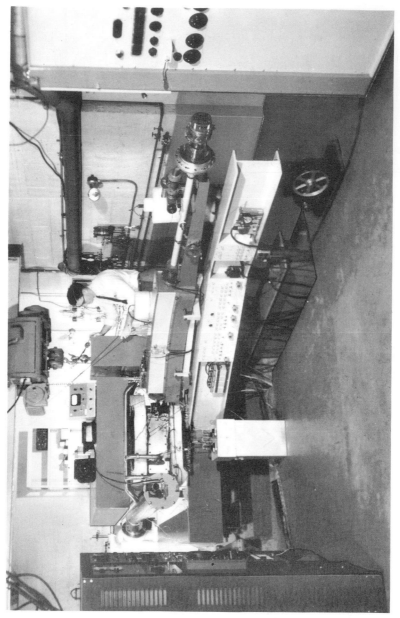

Precision mass spectrometer under construction at Harvard University; see Section 37.2. (Courtesy K. T. Bainbridge, photograph by Paul Donaldson.)

FOUNDATIONS OF
MODERN PHYSICAL
SCIENCE

To

WALTER GUYTON CADY

FOUNDATIONS OF
MODERN PHYSICAL SCIENCE

by

GERALD HOLTON, Ph.D.

Associate Professor of Physics
Harvard University

and

DUANE H. D. ROLLER, Ph.D.

Assistant Professor of the History of Science
University of Oklahoma

under the editorship of

DUANE ROLLER, Ph.D.

Member of the Senior Staff of The Ramo-Wooldridge Corporation
and Professor of Physics at Harvey Mudd College

ADDISON-WESLEY PUBLISHING COMPANY, INC.

READING, MASSACHUSETTS

Copyright © 1958

ADDISON-WESLEY PUBLISHING COMPANY, INC.

Printed in the United States of America

ALL RIGHTS RESERVED. THIS BOOK, OR PARTS THERE-
OF, MAY NOT BE REPRODUCED IN ANY FORM WITH-
OUT WRITTEN PERMISSION OF THE PUBLISHERS.

Library of Congress Catalog Card No. 58-5057

Third printing—October 1965

ADDISON-WESLEY PUBLISHING COMPANY, INC.
Palo Alto · READING, MASSACHUSETTS · London
NEW YORK · DALLAS · ATLANTA · BARRINGTON, ILLINOIS

CONTENTS

PART IX. THE NUCLEUS

"You see, then, Glaucon, that this study is really indispensable for our purpose, since it forces the mind to arrive at pure truth by the exercise of pure thought."

"Yes, Socrates, it has a powerful effect of that kind..."

"Also, it would not be easy to find many branches of study which require more effort from the learner?"

"No."

"Then for all these reasons we must not neglect this study, but those who have the best natures must be trained in it?"

"I agree."

"Then let this be one point settled."

PLATO, *The Republic*, Book VII.

INTRODUCTION

OBJECTIVES. This new book for the introductory course in physics or physical science is the result of two developments. After the appearance of the textbook *Introduction to Concepts and Theories of Physical Science* the demand was voiced that a book with the same approach to the study of physical science be also provided for a wider group of students. The earlier text continues, of course, to be available for the student whom it was intended to serve; the present book develops its mathematical and conceptual material more extensively, and also gives more space to physical optics, electricity and magnetism, and nuclear physics. A choice can therefore be made to provide the text appropriate to the best intellectual effort of a given group of students.

A second point of origin for the new book has been the continued evolution of ideas in recent years concerning instruction in physics and related physical sciences. For example, the Report of a Conference sponsored by the American Association of Physics Teachers (AAPT), entitled "Improving the Quality and Effectiveness of Introductory Physics Courses,"* in summarizing the results of a lengthy study, endorses seven objectives for every introductory physics course, regardless of the level of preparation. In addition to the *sine qua non*, namely "a precise understanding of the basic concepts of physics," the report asks that the course should attempt to impart some of the scientist's characteristic curiosity about the physical world; the instructor is urged to stress the underlying, unifying principles in mathematical form, but should also set forth the scope and limitations of the conceptual tools; special attention is directed to the development of precise methods for measurement; the point is made that "to appreciate fully the physics of today the student must know something of the historical development of underlying ideas, of the struggle of the past and the great strides that were taken by a few individuals in enunciating these broadly applicable unifying principles"; and the timely objective is cited that "through a proper understanding of the laws of nature, people can arrive at more objective judgments and, it is hoped, keep free of many of the popular fears and superstitions involving science itself today."

We believe these objectives to be entirely sound, despite the difficulties that clearly await every attempt at implementation. We also agree fully that the success of a course of study in physics or physical science is de-

---

*American Journal of Physics, v. 25, pp. 417–424 (1957).

termined in large measure by the seriousness with which the instructor heeds the warning in the Report to "reduce drastically the number of topics discussed in introductory physics courses" rather than "sacrifice depth and understanding by attempting to cover too many topics in encyclopedic fashion." The Report makes the bold suggestion that the course should concentrate on "seven basic principles and concepts and the material leading up to them: conservation of momentum, conservation of mass and energy, conservation of charge, waves, fields, the molecular structure of matter, and the structure of the atom."

The Report stresses that the afore-cited statement of objectives is pertinent to *all* types of physics and physical science courses, and it asserts also that the same basic content should be incorporated in all types of courses. We believe that the principle implied can be stated more generally: the same basic conception of the field of physical science can and should be presented in all courses in which physics is taught. We regard it as axiomatic that there is only one physical universe for all of us—not one for physicists and engineers, another for premedical students, a third for liberal arts majors, and so on—and that it is possible to meet the special needs and pedagogic problems of each student group without sacrificing the fundamental unity of the subject.

APPROACH. The present book is intended mainly for courses of two types: (a) the one-year *general physics course* for science majors (including premedical students) outside physics or engineering, and (b) the *course for majors in the humanities and social studies*, including the physical science course for liberal arts students and the integrated or general education course. As with the earlier text, the present book will probably also find use in certain physics courses for physicists and engineers in conjunction with some other text such as that of Sears and Zemansky, or Semat, or Shortley and Williams, or Weber, White and Manning, or White.

To illustrate more concretely how the recommendations of the AAPT Report may be implemented, the publication of sample course syllabi was commissioned by the reporting conference. The following passages from one of these syllabi* present the basis on which the present book was developed:

> The principal aims are the sound presentation of the key concepts and theories of physical science, and the development of intellectual tools for the student's orientation in an age where science has become a dominant cultural force. Physical science is therefore studied both as a body of rigorous knowledge and as a living process of investigation.
>
> The center of the course lies in physics, although connections are made to other physical sciences whenever appropriate. Instead of adhering to the

---

* *American Journal of Physics* v. 25, pp. 425–429 (1957).

ancient but rather arbitrary division of physics into rigid categories (e.g., mechanics, heat, etc.), we let the historical and philosophical development of science suggest the organization and unification of the material. Like others who have tried it, we have found that this approach has several advantages. Occasional well-chosen references to the original work of great scientists can provide the excitement of looking over the shoulder of the originator at his work. A careful study of the meaning of fundamental concepts brings out that feature of science which has made it the proverbial model for effective thinking. And the occasional analysis of procedures and tools of working scientists may help to formulate the student's attitude toward problem situations in general.

However, the main strength of any science course lies in its scientific subject-matter content, and the most important experience we can give a student comes when he finds that he can enjoy and solve a difficult but important problem in science, although it be on the introductory level. This is the prerequisite to an understanding of the physical universe. And if the student does not reach this stage first, attempts to teach the "meaning" or nature or structure of science can hardly succeed. Therefore we avoid following the historical line wherever it does not help to clarify the scientific content. In short, in this course the history of science is necessarily thought of neither as a science nor as the subject of main concern, but as a pedagogic aid.

Encyclopedic coverage—the great stumbling block in elementary courses—has also been discarded; instead of giving a general (and therefore often shallow) survey, we have elected to spend the time on a more careful study of a number of key topics. This choice need not imply a set of unconnected cases; they can be arranged to form a continuously developing story from early beginnings to contemporary research, from Galileo's law of free fall to thermo-nuclear reactions.

The guiding principle in the selection of subject matter for this form of block-and-bridge course is that *each main topic should fulfill two purposes: it must be of interest and importance in its own right, and it must have important links with the rest of the story.* For example, the laws of projectile motion are discussed first in connection with Galileo's contribution to kinematics, but are taken up again several times later: as examples of vector addition; as a special case of motion under Newton's law of universal gravitation; and in connection with the motion of charged particles in the cathode-ray tube and the mass spectrograph. The same selection principle gives one courage to omit many topics which usually have been regarded as indispensable in the classic type of preprofessional physics course (e.g., photometry, lens aberrations).

Some of the developments not brought into the present text have been incorporated in the problems, which are intended partly as assignments of varying difficulty and partly as points of departure for the discussion sections. Other topics are not mentioned at all, and each reader doubtless can make a list of regretted omissions or inclusions. The balance chosen here was dictated by our own response to the important plea of the AAPT Report to make "a more critical and parsimonious selection of content [in order to] permit a pace that encourages both reflection on the part of the student and a proper regard for depth and intellectual vigor."

The Report contains also some pertinent remarks concerning the use of textbooks:

> Although a textbook is usually considered to be essential to an introductory course, the responsibility for teaching rests with the instructor, not with the textbook author. In choosing a text, it is important that the instructor should feel that its general approach is suited to his methods of presentation and to the requirements of his students. It is far less important that the book should cover exactly the subject matter that he plans to teach. He should feel free to omit sections that are not essential to his development of the subject and to add topics not included in the book. Without disparaging the text, he can encourage his students to criticize some of its statements and arguments.

LABORATORY WORK. The AAPT Report suggests that to a greater extent than has sometimes been tried, "the laboratory can be made an integral part of the introductory physics course and can contribute to the objectives outlined above." The laboratory part of a physics or physical science course can be so designed that it includes material not otherwise elaborated upon in the course; thereby each experiment is endowed with additional value and student interest, and more class time can be given to other topics.

Moreover, if the course is to serve a double purpose, the specific experiments can concentrate on topics with which one expects a particular group to be familiar (e.g., for premedical students, geometrical optics and electric circuits). Consequently, physical science courses of the general education type, given on this basis, can provide one way of fulfilling preprofessional requirements, for instance the physics requirement for students who plan to apply for admission to medical schools. Indeed, the development of this type of course is in line with the needs and desires of medical schools as expressed both by their response to this proposal and by the "Severinghaus report."*

ACKNOWLEDGMENTS. We acknowledge with pleasure our debts to colleagues and friends whose advice aided in the preparation of this work. Among those who were especially helpful were Professors I. Kaplan, E. C. Kemble, L. K. Nash, and R. M. Whaley. For help in providing illustrations we are indebted, among others, to K. T. Bainbridge, P. Donaldson, Mrs. Laura Fermi, O. Hahn, Miss Lotte Jacobi, P. A. Macklin, J. J. G. McCue, H. A. Selenkow, and A. K. Solomon; also to the Atomic Energy Commis-

---

*Severinghaus, Carman, and Cadbury, *Preparation for medical education in the liberal arts college* (McGraw-Hill, 1953).

sion, Brookhaven National Laboratory, Cavendish Laboratory, Ealing Corporation, Fogg Art Museum, High Voltage Engineering Corporation, Metropolitan Museum of Art, Rockefeller Institute for Medical Research, and *Scientific American*. Extracts from Galileo's *Dialogue* of 1632 are reprinted from *Dialogue on the great world systems, in the Salusbury translation, revised, annotated, and with an introduction by Giorgio de Santillana*, by permission of the University of Chicago Press; copyright 1953 by the University of Chicago.

The publisher, especially through Mrs. Olga A. Crawford and Mr. Joseph S. Banks, has contributed far beyond the requirement of duty to expedite the completion of the work.

G.H.
D.H.D.R.

March 1958

Part I
THE STUDY OF MOTION

(1564–1642)

THE STUDY OF MOTION

Historically as well as logically, mechanics represents the foundation of physics and the prototype for the study of other physical sciences. The concepts which we shall meet in mechanics will appear again and again throughout this book, as though mechanics provided a frame on which physical science is erected. In this sense, mechanics is to physics what the skeleton is to the human figure—at first glance it may appear stiff and cold, but after even a brief study of its functions one experiences with mounting excitement the discovery of an astonishingly successful design, of a structure that is complex, yet so ingenious and simple as to be almost inevitable.

We shall begin with a key topic in mechanics, namely, with the concepts and formulations for describing some of the simpler motions of objects. For even in Galileo's time there was this axiom: *ignorato motu, ignoratur natura.*

CHAPTER 1

SPEED AND ACCELERATION

1.1 Motion with constant speed. Physical science is the study of nature at the most fundamental level. It starts appropriately with what first draws our attention in watching nature, namely that there is an endless variety of motions. This chapter will establish the concepts of speed and acceleration; although the concepts are relatively simple, we shall introduce them with care and deliberation, using them to demonstrate some useful mathematical methods and cultivate some indispensable intuitions. With this background we shall be able, in the next chapter, to turn to Galileo's historic study of freely falling bodies, which is commonly regarded as the work marking the beginning of modern physical science.

To discuss motion, we must first be able to describe it. Suppose, for example, that a car is traveling along a road, and that we wish to find the relationship between the distance covered and the time required to cover it. The progress of this car may be timed at stations regularly spaced at, say, 20 feet all along the line (Fig. 1.1). We may assume that the car had been brought up to speed before passing through the first station. If the motion had progressed at an even pace, a tabular arrangement of the time schedule for the first five stations might be found to read as in Table 1.1. This is the first and simplest method for describing ordinary motions.

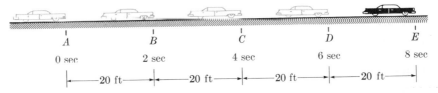

FIG. 1.1. A car moving along a road. The time of its arrival is entered under each of the five stations.

Table 1.1. Data for car moving along road.

Station	Distance from station A (ft)	Time of travel from station A (sec)
A	0	0
B	20	2
C	40	4
D	60	6
E	80	8

1

Another useful way of representing the same information is to make a graph of distance *versus* time (Fig. 1.2). Along the horizontal axis (called the *axis of abscissas*) we note the observed times; along the vertical axis (the *axis of ordinates*) we note the corresponding distances covered. Since the five known points (observations) thus entered on this graph are seen to lie on a straight line, we draw it in as shown to indicate our not unreasonable belief that any additional data taken would also have fallen along this line. For example, on examining the plotted data we could feel fairly confident that the car would have passed a point 30 ft from station A 3 sec after the beginning of our series of observations. A statement such as this, based on a presumed state of affairs between the points of actual observation, is an *interpolation;* the process is easily carried out on a graph of this type. Moreover, we are also fairly sure that after 9 sec the vehicle, if it continued to move in the same way, would have reached a position 90 ft beyond station A. This is an *extrapolation* beyond the region of given data. In general, one must not place too much confidence in information obtained by interpolation, particularly when the basic data are few or widely spaced, and results obtained by extrapolation are often still more uncertain. More will be said about these two processes in Section 1.2.*

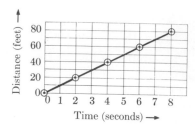

FIG. 1.2. Distance-time graph for motion with constant speed.

To represent motion we can use not only graphs (geometry) but also algebra. If we symbolize by the letter t the time elapsed since station A was passed, and by the letter s the distance covered during that time interval, then we can represent this particular motion by a simple algebraic statement:

$$\frac{s}{t} = \text{a constant.}$$

EXAMPLE 1.1. Using the data of Table 1.1, show that the ratio s/t has the same value (i.e., is a constant) for several different values of t.

---

*Figure 1.2 serves also to illustrate three simple rules that should be followed in plotting any graph from observed data: (1) All known data are preferably represented by points surrounded by small circles; however, if there are many known points close together, it may be better to indicate each point by a $\times$ rather than a circle. (2) The line is neat and is not drawn through the circles. (3) Each coordinate axis is labeled with the name of the physical quantity plotted and, if numerical values are entered, also with the name of the unit of measurement in terms of which this quantity is expressed.

Solution. During the first two seconds ($t = 2$ sec) the car traveled 20 ft ($s = 20$ ft); therefore $s/t = 20$ ft/2 sec $= 10$ ft/sec.

During the first four seconds ($t = 4$ sec) the car traveled 40 ft ($s = 40$ ft); therefore $s/t = 40$ ft/4 sec $= 10$ ft/sec.

Similarly, when t is 8 sec, s is 80 ft; therefore $s/t = 80$ ft/8 sec $= 10$ ft/sec.

Whenever the ratio of two variable quantities is a constant, the graph of one quantity *versus* the other is a straight line. Hence we could have predicted the rectilinear nature of the graph (Fig. 1.2) simply by knowing that the ratio s/t is constant. Conversely, the fact that the graph is found to be a straight line tells us that the ratio will be a constant. The ratio s/t is not by any means a constant for all the motions we shall encounter, but it is nevertheless useful for describing so many motions that we give to this ratio the special name of *speed*. Thus we can describe the motion we have discussed by saying that *the speed of the car is a constant*, having the value 10 ft/sec.

If an object is moving with *constant* speed, this speed can be computed using *any* distance traversed and the corresponding time interval. Thus, in our example, at 4 sec the car was 40 ft from where we started our measurements, and at 6 sec it was 60 ft from the start. During these two seconds (i.e., from the 4th second to the 6th second) the car went 60 ft $-$ 40 ft $=$ 20 ft. Dividing the distance traversed by the time elapsed, we obtain 20 ft/2 sec $= 10$ ft/sec, which is just the value we previously obtained for the speed. Thus if s_1 and s_2 are the distances moved in times t_1 and t_2, respectively, at constant speed, then $s_2 - s_1$ is the distance traveled in time $t_2 - t_1$, and the speed is $(s_2 - s_1)/(t_2 - t_1)$.

PROBLEM 1.1. Obtaining the necessary information from the graph, Fig. 1.2, compute the speed for each of the following time intervals: from $t_1 = 1$ sec to $t_2 = 2$ sec; from $t_1 = 2$ sec to $t_2 = 5$ sec; from $t_1 = 3$ sec to $t_2 = 6$ sec; from $t_1 = 1$ sec to $t_2 = 7$ sec.

(*Note:* In the first reading of a chapter, you may wish to pass over the problems to preserve the sense of continuity; but in the second reading, think about each problem as you reach it.)

Before you proceed, be sure you can answer the following questions:

How is *constant speed* defined (using algebraic notation)? What observations must I make to find out whether a certain body is moving with constant speed? How can I compute the speed once I know that it is constant?

Consider for a moment what an amazing thing has happened. First we watched the actual motion of a car along a road. Then, from the multitude of ever-changing impressions—the blur, the noise, the turning of wheels, the whole chaos of events progressing in time and space—we have isolated two measurable quantities, distance s and time t, both of which take on different numerical values every instant, and we have found that their ratio, called the *speed*, was an unchanging quantity in an otherwise complex situation. Perhaps we are too familiar with the concept of speed to be able to appreciate fully this present experience of *creating order from a chaos of sense impressions* by abstracting some measurable data and by inventing another concept (speed) which enables us to describe one portion of the total situation in a remarkably simple manner. However, we shall return again and again to this method, the very heart of scientific procedure.

1.2 The "text" behind equations. Let us take a second critical look at our study of the motion of the car. We began with Table 1.1, which presents the raw experimental data in tabular form. Figure 1.2 represents these same data in the form of a graph and expands their usefulness by permitting convenient interpolation and extrapolation. Finally we abstracted from these representations a general conclusion which we expressed by means of the equation $s/t =$ a constant (10 ft/sec in this specific case).

In brief, we have proceeded from a bulky table of raw data to a concise generalization ($s/t = 10$ ft/sec). If on repeated observations of this car we always arrived at this same equation, in other words, if the car always moved at a constant speed of 10 ft/sec, we should regard the equation as a rule or an empirical *law* applicable to this restricted type of observation. As it is, our equation arose from a single set of observations and is simply a general description of this one motion of the car which, at other times, may be moving very differently.

At first glance all three stages—table, graph, and equation—seem to afford precisely the same information, with the last stage appearing vastly preferable because it is so brief and comprehensive. However, we must not let a desire for conciseness override caution; the equation $s/t = 10$ ft/sec does, in fact, include everything that the table offers, but it also implies indiscriminately a great deal more that may actually be quite unwarranted. For example, unless you had seen the tabulated data, you might believe on the basis of the equation $s/t = 10$ ft/sec alone that surely $s = 0.12$ in. if $t = 0.001$ sec, or that $s = 864,000$ ft if $t = 1$ day. Both statements are correct if the speed under investigation is truly constant within the limits of such very small time intervals as 0.001 sec and for such a span of time as 1 day; but in our actual, limited experience these conditions are not likely to hold.

The lesson to be drawn here is that *equations in physical science must be thought to have attached an unseen "text,"* a statement that describes the underlying assumptions and other conditions that limit the applicability of the equation. These conditions, this text, may simply be of the following form: "The equation $s/t = 10$ ft/sec describes the result of a certain experiment in which t did not exceed 8 sec, and in which only a few measurements were made, each with such and such accuracy." Without the clear understanding that equations in physical science always have hidden limitations, we cannot expect to interpret or apply them successfully. For instance, we would continually be tempted to make unwarranted extrapolations and interpolations. We would be in the catastrophic position of a navigator who has to negotiate a rocky channel without having any idea of the length, width, and draft of his ship.

1.3 The concept of average speed. Prolonged motion with constant speed occurs so rarely in nature, and the concept of constant speed is so limited, that we have not honored the latter with a special letter symbol of its own. We turn now to motion with any speed, including *varying* speed (accelerated or decelerated motions). The graph for a motion of this type is shown in Fig. 1.3, where a car starts from rest, gains speed until time t_1,

and proceeds with constant speed until time t_2 (as indicated by the straight-line portion between t_1 and t_2), after which it slows down to rest (t_3), waits without moving until time t_4, and then again accelerates to reach a new and higher constant speed. To deal with such variations in speed, it is necessary to introduce a new concept, *average speed*, denoted by the special symbol $\bar{v}$ (read "*v*-bar" or "*v*-average").

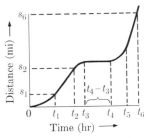

FIG. 1.3. Graph for motion with varying speed.

DEFINITION. *The average speed $\bar{v}$ of an object during a time interval t is the distance covered during this time interval divided by t; that is, $\bar{v} = s/t$.*

Note that when the speed is variable rather than constant, the value of the average speed $\bar{v}$ depends on the length of the time interval chosen. For example, by examining Fig. 1.3, we can see that by our definition $\bar{v}$ for the time interval from the start to t_1 is smaller than $\bar{v}$ computed for the interval from the start to t_2. On the other hand, $\bar{v}$ is zero during the interval $(t_4 - t_3)$.

Although the average speed from t_1 to t_2 may be 30 mi/hr (miles per hour) and that between t_5 and t_6 may be 50 mi/hr, the average speed $\bar{v}$ for the entire motion to time t_6, which is calculated by using $\bar{v} = (s_6/t_6)$, is perhaps 20 mi/hr. We recognize that the meaning of $\bar{v}$ is this: when an object travels a distance s in a time interval t, the average speed $\bar{v}$ given by s/t represents the value of that *constant* speed at which the same object could have traversed the same distance s in the same time interval t.

EXAMPLE 1.2. A train leaves a station and steadily increases its speed for 5 min, going 2 mi in that time. What is the average speed during this time interval?

Solution. As in every problem, we must first translate each separate phrase into mathematical symbols, or else extract from each some clues as to which physical concepts, laws, and limitations are here applicable. The phrase "a train leaves a station and steadily increases its speed for 5 min" is rendered, "the speed is not constant, $t = 5$ min"; "going 2 mi in that time" means "$s = 2$ mi." The final phrase, of course, is "$\bar{v} = ?$" From our definition of average speed $\bar{v}$, we know that $\bar{v} = s/t$ and see that we are now in a position to solve the problem. In summary, $s = 2$ mi, $t = 5$ min, $\bar{v} = s/t$, $\bar{v} = ?$

$$\bar{v} = s/t = 2\,\text{mi}/5\,\text{min} = 0.4\,\text{mi/min}.$$

Although this example may seem simple and spelled out in overelaborate detail, you will find that the steps taken are the same here as in almost every problem, no matter how sophisticated. If you decide from the very start to *translate each phrase separately*, half the initial troubles with problems in physical science will have been avoided.

EXAMPLE 1.3. An airplane flies from New York to Chicago, a distance of 800 mi, in 2 hr and then returns to New York in 4 hr. What is the average speed each way and for the round trip?

Solution. (a) For the westward trip: $s = 800$ mi, $t = 2$ hr, $\bar{v} = ?$ From the definition of average speed, $\bar{v} = s/t = 800\,\text{mi}/2\,\text{hr} = 400\,\text{mi/hr}$. (b) For the eastward trip: $s = 800$ mi, $t = 4$ hr, $\bar{v} = s/t = 800\,\text{mi}/4\,\text{hr} = 200\,\text{mi/hr}$. (c) For the round trip: $s = 1600$ mi, $t = 6$ hr, $s = 1600\,\text{mi}/6\,\text{hr} = 267\,\text{mi/hr}$.

PROBLEM 1.2. A man drives 90 mi in 4 hr. What was his average speed during that time?

PROBLEM 1.3. A man drives 120 mi in 4 hr, stops 1 hr for luncheon, and then drives 120 mi in another 4 hr. Compute: (a) his average speed for the first 4 hr; (b) his average speed for the first 5 hr; (c) his speed if he had driven the same total distance of 240 mi in the same total time at constant speed.

PROBLEM 1.4. A train travels 120 mi in 2 hr and then 120 mi more in 3 additional hours. Find the average speed for the first 2 hr, the last 3 hr, and the whole trip.

1.4 Instantaneous speed. All our speed measurements so far have involved more or less extended time measurements. However, we certainly also want to have a concept that pertains to the speed of an object at one *instant*, the type of information that we read off a speedometer. For example, we may ask, "What is the speed at time t_P for the motion pictured in Fig. 1.4(a)?" Now we *do* know how to find the average speed $\bar{v}$ during a time interval from t_1 to t_2, which includes the instant t_P, that is, $\bar{v} = (s_2 - s_1)/(t_2 - t_1)$. However, since the speed is not constant from t_1 to t_2, we certainly cannot identify the speed *at the instant* t_P with the average speed $\bar{v}$ *during* the interval $(t_2 - t_1)$. Therefore, we must resort to what undoubtedly will look like a trick: we calculate $\bar{v}$ for a very short time interval encompassing the instant t_P, an interval so short that the

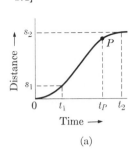
(a)

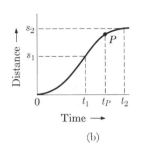
(b)

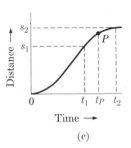
(c)

FIG. 1.4. Determination of instantaneous speed at time t_P. As the interval $(t_2 - t_1)$ is made shorter and shorter, the average speed $\bar{v}$ calculated for $(t_2 - t_1)$ approaches the value of the instantaneous speed at t_P.

Table 1.2. Data for computing instantaneous speed.

$t_2 - t_1$ (sec)	$s_2 - s_1$ (ft)	$\bar{v} = \dfrac{s_2 - s_1}{t_2 - t_1}$ (ft/sec)
10	25	2.5
1.0	2.0	2.0
0.10	0.18	1.8
0.010	0.017	1.7
0.0010	0.0017	1.7

value of $\bar{v}$ computed for it would not change appreciably if the interval were made even shorter.

A concrete example will help here. From the data on which Fig. 1.4(a) is based we might construct Table 1.2 for some space and time intervals that include point P on the curve. We note that the values for $\bar{v}$ calculated for shorter and shorter time intervals approach closer and closer to 1.7 ft/sec, and that, in fact, for *any* time interval less than 0.01 sec, the average speed $\bar{v}$ will be 1.7 ft/sec within the limits of accuracy of the measurement of s and t. Therefore, we now make a leap from the concept of average speed and conclude that the speed at time t_P itself is 1.7 ft/sec, insofar as we can give any meaning at all to the concept of speed *at a particular moment.*

This calculation has illustrated how we can obtain the *instantaneous speed* at t_P by examining $\bar{v}$ for smaller time intervals. Instantaneous speed of an object will be denoted by the symbol v. Problem 1.26 provides the necessary practice for finding the instantaneous speed in a concrete case.

Mainly for the sake of completeness, we note that the procedure illustrated above is sometimes symbolized in mathematical shorthand as follows:

$$v \equiv \lim_{\Delta t \to 0} \bar{v},$$

which means that the instantaneous speed v at a point is, *by definition*, equal to the limiting value reached by the average speed $\bar{v}$ encompassing that point as the time interval Δt (read "delta-t") is made smaller and smaller. The symbol $\equiv$ means "identically the same as." Often the symbol $\bar{v}$ in this equation is replaced by $\Delta s/\Delta t$, which signifies generally the ratio of a distance interval to a time interval; thus $\Delta s \equiv s_2 - s_1$, and $\Delta t \equiv t_2 - t_1$.

We saw previously that *average* speed is defined by the expression $\bar{v} = s/t$. If an object is moving with constant speed, the average speed $\bar{v}$ for any part of the motion is the same as the instantaneous speed v at each moment. Consequently, for *uniform motion* we may write

$$\frac{s}{t} = v$$

or

$$s = vt. \tag{1.1}$$

This equation leads us to an important relationship between the algebraic and geometric representations of motion. Recall the construction of the distance *versus* time graph, Fig. 1.2; it is equally simple to make a speed *versus* time graph for any motion on which there are sufficient data. This is illustrated in Fig. 1.5(a) for the motion of the car discussed at the beginning of this chapter, for which the instantaneous speed is at all times 10 ft/sec. A particularly interesting feature of the speed-time graph for any moving body is that *the area under the curve represents the distance traveled*.

Let us prove this for the special case of a body moving with constant speed. In Fig. 1.5(b) consider the shaded area bounded by four lines: the two coordinate axes, the horizontal line representing the progress of the car with constant velocity v, and the vertical line at the right representing the end of the experiment at some time t. These four lines form a rectangle, and the area of any rectangle is equal to the height multiplied by the base. Here the height is v and the base is t; therefore the area is vt, which, by Eq. (1.1), is equivalent to the distance s traversed in the specified time t.

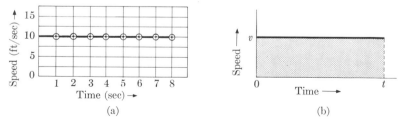

FIG. 1.5. Speed-time graph for motion with constant speed.

One may ask: "How can an area be equal to a distance?" But note that we are measuring the lengths of the sides of the rectangle in very special units: the base is a time interval and the height is a speed, that is, a distance divided by a time. And just as we may *represent* elapsed times by distances along the axis of abscissas, so we may represent distances traveled by areas. The area under the curve in any speed-time graph represents the distance traveled even when the speed is not constant; we shall find this fact useful.

PROBLEM 1.5. A car is driven at constant speeds of 30 mi/hr for one hour, 35 mi/hr for the second hour, and 40 mi/hr for the third hour. (a) Draw the speed-time graph for the whole period. (b) Compute the areas for the first hour, the first two hours, and the first three hours. (c) For these same time intervals, compute the distances traversed by using Eq. (1.1); compare these distances with the values for the corresponding areas.

1.5 Acceleration. Of all motions, the one of most interest for our present purposes is motion with *uniformly changing* speed, that is, motion with constant acceleration or constant deceleration. To a fair approximation this is the type of motion characteristic of an object falling freely to the ground or sliding down a smooth inclined plane, or coasting to a stop on level ground.

Three different situations involving uniformly changing speeds are illustrated in Fig. 1.6. In (a) the speed* at the start is zero ($v_0 = 0$) and uniformly increases, reaching a value v at time t; in (b) v_0 is not zero, and the speed increases uniformly; and in (c) the speed decreases from a large initial value v_0 to reach nearly zero at time t. Concrete situations cor-

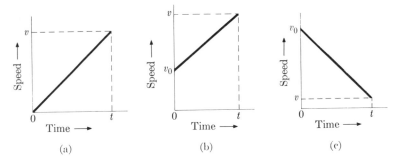

FIG. 1.6. Motion with constant acceleration.

---

*When we use the term speed from now on, we shall mean instantaneous speed unless otherwise specified. The general symbol for instantaneous speed is v, and we shall add subscripts 0, 1, 2, ... to mean the following: v_0 is the speed at the start of some time interval, when $t = 0$; v_1 is the speed at time t_1; v_2 at t_2; and v without subscript the speed at time t in general.

responding to each graph will suggest themselves readily. For instance, they might respectively pertain to a sled on a smooth hill that (a) slides down from rest, (b) slides down after a running start, and (c) having reached the bottom, is sliding up another hill.

For all such cases of uniformly changing motion it is convenient to define the concept of acceleration, for which we shall use the symbol a. *Acceleration is the ratio of the change of speed ($v - v_0$) to the time (t) during which this change occurs;* or, in algebraic form,

$$a = \frac{v - v_0}{t}. \tag{1.2}$$

Since we have agreed to restrict our attention for the time being to motion with *constant* acceleration, we need not distinguish between average acceleration and instantaneous acceleration, for, as in the case of constant speed, the average and instantaneous values are numerically equal.

To illustrate this new concept let us consider some specific examples.

EXAMPLE 1.4. A skier starts to move down an incline and gains speed at a constant rate, reaching a speed of 30 ft/sec in 5 sec. What is his acceleration?

Solution. $v_0 = 0$, $v = 30$ ft/sec, $t = 5$ sec, $a = ?$

$$a = \frac{v - v_0}{t} = \frac{30 \text{ ft/sec} - 0}{5 \text{ sec}} = \frac{6 \text{ ft/sec}}{1 \text{ sec}} = 6\,\frac{\text{ft/sec}}{\text{sec}} = 6 \text{ ft/sec}^2.$$

[The unit (ft/sec)/sec is read "feet per second, per second"; and the equivalent expression ft/sec^2 is read "feet per second squared."]

EXAMPLE 1.5. A car has been traveling on a level road at a speed of 50 mi/hr when suddenly the clutch is disengaged and the car coasts along. During the first minute it loses 20 mi/hr. What was the acceleration during that time?

Solution. Translating, we read $v_0 = 50$ mi/hr, $v = 30$ mi/hr, $t = 1$ min $= 60$ sec, $a = ?$ It is tempting to plunge ahead and write, without qualification,

$$a = \frac{30 \text{ mi/hr} - 50 \text{ mi/hr}}{60 \text{ sec}} = -\frac{1}{3}\frac{(\text{mi/hr})}{\text{sec}}.$$

However, this is true only if we assume that the car coasted with constant acceleration—a good guess but not necessarily the correct one. Therefore we must say $a = -\frac{1}{3}$ (mi/hr)/sec *if* the acceleration was constant. Notice the negative sign, indicating that the car is slowing down.

EXAMPLE 1.6. A car on a roller coaster having variable slopes and many curves changed its speed from 5 mi/hr to 25 mi/hr in 20 sec. What was the acceleration?

Translation. $v_0 = 5$ mi/hr, $v = 25$ mi/hr, $t = 20$ sec, $a = ?$ However, since there is little likelihood that the acceleration was constant, we must simply admit that we cannot solve this problem until further data are given from which the type of motion may be deduced. (It would be a mistake to regard such a statement as an admission of dishonorable defeat; on the contrary, in physical science, as in every other field, the possibility of solving a problem offhand is the exception rather than the rule, and it is a considerable preliminary victory to foresee what additional information is needed for an eventual solution.)

The units for acceleration were here variously given as (ft/sec)/sec or (mi/hr)/sec; others are evidently also possible, for example, (mi/sec)/min. In all these cases, the units correspond to (length/time)/time. It is usually wise but not always necessary to convert all data to the same units of measurement (feet and seconds, or feet and minutes, etc.) before starting on the calculations.*

PROBLEM 1.6.   A rock dropped from a cliff attains a speed of 129 ft/sec in 4.0 sec. What is its acceleration? What will be its speed after an additional 2 sec if the acceleration continues to be constant?

PROBLEM 1.7.   Coasting on a level road, a bicyclist slows from 15 ft/sec to 3 ft/sec in 1 min. What is his acceleration? At this acceleration, how long will it take him to come to rest from a speed of 15 ft/sec?

1.6 Equations of motion for constant acceleration.   The reason for our present preoccupation with uniformly accelerated motion is not only its occasional appearance in nature but also, and primarily, the *ease* with which we can formulate some simple equations of motion, equations that relate the five important variable quantities: distance covered (s), time taken (t), initial speed (v_0) at the beginning of time interval t, final speed (v) at the end of time interval t, and acceleration (a). Equation (1.2) is a good example. It is usually remembered in the alternative form

$$v = v_0 + at \tag{1.3}$$

or, in words, the speed v at the end of a time interval t is the sum of the initial speed v_0 and the change in speed at, which is the constant acceleration a times the elapsed time t. There are other, similar equations relating the five variables. We shall now construct three of them.

We have seen that the area under the speed-time curve is numerically equal to the distance s covered (Section 1.4). For example, we redraw in Fig. 1.7 the second of the set of three graphs in Fig. 1.6. The area under the curve in Fig. 1.7 is now shaded, and may be thought of as a rectangle

---

*The relationship 30 mi/hr $\doteq$ 44 ft/sec $\doteq$ 13 meter/sec is a very useful one to memorize. The symbol $\doteq$ stands for "approximately equals."

with sides v_0 and t, surmounted by a
triangle of altitude $(v - v_0)$ and base t.
The area of the rectangle is $v_0 t$ and the
area of the triangle is $\frac{1}{2}$ altitude $\times$ base,
or $\frac{1}{2}(v - v_0)t$. The total area under
the curve of the speed-time graph is
therefore $v_0 t + \frac{1}{2}(v - v_0)t$; this corresponds again to the total distance
traveled, and we can interpret the
total distance as the sum of two parts,
namely (1) the distance $v_0 t$ covered
during time t if the motion had pro-

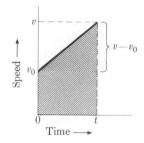

Fig. 1.7. The area under the
speed-time graph represents the
distance covered.

ceeded with a constant speed equal to v_0, plus (2) the distance $\frac{1}{2}(v - v_0)t$
added by virtue of the acceleration of the motion. Thus we may write for
the total distance covered

$$s = v_0 t + \tfrac{1}{2}(v - v_0)t.$$

From Eq. (1.2), we see that $v - v_0 = at$. Substitution of this expression
into the equation just obtained yields

$$s = v_0 t + \tfrac{1}{2}at^2. \tag{1.4}$$

This is the second of our equations for motion with constant acceleration.

We obtain another equation of motion from the consideration that, for
any motion with constant acceleration, the average speed $\bar{v}$ is equal to
one-half the sum of the initial and final speeds, just as one might calculate
the average value of any uniformly changing quantity. In equation form,

$$\bar{v} = \frac{v_0 + v}{2}.$$

Substituting this special expression for $\bar{v}$ into the general equation $s = \bar{v}t$,
we get

$$s = \left(\frac{v_0 + v}{2}\right)t. \tag{1.5}$$

This is the third of our equations of motion.

Finally, a fourth equation of motion may be obtained by combining
Eqs. (1.2) and (1.5) to give

$$v^2 = v_0^2 + 2as. \tag{1.6}$$

PROBLEM 1.8. Derive Eq. (1.6) from Eqs. (1.2) and (1.5).

Equation (1.6), although it is derived from the others and therefore actually contains nothing new, still has a certain advantage which exhibits itself more clearly when all four equations are juxtaposed. The following grouping shows the conventional four combinations of the five quantities s, t, v_0, v, and a, allowing for the fact that only four of them are used in any one equation:

$$v = v_0 + at, \qquad \text{(I)}$$

$$s = v_0 t + \tfrac{1}{2}at^2, \qquad \text{(II)}$$

$$s = \left(\frac{v_0 + v}{2}\right) t, \qquad \text{(III)} \tag{1.7}$$

$$v^2 = v_0^2 + 2as. \qquad \text{(IV)}$$

Now it is possible to step back, so to speak, and to study the over-all pattern of our work so far. Equations (1.7) provide all the important and interesting relations between distances traveled, time needed, and so forth, for an object that is moving with an acceleration that is constant. Whenever we encounter this type of motion, we shall at once know how to calculate any two of the five quantities when given the values of the remaining three. This is what makes the four equations of motion such powerful conceptual tools: they help us to analyze, predict, and thereby understand the motion of bodies.

EXAMPLE 1.7. A stone dropped from a tower arrives at the ground 178 ft below with a speed of 107 ft/sec. Previous analysis has shown that the acceleration throughout the free fall will be very nearly constant in these circumstances. Compute the time of fall and the acceleration.

Solution. Upon translating the foregoing information, we have $v_0 = 0$, $v = 107$ ft/sec, $s = 178$ ft, $t = ?$, $a = ?$ Scanning our four equations, we find that v_0, v, s, and t are related by Eq. (III), which can therefore be used to compute t. For convenience in computation, we rearrange Eq. (III) into the form $t = 2s/(v_0 + v)$. Then $t = (2 \times 178 \text{ ft})/(0 + 107 \text{ ft/sec}) = 3.33$ sec. To compute the acceleration a, we note that Eq. (IV) relates it to v_0, v, and s. Rewriting this equation in the form $a = (v^2 - v_0^2)/2s$, we then obtain $(107 \text{ ft/sec})^2/(2 \times 178 \text{ ft}) = 32.1 \text{ ft/sec}^2$.

EXAMPLE 1.8. A rock dropped from a bridge 11 meters* high is found to reach the water in 1.5 sec. Find the speed of the rock just before it hits the water. What is the acceleration?

_____

Metric units of length are commonly used in scientific work. They include the *meter* (abbreviation, m), the *centimeter* (cm), and the *millimeter* (mm); $1 \text{ m} \equiv 100 \text{ cm} \equiv 1000 \text{ mm}$. One can think of the meter as being a little more than a yard, the centimeter as about a third of an inch, and the millimeter as about the width of a thick pencil line. Exact relationships are given in Appendix B.

Solution. Translating into algebraic language, $v_0 = 0$, $s = 11$ m, $t = 1.5$ sec, $v = ?$, $a = ?$ Then, from Eq. (III), $v = 2(s/t) - v_0 = (2 \times 11 \text{ m})/1.5 \text{ sec} - 0 = 14.7$ m/sec; and from Eq. (II), $a = 2(s - v_0 t)/t^2 = 2(11 \text{ m} - 0)/(1.5 \text{ sec})^2 = 9.8$ m/sec^2.

PROBLEM 1.9. A hawk rises to a vertical height of 300 ft and then drops back to earth with a constant acceleration of 32.2 ft/sec^2.* How long does it take to reach the ground? What is its speed just before hitting? What assumptions have you made? Are they likely to apply to an actual case?

PROBLEM 1.10. A stone thrown directly downward from a bridge was found to strike the water 100 m below in 4.0 sec. With what speed was the stone thrown?

PROBLEM 1.11.   A motorcyclist starts from rest and reaches a speed of 30 mi/hr in 15 sec. Assuming that his acceleration was constant, find its value and also how far he will have moved in 15 sec.

PROBLEM 1.12. An airplane, upon landing, slowed from 150 mi/hr to rest in a distance of 1 mi. Compute the acceleration on the assumption that it was constant.

PROBLEM 1.13. A ship changed its speed from 18 to 20 mi/hr in 5 min. If the acceleration was constant, what was its value? How far did the ship move during this time interval?

We have seen how Eqs. (1.7) function as tools for dealing with motions in which the acceleration is constant. Now that we have developed and established the usefulness of these tools, we shall simply remember and apply them as occasion arises, in much the same manner as a craftsman, once having carefully selected a proper tool kit for his work, ceases to re-invent or justify his tools at every turn, but is content to reach into his bag for the proper instrument demanded by the situation at hand. Before our tool kit begins to fill up, we must take the important step of gaining complete mastery over and confidence in each new concept or law as it is introduced. We can then apply it when called upon without feeling a need to re-examine it in detail.

This is, of course, not at all the same thing as the self-defeating practice of simply learning equations by heart or of looking them up in notes to apply them when called upon. This is bound to fail, because one cannot apply an equation properly without knowing all its intimate strengths and weaknesses, the implied "text" mentioned in Section 1.2. As a final example of this important point, suppose that we are asked to predict the time of fall of an object from the top of the Empire State Building, a distance of 1250 ft. Knowing v_0, a, and s, we might feel justified in substituting them

---

*Unless otherwise instructed, assume in all future problems that the acceleration of a body falling freely near the surface of the earth has the constant value 32.2 ft/sec^2 or 9.80 m/sec^2. This happens to be true, within fairly narrow limits, over the whole earth. The acceleration of a freely falling body is called "the acceleration due to gravity," and it is often symbolized by the letter g.

in the readily memorized Eq. (II). However, the time of fall thus computed would turn out to be appreciably smaller than the observed time of fall. Our equations of motion do not yield accurate results here because the acceleration is not constant for so large a distance of fall through air; as the body falls, the air resistance gradually increases, so that the body can no longer be regarded as falling freely. In fact, as is shown by observation of falling leaves, snow, rain, and notably parachutes, each body sooner or later may reach a terminal speed beyond which there is no acceleration at all. This terminal speed depends on the surface characteristics, shape, volume, and weight of the body, and the properties of the air or other medium through which the fall occurs. Such motions are not described by the set of equations (1.7), but have their own special, more complex laws.

Our study of motion has now provided us with the basis for an investigation of the laws of projectile motion, starting with a historical discussion of the special problem of free fall.

Additional Problems

Note: As a rule, do not spend more than about $\frac{1}{2}$ hour at most on any problem. If unable to solve it in that time, plan to come back to it later, or else finish it by stating what you foresee is likely to be the subsequent procedure and final solution. Note also that not all problems have simple numerical answers, even if the statement of the problem is numerical.

1.14. (a) Copy Fig. 1.2 onto graph paper and find by graphical interpolation the approximate position of the car corresponding to times of travel of 5 sec, 0.5 sec, 7.005 sec. Extrapolate to find the position corresponding to 10 sec, 50 sec, −2 sec. (b) Discuss the limitations of the processes of interpolation and of extrapolation.

1.15. An automobile moves past observing stations A, B, C, D, and E, 60 m apart, passing each station 4 sec after having passed the previous one. Represent this motion by a drawing (as in Fig. 1.1), a table, a graph, and an equation, as we did in the case discussed at the beginning of this chapter.

1.16. A leisurely auto trip from New London, Conn., to Berkeley, Calif., took 15 days, including several long stops en route. Calculate the average speed for this trip in miles per hour. What can you say about the instantaneous speed of the car at any time during this interval? (*Note:* Whenever the data given seem insufficient, you may find the necessary additional information in pertinent books in your library. Technical data needed in many problems are given in Appendixes A and B. Many useful tables of physical constants are given in the *Handbook of chemistry and physics*, in the *American Institute of Physics handbook*, and in other reference works.)

1.17. Make some reasonable assumption about the speed that an automobile can pick up during the first 10 sec after starting from rest; then calculate the acceleration.

1.18. (a) Prove first by algebra and then by geometric reasoning that $\bar{v} = \frac{1}{2}(v_0 + v)$ if the acceleration is constant. (b) On what grounds do we regard these mathematical results as applicable to actually observed situations?

1.19. Five observation stations are spaced 10 m apart along a straight vertical line. A body is released at the topmost station at a known time. It falls freely as it passes each of the others. Compute and tabulate the expected time of arrival and speed at each station. Represent these data by a graph (use graph paper).

1.20. A body falls freely from rest. Compute and tabulate the values of s, v, and $\bar{v}$ when the time of fall t is, in turn, 1 sec, 2 sec, 3 sec, 5 sec, and 10 sec. Represent these results in three graphs on graph paper. (Before starting your work, design a procedure for simplifying the calculations.)

1.21. A boy hurls, rather than simply drops, a stone vertically downward from a building 100 ft high. If the stone hits the pavement below in 1.8 sec, what was its initial speed?

1.22. A stone is thrown vertically downward from the top of a building with a speed of 30 m/sec. If it reaches the ground in 2.0 sec, what was the height of the building?

1.23. Make a list of all the relevant limitations, conditions, and idealizations that were implied in your solutions of Problems 1.21 and 1.22.

1.24. The nucleus of a helium atom is to travel along the inside of a straight tube 2 m long, which forms a portion of a particle accelerator. If the nucleus is to enter with a speed of 5000 m/sec and to leave at the other end at 10,000 m/sec, how long will it be in the tube? What assumptions must you make?

1.25. Describe the possible experimental situations that may have given rise to each of the eight graphs of distance *vs.* time in Fig. 1.8 for motion along one line. Then try to express each of three or four of these graphs in terms of an algebraic equation relating s and t.

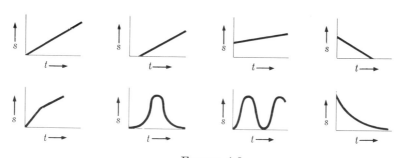

FIGURE 1.8

1.26. During a take-off, a plane is rolling past the position where $s = 0$, $t = 0$, and reaches the following distances during subsequent one-second intervals:

Position	A	B	C	D	E	F
Time t (sec)	0	1	2	3	4	5
Distance s (ft)	0	9	28	57	96	

(a) Plot these data carefully on a large sheet of graph paper, using a hard pencil and making a clean, smooth line. Extrapolate your graph to $t = 5$ sec.

(b) Verify that the equation of the curve is $s = (4 \text{ ft/sec})t + (5 \text{ ft/sec}^2)t^2$.

(c) Define, in words and in symbols, the concept *instantaneous speed*.

(d) Use the graph to find the instantaneous speed of the plane at $t = 3$ sec by the limiting process as in Fig. 1.4 and Table 1.2. That is, first let $t_1 = 1$ sec and $t_2 = 5$ sec, and find the average speed $(\Delta s/\Delta t)$ for this interval. Then find the average speed for the interval between $t_1 = 2$ sec and $t_2 = 4$ sec, then for the interval between $t_1 = 2.5$ sec and $t_2 = 3.5$ sec, etc. These different values of $\bar{v}$ approach the value for the instantaneous speed v at $t = 3$ sec more and more closely as the time interval is made shorter and shorter.

SUPPLEMENTARY READING

BLÜH, O., and J. D. ELDER, *Principles and applications of physics* (Interscience Publishers Inc., 1955). Chapter 1 on standards and measurements.

MICHELS, W. C., and A. L. PATTERSON, *Elements of modern physics* (Van Nostrand, 1951). Chapter 2 on measurement of length and time.

MILLIKAN, R. A., D. ROLLER, and E. C. WATSON, *Mechanics, molecular physics, heat, and sound* (Ginn, 1937). An intermediate textbook with frequent historical references. See pp. 7–22 for an introductory treatment of motion; also pp. 457–458 for significant figures and notation by powers of ten.

POHL, R. W., *Physical principles of mechanics and acoustics* (Blackie & Son, 1932, and later editions). Chapter 1 on measurement of length and time. Chapter 2 on methods of representing motion.

WHITE, H. E., *Modern college physics* (Van Nostrand, 1948, and later editions). Chapters 1 and 2.

CHAPTER 2

GALILEO AND THE KINEMATICS OF FREE FALL

2.1 Introduction. The previous chapter served to clarify the concepts of speed and constant acceleration. Although today these concepts may seem fairly self-evident, they were gained through the centuries only at the cost of enormous effort and long struggle. One of the foremost contemporary historians, Herbert Butterfield, has said,

> Of all the intellectual hurdles which the human mind has been faced with and has overcome in the last fifteen hundred years, the one which seems to me to have been the most amazing in character and the most stupendous in the scope of its consequences is the one relating to the problem of motion . . . (*The origins of modern science*)

The long history of the study of motions of bodies reached a dramatic stage in the early 17th century with the work in kinematics* of Galileo Galilei. We shall examine in some detail the contributions of this remarkable man, often called the father of modern physical science. In particular we shall study his solution of the famous problem of freely falling bodies, analyzing it especially from the point of view of an achievement in the methodology of science.

Galileo is important and interesting to us for several reasons. First, we see in his work the science of kinematics entering into its modern form. Second, he speaks to us as a scientist at his best, as an investigator whose virtuosity in discovery and eloquence in argument excites in his listeners a deep and lasting impression; he will be for us an example of a scientist of the first rank at work.

Third, Galileo's approach to the problems of motion will provide us, both in this chapter and later, with opportunities for discussions of procedures in physical science. We need this. Without an awareness of the character and roles of definition, hypothesis, mathematical deduction, experimentation, and intuition in physical investigations, without a knowledge of the vital processes by which this field of knowledge functions and grows, science would appear as a dry formalism instead of a source of understanding.

2.2 Sources of Scholastic physics. The serious study of the science of mechanics began in Ancient Greece, during one of the great periods of

---

Kinematics means the study of motion without regard to the causes of that motion. It differs from geometry in that it involves the concept of time as well as the dimensions of space.

intellectual advance in our history, from roughly the 6th century B.C. to the 2nd century A.D. While very little of the large store of Greek learning was carried over into early medieval Western Europe, it was preserved in the Arabic countries and from there reintroduced into Europe, beginning in the 12th century. The impact upon Western thought was enormous: European scholars became aware of the existence of a body of knowledge that was of pagan origin and yet vastly superior to their own. The immediate reaction of both Church and schools was to ban this pagan knowledge, but all attempts to stem the flood of translations into Latin failed.

With the Arabs, the scientific work of the Greek philosopher Aristotle (4th century B.C.) and his followers had held a high place, and among the scientific writings eventually reaching Europe there were not only many of Aristotle's, but large numbers of commentaries on his work by Arabic philosophers. In the 13th century Thomas Aquinas succeeded in reconciling the Aristotelian science—especially Aristotle's physics—with Christian theology, and in his great treatise, *Summa theologica*, he secured the establishment of Aristotle as a major authority in philosophic and scientific matters. Furthermore, in the Thomistic "natural theology," science became a field of study in its own right. As the philosopher A. E. Taylor has said:

> With Thomas and his teacher, Albert, the conception of "natural *science*" definitely stamped itself on the thought of Western Europe, never to be forgotten again. (*Platonism and its influence*)

The intellectual followers of Thomas Aquinas came to be known as the Schoolmen or *Scholastics*. Stimulated by the reintroduction of ancient learning, they did important scientific work in the 14th century and became established as the scholars of authority in all the European centers of learning. Galileo was taught by Scholastics, at the University of Pisa, and a good portion of his life was spent in controversy with them. It is therefore of interest to examine Scholastic physics briefly before turning to Galileo's work.

2.3 Scholastic mechanics. In the Aristotelian-Scholastic physical science there was a sharp dividing line between the worlds of terrestrial and celestial objects. All terrestrial matter, all matter within our physical reach, was considered to be a mixture of *four elements*, Earth, Water, Air, and Fire, it being understood that a lump of actual earth or a stone was endowed mainly with the singly unobtainable pure element, Earth. Each of these four elements was thought to have a "natural place" relative to the others in the terrestrial region. The highest place was allotted to Fire. Beneath Fire was Air, then Water, and finally, in the lowest position, Earth. Thus Fire would rise through Air, Air through Water, and Earth would fall through both Air and Water. Whether a particular object would

of its own accord move upward or downward was believed to be determined by the "desire" of the element most abundantly present within the
object to reach its own "natural place."

A good deal of common-sense "evidence" can be cited to support this
view. For example, Water bubbles up through Earth at springs. When
sufficient Fire is added to ordinary water, by heating it, the resulting
mixture of elements, steam, rises; when, on cooling, the steam gives up its
Fire, Water is again the predominant element and the condensed moisture
descends to its natural place. And in the vessel from which water has been
boiled away, a residue of earthy substance is found, showing that common
water contains, besides the element Water, some Earth as well.

There seemed to be abundant observations of this type in support of the
Aristotelian-Scholastic doctrine that a terrestrial object set free and permitted to move of its own accord experiences "natural motion" toward its
"natural place," so that objects move "naturally" straight upward if they
are "light," and straight downward if they are "heavy." But in addition
to natural motion, there is another type: "forced" or "violent" motion.
Thus when a stone is thrown, it is in "violent motion" for a time; it moves
upward and sidewise, which is not "natural" for an object consisting predominantly of the element Earth. Such a violent, unnatural motion can
only result from a violent agent, an external force presumably acting on
the stone for as long as it continues in violent motion. When this violent
motion ceases, natural motion begins, and the rock falls to the ground.

The celestial bodies, the stars and planets, appear to behave in a far
simpler manner. They were believed to consist not of the four ordinary
elements but solely of a fifth element, the *quintessence (quinta essentia)*,
for which the natural motion was endless revolution in circles around the
center of the Aristotelian universe, our earth. In short, although moving,
heavenly bodies were at all times in their natural places. They were thus
set apart from terrestrial objects, whose natural motion was largely a sign
of their absence from their own natural places.

This is a physical science of order and place. It fits many facts of everyday observation well. Moreover, these conceptions, in the original form,
were part of an imposing structure which Aristotle sought to erect in his
search for a unity of *all* thought and experience through an all-embracing
scheme relating elements nowadays separated into scientific, poetic,
ethical, and theological components. Yet difficulties appear when detailed
quantitative or even semiquantitative observations are begun. For instance, Aristotle made the following deduction from his theory:

> A given weight moves [falls] a given distance in a given time; a weight which
> is as great and more moves the same distance in a less time, the times being
> in inverse proportion to the weights. For instance, if one weight is twice
> another, it will take half as long over a given movement. (*De caelo*)

There is no record that Aristotle tested this deduction experimentally. In the 5th century A.D., however, John Philoponus said of it:

> But this is completely erroneous, and our view may be corroborated by actual observation more effectively than by any sort of verbal argument. For if you let fall from the same height two weights of which one is many times as heavy as the other, you will see that the ratio of the times required for the motion does not depend on the ratio of the weights, but that the difference in time is a very small one.*

The idea of violent motion also presented difficulties. Aristotle had generalized the common-sense notion that an object cannot undergo "violent" motion without a mover, without something pushing on it, and had concluded that a projectile must be propelled by a force while moving upward and sidewise through the air. To account for the source of this force he offered an ingenious suggestion: as was known, if one object hits a second and sets it into motion, the second object may set a third into motion by hitting it; since a projectile moving through the air is pushing the air from its path, thereby giving it the ability to move an object, and since this displaced air continuously goes around behind and fills the space being vacated by the projectile, it is this air that is pushing the projectile forward.

Now, in the 14th century, when the Scholastics began anew the study of this problem, they found perplexing difficulties in Aristotle's suggestion. If the air continuously displaced from in front of a projectile rushes around behind and serves as the propelling force, why is it that the projectile eventually stops moving violently and falls to the ground? Or if we throw two javelins, one with a pointed rear end and the other with a blunt rear end, why does not the latter go farther, since it has more surface upon which the air can push? These and other similar examples produced open skepticism in the 14th century as to the role of the air in the continuing motion of projectiles.

Thus by the year 1400 it was clear to European scientists that Aristotle was not an authority on matters of motion. Indeed, at the University of Paris one of the most influential teachers of all time, Jean Buridan, had taught that there was no motion in nature that is properly described by Aristotle. This was the period in which the University of Paris, "mother of universities," was graduating many chancellors of new universities, and Buridan's students included the founders of many of the great European centers of learning.

The realization that Aristotle's teachings concerning motion were untenable had little effect on the important position given to his writings,

---

*M. R. Cohen and I. E. Drabkin, *A source book in Greek science* (McGraw-Hill, 1948), p. 220.

since the study of motion was of major interest to comparatively few scholars. Aristotle had written in practically every area of human knowledge, including philosophy, political theory, literary criticism, and all of the sciences, and in general the Scholastics found what he had to say useful and meaningful. The Aristotelian writings therefore remained an important influence on all intellectual work despite the failings we have noted.

Two influences had a retarding effect even on the study of motion. First, Aristotle had believed that mathematics was of little value in describing change; and this was eventually found to be untrue, as we have already seen (Chapter 1). Second, he had put great emphasis upon qualitative observation as the basis for all theorizing; yet we shall see that too close an attention to mere appearances can place an excessive restraint upon the creative mind of the theorist. Indeed, the modern science of motion came into being with the work of those who, by abandoning the concentration on simply observed natural phenomena that characterized the later Scholastics, were thus able to reach a broader and more commanding view.

2.4 Biographical note on Galileo. We have already seen in Chapter 1 that the modern quantitative and descriptive approach to terrestrial motion is very different from the qualitative approach of Aristotle, and later we shall see that similarly drastic changes occurred in thinking concerning celestial motion. The new developments in both mechanics and astronomy come to fruition in the writings of Galileo Galilei, born in Pisa in 1564, the year of Shakespeare's birth and Michelangelo's death. He was the son of a Florentine nobleman from whom he acquired an active interest in poetry, music, and the classics. Galileo's inventiveness began to show itself early, when as a medical student at the University of Pisa he constructed a simple pendulum-type timing device for the accurate measurement of pulse rates.

Lured from medicine to physical science by the reading of Euclid and Archimedes, Galileo quickly became known for his unusual ability, and at the age of 26 he was appointed to the University Chair of Mathematics at Pisa. There he showed an independence of spirit and an inquisitive and forthright intellect unmellowed by tact or patience. Soon after his appointment he began to challenge the opinions of his colleagues, among whom he acquired many enemies. Indeed, before his tenure was completed he had to leave Pisa, evidently forced out by his enraged opponents. Later we find him at Padua in the republic of Venice, where he began his work in astronomy on behalf of the Copernican theory, which later was to bring him further enemies and suffering—as well as immortal fame.

Drawn back to his native Tuscany in 1610 by a generous offer of the Grand Duke, Galileo became the Court Mathematician and Philosopher, a title he chose himself. From then until his death at 78 in 1642, Galileo's life was continuously productive of excellent work, filled with research, teaching, and writing, despite recurring illness, family and money troubles, and the relentless and tragic fight with his enemies. He left us an orientation toward the world of phenomena that emphasized the mathematical approach to nature, a philosophy that has its roots in the Pythagorean and Platonic tradition and was in conflict with the qualitative approach that marked the Aristotelian tradition.

D I S C O R S I

E

DIMOSTRAZIONI

M A T E M A T I C H E,

intorno à due nuouc fcienze

Attenenti alla

MECANICA & i MOVIMENTI LOCALI,

del Signor

G A L I L E O G A L I L E I L I N C E O,

Filofofo e Matematico primario del Screniffimo
Grand Duca di Tofcana.

Con vna Appendice del centro di grauità d'alcuni Solidi.

I N L E I D A,
Appreffo gli Elfevirii. M. D. C. XXXVIII.

FIG. 2.1. Title page of Galileo's *Two new sciences* of 1638. (From the De-Golyer copy in the University of Oklahoma Library.)

2.5 Galileo's *Two new sciences*.   In his youth Galileo was taught Scholastic physics, and his early writings on mechanics are Scholastic in their approach. He seems to have shown a keen awareness of difficulties inherent in the mechanics he learned in the university, but his principal interest in his mature years was in astronomy. When his important astronomical work, *Dialogue on the great world systems* (1632), was condemned by the Inquisition and he was forbidden to teach the new astronomy in which he so ardently believed, he turned back to mechanics. His book, *Discourses and mathematical demonstrations concerning two new sciences pertaining to mechanics and local motion* (1638), usually referred to as the *"Two new sciences,"* was written while he was technically a prisoner of the Inquisition, and was published surreptitiously in Holland in 1638 (Fig. 2.1). And well might Galileo's enemies have feared his writings, for the mechanics described in the *Two new sciences* was the beginning of the end not only for Scholastic mechanics but for the entire Scholastic-Aristotelian cosmological system of which it was a part.

Even though he was old, sick, and going blind at the time, Galileo wrote in a clear and delightful style. He consciously and deliberately used the Socratic dialogue form—another indication of Plato's influence on him. We are introduced to three "speakers": *Simplicio*, representing the Aristotelian view; *Salviati*, who presents the new views of Galileo; and *Sagredo*, the uncommitted "good mind," willing and indeed eager to learn. Salviati leads his companions to Galileo's ("our author's") views, and even characterizes himself, as did Socrates, as "a good midwife of the mind." Of the four parts of the treatise, it is mainly the third and fourth that deal with the motion of falling bodies. Let us allow ourselves a rare luxury and listen to Galileo's three disputants as they discuss the problem of free fall in the *Two new sciences:**

> *Salviati:* I greatly doubt that Aristotle ever tested by experiment whether it be true that two stones, one weighing ten times as much as the other, if allowed to fall, at the same instant, from a height of, say, 100 cubits,† would so differ in speed that when the heavier had reached the ground, the other would not have fallen more than 10 cubits . . .
>
> *Sagredo:* . . . I, who have made the test, can assure you that a cannon ball weighing one or two hundred pounds, or even more, will not reach the ground by as much as a span ahead of a musket ball weighing only half a pound . . .

---

*Excerpts from the *Two new sciences* are after the translation of Crew and De Salvio, with some changes.

†Several "cubits" had been in use since antiquity, varying between about $17\frac{1}{2}$ and 20 inches. Thus the 181-ft Leaning Tower of Pisa is about 150 cubits in height. Incidentally, there is nothing in Galileo's own writings to substantiate the legend that he dropped objects from that tower in a public demonstration of Aristotle's error, nor do any of his contemporaries mention having witnessed such a public demonstration.

Simplicio: Your discussion is really admirable; yet I do not find it easy to believe that a bird-shot falls as swiftly as a cannon ball.

Salviati: Why not say a grain of sand as rapidly as a grindstone? But, Simplicio, I trust you will not follow the example of many others who divert the discussion from its main intent and fasten upon some statement of mine that lacks a hairsbreadth of the truth and, under this hair, hide the fault of another that is as big as a ship's cable. Aristotle says that "an iron ball of one hundred pounds falling from a height of 100 cubits reaches the ground before a one-pound ball has fallen a single cubit." I say that they arrive at the same time. You find, on making the experiment, that the larger outstrips the smaller by two fingerbreadths . . . ; now you would not hide behind these two fingers the 99 cubits of Aristotle, nor would you mention my small error and at the same time pass over in silence his very large one.

This is as clear a statement as we would wish of the principle that even very careful observation of natural events is not at all a sufficient basis for the formulation of a physical theory; different bodies falling freely in air indeed do *not* reach the ground at the very same instant; but this, on further thought, turns out to be far less significant than the realization that they do arrive at *almost* the same instant. Attention to this last point, one which is actually far removed from the immediate sense impressions gained in this experiment, is suggestive and fruitful, because it regards the failure of equal arrivals as a minor deviation instead of a major truth, as an experimental circumstance explainable by air friction. And indeed, when the air pump was invented soon after the time of Galileo, this hypothesis was confirmed by the observation that a feather and a coin inside an evacuated glass tube fall to the bottom of the tube in the same time.

We are reminded of the old saying that science has grown almost more by what it has learned to ignore than by what it has had to take into account. In this particular case, everything depended on being able to "think away" the effect of the air on free fall. This is easy enough for us who know of air pumps, but it was at that time conceptually almost impossible for several reasons, some evident, others quite subtle: for instance, the possibility of a vacuum existing in the terrestrial region had been denied by Aristotle as contrary to experience and incompatible with theory.

2.6 The motion of freely falling bodies. It was widely known before Galileo that the Aristotelian mechanics was inadequate, and hence a good deal of attention had been given to motion in a free fall. In attacking Aristotelian cosmology Galileo set himself the task of assembling concepts, methods of calculation and of measurement, and so forth, to arrive at a description of the motion of objects in rigorous mathematical form. Little of the detail of this work is new, but the whole provides a coherent and satisfactory theory of projectile motion. In the following excerpts from his *Two new sciences*, dealing directly with the motion of freely falling bodies, we must not lose sight of the main plan. First, Galileo will discuss the mathematics of a *possible*, simple type of motion, namely, motion with constant acceleration. Then he will assume or hypothesize that this is the type of motion that a heavy body undergoes during free fall. Third, he will deduce from this hypothesis some predictions that are amenable to experimental tests. Lastly, he will show that these tests do indeed bear out the predictions, thus confirming the fundamental assumption, namely, the constancy of acceleration in free fall.

Galileo introduces the discussion with these remarks:

> My purpose is to set forth a very new science dealing with a very ancient subject. There is, in nature, perhaps nothing older than motion, concerning which the books written by philosophers are neither few nor small; nevertheless I have discovered some properties of it that are worth knowing and that have not hitherto been either observed or demonstrated. Some superficial observations have been made, as, for instance, that the natural motion of a heavy falling body is continuously accelerated; but to just what extent this acceleration occurs has not yet been announced; for so far as I know, no one has yet pointed out that the distances traversed, during equal intervals of time, by a body falling from rest, stand to one another in the same ratio as the odd numbers beginning with unity [namely, 1:3:5:7 . . .].
>
> It has been observed that missiles and projectiles describe a curved path of some sort; however, no one has pointed out the fact that this path is a parabola. But this and other facts, not few in number or less worth knowing, I have succeeded in proving; *and what I consider more important*, there have been opened up to this vast and most excellent science, of which my work is merely the beginning, ways and means by which other minds more acute than mine will explore its remote corners.
>
> This discussion is divided into three parts: the first part deals with motion that is steady, or uniform; the second part, with motion as we find it accelerated in nature; the third part, with the so-called violent motions and with projectiles.

In the first part there is a thorough and searching discussion of motion with constant speed, along the lines indicated in our previous chapter. Then follows the second part, on "uniformly accelerated motion":

> We shall consider now naturally accelerated motion, such as that of falling bodies . . .
>
> First of all it seems desirable to find and explain a definition that best fits natural phenomena. Although certainly it is quite permissible to invent an arbitrary type of motion and study its course (as, indeed, some have proposed to themselves helices and conchoids as the paths described in certain motions—it being granted that nature does not make use of such—and have very commendably deduced the properties of these from their definitions), we however have decided to consider the phenomena of freely falling heavy bodies with an acceleration *such as actually occurs in nature*, and to make our definition

of accelerated motion exhibit the essential features of this type of natural accelerated motion. And this, at last, after repeated efforts we trust we have succeeded in doing. We are confirmed in this belief mainly by the consideration that experimental results are seen to agree and exactly correspond with those properties which have been described by us.

Finally, in the investigation of naturally accelerated motion we have been led, as if by the hand, by careful observation of the usage and precept of nature herself in all her other actions, in which she is accustomed to employ the simplest and easiest means . . .

When, therefore, I observe a stone initially at rest falling from an elevated position and continually acquiring new increments of speed, why should I not believe that such increases take place in a manner which is exceedingly simple and fairly easily apprehended by everybody? If now we examine the matter carefully, we find no addition or increment more simple than that which repeats itself always in the same manner. This we readily understand when we consider the intimate relationship between time and motion; for just as uniform motion is defined by and thought of in terms of equal time intervals and equal distances (thus we call a motion uniform when equal distances are traversed during equal time intervals), so also we may, in similar manner, by thinking in terms of equal time intervals, conceive additions of velocity as taking place without complication; . . .

Hence the definition of the motion which we are about to discuss may be stated as follows:

A body is said to be uniformly accelerated when, starting from rest, it acquires equal increments of velocity during equal time intervals.

Sagredo: Although I can offer no rational objection to this or indeed to any other definition, devised by any author whosoever, since all definitions are arbitrary, I may nevertheless without offense be allowed to doubt whether such a definition as the foregoing, established in an abstract manner, corresponds to and describes that kind of accelerated motion which we meet in nature in the case of freely falling bodies. . . .

The discussion now turns toward the only correct answer to this excellent question, namely, that Galileo's "arbitrary" definition of acceleration [which we may write as $a = (v - v_0)/t$ for this case of constant acceleration] happens to be most useful for describing the experimental facts of real, observable motion. But there is first a significant little excursion when Sagredo proposes:

From these considerations perhaps we can obtain an answer to a question that has been argued by philosophers, namely, what is the *cause* of the acceleration of the natural motion of heavy bodies . . .

Salviati, the spokesman of Galileo, sternly turns away from this persistent preoccupation of the previous two millennia with the exhortation that it is premature to inquire into the cause of motion until one has obtained an accurate description of motion:

Salviati: The present does not seem to be the proper time to investigate the cause of the acceleration of natural motion concerning which various opinions have been expressed by various philosophers, some explaining it by attraction to the center, others by repulsion between the very small parts of the body, while still others attribute it to a certain stress in the surrounding medium which closes in behind the falling body and drives it from one of its positions to another. Now, all these fantasies, and others too, ought to be examined; but it is not really worth while. At present it is the purpose of our Author [Galileo] merely to investigate and to demonstrate some of the properties of accelerated motion whatever the cause of this acceleration may be.

Galileo at this point admits having at one time entertained a different hypothesis about freely falling bodies, namely, that the speed acquired is proportional, not to the time of fall, but to the *distance* covered. Both of these hypotheses had been advanced as early as the 14th century, and both evidently meet Galileo's requirement of simplicity of relationship. However, by appealing to a plausible experiment which he asks us to *imagine* (a *thought experiment*, one of the very useful devices in the physicist's kit of methods) he shows how the hypothesis that the speed acquired is proportional to the distance fallen leads to predictions that are not in accord with the facts of observation. We shall omit the argument that Galileo employed, but it should be remarked at this point that his argument turned out to be faulty, although the conclusion he reached is correct.

2.7 The experimental test of Galileo's hypothesis. Galileo is now convinced that the most reasonable hypothesis for a freely falling body is that the speed v acquired is proportional to the time t elapsed; in other words, that the acceleration a, given by $(v - v_0)/t = a$, is constant. But "reasonableness" is not sufficient to justify acceptance of a hypothesis, so his next step is to show that the hypothesis is in accord with the observed facts. This would seem to be easy: simply drop a heavy object from several different heights, say from windows on different floors of a building or tower, always with an initial speed of zero ($v_0 = 0$), and for each height of fall observe the time of fall t and the speed v just before the object strikes the ground; then compute the ratio v/t ($=a$) for each height to see whether it does always have the same value. But to make *direct* measurements of the speed v would be difficult even today, and as for the times of fall t, they are far too small (less than 3 sec even from the top of a 10-story building) to have been measured accurately with the crude clocks available to Galileo.

The inability to make *direct* tests of his "reasonable" hypothesis that $a = $ constant does not stop Galileo. Instead, he characteristically turns to mathematics and seeks to derive from his hypothesis some other relationship that possibly can be tested with the facilities available to him. Using a method of derivation similar to the one we employed in the preceding chapter, he succeeds in deriving the relation which is now written $s = v_0 t + \frac{1}{2}at^2$, where s is the distance that will be traversed in time t by a body assumed to be moving with a constant acceleration a. For a body dropped from rest ($v_0 = 0$), the relationship to be tested becomes $s = \frac{1}{2}at^2$, which we may rewrite as $s/t^2 = \frac{1}{2}a$. Then, if measurements made on falling bodies show that s/t^2 has the same value for various heights of fall s, it follows that the acceleration a is constant.

The advantage of this new relationship is that, unlike the previous one, it does not contain the speed v, which Galileo could not measure. Instead, it contains the distance s, which is directly and easily measured. But with the times of fall t there is the same difficulty as before. Only in the present century has it been possible to make accurate *direct* tests of the relationship $s/t^2 = \frac{1}{2}a$ in free fall, for example by dropping an illuminated object at night from an airplane and photographing its path of fall. The times along the path are marked on the photographic plate by means of a device attached to the camera shutter, which momentarily closes the shutter at intervals known to an accuracy of about 0.003 sec.

Galileo, realizing that it will still be impossible for him to carry out quantitative tests with freely falling bodies, continues the chain of argument and proposes another and much more easily testable consequence of his hypothesis, "the truth of which will be established when we find that the inferences from it correspond and agree exactly with experiment."

The new consequence which he deduces is this: if a freely falling body has an acceleration that is constant, then it follows that a "perfectly round" ball rolling down a "perfectly smooth" inclined plane will also have a constant, though smaller, acceleration. Thus, if s/t^2 ($=\frac{1}{2}a$) is constant for a body falling freely from rest, this ratio will also have a constant value, although a smaller one, for a ball released from rest and rolling different distances down an inclined plane. The effect of the inclined plane is merely to slow down the whole experiment, to "dilute" the effect of gravity. Here is an experiment that provides an indirect test of Galileo's "reasonable hypothesis" and that can be carried out with acceptable accuracy. On an inclined plane of gentle slope, the times of descent of the ball are of conveniently measurable magnitude. Moreover, the ball travels distances so short that the same observer can without difficulty both control its time of release and note the time of arrival at any given point.

Let us listen to Salviati describing the experimental test:

> We took a piece of wooden scantling, about 12 cubits long, half a cubit wide, and three fingerbreadths thick. In its top edge we cut a straight channel a little more than one finger in breadth; this groove was made smooth by lining it with parchment, polished as smooth as possible, to facilitate the rolling in it of a smooth and very round ball made of the hardest bronze. Having placed

the scantling in a sloping position by raising one end some one or two cubits above the other, we let the ball roll down the channel, noting, in a manner presently to be described, the time required for the descent. We repeated this experiment more than once in order to be sure of the time of descent and found that the deviation between two observations never exceeded one-tenth of a pulse beat. Having performed this operation until assured of its reliability, we now let the ball roll down only one-quarter of the length of the channel; and having measured the time of its descent, we found it to be precisely one-half of the former. Next we tried other distances, comparing the time for the whole length with that for the half, or for two-thirds, or for three-fourths, or indeed for any fraction. In such experiments, repeated a full hundred times, we always found that the distances traversed were to each other as the squares of the times, and this was true for *any* inclination of the . . . channel along which we rolled the ball . . .

The last sentence contains two crucially important points. For any two distances s_1 and s_2 covered by the rolling ball on an incline of fixed angle θ with the horizontal, the corresponding intervals t_1 and t_2 are, by measurement, related as $s_1/s_2 = t_1^2/t_2^2$; hence $s_1/t_1^2 = s_2/t_2^2 = $ constant, as Galileo had expected to find. In a concrete case, for a given angle θ and the distances $s_1 = 20$ ft and $s_2 = 5.0$ ft measured from the top along the inclined plane, we may find experimentally that the time taken for the rolling motion is $t_1 = 2.0$ sec and $t_2 = 1.0$ sec respectively. We note that $s_1/t_1^2 = 5.0$ units and $s_2/t_2^2 = 5.0$ units also; hence $s_1/t_1^2 = s_2/t_2^2 = $ constant.

The second main point is this: when the angle θ of the inclined plane is changed, say increased by $10°$, the ratio s/t^2 is again found to have the same value for long and short distances of descent of the rolling ball, although of course the whole motion is now faster. For example, if $s_1 = 20$ ft and $s_2 = 5.0$ ft, as before, the time of descent may now be found to be $t_1 = 1.7$ sec and $t_2 = 0.85$ sec respectively, so that the ratios s_1/t_1^2 and s_2/t_2^2 again have equal values (6.9 units in this case). Now clearly, if the statement $s/t^2 = $ constant is found to be independent of the angle of inclination θ for those values of θ where measurements of t can be carried out conveniently, we shall be tempted to propose that the same statement holds even for larger values of θ where the motion of the ball is too fast for accurate measurements of t to be made. And then it is only one step more to regard *free fall* merely as the extreme case in this series of experiments, namely, the case where the angle of inclination, θ, has become $90°$, and the ball descends along a straight vertical line. *Hence the statement $s/t^2 = $ constant, verified on the inclined plane, may be assumed to apply to free fall also.*

But some obvious doubts arise concerning the validity of this chain of reasoning. First, was Galileo's measurement of time t accurate enough to establish the constancy of s/t^2 even for the earlier case of a slowly rolling object? Galileo tries to reassure expected critics by continuing his rather detailed description of the experimental arrangement, and thereby also invites indirectly the repetition of the experiments he is describing:

> For the measurement of time, we employed a large vessel of water placed in an elevated position; to the bottom of this vessel was soldered a pipe of small diameter giving a thin jet of water, which we collected in a small cup during the time of each descent, whether for the whole length of the channel or for a part of its length; the water thus collected was weighed on a very accurate balance; the differences and ratios of these weights gave us the differences and ratios of the time intervals, and this with such accuracy that, although the operation was repeated many, many times, there was no appreciable discrepancy in the results.

A second cause for doubting the series of hypotheses above is one evident difference between a rolling ball and a falling ball. As the angle θ of the inclination is increased, there comes a point where the ball starts to move forward without rotating on its central axis. This is a discontinuity in behavior, and endangers the assumption that the same general law applies to both cases. Galileo does not explicitly answer this objection; we could do it for him by showing that experimentally the same constancy of the ratio s/t^2 is observed to hold for blocks which slide without rolling on a smooth incline, and framing all conclusions in terms of this modification of the experiment. Moreover, we should stress that the material of the object and its weight do not affect the constancy relation either.

In summary, observation on bodies moving on a smooth inclined plane shows, within the limits of accuracy of the experiment, that the ratio s/t^2 is constant, and that this constancy is not dependent on the angle of inclination. Hence the relation may be assumed to apply to the case of free fall also. But the relation $s/t^2 = $ constant was derived on the assumption that the *acceleration* of the object is constant. Turning the argument around, we say with Galileo that our experimental verification of a consequence deduced from the assumption has put the assumption itself in a good light; *the hypothesis that in free fall bodies have a constant acceleration has yielded a verifiable prediction and thereby has become more than merely "reasonable."*

This is a typical method of testing hypotheses. We note that we cannot strictly claim that this process yields certainty. A wrong hypothesis can sometimes also lead to correct predictions; these and other methodological problems will be discussed in greater detail in Part IV. But in the present case, the belief in the correctness of the hypothesis may be quickly strengthened by showing additional successes deriving from it—for example, by its subsequent application in the prediction of more general projectile motions, to which the next chapter is dedicated. Galileo himself was aware of the potentialities inherent in both the results and the methods of his pioneering work on motion, of which we have so far discussed only a brief fragment. He concluded his treatment of naturally accelerated motion on a prophetic note:

> The theorems set forth in this brief discussion, if they come into the hands of other investigators, will continually lead to wonderful new knowledge. It is conceivable that in such a manner a worthy treatment may be gradually extended to all the realms of nature.

PROBLEMS

2.1. What are our present-day objections to Aristotle's system of elements? Why might these objections have been unimportant in the eyes of an Aristotelian?

2.2. Read through Galileo's "Third day" in the *Two new sciences* in order to find what his arguments were for thinking that the law of motions for a smooth inclined plane are the same as for free fall.

2.3. List the steps outlined in this chapter by which Galileo progressed from his first definition of uniformly accelerated motion to his final confirmation that this definition is useful for describing the motion of a freely falling body. Identify each step as a hypothesis, deduction, observation, or computation, etc. What limitations and idealizations entered into the argument?

2.4. Read Galileo's "Third day" to Theorem IV. Then restate as concisely as possible the argument leading to the conclusion that the acceleration a of an object sliding on a smooth inclined plane is to the acceleration in free fall g as the vertical height of the plane h is to the length of the plane l or, in short, that $a = g \sin \theta$ (Fig. 2.2).

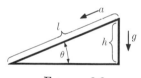

FIGURE 2.2

2.5. At the very start of his discussion of free fall, Galileo, as quoted, points out that "the distances traversed, during equal intervals of time, by a body falling from rest, stand to one another in the same ratio as the odd numbers beginning with unity [namely, $1:3:5:7\ldots$]." Prove that this statement is correct, starting with the assumption that freely falling bodies are uniformly accelerated.

SUPPLEMENTARY READING

Note: The references listed here are intended to guide you to stimulating sources if you wish to carry this subject further. The excepts from the original writings are especially recommended, for, as Ernst Mach wrote, "There is no grander nor more intellectually elevating spectacle than that of the utterances of the fundamental investigators in their gigantic power."

BUTTERFIELD, H., *The origins of modern science: 1300–1800* (G. Bell, London, 1949; Macmillan, 1951 and later), Chaps. 1 and 5.

COOPER, L., *Aristotle, Galileo, and the tower of Pisa* (Cornell University Press, 1935).

CREW, H., *The rise of modern physics* (Williams and Wilkins, Baltimore, 1935), Chap. IV.

DE SANTILLANA, G., *The crime of Galileo* (University of Chicago Press, 1955).

FAHIE, J. J., *Galileo, his life and work* (James Pott, New York, 1903).

GALILEO GALILEI, *Two new sciences,* trans. by H. Crew and A. De Salvio under the title of *Dialogues concerning two new sciences* (Macmillan, 1914, 1933; Northwestern University Press, 1936, 1946, 1950; Dover Publications, 1952). See pp. 105–112 (bracketed page numbers) of the "First day" and all the "Third day." Excerpts of the latter are in Vol. 2 of James R. Newman's *The world of mathematics* (Simon and Schuster, 1956).

HALL, A. R., *The scientific revolution 1500–1800* (Longmans, Green, 1954; Beacon Press, 1956), Chaps. III and VI.

KLINE, M., *Mathematics in western culture* (Oxford University Press, 1953), Chaps. VII, VIII, and XIII.

KNEDLER, J. W., JR., *Masterworks of science* (Doubleday, 1947). Biographical notes and condensed excerpts, e.g., pp. 75–151, Galileo.

KOYRÉ, A., "Galileo and Plato," *Journal of the History of Ideas,* v. 4 (1943), pp. 400 ff. Reprinted in P. P. Wiener and A. Noland, *Roots of scientific thought* (Basic Books, 1957).

MAGIE, W. F., *A source book in physics* (McGraw-Hill, 1935). Short and valuable biographical notes and excerpts, e.g., Galileo's work on falling bodies, pp. 1–17.

WERTHEIMER, M., *Productive thinking* (Harper, 1945), Chap VI. The thought processes which may have guided Galileo in his development of the laws of motion are discussed from the point of view of Gestalt psychology with insight and lucidity.

WHITEHEAD, A. N., *Essays in science and philosophy* (Philosophical Library, 1947), pp. 227–242.

WHITEHEAD, A. N., *Science and the modern world* (Macmillan, 1925; also Pelican Mentor Book M28, 1948), Chap. I.

CHAPTER 3

PROJECTILE MOTION

3.1 Galileo's discussion of projectile motion. To this point we have been solely concerned with the motion of objects as characterized by their speed; we have not given much consideration to the *direction* of motion, or to changes in direction of motion. Turning now to the more general problem of projectile motion, we leave the relatively simple case of bodies moving in a *straight line* only and expand our methods to deal with projectiles moving along curved paths. Our understanding of this field will hinge largely on a far-reaching idea: the observed motion of a projectile may be thought of as the result of two *separate* motions, combined and occurring *simultaneously;* one component of motion is in a horizontal direction and without acceleration, whereas the other is in a vertical direction and has a constant acceleration downward in accordance with the laws of free fall. Furthermore, these two components do not interfere with each other; each component may be studied as if the other were not present. Thus the whole motion of the projectile at every moment is simply the result of the two individual actions.

This principle of the independency of the horizontal and vertical components of projectile motion was set forth by Galileo in his *Dialogue on the great world systems* (1632). Although in this work he was principally concerned with astronomy, Galileo already knew that terrestrial mechanics offered the clue to a better understanding of planetary motions. Like the *Two new sciences*, this earlier work is cast in the form of a discussion among the same three characters, and also uses the Socratic method of the Platonic dialogues. Indeed, the portion of interest to us here begins with Salviati reiterating one of Socrates' most famous phrases, as he tells the Aristotelian Simplicio that he, Simplicio, knows far more about mechanics than he is aware:*

> *Salviati:* ... Yet I am so good a midwife of minds that I will make you confess the same whether you will or no. But Sagredus stands very quiet, and yet, if I mistake not, I saw him make some move as if to speak.
> *Sagredo:* I had intended to speak a fleeting something; but my curiosity aroused by your promising that you would force Simplicius to uncover the knowledge which he conceals from us has made me depose all other thoughts. Therefore I pray you to make good your vaunt.

---

*These extracts from Galileo's *Dialogue on the great world systems,* as well as those appearing in later chapters, are taken from the translation of T. Salusbury, edited and corrected by Giorgio de Santillana (University of Chicago Press, 1953).

Salviati: Provided that Simplicius consents to reply to what I shall ask him, I will not fail to do it.

Simplicio: I will answer what I know, assured that I shall not be much put to it, for, of those things which I hold to be false, I think nothing can be known, since Science concerns truths, not falsehoods.

Salviati: I do not desire that you should say that you know anything, save that which you most assuredly know. Therefore, tell me; if you had here a flat surface as polished as a mirror and of a substance as hard as steel that was not horizontal but somewhat inclining, and you put upon it a perfectly spherical ball, say, of bronze, what do you think it would do when released? Do you not believe (as for my part I do) that it would lie still?

Simplicio: If the surface were inclining?

Salviati: Yes, as I have already stated.

Simplicio: I cannot conceive how it should lie still. I am confident that it would move towards the declivity with much propenseness.

Salviati: Take good heed what you say, Simplicius, for I am confident that it would lie still in whatever place you should lay it.

Simplicio: So long as you make use of such suppositions, Salviatus, I shall cease to wonder if you conclude most absurd conclusions.

Salviati: Are you assured, then, that it would freely move towards the declivity?

Simplicio: Who doubts it?

Salviati: And this you verily believe, not because I told you so (for I endeavored to persuade you to think the contrary), but of yourself, and upon your natural judgment?

Simplicio: Now I see your game; you did not say this really believing it, but to try me, and to wrest words out of my mouth with which to condemn me.

Salviati: You are right. And how long and with what velocity would that ball move? But take notice that I gave as the example a ball exactly round, and a plane exquisitely polished, so that all external and accidental impediments might be taken away. Also I would have you remove all obstructions caused by the air's resistance and any other causal obstacles, if any other there can be.

Simplicio: I understand your meaning very well and answer that the ball would continue to move *in infinitum* if the inclination of the plane should last so long, accelerating continually. Such is the nature of ponderous bodies that they acquire strength in going, and, the greater the declivity, the greater the velocity will be.

Simplicio is next led to express his belief that if he observed the ball rolling *up* the inclined plane he would know that it had been pushed or thrown, since it is moving contrary to its natural tendencies. Then Salviati turns to the intermediate case:

Salviati: It seems, then, that hitherto you have well explained to me the accidents of a body on two different planes. Now tell me, what would befall the same body upon a surface that had neither acclivity nor declivity?

Simplicio: Here you must give me a little time to consider my answer. There being no declivity, there can be no natural inclination to motion; and there being no acclivity, there can be no resistance to being moved. There would then arise an indifference between propulsion and resistance; therefore, I think it ought naturally stand still. But I had forgot myself; it was not long ago that Sagredus gave me to understand that it would do so.

Salviati: So I think, provided one did lay it down gently; but, if it had an impetus directing it towards any part, what would follow?

Simplicio: That it should move towards that part.

Salviati: But with what kind of motion? Continually accelerated, as in declining planes; or successively retarded, as in those ascending?

Simplicio: I cannot tell how to discover any cause of acceleration or retardation, there being no declivity or acclivity.

Salviati: Well, if there be no cause of retardation, even less should there be any cause of rest. How long therefore would you have the body move?

Simplicio: As long as that surface, neither inclined nor declined, shall last.

Salviati: Therefore if such a space were interminate, the motion upon it would likewise have no termination, that is, would be perpetual.

Simplicio: I think so, if the body is of a durable matter.

Salviati: That has been already supposed when it was said that all external and accidental impediments were removed, and the brittleness of the body in this case is one of those accidental impediments. Tell me now, what do you think is the cause that that same ball moves spontaneously upon the inclining plane, and does not, except with violence, upon the plane sloping upwards?

Simplicio: Because the tendency of heavy bodies is to move towards the center of the Earth and only by violence upwards towards the circumference. [This is the kernel of the Scholastic viewpoint on falling bodies (see Section 2.3). Salviati does not refute it, but turns it to Galileo's purposes.]

Salviati: Therefore a surface which should be neither declining nor ascending ought in all its parts to be equally distant from the center. But is there any such surface in the world?

Simplicio: There is no want of it, such is our terrestrial globe, for example, if it were not rough and mountainous. But you have that of the water, at such time as it is calm and still.

Here is the genesis of one of the fundamental principles of the new mechanics: if all "accidental" interferences with an object's motion are removed, the motion will endure. The "accidents" are eliminated in this thought experiment by: (1) proposing the use of a perfectly round, perfectly hard ball on a perfectly smooth surface, and (2) by imagining the surface to be a globe whose surface is everywhere equidistant from the center of the earth, so that the ball's "natural tendency" to go downward is balanced by the upward thrust of the surface. (We shall return to this latter point in our discussion of isolated systems in Chapter 16.) Note carefully the drastic change from the Scholastic view: instead of asking "What makes the ball move?" Galileo asks "What might change its motion?"

Having turned the conversation to smooth water, Galileo brings in the motion of a stone dropping from the mast of a moving ship. Since the stone is moving horizontally with the ship before it is dropped, it should continue to move horizontally while it falls.

Sagredo: If it be true that the impetus with which the ship moves remains indelibly impressed in the stone after it is let fall from the mast; and if it be further true that this motion brings no impediment or retardment to the motion directly downwards natural to the stone, then there ought to ensue an effect of a very wonderful nature. Suppose a ship stands still, and the time of the falling of a stone from the mast's round top to the deck is two beats of the pulse. Then afterwards have the ship under sail and let the same stone depart from the same place. According to what has been premised, it shall still take up the time of two pulses in its fall, in which time the ship will have gone, say, twenty yards. The true motion of the stone then will be a transverse line [i.e., a curved line in the vertical plane, see Fig. 3.1], considerably longer than the first straight and perpendicular line, the height of the mast, and yet nevertheless the stone will have passed it in the same time. Increase the ship's velocity as much as you will, the falling stone shall describe its transverse lines still longer and longer and yet shall pass them all in those selfsame two pulses. In this same fashion, if a cannon were lev-

FIG. 3.1. A stone dropped from the mast of a ship in uniform motion. From the shore the trajectory of the stone is seen to be a curved line (parabola).

eled on the top of a tower, and fired point-blank, that is, horizontally, and whether the charge were small or large with the ball falling sometimes a thousand yards distant, sometimes four thousand, sometimes ten, etc., all these shots shall come to ground in times equal to each other. And every one equal to the time that the ball would take to pass from the mouth of the piece to the ground, if, without other impulse, it falls simply downwards in a perpendicular line. Now it seems a very admirable thing that, in the same short time of its falling perpendicularly down to the ground from the height of, say, a hundred yards, equal balls, fired violently out of the piece,

Fig. 3.2. For cannon balls fired horizontally with different initial forward speeds, "all the balls in all the shots made horizontally remain in the air an equal time."

should be able to pass four hundred, a thousand, even ten thousand yards. All the balls in all the shots made horizontally remain in the air an equal time [Fig. 3.2].

Salviati: The consideration is very elegant for its novelty and, if the effect be true, very admirable. Of its truth I make no question, and, were it not for the accidental impediment of the air, I verily believe that, if at the time of the ball's going out of the piece another were let fall from the same height directly downwards, they would both come to the ground at the same instant, though one should have traveled ten thousand yards in its range, and another only a hundred, presupposing the surface of the Earth to be level. As for the impediment which might come from the air, it would consist in retarding the extreme swift motion of the shot.

3.2 Projectile launched horizontally. Galileo's two thought experiments may be rephrased and analyzed in terms of two modern examples.

(1) If we watch an airplane in steady horizontal flight drop a small, heavy object, we shall see that the object remains very nearly *directly below* the plane while, of course, dropping closer and closer to the ground (Fig. 3.3). If we had been riding in the plane when the object was dropped, we would have seen only the horizontal part (component) of the motion; that is, we would have seen the object traveling along directly under the plane, although of course appearing to become smaller and smaller as it receded toward the ground. The clear implication is that *the horizontal component of the motion of the object remains what it was at the moment of release from the plane*, even though there is superposed on it the ever-increasing speed downward.

(2) In the second experiment we place two similar small spheres at the

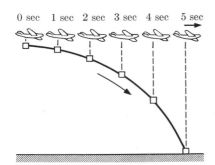

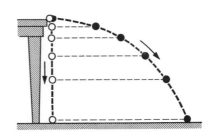

FIG. 3.3. Successive positions, at equal time intervals, of an object dropped from an airplane.

FIG. 3.4. Trajectories of an object projected horizontally (solid circles) and of an object dropped simultaneously (open circles).

edge of a table (Fig. 3.4). At the moment that one sphere is given a strong horizontal push, so that it flies off rapidly and makes a wide, curved trajectory, the other is touched only very gently so that it drops straight down to the floor. Which sphere will land first?

Experience shows that they land together, no matter what the initial horizontal speed of the pushed ball. Furthermore, the balls remain at equal levels throughout their fall, though of course the horizontal distance between them gradually increases, one having a large (and, by the previous experiment, presumably undiminishing) horizontal speed and the other having none. The conclusion here is that *the vertical component of the motion is quite independent of any accompanying horizontal movement.*

The conclusion from both experiments is that motion in a plane can be resolved into two components, the horizontal and the vertical, and that these are independent. This means that we may treat them separately and individually. Since the horizontal part of the motion occurs with constant speed, as shown by the first experiment, it is completely described by Eq. (1.1),

$$s = vt. \tag{1.1}$$

As for the vertical part of the motion, it occurs without initial downward speed ($v_0 = 0$) and with a constant acceleration g, and is completely described by Eqs. (1.7). Setting $v_0 = 0$ and $a = g$ in those equations yields

$$
\begin{aligned}
v &= gt, & \text{(I)} \\
s &= \tfrac{1}{2}gt^2, & \text{(II)} \\
s &= \tfrac{1}{2}vt, & \text{(III)} \\
v^2 &= 2gs. & \text{(IV)}
\end{aligned}
\tag{3.1}
$$

Thus Galileo's principle of the independency of the horizontal and vertical components of projectile motion enables us to study such motion, even though it is complicated, with the help of equations that are already familiar to us. For example, consider these questions: for the projectile pictured in Fig. 3.3, (1) what was its range (the horizontal distance from the starting to the landing point) and (2) what was the total vertical distance through which it fell? Suppose that the speed of the airplane was v (ft/sec) and that the total time of fall of the projectile was t (sec). Then, assuming that the horizontal part of the motion occurred with constant speed, the range of the projectile was equal to v (ft/sec) $\times$ t (sec), that is, vt (ft). Simultaneously, the projectile underwent a vertically downward displacement equal to that of a body falling freely from rest in the time t; that is, its downward acceleration was g (ft/sec^2) and therefore the vertical distance fallen was $\frac{1}{2}gt^2$ (ft).

In dealing with projectile motion, the s and v in Eq. (1.1) refer to the horizontal component of motion, whereas the s and v in Eqs. (3.1) refer to the vertical component. It is obviously desirable to distinguish between these symbols, and a simple way to do this is to attach the subscript x to the symbols for horizontal quantities, and the subscript y to those for vertical quantities. Thus, we rewrite Eq. (1.1) in the form

$$s_x = v_x t, \tag{3.2}$$

where s_x is the distance that the projectile has moved horizontally in the time interval t, *without regard to the distance fallen*, and v_x is the constant speed of the projectile in the horizontal direction. If, for example, the projectile is dropped from an airplane in horizontal flight, v_x is the speed of the plane at the moment of release.

Similarly, for the vertical part of the motion, we rewrite Eqs. (1.7) in the forms

$$
\begin{aligned}
v_y &= gt, &\text{(I)}\\
s_y &= \tfrac{1}{2}gt^2, &\text{(II)}\\
s_y &= \tfrac{1}{2}v_y t, &\text{(III)}\\
v_y^2 &= 2gs_y, &\text{(IV)}
\end{aligned}
\tag{3.3}
$$

where s_y is the distance moved vertically and v_y is the vertical speed acquired during the time interval t.

Notice that we do not need a subscript for t; this symbol represents the time required for the projectile to reach any particular point on its trajectory, and is the same for both the horizontal and vertical parts of the motion undergone in reaching that point. Finally, we must remember the "text" that goes along with our equations, for example, that they are valid only so long as air resistance does not appreciably retard the motion of the projectile.

EXAMPLE 3.1. A plane flying south in a horizontal line at 300 mi/hr drops a bomb. How far south of the point of release will the bomb be 5.0 sec later?

Solution. Assuming that the bomb has not reached the ground in 5 sec and that the the effect of air resistance is inappreciable, we have $v_x = 300$ mi/hr $= 440$ ft/sec, $t = 5.0$ sec, $s_x = ?$, and from Eq. (3–2),

$$s_x = v_x t = (440 \text{ ft/sec}) \times (5.0 \text{ sec}) = 2.2 \times 10^3 \text{ ft.}$$

EXAMPLE 3.2. How much time was needed for the bomb in Example 3.1 to move 1500 ft south of the point of release?

Solution. $s_x = 1500$ ft, $v_x = 440$ ft/sec, $t = ?$, and from Eq. (3.2),

$$t = s_x/v_x = (1500 \text{ ft})/(440 \text{ ft/sec}) = 3.4 \text{ sec.}$$

EXAMPLE 3.3. A ball is thrown horizontally from the top of a building 20.0 m high. How far below the starting point will it be in 2.00 sec?

Solution. $g = 9.80$ m/sec^2, $t = 2.00$ sec, $s_y = ?$, and from Eq. (3.3, II),

$$s_y = \tfrac{1}{2}gt^2 = \tfrac{1}{2}(9.80 \text{ m/sec}^2) \times (2.00 \text{ sec})^2$$
$$= \tfrac{1}{2} \times 9.80 \times 4.00 (\text{m/sec}^2)(\text{sec}^2) = 19.6 \text{ m.}$$

EXAMPLE 3.4. How long will it take the ball of Example 3.3 to reach the street?

Solution. $s_y = 20.0$ m, $g = 9.80$ m/sec^2, $t = ?$ Solving Eq. (3.3, II) for the time, we have $t^2 = 2s_y/g$, or

$$t = \sqrt{2s_y/g} = \sqrt{2 \times 20.0 \text{ m}/(9.80 \text{ m/sec}^2)} = \sqrt{4.08 \text{ sec}^2} = 2.02 \text{ sec.}$$

PROBLEM 3.1. A ball is thrown horizontally from a window, with a speed of 10 ft/sec. How far will it move horizontally in 3.0 sec?

PROBLEM 3.2. A stone is thrown horizontally from the top of a building 50.0 m high. How far will it fall in 3.00 sec?

3.3 Displacement of a projectile. Vector quantities.

When a projectile has reached a point P of its trajectory (Fig. 3.5), it is a straight-line distance s ($=OP$) away from the point of release. Since s corresponds in magnitude to the diagonal of a rectangle of which s_x and s_y are adjacent sides, we may compute its magnitude with the help of the Pythagorean theorem of plane geometry:

$$s = \sqrt{s_x^2 + s_y^2}. \qquad (3.4)$$

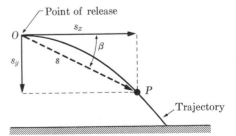

FIG. 3.5. The displacement s of a projectile has both magnitude and direction.

The distances s_x and s_y are called the *x- and y-components of the total displacement s*. This total displacement s of the projectile from the point of release is in a certain definite direction. A convenient way to describe this direction is to state the angle β which the displacement makes with the horizontal, since this angle can be computed from the relation*

$$\tan \beta = \frac{s_y}{s_x}. \tag{3.5}$$

To specify *completely* the displacement of an object we must give both its *magnitude* (s in Eq. 3.4) and its *direction* (by calculating angle β in Eq. 3.5). A physical quantity that has both magnitude and direction is known as a *vector quantity*, whereas one that has magnitude only is called a *scalar quantity*. Displacement is a vector quantity and we shall later encounter others, such as *velocity* and *force;* further details on vector calculations will be presented in Section 5.4 and in Appendix G.

It is a more difficult problem, and one that we shall not try to solve, to determine not the displacement s of the projectile but the distance it actually travels along the curved trajectory. This quantity happens to be fairly unimportant to us; the displacement s or its components s_x and s_y are the more sought-after quantities.

EXAMPLE 3.5.   A projectile falls 900 ft while moving 100 ft horizontally. Compute its displacement.

Solution. $s_x = 100$ ft, $s_y = 900$ ft, $s = ?$ From Eq. (3.4),

$$s = \sqrt{s_x^2 + s_y^2} = \sqrt{(100 \text{ ft})^2 + (900 \text{ ft})^2}$$

$$= \sqrt{82.0 \times 10^4 \text{ ft}^2} = 9.06 \times 10^2 \text{ ft}.$$

From Eq. (3.5),

$$\tan \beta = s_y/s_x = (900 \text{ ft})/(100 \text{ ft}) = 9.00.$$

From the table of Appendix F,

$$\beta = 83.6°,$$

and from the context it is clear that the angle is 83.6° below the horizontal. Thus the displacement is 9.06×10^2 ft at 83.6° below the horizontal.

PROBLEM 3.3.   At a certain moment a projectile has reached a point P on its trajectory such that the horizontal and vertical components of its displacement from the starting point O are 210 m and 280 m, respectively. Find the magnitude and direction of the displacement.

3.4 Plotting the trajectory.   We have seen how, for an object projected horizontally, Eqs. (3.2) and (3.3, II) enable us to compute the two displacement components s_x and s_y for any particular time interval t after release. Calculation of the values of these two components for a number of

---

*See Appendix E for a summary of trigonometric relations.

different time intervals evidently will give us the data needed to plot a graph showing the location of the projectile at any moment during its flight.

EXAMPLE 3.6. A plane flying 225 mi/hr west at an altitude of 1000 ft drops an object. Compute the components of the displacement for successive seconds after release, and plot the trajectory.

Solution.　$v_x = 225$ mi/hr $= 330$ ft/sec; $s_x = v_x \times t = 330$ (ft/sec) $\times t$; $g = 32.2$ ft/sec², $s_y = \frac{1}{2}gt^2 = \frac{1}{2} \times 32.2$ (ft/sec²) $\times t^2 = 16.1t^2$ (ft/sec²).

Substituting values of $t = 1$ sec, 2 sec, ... successively into Eqs. (3.2) and (3.3, II), we obtain pairs of values of s_x and s_y that yield a series of points determining the trajectory. This is shown in the following tabulation, and the graph of Fig. 3.6 is derived from these values. (Note that this type of calculation can be made with incredible speed by electronic computers such as help to guide an interceptor toward an approaching ballistic projectile.)

t (sec)	1	2	3	4	5	6	7
s_x (ft)	330	660	990	1320	1650	1980	2310
s_y (ft)	16.1	64.4	145	258	403	580	789

If we are interested merely in the shape of the trajectory rather than in the location of the projectile at each instant of time, we can obtain the *equation of the trajectory*. This is the equation relating s_x and s_y directly, and can be obtained by eliminating the parameter t between Eqs. (3.2) and (3.3). From the former,

$$s_x = v_x t, \quad \text{or} \quad t = s_x/v_x;$$

therefore

$$t^2 = s_x^2/v_x^2.$$

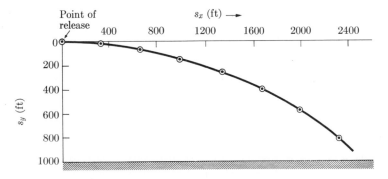

FIG. 3.6. The parabolic trajectory of the object discussed in Example 3.6.

Substitution of this value for t^2 into the second of Eqs. (3.3) yields

$$s_y = \tfrac{1}{2}gt^2 = \tfrac{1}{2}g\left(\frac{s_x^2}{v_x^2}\right),$$

which may be written

$$s_y = \left(\frac{g}{2v_x^2}\right)s_x^2. \tag{3.6}$$

Since the quantity $g/2v_x^2$ has a constant value throughout a particular projectile motion, it follows from Eq. (3.6) that s_y is proportional to s_x^2. This may be written $s_y \propto s_x^2$. We know that whenever one of two variables is directly proportional to the square of the other, the graph obtained by plotting corresponding values of the two variables is a *parabola*. Thus trajectories such as we have been discussing (Figs. 3.5, 3.6) are parabolic.

EXAMPLE 3.7. A bullet is fired horizontally from a height of 1.5 m with an initial speed of 120 m/sec. Neglecting air resistance, compute the range.

Solution. Solving Eq. (3.6) for the horizontal component s_x, we obtain $s_x = \sqrt{2s_yv_x^2/g} = v_x\sqrt{2s_y/g}$. We wish to know the value of s_x when the bullet has reached the ground, that is, when $s_y = 1.5$ m. Our other data are $g = 9.80$ m/sec^2, $v_x = 120$ m/sec, $s_x = ?$ Therefore $s_x = v_x\sqrt{2s_y/g} = (120$ m/sec$)\sqrt{2 \times 1.5 \text{ m}/(9.8 \text{ m/sec}^2)} = (120$ m/sec$)\sqrt{0.306 \text{ sec}^2} = 66$ m.

Since Eq. (3.6) for the path was deduced from the two equations of motion (3.2) and (3.3, II), it of course applies only to situations for which the latter equations are valid. Thus it holds only when an object is projected horizontally and only when the air resistance is small. A scrap of paper, even though thrown horizontally, will flutter down along a path very different from a parabola. A bomb dropped from a high altitude at first follows a path that is very nearly parabolic, but soon its speed and consequently the effect of air resistance become so large that these equations no longer apply.

3.5 The use of mathematics in physics. After Galileo had deduced the parabolic nature of the trajectory (by an original argument similar to the one we used), the study of projectile motion became a simpler matter, for the geometric properties of the parabola had long before been established by Greek mathematicians in their pursuit of principles of abstract geometry.

We find here a first clue to three important "facts of life" in modern physical science: (1) If we can express the features of a phenomenon quantitatively and cast the relations between observables into equation form, then we can use the rules of mathematics to manipulate the equations and so open the way to unexpected insights. Galileo always insisted *that the proper language of nature is mathematics*, and that a full understanding of natural phenomena depends on translating our qualitative experiences into quantitative terms. Having, for example, found that our trajectories are parabolic, we could confidently calculate, if required, the length of the actual curved path of the projectile by means of formulas proposed to us by a mathematician who is familiar with the properties of parabolas, even though he may never even have seen an actual projectile motion. (2) Consequently there is always an imperative need for a well-developed system of pure mathematics from which the physicist may draw as needed. (3) The physical scientist always tries to cast a problem into such a form that methods from another branch of science or from mathematics will aid in the solution. For example, just as Galileo applied the already known mathematics of parabolas to actual projectile motions, so does the modern acoustical engineer solve his problems by means of the mathematical schemes developed quite independently by electrical engineers for their own field. Whatever the methods of science may be, they have shown themselves to be transferable from one specialty to another in a remarkable and fruitful way.

3.6 The concept of velocity; velocity of a projectile. As Eqs. (3.2) and (3.3) show, it is desirable in describing projectile motion to distinguish between v_x, the speed in the horizontal direction, and v_y, the speed in the vertical direction. This suggests that there is need for a new concept that involves direction as well as speed, and this we call *velocity*. Like displacement, velocity is a vector quantity, because it requires for its complete description both a direction and a magnitude. Two automobiles moving at a rate of 40 mi/hr in opposite directions on a straight east-west road have the same speed (namely, 40 mi/hr), but their velocities are different, one being 40 mi/hr east and the other 40 mi/hr west. Thus one might think of velocity as speed together with direction of motion, and of speed as the *magnitude* of velocity, without regard to the direction of motion.

We now ask: How do we find the velocity of a projectile when it is at any particular point on its trajectory; that is, what is its speed and in what direction is it moving? The answer is gratifyingly simple (Fig. 3.7). The velocity v is determined by its components v_x and v_y, just as the displacement s is determined by its components s_x and s_y (Section 3.3). Thus, the magnitude of the velocity is given by

$$v = \sqrt{v_x^2 + v_y^2},\qquad(3.7)$$

and the angle γ that it makes with the horizontal is given by

$$\tan \gamma = v_y/v_x.\qquad(3.8)$$

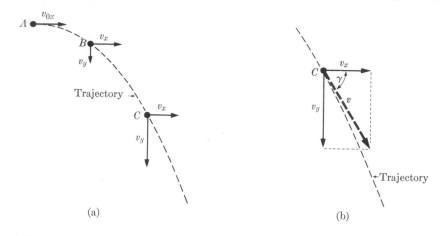

FIG. 3.7. The velocity v at any point on the trajectory can be obtained from its components v_x and v_y.

EXAMPLE 3.8. A ball is projected horizontally from the top of a tower with a speed of 40 m/sec. It is still in flight 3.1 sec later. Compute, for this instant, (a) the horizontal and vertical components of the velocity, and (b) the actual velocity.

Solution. (a) Since the horizontal component v_x remains constant throughout the flight, its magnitude at the end of 3.1 sec is the same as the speed of projection, or $v_x = v_{0x} = 40$ m/sec; the downward component of velocity is $v_y = gt = (9.8 \text{ m/sec}^2) \times (3.1 \text{ sec}) = 30$ m/sec. (b) The magnitude of the actual velocity is $v = \sqrt{v_x^2 + v_y^2} = \sqrt{(40 \text{ m/sec})^2 + (30 \text{ m/sec})^2} = \sqrt{(1600 + 900)}$ m/sec $= 50$ m/sec; the angle between the direction in which the projectile is moving and the horizontal is given by $\tan \gamma = v_y/v_x = (30 \text{ m/sec})/(40 \text{ m/sec}) = 0.75$; thus, from Appendix F, $\gamma = 37°$. The answer to the question "What is the velocity?" is therefore: "50 m/sec in a direction 37° below the horizontal."

PROBLEM 3.4. A stone is thrown horizontally from a window with a speed of 12 m/sec. What is the velocity 1.0 sec later?

PROBLEM 3.5. A projectile has components of velocity $v_x = 19$ m/sec (to the right) and $v_y = 14$ m/sec (downward). What is its velocity at this moment?

PROBLEM 3.6. The velocity of a projectile is 200 m/sec in a direction 10° below the horizontal. What are the horizontal and vertical components of the velocity at this moment?

Equations (3.7) and (3.8) for computing the velocity of a projectile, like the corresponding equations for displacement, are based on the principle that the horizontal and vertical motions of a projectile combine, to use Galileo's words, "without altering, disturbing, or hindering each other." This is not a self-evident principle, but one that had to be tested against experience.

The importance of this principle here is that it enabled Galileo, and has enabled us, to study projectile motion by the method of analysis and subsequent synthesis. Thus we began by discussing motion with constant speed, that is, the type of motion that a ball, say, would have if it were rolling on a horizontal surface and there were no frictional forces or air resistance to retard it. Next we studied the motion of a freely falling body and found that it occurs with an acceleration that is constant so long as the air resistance is negligibly small. Then we considered the possible relations between these two motions when they occur simultaneously, as in projectile motion, and concluded that they take place independently. Finally, we synthesized the results of the two separate studies, thus arriving at the method which we have just used for computing velocities. This method can be restated as follows: instantaneous velocity can be obtained by *superposing the two independent components* v_x *and* v_y *in a simple parallelogram construction*, where v, the resultant, is given in both direction and magnitude by the diagonal, as shown in Fig. 3.7(b).

This statement is a special case of a general principle called the *principle of superposition*, according to which many physical situations may be understood as the combined effect of two or more parts, each acting as though the other were not there. In one form or another the superposition principle is so simplifying a device that it may seem to have been too much to hope for; yet natural phenomena graciously do exhibit such features at times, and it is practically unthinkable that physics could have embarked on its great journey of vigorous discovery from Galileo on without his having intuited many such "simple" fundamentals.

EXAMPLE 3.9. A stone was dropped from a plane flying horizontally with a speed of 200 ft/sec. If the stone reached the ground in 5 sec, (a) from what height was the projectile released? What was (b) the range, (c) the total displacement, and (d) the velocity just before striking the ground? Translating phrase by phrase, we write, $v_{0x} = 200$ ft/sec, $v_{0y} = 0$, $t = 5$ sec, $s_x = ?$, $s_y = ?$, $s = ?$, $\beta = ?$, $v = ?$, $\gamma = ?$

Solution. $s_x = v_{0x}t = 10^3$ ft; $s_y = \frac{1}{2}gt^2 = 4 \times 10^2$ ft; $s = \sqrt{10^6 + (16 \times 10^4)}$ ft; $\tan \beta = (4 \times 10^2)/10^3 = 0.4$; and so on.

PROBLEM 3.7. Show that the principle of superposition can be used to calculate a displacement if we know its components. For an example use the simultaneous effects of a wind and a water current on a boat.

3.7 Projectile motion with initial velocity upward. The previous sections have been concerned with projectiles whose initial velocity was always horizontal, so that $v_{0y} = 0$. Now let us consider a projectile thrown or shot straight upward. In this case there is no horizontal motion; that is, $v_{0x} = 0$, and so v_x is always zero. The projectile rises vertically, steadily losing speed until at last it stops and begins to fall. Since this vertical motion occurs with constant acceleration, it is describable by Eq. (1.3), and we may write

$$v_y = v_{0y} + gt, \tag{3.9}$$

where v_y is the velocity at any time t. Clearly, v_y consists of two parts: the constant term v_{0y} which is the initial, or "muzzle" velocity, and the oppositely directed term gt, where g represents the rate at which the second component is changing, and gt is the total change that has occurred when time t has elapsed.

We will find it useful here to assume that upward vectors take on positive values and downward vectors take on negative values. Thus, in computing the value of v_y, we use Eq. (3.9), with v_{0y} positive since it is upward, and $g = -9.80$ m/sec^2 or -32.2 ft/sec^2 since this gives the downward velocity component when multiplied by t. Then, when the computation yields a positive value of v_y, we know that the projectile is moving upward, and when it yields a negative value of v_y, the projectile is moving downward.* Physically we may picture the projectile as having an upward velocity of magnitude v_{0y} which steadily decreases by an amount gt. When gt has become as large as the initial amount v_{0y}, the total value v_y has dropped to zero and the projectile has reached its highest point. As the time of flight t continues to increase, the projectile's downward velocity gt increasingly overwhelms the fixed initial upward velocity v_{0y}, with the net result that the projectile picks up speed downward.

Note that at any particular level the *magnitude* of the velocity is the same whether the projectile is passing that level on the way up or on the way down. This can best be seen by rewriting Eq. (1.7, IV) in the form

$$v_y = \pm \sqrt{v_{0y}^2 + 2gs_y}. \tag{3.10}$$

For any particular value of s_y, this equation will yield two values of v_y, equal in magnitude but positive for the rising projectile and negative for the falling projectile.

EXAMPLE 3.10.   A projectile is fired straight upward with a velocity of 50 ft/sec. Compute its velocity when its distance s above the ground is 10 ft.

Solution.
$$v_{0y} = 50 \text{ ft/sec upward}, \qquad s_y = 10 \text{ ft},$$

$$v_y = \pm\sqrt{v_0^2 + 2gs} = \pm\sqrt{2500 \text{ ft}^2/\text{sec}^2 - (2 \times 32 \text{ ft/sec}^2) \times 10 \text{ ft}}$$

$$= \pm\sqrt{(2500 - 640)\text{ft}^2/\text{sec}^2} = \pm 43 \text{ ft/sec}.$$

---

*We could just as well have considered upward vector quantities as negative and downward vectors as positive. This is purely a matter of convenience. In fact, in Chapter 1, where v_{0y} and gt were in the same direction, we considered both quantities positive, even when downward. Either sign convention will work, so long as it is used consistently in each problem.

The positive value indicates the speed on rising, and the negative value the speed on falling. They are numerically equal.

PROBLEM 3.8. For a projectile fired vertically upward, derive an expression for the time of rise to the highest point in terms of the initial velocity and g. Then derive the expression for the total time of flight. How do these two times compare? [*Note:* Whenever you are asked to "derive an expression," start with the laws of nature describing the phenomenon. In this simple case, start with the equation of motion in the form of Eq. (3.9).]

Since our projectile moves with constant (downward) acceleration, Eq. (1.7, II) may be modified by setting $a = g$ and adding subscripts:

$$s_y = v_{0y}t + \tfrac{1}{2}gt^2. \tag{3.11}$$

This equation enables us to find the projectile's displacement s_y at any particular time t. If we visualize the movement of the projectile, we see that s_y increases until the highest point is reached and then decreases, becoming zero again as the projectile returns to the starting level. From our convention that upward vector quantities are positive, we see that the first term in the right-hand member of Eq. (3.11) will be positive because both v_{0y} and t have positive values, while the second term will be negative, g having been assigned a negative value; s_y is thus the sum of a positive and of a negative term.

EXAMPLE 3.11. A projectile is hurled straight upward at the edge of a cliff with an initial velocity of 25 m/sec. Compute $v_{0y}t$, $\tfrac{1}{2}gt^2$, and s_y for the first six seconds of flight.

Solution. $v_{0y} = 25$ m/sec, $g = -9.8$ m/sec², $v_{0y}t = (25$ m/sec$) \times t$, $\tfrac{1}{2}gt^2 = (-4.9$ m/sec²$) \times t^2$. We may summarize our computations in tabular form:

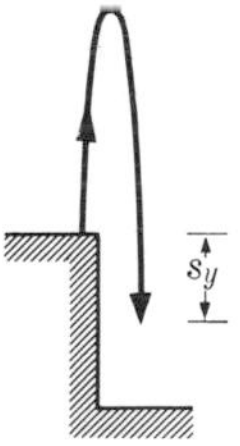

FIG. 3.8. Displacements *below* the initial level are considered to have negative values.

t (sec)	1	2	3	4	5	6
$v_{0y}t$ (m)	25	50	75	100	125	150
$\tfrac{1}{2}gt^2$ (m)	—4.9	—20	—44	—78	—120	—180
s_y (m)	20	30	31	22	5	—30

Since our last value for s_y (at $t = 6$ sec) is negative, it must be interpreted to mean that the projectile is then 30 m *below* the starting level (Fig. 3.8).

PROBLEM 3.9. The initial velocity components of a certain projectile are $v_{0x} = 0$, $v_{0y} = 50$ ft/sec upward. To what height does the projectile rise in 1.5 sec? What is the magnitude and direction of the velocity at this time?

PROBLEM 3.10. A projectile is fired with an initial velocity of 50.0 ft/sec upward. (a) How long does it rise? (b) How high does it rise? (c) What is its speed 1.00 sec after it begins to return to the ground?

PROBLEM 3.11. A bullet is fired vertically upward with a muzzle speed of 3.00×10^2 m/sec. Assuming that the air resistance is negligibly small, compute (a) the velocity and the height for every 10-sec interval of the flight, and (b) the total time of flight.

3.8 The general case of projectile motion. In Chapter 1 we discussed the motion of objects thrown or dropped straight down. In this chapter we have considered two other cases of projectile motion. In each of these three cases, either v_{0x} or v_{0y} was zero. We now have sufficient conceptual equipment to attack the general case of a projectile fired in any direction; the previously discussed motions will then be seen to be merely special applications of the general case.

Suppose that the initial velocity v_0 is in a direction making an angle θ with the horizontal. By resolving the initial velocity into horizontal and vertical components, we are able to treat each component of motion separately, in the same manner as in our previous examples. The components of the initial velocity may be computed with the help of trigonometry, for they correspond to the sides of a rectangle of which the velocity corresponds to the diagonal [Fig. 3.9(a)]. The components are

$$v_{0x} = v_0 \cos \theta, \tag{3.12}$$

$$v_{0y} = v_0 \sin \theta. \tag{3.13}$$

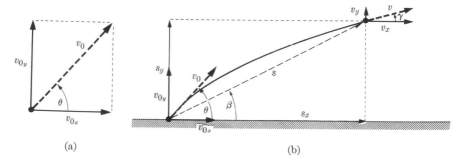

(a)   (b)

FIG. 3.9. (a) The initial velocity v_0 of a projectile may be resolved into a horizontal and a vertical component. (b) Identification of symbols in Eqs. (3.14).

The motion in the horizontal direction occurs with constant speed $v_x = v_{0x}$, and thus the horizontal component of displacement is given by Eq. (3.2). The motion in the vertical direction always has a constant (downward) acceleration g, and Eqs. (1.7) can be adapted to its description by introducing the subscript y and setting $a_y = g$. Knowing the components of the displacement and velocity at any time t, we can compute the total displacement and total velocity as we did in Sections 3.3 and 3.6.

This information may be summarized in the following set of *general equations of projectile motion* for constant acceleration [Fig. 3.9(b)]:

$$\textit{Horizontal Components}$$

$$s_x = v_x t = v_{0x} t \qquad \text{(A)}$$

$$v_x = v_{0x} = v_0 \cos \theta \qquad \text{(B)}$$

$$\textit{Vertical Components}$$

$$s_y = \tfrac{1}{2}(v_{0y} + v_y)t \qquad \text{(C)}$$

$$s_y = v_{0y} t + \tfrac{1}{2}gt^2 \qquad \text{(D)}$$

$$v_y = v_{0y} + gt \qquad \text{(E)}$$

$$v_y^2 = v_{0y}^2 + 2gs_y \qquad \text{(F)}$$

$$v_{0y} = v_0 \sin \theta \qquad \text{(G)}$$

$$\textit{Total Quantities}$$

$$s = \sqrt{s_x^2 + s_y^2}, \qquad \tan \beta = s_y/s_x \qquad \text{(H)}$$

$$v = \sqrt{v_x^2 + v_y^2}, \qquad \tan \gamma = v_y/v_x \qquad \text{(I)}$$

$$(3.14)$$

Conventions Regarding Sign

Vector components in the upward $(+y)$ direction are given positive values.

Vector components in the downward $(-y)$ direction are given negative values.

The value of g will be taken as -9.8 m/sec^2 or -32.2 ft/sec^2, unless otherwise specified.

The above set of equations is not as formidable as it might seem at first glance. Equation (A) is the formula that we use daily to find out how far an object moves, at a constant speed, in a certain time; and equation (B) merely tells us that this constant speed component is equal to the initial speed component; equations (C) through (F) are the equations for motion with constant acceleration along the vertical axis of coordinates; equation (G) gives us the vertical component of the initial velocity. Equations (H) and (I) are those encountered in Sections 3.3 and 3.6 for computing the displacement and velocity from their components. Finally, the sign conventions, which quickly become second nature in use, reflect only a useful way of differentiating between addition and subtraction of quantities.

Now comes the reward for this work—the ability to solve a wide variety of problems by means of this set of equations.

EXAMPLE 3.12. A gun pointed at an angle θ above the horizon fires a projectile with muzzle velocity v_0. What is the time t needed for the projectile to return to level ground? That is, given v_0, θ, and, of course, g, derive an expression for the total time of flight, or the time t when $s_y = 0$ (Fig. 3.10).

Solution. Since in general

here
$$s_y = v_{0y}t + \tfrac{1}{2}gt^2,$$

and
$$0 = (v_0 \sin \theta)t + \tfrac{1}{2}gt^2,$$

$$t = -2v_0 \sin \theta/g.$$

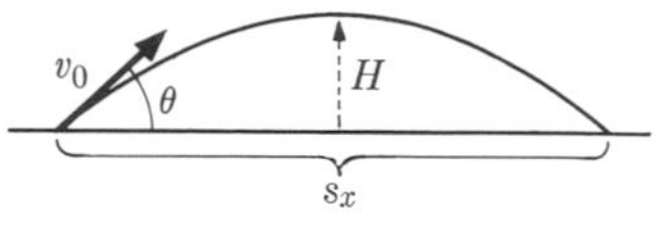

FIGURE 3.10

Since g has a negative value, t will come out positive, as it surely must. For example, a shell fired at an angle of 30° with a muzzle velocity of 700 ft/sec will remain in the air for a time $t = -2 \times 700$ (ft/sec) $\times 0.50/(-32 \text{ ft/sec}^2) = 22$ sec. In actual cases the time would be less than the computed value because of air resistance; this effect is not accounted for in our set of equations, but can be included in more complex equations, modifications of those we have derived here.

EXAMPLE 3.13. In the previous example, what is the maximum height reached? That is, given v_0, θ, g, find s_y ($\equiv H$) if $v_y = 0$.

Solution. By Eq. (IV), $0 = (v_0 \sin \theta)^2 + 2gs_y$, and

$$s_y (\equiv H) = \frac{-(v_0 \sin \theta)^2}{2g} = \frac{-(700 \times 0.50)^2 \text{ ft}^2/\text{sec}^2}{-2 \times 32 \text{ ft/sec}^2}$$

$$= 1.9 \times 10^3 \text{ ft.}$$

EXAMPLE 3.14. Find an expression for the range on level ground of a projectile in terms of v_0, θ, and g.

Solution. The range is given by $s_x = v_{0x}t = (v_0 \cos \theta)t$, where t is the total time of flight. From Example 3.12, $t = -2v_0 \sin \theta/g$. Thus $s_x = (v_0 \cos \theta) \times (-2v_0 \sin \theta/g) = -2v_0^2 \cos \theta \sin \theta/g = -v_0^2 \sin (2\theta)/g$. Thus, for a projectile fired with a muzzle velocity of 700 ft/sec at angle of elevation 30°, the range is $s_x = -(700 \text{ ft/sec})^2 \sin 60°/(-32 \text{ ft/sec}^2) = 1.3 \times 10^4$ ft.

EXAMPLE 3.15. Show that for a given initial speed v_0 the range on level ground is a maximum when the angle of elevation θ is 45°.

Solution. Inspection of the expression for the range (Example 3.14), $s_x = -v_0^2 \sin (2\theta)/g$, shows that the range is maximum when $\sin (2\theta)$ is maximum; and the latter has its largest value, 1, when θ is 45°.

It should be emphasized again that all these results would hold strictly only for *ballistic* (i.e., not self-propelled) projectiles moving without air resistance above a part of the earth that can be regarded as a flat plane. The actual effects of air resistance alone may decrease the effective range by 50 percent, but for practical applications this can be predicted by means of theoretical and empirical corrections.

3.9 Galileo's conclusions. Galileo himself carried his work on projectile motion to the point of computing fine tables of ranges and heights of trajectories over level ground for various muzzle velocities v_0 and angles of elevation θ. And he also derived additional results of a general character, for example, that for a given muzzle velocity v_0 the range is equally great for any two values of θ differing from 45° by an equal amount in each direction (e.g., 38° and 52°). He very penetratingly remarks at this point:

> The force of rigorous demonstrations such as occur only by use of mathematics fills me with wonder and delight. From accounts given by gunners, I was already aware of the fact that in the use of cannon and mortars, the maximum range, that is, the one in which the shot goes farthest, is obtained when the elevation is 45° . . . ; but to understand *why* this happens far outweighs the mere information obtained by the testimony of others or even by repeated experiment . . . The knowledge of a single effect apprehended through its cause opens the mind to understand and ascertain other facts *without need of recourse to experiment*, precisely as in the present case, where, having won by demonstration the certainty that the maximum range occurs when the elevation [θ] is 45°, the Author [Galileo] demonstrates what has perhaps never been observed in practice, namely, that for elevations which exceed or fall short of 45° by equal amounts, the ranges are equal . . .

Note the pleasure which he finds in discovering a mathematical law, and how he regards it as the way "to understand *why*" projectiles move as they are observed to do. Note also especially the phrase "without need of recourse to experiment"; Galileo, traditionally regarded as the patron saint of experimental science, clearly warns us that the continual experimental verification of a prediction from a law is unnecessary once the law is sufficiently well established. After the initial mandatory doubts are satisfied, one must believe in the law to obtain benefit from its use.

A second important conclusion from the work on projectiles may seem almost trivial at first glance. In support of the Copernican thesis that the earth moves about its axis and around the sun, Galileo offered an answer to critics who argued that if the earth moved, a stone dropped from a tower would be left behind while falling through the air, and con-

FIG. 3.11. Projectile motion in the 16th century, symbolizing the connection between science and philosophy; (from Tartaglia's *La nuova scientia*, Venice, 1537). In A. C. Crombie's words, "The student is met by Euclid at the outer gate. Inside he finds Tartaglia surrounded by the mathematical disciplines: Arithmetic, Music, Geometry, Astronomy, Astrology, etc. A cannon is firing, showing the trajectory of the projectile. At the far gate stand Aristotle and Plato to welcome the student into the presence of Philosophy. Plato holds a scroll with the inscription *No-one inexpert in geometry may enter here.*" (*Augustine to Galileo*, Falcon Press, London, 1952)

FIG. 3.12. Projectile motion in the 20th century, symbolizing the connections between science, technology, and warfare; (courtesy of Lockheed Aircraft Co., Missile Systems Division). The X–17 three-stage rocket is described by the company as follows: The first stage is a solid propellant rocket, launched at 85° to lift it to an altitude of several miles in a few seconds; then the 6-ton, 40-foot tall missile follows a trajectory to its peak altitude. On re-entering into denser atmosphere, the first stage is ejected, the second stage is ignited, and a few seconds later "the third and final stage, with the nose cone, fires and drives the X-17 downward."

sequently would not land directly at the foot of the tower as observed, but much beyond. Galileo assumes that during the *short* time of fall, the earth, and the top and the foot of the tower, may be thought to move forward equally far with uniform velocity. If, then, the whole tower moves with the same speed v_{0x}, the dropped stone must fall along the side of the tower, because it will retain this "initial" horizontal component of speed, as truly as a parcel dropped from a moving plane lands below the plane or, in Galileo's analogy, as an object falling from the mast of a moving ship lands at the foot of the mast. From this and equivalent observations concerning the other laws of mechanics has been developed a most valuable generalization, usually called the *Galilean relativity principle:* Any mechanical experiment, such as on the fall of bodies, carried out in a stationary "laboratory" (e.g., on a stationary ship) will come out precisely the same way when repeated in a second, moving "laboratory" (say on a moving ship) so long as the second laboratory moves with *constant velocity* as measured from the first.

To express this more elegantly, let us use the words "coordinate system" instead of "laboratory," since all that counts in the description of experiments is the system of reference used for measurements. Some corner of the rectangular laboratory table might be the origin for all our measurements of distance, and the three edges of the table may correspond to the x-, y-, and z-directions. Then we may restate the Galilean relativity principle: "All laws of mechanics observed in one coordinate system are equally valid in any other coordinate system moving with a constant velocity relative to the first." If you drop a suitcase in a compartment in a train, be it at rest or speeding at 30 mi/hr or at 60 mi/hr straight across level terrain, the case will always hit the floor below its point of release, and will fall downward with the same acceleration as measured in the car. Consequently, from the motion of a projectile in a car you cannot decide whether the car itself is moving. If the principle is true in its general form, it follows that no *mechanical* experiment made on our earth can decide such intriguing questions as whether the solar system as a whole proceeds with some constant velocity through the space about us.

3.10 Summary. Evidently, this discussion has carried us far from our starting point. Recall that we began with the simple case of projectile motion in a plane, θ being 0° at first. Then we deduced the superposition principles for velocities, and extended our treatment to the general case, obtaining the *general equations of projectile motion* without any restrictions on the initial direction of motion. Finally, we learned that even more general principles were obtainable from these equations. In passing, we also noted the power and meaning of the mathematical formulation of physical events, and the multifold predictions flowing from mathematical expressions—whether theoretical, as the determination of a maximum range for $\theta = 45°$, or practical, as the construction of gunnery tables.

With these examples of the development and power of mathematical physics in mind, we shall later return to a discussion of "scientific methods." But, throughout the rest of this study, we shall encounter influences of Galileo's work from time to time, as one might find an ancestral trait running through generations of one family.

We saw (Section 2.6) that Galileo began his studies with the insistence that descriptions of motions be obtained, and that he firmly turned away from digressions into the causes of these motions. This was very appropriate, in view of the state of knowledge at the beginning of the 17th century. The time was ripe for the development of the science of kinematics, but until progress was sufficient to give a precise description of the motions of, say, projectiles, inquiry into the "causes" of these motions was likely to be fruitless.

Now that we have reached a method of describing motions, we may broaden our inquiry to include such "causal" concepts as *force* and *mass*, which help to provide the basis for the science of *dynamics*. Kinematics and dynamics are as the two sides of a coin: without both, we cannot purchase the full understanding of mechanical phenomena.

ADDITIONAL PROBLEMS

3.12. What is the general procedure for "deriving an expression" or "deriving a formula"?

3.13. What is meant by saying that the paths of projectiles are parabolic? When we find by experiment that the paths *are* parabolic, what help is that in solving projectile problems?

3.14. You are required to design a projectile that will have a range of 5000 mi. List the main effects not included in the equations of motion given in this chapter which must be considered in setting up a useful modification of these equations.

3.15. A stone is thrown virtually vertically upward with an initial speed $v_{0y} = 100$ ft/sec (Fig. 3.8). Find, at the end of the 1st, 3rd, and 7th seconds, (a) the displacement s_y of the stone, and (b) the instantaneous velocity. Use your data to plot a v vs. t graph (on graph paper) and find from it (*graphically*), (c) when the stone will have a speed of 20 ft/sec.

3.16. How long will the stone in Problem 3.15 take to reach the ground again? Obtain this result first from your graph for Problem 3.15, then check it by independent direct calculation.

3.17. A self-propelled research rocket starts from rest and moves straight upward, increasing its speed on a vertical path so that at an altitude of 80 mi, when the fuel is exhausted, it has attained a speed of 9000 ft/sec. From that point on, the instrument-carrying part of the rocket continues upward as an ordinary projectile. (a) What time interval (in sec) is available for measurements of the conditions existing in the relatively air-free region above 80 mi? (b) What maximum height does the instrument part of the rocket reach? (c) What is the total time from the firing of the rocket to the instant it comes to earth? (d) What assumptions have you made and how good are they likely to be?

3.18. A gun fires a shell with a muzzle velocity of 1000 ft/sec and at an angle of 30° above the horizon. How long will it take the projectile to return to earth, how high will it rise, and what is its range on level ground? (Neglect air friction.)

3.19. During World War I there was a famous gun known as Big Bertha that had a maximum range of about 75 mi on flat territory. Supposing that this had been the range *in vacuum*, what would have been the muzzle velocity of the projectile? (The actual muzzle velocity was, of course, somewhat larger.)

3.20. A baseball is thrown with a speed of 50 ft/sec at an angle of elevation θ of 60°. Show that after 2.0 sec it has risen 23 ft, has traveled 50 ft horizontally, and is moving in a direction 40° below the horizontal.

3.21. A hunter points his gun barrel directly at a monkey in a distant palm tree. Where will the bullet go? If the animal, startled by the flash, drops out of the branches at the very instant of firing, will it then be hit by the bullet? Explain. Would this last answer hold if the acceleration due to gravity were not 32 ft/sec^2 but only $\frac{1}{6}$ as great, as on the moon?

3.22. For each of the following cases sketch two graphs, one of total displacement *vs.* time elapsed, the other of velocity *vs.* time elapsed. Carefully use the convention concerning positive and negative values. (a) A parachutist falls from a plane, after a while opens the 'chute, and floats to the ground. (b) A marble drops from your hand and bounces back three times before coming to rest on the floor. (c) A shell is fired at 60° elevation and falls into a deep valley.

3.23. Read through the "Fourth day" (Motion of projectiles) in Galileo's *Two new sciences*, and on this basis briefly discuss (a) Galileo's examination of the role of air resistance in projectile motion, (b) Galileo's use of experiments to further his arguments, (c) Galileo's interest in practical applications of his work.

3.24. Prove Galileo's statement that "for elevations which exceed or fall short of 45° by equal amounts, the ranges are equal."

Supplementary Reading

GALILEO GALILEI, *Dialogue on the great world systems*, edited by G. de Santillana (University of Chicago Press, 1953), pp. 1–25, 140–200.

GALILEO GALILEI, *Two new sciences*, the "Fourth day."

Part II
THE STUDY OF FORCES

Isaac Newton.

(1642–1727)

THE STUDY OF FORCES

Occasionally a science reaches dramatic culmination in the work of a single man who, drawing upon centuries of previous work, provides a synthesis that furnishes a firm foundation for further investigation. Isaac Newton was such a man in that branch of mechanics called *dynamics*, the science that is concerned with the effects of forces on moving objects.

The study of dynamics is the substance of Part II, and it complements and extends our study of kinematics in Part I. These two Parts, together, will provide us with a basis for moving on into other areas of physical science.

CHAPTER 4

NEWTON'S LAWS OF MOTION

For all the ingenuity and penetration, variety and bulk of Galileo's work in mechanics, much of it was concerned with special types of motion, such as that of projectiles. Newton's work is different in this respect: his concern is with all motions of all bodies, heavenly as well as terrestrial. His work, in outline and detail, still is the basis of introductory treatments of dynamics.

More than that, not only dynamics, but virtually all of our physical sciences depend on the key concept of force, still definable in essentially the same words that Newton employed in 1687. We shall hear more about his position and person later on, in connection with his discovery of the law of universal gravitation. But now we proceed to a more or less didactic treatment of his famous three Laws of Motion (also called Axioms, Postulates, or Principles) and some of their consequences.

4.1 Newton's first law. We may phrase the first law, often called the *Principle of Inertia*, as follows:

Every material body persists in its state of rest or of uniform (unaccelerated) motion in a straight line if and only if it is not acted upon by a net (i.e., unbalanced) external force.

The essence is this: if we see an object speeding up, slowing down, or changing its direction of motion, then we must assume that a net force is acting on the object. Since a change in either speed or direction of motion means a change of velocity (Section 3.6), we may look upon change of velocity as the criterion for the *presence* of an unbalanced force. It is important to recall that a change in direction of motion without change in speed also corresponds to a change in velocity; hence, by the first law of motion, a change in direction of motion is the result of an unbalanced force. On the other hand, if an object is at rest or is moving with constant velocity, this does not mean that there can be no external forces acting on the object. Indeed, no one has ever observed an object upon which there are no forces whatever. All that matters so far as the first law is concerned is that the *net* external force be zero—that is, that all the individual forces applied to the object be in balance. For example, suppose that two men push on a stationary object in opposite directions but with forces of the same magnitude. Since the unbalanced force, or net force, is here zero, the object remains in its state of rest.

4.2 The changing point of view in mechanics. The first law implies that a net force is the "cause" of change of velocity. We recall that the Aristotelian Scholastics had a different view of the role of force; they held that force was also the cause of *uniform* (unaccelerated) motion. As an example, consider the two opposing opinions that would exist concerning a cart pulled by a horse in steady motion on a level road. The Galilean-Newtonian commentator would hold that the horse's efforts serve solely to equal and cancel the force of friction on the wheels, so that the *net* force, i.e., the pull of the animal minus the force of friction, is zero, the cart being consequently in a state of equilibrium, a state which by definition includes motion with constant velocity as well as rest. On the other hand, the Aristotelian scholar would say that since the "natural" state of the cart is rest, a force has to be supplied by the horse to keep it in uniform motion— even in the absence of friction, if such a circumstance could be approached.

We have here not so much a dispute about experimentally observable facts as a difference in the whole conceptual scheme for dealing with motion, complicated by the use of the same word, *force*, with two such disparate meanings. As a matter of fact, the Aristotelian view, here as in some other contexts, is the one closer to contemporary common-sense opinion; since friction is in actuality never absent and is often a very real hindrance in moving an object, it is natural to develop the intuitive idea that a force is needed to "keep things moving," and, as a next step, to define force as "the cause of continued motion." The difficulty with this view is that the concept of force, so defined, does not (or at any rate, *did* not) lead to as powerful a scheme of mechanics as the other view.

Some of the consequences of the first law of motion are immediately recognizable as potential battlegrounds. For example, if a change in the direction of a motion implies the action of a net force, we cannot think, as the ancients did, that no force need act on the planets in their orbits to keep them moving around the sun; on the contrary, we must consider that the planets are subjected to forces which draw them continually from a straight-line course.

To summarize, the first law makes it plain that a net force must be supplied to change an object's state from rest to motion or from motion to rest, from one speed to another, or from one direction of motion to another even at the same speed. Material bodies are, so to speak, the victims of habit, of inertia, so far as motion is concerned; they continue in their state of rest or of motion unless compelled by some external agent to do otherwise. There is little profit in trying to account for this experimental fact in terms of some physical model or picture; let us simply accept the fact that physical bodies are characterized by inertia just as they are by such other fundamental attributes as volume, chemical constitution, and so forth.

PROBLEM 4.1. In terms of Newton's first law, explain: (a) the common experience of lurching forward when a moving train suddenly decelerates; (b) what happens to the passengers of a car that makes a sharp and quick turn; (c) why, when a coin is put on a phonograph turntable and the motor is started, the coin flies off when the turntable has reached a certain speed.

PROBLEM 4.2. Assume that the floor of a laboratory could be made perfectly horizontal and perfectly smooth. A block of wood is placed on the floor and given a small push. Predict the way in which the block would move. How would this motion differ if the whole laboratory were moving with constant velocity during the experiment (if, for example, it were mounted on wheels or were in a space ship)? How would it differ if the whole laboratory were accelerating along a straight line? If the block were seen to move in a curved path along the floor, how would you explain this?

4.3 Newton's second law. So far, we have mainly a qualitative notion of the concept of force and, incidentally, of the property of bodies called *inertia*. But to develop a science of dynamics that will be most useful we must be able to determine forces and inertias quantitatively. This need for quantification is met by Newton's second law of motion, which we can phrase as follows:

The net (i.e., unbalanced) external force acting on a material object is directly and linearly proportional to, and in the same direction as, the acceleration of the object.

Here the point is this: if the presence of a net force on any particular object is qualitatively detected by changes of velocity (referring to the first law), let us precisely define this net force as proportional to the rate at which the velocity of the object is changing, namely, its acceleration. Of course we remember, as Galileo had Sagredo say (Section 2.6), that any definition is *possible*. Whether the concept so defined is *useful* must be demonstrated later.

If we adopt the symbols F_{net} and a for the net force and the acceleration, we can write

$$F_{net} \propto a$$

for a given object. The symbol $\propto$ is read "is proportional to." Whenever one quantity is proportional to another, their ratio must be a constant. So we may write

$$\frac{F_{net}}{a} = \text{a constant for a given object.} \tag{4.1}$$

One may ask how we know that this ratio will be a constant for a given object. We make it so by our definition of net force. If a net force F_{net} gives a certain acceleration to an object and another net force F'_{net} produces twice as much acceleration in the same object, then $F'_{net} = 2F_{net}$, by our definition.

The constant in Eq. (4.1) may be regarded as a measure of the object's inertia; for clearly a large ratio of F_{net} to a means that a large net force is required to produce a desired acceleration—just what we expect for large, massive objects, to which we intuitively assign larger inertias than to small objects of little bulk. If we now symbolize the constant in Eq. (4.1) by the letter m and give to it the alternative name *mass,* we can write

$$F_{net}/a = m \quad \text{or} \quad F_{net} = m \times a. \tag{4.2}$$

(It is suggested that you always use the lower-case letter m for mass, reserving M for another concept.)

4.4 The measurement of force by use of a standard mass. Equation (4.2) permits us in principle to assign a numerical value to a net force if we measure the acceleration it produces on a body of known mass, or conversely we could in principle obtain a numerical value for the mass in terms of the acceleration and the net force. But of course you notice the vicious circle: unhappily we find that inertia and force, the two concepts we are trying to quantify rigorously, are mutually interconnected. To find one we seemingly would have to know the other in advance.

There is one straightforward solution for this apparent dilemma. Before attempting to measure any masses or forces, we first choose some convenient object, perhaps a certain small piece of polished rock or metal, as the universal *standard of mass*, and regard it arbitrarily as having an inertia of unity, or *unit mass;* for example, we may name it the *standard mass of one kilogram* (abbreviated 1 kgm). Then, by Eq. (4.2), any net force can be evaluated by observing the acceleration it produces on our standard object.

This important point will be clearer if we resort to an imaginary, idealized experiment ("thought experiment"). Place the standard 1-kgm object on a horizontal surface that is so smooth that we may speak of it as frictionless.* Now attach a string to the standard and pull on it horizontally, as shown in Fig. 4.1. Here the applied force is the only unbalanced external force and hence is indeed the net force. If this force is kept constant, the acceleration of the object will also be constant, and therefore ascertainable without fundamental diffi-

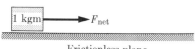

Frictionless plane

FIG. 4.1. Thought experiment to define the unit of force.

---

*A strikingly close approximation to this ideal is reached when a smooth block of "dry ice" (solid carbon dioxide) is placed on a flat, horizontal sheet of plate glass. The block rides on a thin layer of vapor between the two surfaces, which keeps the frictional force to a minimum. Any external push or pull applied to this block can be regarded as the net force on the object.

culties. Suppose it is 2 m/sec² for a given steady pull in this particular example. This is all that is needed to compute the magnitude of the pull; it is, by Eq. (4.2),

$$F_{net} = m \times a = 1 \text{ kgm} \times 2 \text{ m/sec}^2 = 2 \text{ kgm·m/sec}^2.$$

The unit of force (kgm·m/sec²) has been given the shorter name *newton* (abbreviated "new"). Thus the force applied in our example is 2 newtons (written 2 new).

We can in this way determine the magnitude of any constant force applied to the standard 1-kgm mass on the frictionless plane. Furthermore, we can easily conceive of a way of adjusting the applied force to have any desired value: if we wish the force to be 2 new, we pull on the 1-kgm object and adjust the pull as necessary to obtain an observed acceleration of 2 m/sec². Similarly, a 4-new force is one that produces an acceleration of 4 m/sec² in the standard 1-kgm object.

Yet this scheme is, in itself, of little practical value, since with it we can measure forces only when they are applied to the standard 1-kgm object. What is needed is a general way of reproducing forces, so that having applied a force to the 1-kgm standard, we can then apply the *same* force to other objects in a great variety of physical situations. In other words, we wish to be able to apply or to measure forces on any object whatever.

4.5 Calibration of a spring balance and a first determination of mass. Let us resort to a second thought experiment. Here we will replace the string by a spring. When we pull on the spring the body is accelerated as before, but at the same time the spring stretches. A scale may be attached to the spring so that we can determine just how far it stretches (Fig. 4.2). Such a spring with attached scale is known as a *spring balance* (Fig. 4.3).

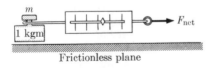

FIG. 4.2. Calibration of a spring balance in a thought experiment.

FIG. 4.3. Cutaway view of a spring balance.

Experience with springs assures us of two things: (a) the larger the applied force (determined perhaps by measuring the acceleration of the standard 1-kgm object on a frictionless plane), the greater the stretch of the spring; (b) for a particular value of the force, the amount the spring stretches is always the same. (In practice, we must be careful not to stretch the spring so far as to distort it permanently.) Thus we can pull with a steady force sufficient to give the 1-kgm standard an acceleration of 1 m/sec^2 and mark the position of the pointer during the process with the symbol "1 newton." Then, pulling harder, until the acceleration increases to 2 m/sec^2, we can mark the new position of the pointer "2 newtons." Continuing in this way, we can *calibrate* the spring balance. It is not necessary to restrict the calibration to integral values of the force. When the 1-kgm standard is given an acceleration of, say, 1.5 m/sec^2, the force is $F_{net} = m \times a = 1$ kgm $\times$ 1.5 m/sec^2 = 1.5 new, and we may mark the pointer position "1.5 newtons."

After such a calibration the spring balance can always be used to apply known forces to any other object. Furthermore, we may also use it, together with Eq. (4.2), to compute the unknown mass m of any object. To do this, we attach the balance to the object resting on the smooth plane and, by pulling on the balance, apply a steady force of, say, 6.0 new, until the pointer reaches the 6.0-new mark. If the resulting acceleration, measured simultaneously, is found to be 1.5 m/sec^2, then, by Eq. (4.2),

$$m = \frac{F_{net}}{a} = \frac{6.0 \text{ new}}{1.5 \text{ m/sec}^2} = \frac{6.0 \text{ kgm·m/sec}^2}{1.5 \text{ m/sec}^2} = 4.0 \text{ kgm.}$$

In summary, Newton's second law, in conjunction with the arbitrary choice of a single standard of mass, conveniently fixes the unit of force, permits the calibration of balances, and gives us an operational determination of the mass of any other object.

PROBLEM 4.3. What is the mass m of a certain block of lead if its observed acceleration on a very smooth horizontal plane is 0.85 m/sec^2 when the reading of the spring balance is 1.7 new?

PROBLEM 4.4. What acceleration will a net force of 1.0 new give to an object of mass 3.8 kgm?

PROBLEM 4.5. Recount in detail what steps you must take (in idealized experimentation) to determine the unknown mass m (in kilograms) of a certain object if you are given nothing but a frictionless horizontal plane, a 1-kgm standard, an uncalibrated spring balance, a meter stick, and a stop watch. (*Note:* Your answer represents a first approach toward an "operational definition" of mass, and will prove a great aid in comprehension of dynamical problems.)

EXAMPLE 4.1. A certain block is dragged with *constant velocity* along a *rough* horizontal table top, by means of a balance attached to it which reads 0.40 new (Fig. 4.4) no matter what the velocity happens to be; this means that the re-

tarding frictional force between block
and table is 0.40 new. When the block
is given a constant acceleration of 0.85
m/sec^2, the balance is found to read 2.1
new. Compute the mass of the block.

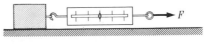

FIGURE 4.4

Solution. As before, $m = F_{net}/a$. But here the net force is the difference
between the forward force and the retarding frictional force; or $F_{net} = 2.1$ new $-$
0.40 new $= 1.7$ new. The mass then is $m = 1.7$ new/$(0.85 \text{ m/sec}^2) = 2.0$
new·sec^2/m $= 2.0$ (kgm·m/sec^2) $\times$ (sec^2/m) $= 2.0$ kgm.

PROBLEM 4.6. Referring to Example 4.1, show that a forward force of 5.4 new
would have to be applied to the 2.0-kgm block to keep it moving with an acceleration of 2.5 m/sec^2.

PROBLEM 4.7. The mass of an average person is about 75 kgm. If he is seated
in a car that starts up with an acceleration of 1.20 m/sec^2, what net force must
he experience? How is this force applied to him? In what direction is this force?

4.6 Standard of mass. It will be readily appreciated that the standard
of mass that represents one kilogram, though essentially arbitrary, has
been chosen with care. For scientific work, *one kilogram* was originally
selected to be the inertia offered by 1000 cm^3 of distilled water at 4°C.
This decision, dating from the late 18th century, is rather inconvenient in
practice. Although standardizing on a certain quantity of water has the
important advantage that it permits cheap and easy reproduction of the
standard anywhere on earth, yet there are obvious experimental difficulties
owing to the effects of evaporation, the additional inertia of the necessary
containers, the relatively poor accuracy with which volumes can be
measured, and so on. Therefore, it has become accepted custom to use as
the primary standard of mass a cylinder of platinum alloy, kept under
careful guard at the *Bureau Internationale des Poids et Mesures* at Sèvres,
a suburb of Paris. Accurate replicas of this international primary standard
of mass have been deposited at the various bureaus of standards throughout
the world. Figure 4.5 is a photograph of the standard of mass in the
National Bureau of Standards in Washington, D.C., alongside the standard
of length, a metal bar which represents *one meter*. From secondary standards, in turn, auxiliary replicas are made for distribution to manufacturers
and laboratories, etc. Since the pound is the unit used for most commerical
purposes in the United States and England, it is helpful to remember that
one kilogram of mass is equivalent to about 2.2 pounds of mass and that
one pound is equivalent to about 0.45 kilogram.* One gram (1 gm) is
one-thousandth of the mass of one kilogram; the U. S. one-cent piece has
a mass of a little more than 3 gm.

---

*More strictly, the pound is defined, by U. S. law, as precisely equivalent to
0.4535924 kgm; and similarly, 1 kgm $\equiv$ 2.204622 lb.

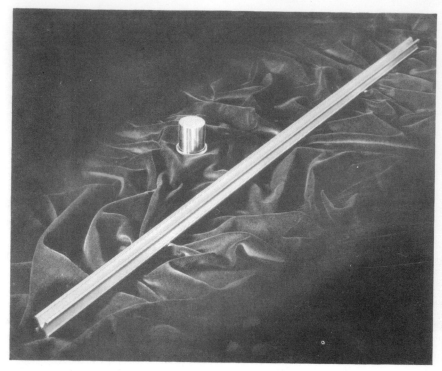

Fig. 4.5. United States secondary standards for mass and length.

4.7 Weight. Objects can be acted on by all kinds of forces: by a push from the hand, by the pull on a string attached to the object, by a magnetic attraction or repulsion if the object is made of iron or other magnetic material, by the action of electric charges, or by the gravitational attraction that the earth exerts on bodies. But no matter what the origin of the forces, their effect is always given by the same equation, $F_{net} = m \times a$. Newton's second law is so powerful precisely because it is so general, and because we can apply it even though at this stage we may be completely at a loss to understand exactly why and how a particular force (like magnetism or gravity) should act on a body. We shall use the symbol F_{grav} when the particular force involved is the gravitational pull of the earth. Because this force, F_{grav}, is so frequently considered, a special name for it, *weight*, is generally used.

Of all the forces a body may experience, gravitational force is perhaps the most remarkable. Let us discuss it in detail. First of all, we are struck by the fact that the gravitational force acts between two bodies (such as a stone in one's hand and the earth below) without any need to prepare them for it—simply by holding them near each other. Before two pieces of steel will attract each other magnetically, we must specially treat at least one of them to magnetize it; and before electric forces can act between two objects, at least one has to be electrified. But mutual gravitational attractions between all bodies are inherently present, although they are usually too feeble to be detected by ordinary means. At any rate, we shall concentrate at first on the more spectacular case of the earth's pull on bodies at or near its surface. There, F_{grav} acts whether we wish it or no, whereas we can apply or remove at will elastic, magnetic, and electric forces.

Furthermore, no matter what we may try to do about it, a body's weight F_{grav} at a given locality is essentially constant. To be sure, the farther the two bodies are separated, the less the gravitational attraction between them, as borne out by experiment, so that the weight of an object approaches zero as we remove the object to a spot extremely far from the earth, for example to interstellar space. But if *at a certain spot* on this globe the weight of a block of metal is, say, 2 new, nothing will change this value short of destroying the identity of the object by cutting something off or by adding to it. Even if we interpose screens of all kinds between block and earth, their mutual gravitational pull remains unchanged, as has been shown by careful experimentation.

Yet another remarkable attribute of gravitational force is revealed by Galileo's observation that (again at a given locality) *all objects* fall with the same gravitational acceleration g. This can mean only that the gravitational attraction F_{grav} is proportional to the mass of the attracted object, and to nothing else; that is, F_{grav} is not influenced by any of the other properties of the object, such as its composition or shape. On reflection, this is an astonishing discovery. Other forces (e.g., electric and magnetic ones) are not simply proportional to the mass of the affected object. On the contrary, objects of equal mass but of different materials will generally behave entirely differently when in the presence of the same magnet or electric charge.

That there should exist a universal and strictly linear proportionality between weight and mass is logically as unexpected as if we had found that the weights of all objects are proportional exactly to the value of their surface areas or, to use an analogy, if it were discovered that on some far-off planet a man's wealth is proportional to the size of his person. Certainly, wealth and size would not thereby become identical concepts, but such a simple empirical relationship between them would allow us quickly to judge a man's bank account by surveying his bulk, and vice versa. Similarly, although weight and mass are entirely different concepts, the simple proportionality between their corresponding values soon puts us in the habit of judging the weight of an object from an estimate of its mass, and vice versa.

4.8 Two methods for measuring weight. We have been discussing *weight*, that is, the gravitational pull of the earth on an object, and thus, as with all physical quantities, we are interested in methods for measuring the weight of any particular object. One method, which we shall refer to as *dynamic*, is simply to drop the object, thus allowing its weight F_{grav} to accelerate it in free fall. By determining the acceleration g during this fall, and then determining the mass m of the object by a separate experiment (Section 4.2), we can at once compute the weight F_{grav} by employing the equation $F_{net} = ma$, which here becomes $F_{grav} = mg$.

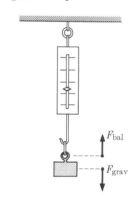

Happily, there is another method, easier and more direct. We need only our previously calibrated spring balance; from it we hang the object whose weight F_{grav} is to be found, and then wait until equilibrium is established (Fig. 4.6). In this method F_{grav} is not the only force acting on the object; instead it is balanced by the upward force F_{bal} of the spring. When the pointer comes to rest, say at the 2.6-new mark, then we know (by either Newton's first law or second law) that the net force on the object is zero, hence the pull of the spring, F_{bal}, must be equal in magnitude, but

Fig. 4.6. Weighing with a spring balance.

opposite in direction, to the weight F_{grav}. Thus if F_{bal} is 2.6 new, then F_{grav} is also 2.6 new. In passing, we note that in "weighing" we "read off" not the weight F_{grav}, but the magnitude of an oppositely directed balancing force F_{bal}. This method, in which the object is in equilibrium (has no acceleration) during the weighing, is called a *static* determination of weight, whereas the previous one, involving the free fall of the object, was dynamic. Experiments show that both procedures, although so different, yield equal values at the same locality. Indeed, if they failed to do so, they would not constitute valid alternative methods for determining weight.

As the discussion of the dynamic method brought out, the weight F_{grav} of any object is equal to mg, the product of the mass m of the object and the gravitational acceleration g at the place where the object is located. Now, while g has the same value for all objects in a given locality, and for most purposes may be taken as 9.80 m/sec^2 or 32.2 ft/sec^2 at the earth's surface, it has measurably different values in different localities. As Table 4.1 shows, the variation is approximately 0.5%, from about 9.78 m/sec^2 at the equator to about 9.83 m/sec^2 at the North Pole. An object of mass 1 kgm will have a weight mg of about 9.79 new in Key West and

9.80 new in Baltimore. Moreover, at the same latitude, the value of g decreases with increasing height above sea level and, although the differences are generally small, so accurate are modern methods of measurement that the minute change in g from one floor of a building to the next is actually discernible!

Table 4.1. Local values of the acceleration due to gravity, g.

Location	g (m/sec^2)
Baltimore, Md.	9.801
Cambridge, Mass.	9.804
Chicago, Ill.	9.803
Denver, Col.	9.796
Key West, Fla.	9.790
San Francisco, Calif.	9.800
Washington, D. C.	9.801
Greenwich, England	9.812
Paris, France	9.809
Latitude 0°, sea level	9.78049
Latitude 90°, sea level	9.83223
Sun's surface, due to sun's gravitational force	274.40
Moon's surface, due to moon's gravitational force	1.67

PROBLEM 4.8. Imagine that you are given a perfectly smooth horizontal surface, a 1-kgm standard mass, an *uncalibrated* spring balance, a meter stick, stop watches, and assistants. Without further aids, and invoking Newton's laws of motion, recount in complete detail what steps you should take in idealized experimentation to determine the unknown weight F_{grav} (in newtons) of an object by two essentially different methods.

PROBLEM 4.9. A replica of the standard kilogram is constructed in Paris and then sent to the National Bureau of Standards in Washington. Assuming that this secondary standard is not damaged in transit, compute (a) its mass in Washington, (b) its weight in Paris and in Washington, (c) the percentage differences in its mass and in its weight in the two localities. (See Table 4.1 for necessary data.)

PROBLEM 4.10. A space traveler whose mass is 75 kgm (165 lb) leaves the earth. What is his weight (a) on the earth, (b) 500 mi above the earth (where the gravitational pull is 20% less), and (c) in interplanetary space? (d) What is his mass at these three locations?

4.9 The equal-arm balance. To return now to the important (and perhaps initially troublesome) concept of mass, we must mention a way to measure the mass of an object that, in everyday practice, is by far the most accurate as well as the most favored method.

By way of review, recall first that we need an arbitrarily selected standard of mass, such as the standard kilogram. Once this has been generally agreed upon, we can calibrate a spring balance (in newtons) by using it to impart measurable accelerations to the standard mass placed on a smooth horizontal surface. Then the calibrated spring balance can serve for determining the masses of various objects, either (1) by using it to pull the object along the surface, noting the pull F and resulting acceleration a, and computing the mass m ($=F/a$); or (2) by hanging the object on the balance, noting its weight F_{grav}, and computing its mass from the relation $m = F_{\text{grav}}/g$, where g is the measured gravitational acceleration at the place in question.

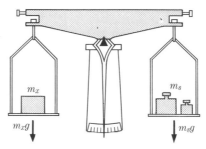

Fig. 4.7. Weighing with an equal-arm balance.

To these methods we now add another, (3), known as "weighing" on an equal-arm balance. At first glance this method seems simple and straightforward, but it is in fact conceptually subtle. We place the object of unknown mass m_x in one pan (Fig. 4.7) and place a sufficient number of marked auxiliary standard masses m_s in the other pan to render the beam horizontal. When this has been done, we know that $m_x g$, the weight of the unknown mass, is counterbalanced by $m_s g$, the combined weight of the standard masses, or $m_x g = m_s g$. The value of g is the same in both members of the equation because both pans of the balance are in essentially the same locality; hence g cancels out, and we have $m_x = m_s$. Adding the individual values m_s of the standard masses in one pan immediately gives us the mass m_x of the object to be weighed in the other pan.

This procedure is much to be preferred over methods (1) and (2) since the range, the accuracy of calibration, and the consistency of a spring balance are all quite limited, whereas the equal-arm balance can accurately handle a very large range of masses. The accuracy of individual measurements on an equal-arm balance is easily better than one-millionth of a kilogram (10^{-6} kgm), and with refinements in apparatus and special care can be made better than 10^{-10} kgm. Also, the results from repeated measurements are consistent, provided only that the arms of the balance remain straight and equally long, that the value of g is the same at each pan, and that the markings of the auxiliary standard masses remain correct. These conditions can be tested experimentally from time to time to make sure that they continue to hold.

4.10 Inertial and gravitational mass. It is remarkable that method (1) of Section 4.9 yields the same value for the mass of an object as do methods (2) and (3). Some thought should convince us that this is either an incredible coincidence or a symptom of a profound new law of nature. To begin with, consider that method (1) is dynamic in that the object is undergoing acceleration (having its inertia overcome) due to the pull of the horizontally moving spring balance, and that the mass so determined is a measure of the inertia of the object. Gravitational forces do not enter at all into the determination; indeed, the measurements presumably could be carried out just as well or better in gravitation-free space. On the other hand, the static methods (2) and (3) involve weighings on balances, and could not be invoked at all in the absence of gravity; inertia plays no role whatever. Thus we see that method (1) on the one hand and methods (2) and (3) on the other measure two entirely different properties of matter, to which we may assign the terms *inertial mass* and *gravitational mass* respectively.

For practical purposes we shall make little distinction between the two types of mass, because the evidence to date is that the values are always the same. But in order to remind ourselves how essential and rewarding it may be to keep a clear notion of the operational significance of scientific concepts, and that, historically, considerable consequences may follow from a reconsideration of long-established ideas in a new light, there are these words from Einstein's and Infeld's book *The evolution of physics:**

> . . . is this identity of the two kinds of mass purely accidental, or does it have a deeper significance? The answer, from the point of view of classical physics, is: the identity of the two masses is accidental and no deeper significance should be attached to it. The answer of modern physics is just the opposite: the identity of the two masses is fundamental and forms a new and essential clew leading to a more profound understanding. This was, in fact, one of the most important clews from which the so-called general theory of relativity was developed.

*A. Einstein and L. Infeld, *The evolution of physics* (Simon and Schuster, 1942), p. 36.

A mystery story seems inferior if it explains strange events as accidents. It is certainly more satisfying to have the story follow a rational pattern. In exactly the same way a theory which offers an explanation for the identity of gravitational and inertial mass is superior to the one which interprets their identity as accidental, provided, of course, that the two theories are equally consistent with observed facts.

PROBLEM 4.11. It is conceivable that, in another universe, some materials have only gravitational mass and others only inertial mass. Describe how some everyday objects would behave if made only of one or only of the other type of material.

4.11 Systems of units. In the system we have been using in the present chapter, the meter, the kilogram, and the second are the units in terms of which we have expressed the basic quantities length, mass, and time. Therefore it is called the *meter-kilogram-second* or *mks* system. This is, in fact, the system of units which is to be generally used for scientific work, according to an international agreement among the representatives of professional societies. But the laws of nature do not depend on the magnitudes of the arbitrarily chosen standards. In particular, we might instead have used the units of common daily transactions in the U. S. A. and Great Britain, namely, the *foot* for length, the *pound avoirdupois* (lb) for mass, and the *second* for time. This is the *foot-pound-second* or *fps* system. The relations between the mks and fps systems (1 lb $\doteq$ 0.454 kgm and 1 ft $\doteq$ 0.305 m) have no fundamental significance, and are historically rather accidental.

A spring balance may, of course, be calibrated by using it to accelerate a 1-lb object on a smooth horizontal surface and then using the equation $F_{\text{net}} = m$ (in lb) $\times a$ (in ft/sec^2). The unit of force so obtained is lb·ft/sec^2, called the *poundal*. This is the unit of force in the fps system, just as kgm·m/sec^2, or the newton, is the force unit in the mks system. As you should confirm by direct calculation, 1 pdl = 0.138 new.

A third system of units that has been widely used in physics is the *centimeter-gram-second* or *cgs* system. Like the mks system, it is a metric system, but uses the centimeter (0.01 m) and the gram (0.001 kgm) as the units of length and mass. The logical cgs unit of force is the net force which will impart to an object of mass 1 gm an acceleration of 1 cm/sec^2, that is, 1 gm·cm/sec^2, to which the name *dyne* is given. Since 1 gm $\equiv 10^{-3}$ kgm and 1 cm $\equiv 10^{-2}$ m, it follows that the dyne is equivalent to 10^{-5} new.

A possible fourth choice is the British engineering system, which must be described here because it is so widely used among engineers in English-speaking countries. As we have seen, in the mks, cgs, and fps systems the units of force (newton, dyne, or poundal) are defined in terms of the units of mass, length, and time. But in the British engineering system the unit of force is defined independently; specifically, it is taken to be the force equal to the earth's gravitational pull on a standard object whose mass is one pound. This unit is called a pound of force (lbf). In brief, one pound of force (lbf) is equal to the weight of an object of mass one pound (lb) at the earth's surface. Since this weight, in fps units, is $mg = 1$ lb $\times$ 32.2 ft/$\sec^2 \doteq 32$ pdl, we see that 1 lbf $\doteq 32$ pdl.

This recital actually has barely hinted at the number and richness of detail of different unit systems in use throughout the world. Hidden behind the multiplicity of existing systems lies a story with many facets, involving the arbitrary choice of the physical quantities that are to be regarded as basic or fundamental, the process of growth from diverse individual fields of knowledge, the role of measurement, and the operational nature of physical concepts. Here, too, we find clues concerning the international character of science, the cooperation and disputes among groups of scientists, and the relation between science and industry and between science and government. Even the passion with which certain systems of units are often advocated or attacked helps to reveal a little of the essentially human side of science.

But for the moment we cannot follow these tempting side roads. As for practical applications, it will save us a great deal of confusion at this stage if we do most of our work in a single system widely used among scientists today, namely, the mks system, in which the unit of length is 1 meter, that of mass is 1 kilogram, that of force is 1 newton, that of acceleration is 1 meter per second, per second, and so on. Appendix B lists factors for converting from any one system to another; it will be found helpful for expressing all problems and results in a consistent manner.

PROBLEM 4.12. Express the following quantities in mks units: (a) 350 cm, 12 cm^2, 9400 cm^3; (b) 30 cm/sec, 453 cm/sec; (c) 270 gm, 870 gm; (d) 37,400 gm·cm/sec^2, 37,400 dynes; (e) 980 cm/sec^2, 1000 cm/sec^2.

PROBLEM 4.13. Express the following quantities in mks units: (a) 3 ft, 1 mi; (b) 1 ft^2, 1 in^2; (c) 1 in^3, 1 ft^3; (d) 160 lbf; (e) 32 ft/sec^2.

PROBLEM 4.14. Construct a list of the multiplying factors for converting the following units to mks units: (a) pound of mass; (b) dyne; (c) foot; (d) hour; (e) mile; (f) cm/sec^2.

PROBLEM 4.15. After ascertaining your weight on a scale (in lbf), compute your *mass* in pounds, kilograms, and grams. Express your weight in newtons, dynes, and poundals.

PROBLEM 4.16. To check on your own ability to handle conversions quickly, find the average acceleration, expressed in units of m/sec^2, of a car of mass 4000 lb that starts from rest and acquires a speed of 50 mi/hr in 2 min. What net force, in newtons, is needed to produce this acceleration?

4.12 Frictional forces between solids.

Although we have used the notion of a frictionless plane in our discussion of force, and although friction may be a negligible factor in some experiments, we know from every-day experience that when one object slides or rolls over another, the frictional forces may be very large. They often enter prominently into problems involving motion.

Some main experimental facts about friction can be generalized in a remarkably simple manner. The frictional force F_f between two solid bodies is always opposite in direction to the force tending to produce motion. To a fair degree of accuracy it may be said to depend on only three factors: (1) it is proportional to the normal force F_n with which one body presses perpendicularly against the surface of the other (in Fig. 4.8, F_n is simply the weight mg of the block), (2) it depends on the materials of which the surfaces are made and the condition of these surfaces, and (3) it depends on the type of relative movement of the objects, that is, whether they slide over each other (*sliding* friction), or whether not quite enough force has been applied to produce relative motion (*starting* or *static* friction), or whether one object rolls on the other without slipping (*rolling* friction). All this is summarized in the expression for the law of friction, namely,

$$\text{frictional force } F_f = \mu F_n. \qquad (4.3)$$

The constant μ (Greek letter *mu*) is called the *coefficient of friction;* values are given in Table 4.2 for a few materials and for the cases of sliding and rolling frictions; for static friction the coefficient μ is usually a little larger than the corresponding value for sliding friction. All values depend on the preparation of the surfaces.

FIG. 4.8. The frictional force F_f is in the direction opposite to the force F_1 tending to produce motion.

Table 4.2. Coefficients of friction, μ.

(Approximate values for dry surfaces.)

Materials	Sliding	Rolling
Oak on oak	0.25	
Metals on oak	0.4–0.6	
Steel on steel	0.4	0.003
Rubber on concrete	0.7	0.03
Greased surfaces	0.2–0.03	

EXAMPLE 4.2. In Fig. 4.9 a block of oak of mass $m_1 = 1.2$ kgm is dragged across an oaken table top by a string passing over a small "frictionless" pulley and attached to another block of mass $m_2 = 2.0$ kgm. Compute (a) the frictional force F_f between block and table, (b) the force causing the system to accelerate, and (c) the acceleration.

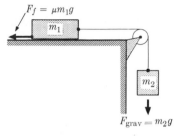

$F_f = \mu m_1 g$

$F_{\text{grav}} = m_2 g$

FIGURE 4.9

Solution. (a) From Eq. (4.3) and Table 4.2, $F_f = \mu F_n = \mu m_1 g = 0.25 \times 1.2$ kgm $\times 9.8$ m/sec$^2 = 2.9$ new. (b) Since one block is supported by the table, its weight produces no acceleration of the system; thus the accelerating force F_{net} is simply the weight $m_2 g$ of the other block diminished by the frictional force F_f, or $F_{\text{net}} = m_2 g - \mu m_1 g = (2.0$ kgm $\times 9.8$ m/sec$^2) - 2.9$ new $= 17$ new. (c) The total mass m that undergoes acceleration here is $m_1 + m_2$. In Eq. (4.2), $F_{\text{net}} = m \times a$, we realize that m refers to the total mass (here, $m_1 + m_2$); hence $a = F_{\text{net}}/m = 17$ new/$(1.2 + 2.0)$ kgm $= 5.3$ new/kgm $= 5.3$ kgm·m/sec^2·kgm $= 5.3$ m/sec^2.

PROBLEM 4.17. A sled of mass 6.2 kgm is pulled across a horizontal surface with a horizontal force of 12 new. What is the coefficient of friction μ between sled runners and surface?

PROBLEM 4.18. Suppose that the blocks and table top in Fig. 4.9 are made of steel, and that m_1 and m_2 are 4 and 2 kgm, respectively. Compute the acceleration of the system.

4.13 Another application of the second law: Atwood's machine. To study further the range of application of Newton's second law in mechanics, consider two objects of masses m_1 and m_2, connected by a string passing over a very light pulley which turns with negligible friction (Fig. 4.10). If one of the masses is larger than the other, both objects will be accelerated, the more massive one downward and the other upward. This device is known as Atwood's machine, after the 18th-century British physicist who originated it. Although both weights, $m_1 g$ and $m_2 g$, act downward, one is in the direction of acceleration and the other is in the opposite direction. Therefore the accelerating force is the difference between these weights. For example, if m_2 is larger than m_1, the net accelerating force F_{net} will be $m_2 g - m_1 g = (m_2 - m_1)g$. The total mass m undergoing the acceleration

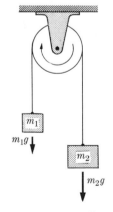

m_1

$m_1 g$

m_2

$m_2 g$

FIG. 4.10. Atwood's machine.

is the sum of the two masses, $m_1 + m_2$. Hence, by Eq. (4.2), the magnitude of the acceleration is

$$a = \frac{F_{net}}{m} = \frac{(m_2 - m_1)g}{(m_1 + m_2)}. \tag{4.4}$$

This equation reveals a main use of Atwood's machine: if m_1 and m_2 are independently known, and if a is accurately determined, g can be computed.

EXAMPLE 4.3. If the masses of the two suspended objects in an Atwood's machine are 3.0 and 4.0 kgm, and the masses move, from rest, 0.70 m in the first second, what is the magnitude of the acceleration due to gravity?

Solution. $m_1 = 3.0$ kgm, $m_2 = 4.0$ kgm, $s = 0.70$ m, $v_0 = 0$, $t = 1.0$ sec. From Eq. (1.3), $s = v_0t + \frac{1}{2}at^2$, or $a = (2s - v_0t)/t^2 = (1.4$ m$)/1.0$ sec$^2 = 1.4$ m/sec^2. From Eq. (4.4), $g = a(m_1 + m_2)/(m_2 - m_1) = (1.4$ m/sec$^2) \times (7.0$ kgm$)/1.0$ kgm $= 9.8$ m/sec^2.

PROBLEM 4.19. If the masses in an Atwood's machine are 200 and 400 gm, what is the acceleration?

Preparatory to a study of the forces on the individual objects of an Atwood's machine, consider an object of mass m at rest, hanging from a string (Fig. 4.11). Since the object is unaccelerated, the net force on it is zero; that is, the upward force F_t exerted by the string must be equal in magnitude to the downward gravitational force F_{grav} [$\equiv mg$], or $F_t = mg$. But if F_t were larger than the weight mg, the net force would be $F_{net} = F_t - F_{grav}$

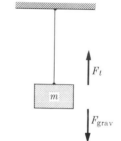

FIG. 4.11. For an object hanging at rest from a string, the tensile force F_t in the string must equal the weight of the object, F_{grav}.

$= F_t - mg$, and would be directed upward, so that the object would accelerate upward. If F_t were smaller than the weight, the net force would be given by $F_{net} = F_{grav} - F_t = mg - F_t$, and the acceleration would be downward. Indeed, even when the object is first hung on the string, it moves a little downward, stretching the string, F_t being the resulting elastic (tensile) force that originates in the stretch of the string. So long as the string has negligibly small mass, the tensile force F_t will be the same at every point of the string, including the ends.

In accordance with the above, if the two suspended objects in an Atwood's machine are of unequal mass, so that there is an acceleration, the tensile force in the string will differ in magnitude from the weight of either object (Fig. 4.12). Let us consider the forces first on one object and then on the other.

Suppose, as before, that $m_2 >$ m_1. Since the more massive object with mass m_2 will accelerate downward, its weight m_2g must exceed the tensile force F_t. The net force on m_2 alone is therefore $F_{\text{net}} = m_2g - F_t$. From Eq. (4.2), $m_2g - F_t = m_2a$, or

$$F_t = m_2(g - a). \qquad (4.5)$$

It is evident that given m_2, g, and the value of a, we can calculate the tensile force F_t.

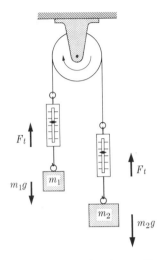

FIG. 4.12. Forces in Atwood's machine.

The second object, of mass m_1, is accelerated upward, so that the tensile force must be greater than its weight, and the net force on it is $F_{\text{net}} = F_t - m_1g$. Again using Eq. (4.2), we get $F_t - m_1g = m_1a$, or

$$F_t = m_1(g + a). \qquad (4.6)$$

Either (4.5) or (4.6) can be used to compute the tensile force in the string which is, as mentioned, the same at both ends. Moreover, juxtaposing these two expressions for F_t yields $m_2(g - a) = m_1(y + a)$, from which we obtain

$$a = \frac{(m_2 - m_1)}{(m_1 + m_2)} g, \qquad (4.4)$$

which is the same as the expression previously derived by an argument applied to Atwood's machine as a whole. This result gives us confidence in the analysis of the machine by isolating the parts.

Note also that Eq. (4.4) can be used to compute the mass of the object on one side of the pulley (say m_1) solely from data obtained from observations on the other side (that is, from m_2, g, and a). For example,

$$m_1 = \frac{m_2(g - a)}{(g + a)}. \qquad (4.7)$$

Equation (4.7) shows that m_1 could be computed even if this portion of the assembly were hidden in the inaccessible interior of a sealed box (Fig. 4.13). In a similar way we can often learn something about the "inside" of other "boxes," although we must remain "outside." In short, this example provides a simple illustration of a very powerful procedure in physical science, *the isolation and individual study of a specific and small part of the total situation* when the remainder is either inaccessible or too complex for a successful study as a whole.

Nature frequently confronts the scientist with "black-box problems." With the aid of the general laws of nature and a few observables he must see through a complex scheme or hidden mechanism. The problem may be as humble as finding m_1 by observations made on m_2, or it may be as general as deducing the temperature, velocity, diameter, mass, and composition of a distant star by analyzing a thin beam of its faint light.

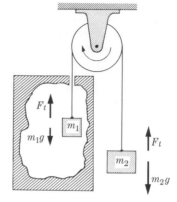

FIG. 4.13. Experiments with the right side of Atwood's machine yield information about the inaccessible left side.

EXAMPLE 4.4. The descending object of an Atwood's machine has a mass of 0.500 kgm and an acceleration of 0.20 m/sec². What is the mass of the other object?

Solution. From Eq. (4.7), $m_1 = 0.500$ kgm $\times$ (9.80 $-$ 0.20)(m/sec²)/(9.80 + 0.20) m/sec² = 0.480 kgm.

EXAMPLE 4.5. The lessons taught by the analysis of Atwood's machine are applicable in a wide range of mechanical situations. Consider Fig. 4.14. (a) What total force F_1 is needed to given an acceleration of 90 cm/sec² to the two blocks if they are of the same material and of mass $m_1 = 250$ gm and $m_2 = 400$ gm. The coefficient of sliding friction is here known to be 0.20. (b) Find the tensile force F_t in the string connecting the two blocks.

FIGURE 4.14

Solution. (a) To move the blocks steadily, without acceleration, would require a forward force equal in magnitude to the sum of the two frictional forces, namely, $\mu m_1 g + \mu m_2 g$. To give the blocks an acceleration a requires an additional forward force of amount $(m_1 + m_2)a$. Thus the total force needed is $F_1 = (\mu m_1 g + \mu m_2 g) + (m_1 + m_2)a = (\mu g + a)(m_1 + m_2) = [(0.20 \times 9.8$ m/sec²$) + 0.90$ m/sec²$] \times (0.250 + 0.400)$ kgm = 1.9 new.

(b) Consider only the second block, of mass $m_2 = 400$ gm = 0.400 kgm. The frictional force to the left is $F_f = \mu m_2 g$, so that the net force is $F_{net} = F_t - \mu m_2 g = m_2 \times a$. Since $\mu = 0.20$, $m_2 = 0.400$ kgm, $g = 9.8$ m/sec², $a = 0.90$ m/sec², $F_t = m_2 \times a + \mu m_2 g = m_2(a + \mu g) = 0.400$ kgm $\times (0.90$ m/sec² $+ 0.20 \times 9.8$ m/sec²$) = 0.40$ kgm $\times (2.86$ m/sec²$) = 1.1$ new.

PROBLEM 4.20. The ascending object of an Atwood's machine has a mass of 380 gm and an acceleration of 15 cm/sec^2. Derive the expression for the mass of the descending object from Eq. (4.4), and compute its numerical value.

PROBLEM 4.21. In Fig. 4.14 assume that the left-hand "block" is the standard kilogram and the right-hand "block" is a spring balance to be calibrated, as in Fig. 4.4. (a) Which force is registered on the balance while it is being pulled, F_1 or F_t? (b) Outline a method for determining the other force and the mass of the balance.

PROBLEM 4.22. In Fig. 4.15, the table top and pulleys are "frictionless," and the masses of the three blocks are $m_1 = 1.0$ kgm, $m_2 = 1.5$ kgm, and $m_3 = 2.5$ kgm. Find the magnitude of the acceleration of the system and the tensile force in the cord connecting m_1 and m_2.

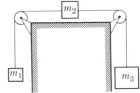

FIGURE 4.15

PROBLEM 4.23. A man tries to obtain a value for the gravitational acceleration g with an Atwood's machine while he and his whole laboratory are falling freely through space. What will be his experimental result for g, and why?

PROBLEM 4.24. If tomorrow the whole earth were to move with large acceleration in a direction toward the North Star, how would this manifest itself mechanically in different parts of the world?

4.14 Newton's third law. Newton's second law of motion provided a quantitative definition of force and introduced the concept of mass. To it Newton added the important *third* law of motion, which completes the general characterization of the concept of force by explaining, in essence, that each existing force has its mirror-image twin. In Newton's words,

> To every action there is always opposed an equal reaction: or, the mutual actions of two bodies upon each other are always equal, and directed to contrary parts.
> Whatever draws or presses another is as much drawn or pressed by that other. If you press a stone with your finger, the finger is also pressed by the stone. If a horse draws a stone tied to a rope, the horse (if I may so say) will be equally drawn back towards the stone; for the distended rope, by the same endeavor to relax or unbend itself, will draw the horse as much towards the stone as it does the stone towards the horse, and will obstruct the progress of the one as much as it advances that of the other. (*Principia*)

The point is rather startling: a single object, all by itself, can neither exert nor experience any force at all. Forces spring up only as the result of interactions, and during such interaction of two objects one object pushes or pulls on the other just as much as it is being pushed or pulled in return. The earth is attracted upward to a falling apple with just as much force as the falling apple is attracted downward toward the earth. We may choose to call the one force "active" and the other "reactive," (sometimes "the action and the reaction") but the order of naming is really arbitrary. It is not that one of the forces appears first and *causes* the other; they both "cause" each other simultaneously. Two men, caught in a crowd and pressing against each other, may each complain that it is the other who is doing the pushing; actually each man is both pushing *and* being pushed. Analogously, the borrowing of money may be said to have caused a debt, but it is equally correct that the lending of money was the cause of the credit. Action and reaction do stand to each other in a relation similar to that of debit to credit: one is impossible without the other, they are equally large but in an opposite sense, the causal connection is introduced only artificially, and, most important, they happen respectively to two different objects.

To emphasize all these points, we might rephrase Newton's third law of motion thus:

In the interaction of any two objects—whether this interaction be by contact, by gravitational or electrical or magnetic means, or in any manner whatsoever— the first object exerts a force on the second and, at the same time, the second exerts a force on the first; these two forces have the same magnitudes but opposite directions.

4.15 Examples and applications of Newton's third law. The easiest way to gain understanding of the third law is to analyze some specific and typical situations, as in the four examples that follow.

Example A. As the simplest case, consider the forces involved when a ball B falls freely to the earth E. Probably the force that comes to mind first is the weight of the ball; we will denote it here by the symbol F_{1B} and indicate it in Fig. 4.16(a) by a vertically downward arrow "anchored" to the ball. Coexisting with this pull of the earth on the ball is the reactive gravitational pull of the ball on the earth, equally large (by the third law) and indicated in Fig. 4.16(a) by the arrow F_{1E} drawn vertically upward.

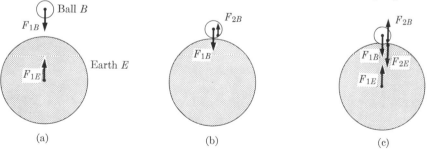

Fig. 4.16. (a) Ball and earth approaching each other. (b) The ball makes initial contact with the ground; only the forces on the ball are shown, and they do not cancel until the ball has fully come to rest. (c) System in equilibrium; all forces are shown.

This completely fulfills the requirements of the third law. Independently, the second law informs us that an observer at some fixed point in space would see the ball and the earth accelerate toward each other.

Example B. Resorting again to a thought experiment, we place the ball gently in contact with the ground. During the first moments of contact, the ball, owing to its weight F_{1B}, compresses the ground below it, "sinking in" during a brief time interval. The ground meanwhile is pressing upward on the ball [Fig. 4.16(b)]; and the more the ground is compressed, the more it presses, until this upward force F_{2B} on the ball has become as large as the ball's weight F_{1B} [Fig. 4.16(c)]. The net force *on the ball* is now zero. At the same time, by the third law, the upward force F_{2B} exerted by the ground on the ball must be accompanied by an equally large downward force F_{2E} exerted by the ball against the ground.

Note that from the moment of contact each body has two separate forces acting on it. When it finally has come to rest, the ball is in equilibrium (has no acceleration) because the two forces on it, F_{1B} and F_{2B}, are equal in magnitude and opposite in direction; the earth is similarly in equilibrium under the two forces acting on it, namely, F_{1E} and F_{2E}. But beware! F_{1B} and F_{2B} *both act on the ball* and are not to be interpreted as an active and a reactive force; rather the reaction to F_{1B} is F_{1E}, which acts on the earth. Similarly, F_{1E} and F_{2E} both act on the earth and hence are not an active and a reactive force. Note further that the forces denoted by the subscript 1 are gravitational forces and thus different in origin from the elastic forces denoted by the subscript 2. In short, F_{1B} and F_{1E} are equally large by Newton's *third* law, whereas F_{1B} is as large as F_{2B} (and F_{1E} as large as F_{2E}) by the condition of equilibrium, derived from Newton's *second* law.

Example C. The situation sketched in Fig. 4.17 involves four interacting objects: a horizontal stretch of ground G on which a recalcitrant beast of burden B is being pulled by its master M by means of a rope R. There are four pairs of active and reactive forces: (1) F_{1G} is the force communicated to the ground by the man's heels (mainly by static friction), and F_{1M} is the equally large reactive force exerted on the man by the ground; (2) F_{2R} is the force with which the man pulls on the rope, and F_{2M} is the equally

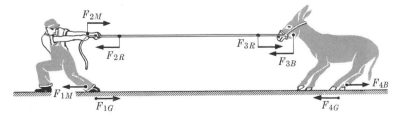

Fig. 4.17. Forces on four interacting objects.

large reactive force exerted by the rope on the man; (3) F_{3B} and F_{3R} are the interaction forces on the donkey and on the rope, respectively; and (4) F_{4G} and F_{4B} are the interaction forces between ground and donkey.

In equilibrium, when the donkey is successfully asserting his right to remain unaccelerated, the net force on each of the four objects is zero; for example, $F_{1M} - F_{2M} = 0$. But if the man succeeds in establishing his authority and the donkey accelerates toward the left, then the net force on the donkey, namely $F_{3B} - F_{4B}$, must have the same value as the product of its mass and acceleration, or $F_{net} \equiv F_{3B} - F_{4B} = m_B a_B$. Similarly, by Newton's second law, whenever the other objects are accelerated, the net force on each must equal the product of its own mass and acceleration. And whether or not there is equilibrium, any active force is equal in magnitude and opposite in direction to its reactive force.

The essential points may be phrased this way: By the third law $F_{1G} = F_{1M}$; similarly, $F_{2M} = F_{2R}$. But that law yields no information whatever about the relationship of F_{1M} to F_{2M}, two forces that act on the man by virtue of his decision to pull on a rope, not by any necessity or law of physics. It is only when he is in equilibrium that the net force on him is zero, or $F_{1M} = F_{2M}$, in terms of their numerical values.

Incidentally, to the donkey driver the difference between zero velocity and some larger, though constant, velocity is of course all that matters; and so he would naturally consider Newtonian physics contrary to common sense if he heard that it lumps two such differently prized states, rest and uniform motion, under one name, equilibrium, and treats them as dynamically equivalent. The donkey driver's viewpoint would certainly be understandable, but it is often by going beyond such viewpoints and breaking with common-sense preconceptions that we gain greater insight into natural phenomena.

Example D. Consider a car that is speeding up on a straight, level road. The force developed by the car's engine is transmitted to the wheels, and so the force propelling the car is, in the last analysis, due to the static friction between the tires and the road at their surfaces of momentary contact. This propelling force, F_C, by the third law, is equal in magnitude to the force F_E which the earth experiences. Consequently an observer fixed in space should ideally be in a position to observe the earth's surface moving backward under the car while the latter moves forward over the earth. But it is easy to show that two forces, although equal in magnitude, would produce unequal accelerations. We first write the equations for each object,

$$F_{net} \text{ on } C \equiv F_C = m_C a_C$$

and

$$F_{net} \text{ on } E \equiv F_E = m_E a_E.$$

But in numerical value, $F_C = F_E$, by the third law, and so we can combine the foregoing to obtain

$$m_C a_C = m_E a_E$$

or

$$a_C/a_E = m_E/m_C. \tag{4.8}$$

The mass of the earth, m_E, is approximately 6×10^{24} kgm, while m_C, the mass of an automobile, is approximately 2×10^3 kgm; therefore the ratio of the accelerations will be

$$a_C/a_E = 6 \times 10^{24} \text{ kgm}/(2 \times 10^3) \text{ kgm} = 3 \times 10^{21}.$$

Thus the acceleration of the car is about three thousand million million million times larger than the simultaneous acceleration of the earth.

Implied in this example is an important conceptual clarification. Strictly speaking, the a in $F = ma$, the acceleration produced by forces on the earth, should be measured not with respect to the earth itself, but rather with respect to some fixed point in space; a "fixed star" would serve the purpose. In practice, we do allow ourselves to use the earth as a frame of reference for the measurement of accelerations because the earth's large inertia ensures that it will respond only negligibly to the forces of reaction communicated to it by mutual gravitation, friction, elastic interactions, and the like.

4.16 The reaction-car experiment. As a summary of Newtonian mechanics in terms of a concrete situation, consider the following "thought experiment" first proposed by the 19th-century Austrian scientist, Ernst Mach.

The two cars in Fig. 4.18 are equipped with light "frictionless" wheels and are initially at rest on a "frictionless" track; their masses are respectively m_1 and m_2. The spring between the cars is compressed, but the cars are tied together with a string to keep them from moving in opposite directions. When the string is cut or burned, the oppositely directed forces F_1 and F_2 exerted on the cars by the spring assert themselves, and impart to the cars oppositely directed accelerations a_1 and a_2. Thus, by the second law, at any instant,

$$F_1 = m_1 a_1, \qquad F_2 = m_2 a_2. \tag{4.9}$$

By Newton's third law, F_1 and F_2, which are forces of mutual interaction, are equally large. Although each of these forces steadily diminishes as the

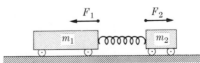

FIG. 4.18. The reaction-car experiment.

spring relaxes, at any instant they are equal in magnitude; that is, $F_1 = F_2$ at any instant. By taking the *average* force $\overline{F}$ and average acceleration $\bar{a}$, from the moment that motion starts until the spring falls away from between the cars, we have $\overline{F}_1 = m_1\bar{a}_1$, $\overline{F}_2 = m_2\bar{a}_2$, and $\overline{F}_1 = \overline{F}_2$. Hence,

$$m_1\bar{a}_1 = m_2\bar{a}_2. \tag{4.10}$$

Now any average acceleration $\bar{a}$ is, by definition, the change in velocity divided by the time needed for the change to occur. Thus, if the velocity changes from v_0 to v in time t, then $\bar{a} = (v - v_0)/t$. In the present experiment, $v_0 = 0$ for both cars. Therefore, if v_1 and v_2 are the final speeds of the cars, reached at the moment the spring falls away, the average accelerations are $\bar{a}_1 = v_1/t_1$ and $\bar{a}_2 = v_2/t_2$. Substituting these values in Eq. (4.10), we obtain

$$m_1v_1/t_1 = m_2v_2/t_2$$

or, since both cars are acted upon by the spring for the same time $t = t_1 = t_2$,

$$m_1v_1 = m_2v_2,$$

or

$$m_1/m_2 = v_2/v_1. \tag{4.11}$$

In words, Eq. (4.11) states that the final speeds produced in two bodies initially at rest by a pair of mutually interacting forces are inversely proportional to the masses of the objects. In the absence of friction, the cars will continue to move at these respective speeds in accordance with Newton's first law.

But one of the main reasons for presenting this example is the further importance of Eq. (4.11). If the mass of one of the interacting objects, say m_2, is chosen to be a *standard of mass*, then the mass of the other object can be measured simply by observing v_1 and v_2 and computing their ratio. Specifically, suppose that m_2 is 1.0 kgm, by definition, and that the magnitudes of the final velocities v_2 and v_1 are observed to be 0.15 m/sec and 0.050 m/sec, respectively. Then, from Eq. (4.11), $m_1 = m_2(v_2/v_1) = 1.0 \text{ kgm} \times (0.15 \text{ m/sec})/(0.050 \text{ m/sec}) = 3.0 \text{ kgm}$.

Thus we see that this so-called "reaction-car experiment" affords us a fourth method for determining the mass of an object: comparing the accelerations produced when the net force experienced by each of two objects is equally large constitutes a direct method for measuring *inertial* masses. It has the profound advantage that there enters nowhere a calibration or use of spring balances, or any *measurement of forces*. So long as we know, by Newton's third law, that the mutual forces between these two cars are equally large and oppositely directed, there is no need to investigate their actual magnitudes.

In summary, the four methods of determining the mass of an object which have been examined in this chapter are:

(1) Apply a measured force to the object by means of a calibrated spring balance, measure the resultant acceleration, and compute the mass by means of the relationship $m = F_{net}/a$.

(2) Measure the weight, F_{grav}, of the object by means of a calibrated spring balance, measure the gravitational acceleration g, and compute the mass by means of the relationship $m = F_{grav}/g$.

(3) Balance the weight of the object against the weight of objects of known mass, using an equal-arm balance. When the weights are equal the masses are equal.

(4) Perform an experiment with a reaction car of known mass m_2, and measure the final speeds. The unknown mass m_1 is then computed by means of the relationship $m_1 = m_2(v_2/v_1)$.

Note the differences among these methods: (1) and (2) require calibrated spring balances, (3) requires an equal-arm balance, (4) needs no balance at all; (1) and (4) involve determination of the motion of the objects, while (2) and (3) are static methods. But in every case the unknown mass is determined directly or indirectly in terms of the standard of mass.

ADDITIONAL PROBLEMS

4.25. Make a set of drawings analogous to Fig. 4.16(c) but involving an apple hanging from a tree.

4.26. Make a drawing of the situation in Fig. 4.17, but enter the pertinent force pairs for the particular case when man, rope, and donkey *do* accelerate to the left. Represent forces of different magnitudes by arrows of different lengths.

4.27. Discuss in terms of Newton's third law of motion (a) why the tensile force F_t could be assumed to be the same on both ends of the rope in the Atwood's machines of Figs. 4.10 and 4.12, and (b) why the forces F_1 and F_2 exerted by the two ends of the spring in Fig. 4.18 could be assumed to be equally large.

4.28. A projectile of mass 3 kgm is shot almost vertically upward with an initial speed of 1000 m/sec. What will be the change of speed of the earth during the launching? (Mass of earth is about 6×10^{24} kgm.)

4.29. Referring to the "thought experiment" of Ernst Mach involving the reaction cars for the determination of relative masses, (a) describe in detail his procedure for finding the inertial mass of an object in kilograms, (b) then describe how you would go on to prove experimentally that the gravitational and inertial masses of the object are identical in value. (c) Suggest how one might measure the quantities v_1 and v_2 needed in Eq. (4.11).

4.30. Is the equation $F_{net} = ma$ true by definition or is it subject to experimental confirmation?

4.31. Write a brief essay on the differences between the concept *weight* and the concept *mass*.

4.32. In an industrial plant a cart on rails is loaded with newly painted parts (total mass $= m_1$) and sent through a hot drying-tunnel by means of a cable and counterweight m_2 (Fig. 4.19). The total time spent by the cart in the hot region can, of course, be controlled by selecting the appropriate value for m_2. The force of friction F_f on the cart is known by measurement.

(a) Starting with Newton's second law of motion, derive a formula for the acceleration a of the cart along the track, giving a in terms of the known quantities m_1, m_2, F_f, and whatever else may be needed.

(b) Then assume that the cart is allowed to start from rest at the entrance to the hot tunnel, and derive an expression for the total time t spent by the cart in the tunnel of length s, giving t in terms of m_2 and whatever else may be needed.

(c) State in one sentence what assumptions must be fulfilled if your results are to be applicable in practice.

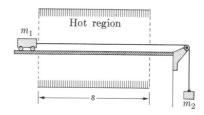

FIGURE 4.19

SUPPLEMENTARY READING

KNEDLER, J. W., *Masterworks of science* (Doubleday, 1947), pp. 171–189. Excerpts from the *Principia*.

LINDSAY, R. B., and H. MARGENAU, *Foundations of physics* (Wiley, 1936), pp. 85–92. An excellent discussion of the laws of motion.

MAGIE, W. F., *A source book in physics* (McGraw-Hill, 1935), pp. 30–46. Excerpts from the *Principia*.

MORE, L. T., *Isaac Newton, a biography* (Scribner's, 1934).

NEWTON, ISAAC, *Philosophiae naturalis principia mathematica*, trans. by A. Motte, revised by F. Cajori (University of California Press, 1934, and later printings). All Prefaces and pp. 1–28; glance through the rest of this magnificent work.

SULLIVAN, J. W. N., *Isaac Newton, 1642–1727* (Macmillan, 1938).

CHAPTER 5

UNIFORM CIRCULAR MOTION

5.1 Introduction. In the previous chapters we first solved the problem of how to describe motions with constant velocity. Next we investigated motions with constant acceleration and, in particular, the historically important case of free fall. Then came general projectile motion, an example of motion in a plane considered as the superposition of two simple motions. Finally we turned to a consideration of the forces needed to accelerate bodies along a straight line. But whereas all of these cases are concerned with constant acceleration, most of the motions observed in nature occur with changing accelerations. Among such motions are those that are classed as *rotational*, the motion of an object in a plane and around a central point. This topic subsumes the movement of planets, propellers, satellites, and electrons alike. In each case, the object is subject to a net force (and consequently to an acceleration) that continuously changes in direction.

We shall follow the same pattern as before and concentrate initially on the simplest type of rotational motion, motion of an object in a circular path with constant speed. First to be discussed is the kinematics of such motion, to be followed by the dynamics. These concepts prepare us for the discussion, in later chapters, of the theories of motions in our planetary system.

5.2 Definitions: period, frequency, radian measure. Consider a particle P moving with constant speed in a circular path (Fig. 5.1); the particle may be a speck of dust on a rotating phonograph turntable, or a stone on the surface of our rotating globe, or, to a good approximation, a planet in its path around the sun. The motion is *periodic*, a term applied to any process in which some definite physical process recurs regularly. To describe such rotational, periodic motions with economy and precision, we need the new concepts of *period* and *frequency*.

The *period*, T, is the time required for each cycle or repetition. For uniform circular motion, the period T is the time (usually measured in seconds) elapsing while the particle moves once around the circle.

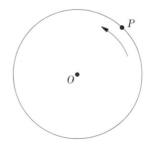

FIG. 5.1. A particle P moving in a circle.

The *frequency*, n, is the number of repetitions per unit time. The frequency n of a body in uniform circular motion is the number of complete revolutions which the body undergoes per unit time. From this definition it can be seen that the frequency is the reciprocal of the period, or

$$n \equiv 1/T. \tag{5.1}$$

EXAMPLE 5.1. A phonograph turntable is turning with a frequency n of 45 rev/min. Compute the frequency in rev/sec and the period T in sec/rev.

Solution. $n = 45$ rev/min $= 45$ rev/60 sec $= 0.75$ rev/sec. From Eq. (5.1), $T = 1/n = 1/(0.75$ rev/sec$) = 1.3$ sec/rev.

Since the period, by definition, is always the time taken *per complete revolution*, it is common practice to omit the phrase "per complete revolution" and express the period simply as a time. Thus, in Example 5.1, the period can be said to be 1.3 sec. Similarly, the frequency could be expressed as 0.75/sec or 0.75 sec^{-1}.

A third concept that we will find useful here is the angle θ turned through by the line OP drawn from the center O of the circle to the moving particle. In Fig. 5.2, as the particle moves from position P_1 to position P_2, the radial line sweeps through the angle θ. This angle may be expressed in *degrees*, or in *revolutions* (1 rev $\equiv$ 360°), or in terms of any other unit of angular measure. In particular, the unit called the *radian* is especially useful for our present purposes. It is defined by

$$\theta \text{ (in radians)} = s/r, \tag{5.2}$$

where s is the length of the arc that subtends the angle θ, and r is the radius of the circle (Fig. 5.3). For example, if s is 6 ft and the radius r of the circle is 2 ft, the angle θ in radians is 6 ft/2 ft, or 3 rad. Note that although the units in numerator and denominator cancel, it is nevertheless customary to specify that the angle is measured in radians.

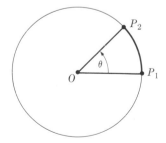

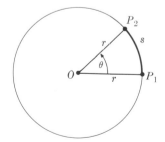

FIG. 5.2. As a particle moves from P_1 to P_2, the radial line sweeps through the angle θ.

FIG. 5.3. The angle θ, in radians, is the length s of the arc divided by the radius r.

The relations between the radian and some of the other angular units are quickly found. In making one complete revolution, a particle describes an arc length s equal to the circumference of the circle, or $2\pi r$. Thus for the specific case of one whole revolution, θ (in radians) $= s/r = 2\pi r/r = 2\pi$ rad. But since 1 rev $\equiv 360°$, it follows that 2π rad $= 360°$. Consequently 1 rad $= 360°/2\pi = 57.3°$. Appendix F lists angles expressed in degrees and the equivalent values in radians.

EXAMPLE 5.2. A chalk mark is made on the side of a flywheel at a point 2 ft from the axle of the wheel. Through what distance s does the chalk mark move when the wheel is rotated through an angle (a) of 4 rad, (b) of 200°?

Solution. (a) From Eq. (5.2), $s = r\theta = 2$ ft $\times 4$ rad $= 8$ ft·rad $= 8$ ft·ft/ft $= 8$ ft. (b) Since 1 rad $= 57.3°$, 200° is equivalent to $(200/57.3)$ rad; so s in this case is given by $s = r\theta = 2$ ft·$(200/57.3)$ rad $= 7.0$ ft·rad $= 7.0$ ft.

Note the relative ease with which s is computed when θ is expressed in radians rather than in degrees. For any angle such as the one shown in Fig. 5.4, by definition, θ (in radians) $= s/r$, $\sin \theta = y/r$, and $\tan \theta = y/x$. But if the angle θ is very small, s and y are almost equally large; and similarly for r and x. Therefore for such small angles (say less than 5°), $\sin \theta \doteq s/r$ and $\tan \theta \doteq s/r$ also, or $\sin \theta \doteq \tan \theta \doteq s/r = \theta$ (in radians); the sine and the tangent of the angle are then both very nearly equal to the angle itself, provided the angle is expressed in radians.

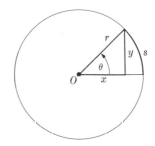

FIG. 5.4. If θ is made very small, $y \doteq s$, $x \doteq r$.

PROBLEM 5.1. Using the table of Appendix F, find the largest angle for which the angle, when expressed in radians, differs from the sine of that angle by no more than (a) 0.001, (b) 0.01, (c) 0.1.

5.3 Angular speed. In our study of motion in a circle with constant speed, we can use the concepts just defined to obtain some useful relations. Since the speed v of the particle is constant, it is defined by Eq. (1.1):

$$v = s/t, \qquad (1.1)$$

where s is the distance moved along the circular path in time t. When the particle makes one revolution, the distance moved is $s = 2\pi r$ and the time required to make the one revolution is, by definition, the period T. Hence,

$$v = 2\pi r/T. \qquad (5.3)$$

By combining this equation with Eq. (5.1), we can also express the speed in terms of the frequency n; thus

$$v = 2\pi r n. \tag{5.4}$$

EXAMPLE 5.3. A particle moves with a speed of 6 ft/sec in a circular path of radius 6 in. What is the frequency n?

Solution. Here $v = 6$ ft/sec, $r = 6$ in. $= 0.5$ ft; from Eq. (5.4), $n = v/2\pi r = $ (6 ft/sec)/($2\pi \times 0.5$ ft) $= 2$/sec, that is, 2 rev/sec.

PROBLEM 5.2. A phonograph record is 7 in. in diameter and turns with a frequency of 45 rev/min. What is the speed of a point on its edge?

PROBLEM 5.3. The first artificial earth satellite was initially put into an orbit averaging 350 mi above the surface of the earth; it took 96 min to make one revolution about the earth. What was its period, frequency, and speed? (Mean radius of earth $= 6.37 \times 10^6$ m.)

PROBLEM 5.4. (a) With what frequency and speed does a stone move around the earth's axis if it is located at the equator? (The equatorial radius of the earth is 3963 mi or 6.38×10^6 m, and the period of rotation of the earth about its axis is approximately 23 hr 56 min per revolution.) (b) Find the approximate speed of the earth in its yearly path around the sun. (The average distance between sun and earth may be taken to be 92.9×10^6 mi.)

The above examples and problems point up a simplification of the description of rotation through the use of angular measures. When any rigid body such as a wheel or a turntable rotates, all the different points of the body travel during a given time interval through *different* linear distances s, depending on their respective distances from the axis of rotation. But during this motion, these points turn through *the same angle* (or *angular distance*) θ. For example, all fixed parts of our spinning earth sweep through the same angle θ in a given time t, but the linear distance s that any part moves in its circular path about the earth's axis is given by $s = r\theta$, where r is the distance of the part from the axis; therefore s may have any value between zero (at the poles) and about $4000\,\theta$ mi (at the equator).

The concept of angular distance θ is supplemented by a concept for dealing with speeds of rotation. This *angular speed* ω (Greek letter omega) is defined as the time rate of change of angular distance, that is,

$$\omega = \frac{\theta}{t}. \tag{5.5}$$

For example, if a particle in uniform circular motion describes an angle of 8 rad in 2 sec, its angular speed is 4 rad/sec.

For one revolution of an object in uniform circular motion, θ (in radians) $= 2\pi$ and $t = T$; thus Eq. (5.5) can be written in the alternative forms $$\omega = \frac{2\pi}{T} = 2\pi n. \tag{5.6}$$

Note that the definition for angular speed, $\omega = \theta/t$, is precisely analogous to the definition for linear speed, $v = s/t$. To obtain the relation between these two quantities, we need only divide both members of the equation $s = r\theta$ by the time t:

$$\frac{s}{t} = \frac{r\theta}{t},$$

$$v = r\omega. \tag{5.7}$$

The concept of angular speed has the same simplifying advantage as that of angular distance: all the parts of a rigid rotating body have the same angular speed ω at the same instant. Linear speeds v, on the other hand, depend on the respective distances r from the axis of rotation.

PROBLEM 5.5. A turntable rotates for 5 min with a constant frequency of 78 rev/min. (a) What angle (in radians and in degrees) is described by a spot situated anywhere on the turntable? (b) What are the linear speeds of two spots at distances of 3 and 12 in. from the central axle? (c) What are the corresponding angular speeds?

5.4 Centripetal acceleration. Although an object moving in a curved path may have a constant *speed*, its *velocity* is not constant, since the direction of motion is changing. Thus in Fig. 5.5 the arrows representing the vector velocities at points P_1 and P_2 are the same length, since the speed (the magnitude of the velocity) is constant; but their directions are markedly different. Now any change in velocity with time constitutes an acceleration, whether this change be one of speed alone, or of direction alone, or of both speed and direction. For the first case, where the direction of the velocity does not change, we were able to apply the defining equation for the magnitude of acceleration, $a = (v_2 - v_1)/t$, assuming it to be constant. Or, to be more rigorous, we write that the magnitude of the *average* acceleration, $\bar{a}$, is

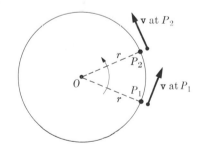

FIG. 5.5. A particle moving in a circle with constant speed nevertheless has a changing velocity.

$$\bar{a} = \frac{(v_2 - v_1)}{t}. \tag{5.8}$$

Thus if the velocity changes from 2 m/sec north (v_1) to 6 m/sec north (v_2), the *change* ($v_2 - v_1$) is clearly 4 m/sec north, and adding this change to the first velocity yields the second velocity [that is, $v_1 + (v_2 - v_1) = v_2$]. If, however, the velocity changes from 4 m/sec north to 4 m/sec west, simple subtraction of the magnitudes alone would indicate (incorrectly) that no change in velocity has occurred. To learn the extent of such a change of velocity, another type of calculation must be employed.

To assist us in focusing upon the problem, we now introduce the convention of designating vector quantities (see Section 3.3) by boldface type, so that a vector velocity will be designated by $\mathbf{v}$ (or, when writing longhand, by $\vec{v}$), while its magnitude, the speed, will be designated by the same letter in italic type, v. In this symbolism we might, for a given motion, write $\mathbf{v} = 3$ m/sec north and $v = 3$ m/sec.

Returning now to the problem of computing the average acceleration involved in a change of velocity, we redefine the average acceleration:

$$\bar{\mathbf{a}} = \frac{(\mathbf{v}_2 - \mathbf{v}_1)}{t} = \frac{\Delta \mathbf{v}}{t}, \tag{5.9}$$

where $\Delta \mathbf{v}$ is an abbreviation for $\mathbf{v}_2 - \mathbf{v}_1$. Not only are velocities vectors, but the average acceleration itself is a vector having the same direction as the *change* in velocity, $\Delta \mathbf{v}$. This redefinition of the average acceleration $\bar{\mathbf{a}}$ is very general; it includes $\bar{\mathbf{a}}$ for the case in which only the magnitude of the velocity changes. Thus in the example previously considered, where $\mathbf{v}_1 = 2$ m/sec north and $\mathbf{v}_2 = 6$ m/sec north, the change in velocity, $\Delta \mathbf{v} = \mathbf{v}_2 - \mathbf{v}_1$, is 4 m/sec north. If this change occurs in, say, 2 sec, the average acceleration, by Eq. (5.9), is

$$\bar{\mathbf{a}} = \frac{(\mathbf{v}_2 - \mathbf{v}_1)}{t} \equiv \frac{\Delta \mathbf{v}}{t} = \frac{4 \text{ m/sec north}}{2 \text{ sec}}$$

$$= 2 \frac{\text{m}}{\text{sec}^2} \text{ north.}$$

In this and every other case, the change in velocity, $\Delta \mathbf{v}$, is the vector quantity that we must add to $\mathbf{v}_1$ in order to compute $\mathbf{v}_2$.

For an object moving with constant speed in a circle, the acceleration is due to changes of direction of motion only. We shall now see how to compute $\Delta \mathbf{v}$ for such a case (Fig. 5.5), and we shall find that *a body moving with constant speed v in a circular path of radius r has at every moment an acceleration of constant magnitude v^2/r directed toward the center of the circle*. Since it is centrally directed at all times, this acceleration is called *centripetal*, or center-seeking (a term proposed by Newton), and the symbol to be used is a_c. A thorough analysis of centripetal acceleration was first published in 1673 by Newton's great contemporary, the Dutch scientist

Christiaan Huygens (1629–1695), but it was probably known to Newton in all its essential details some years earlier. The importance of this concept will appear more fully in the later discussion of the law of universal gravitation (Chapter 11), where it holds a key position in the arguments that led historically to the universal recognition of both the genius of Newton and the full power of physical inquiry.

To obtain an expression for $\Delta \mathbf{v}$, the change in velocity as the body moves from P_1 to P_2, let us first redraw only the arrows representing the velocity vectors of Fig. 5.5, remembering that their magnitudes and directions must be unchanged [Fig. 5.6(a)]. Our question is: what is $\Delta \mathbf{v}$, that is, what must be added to $\mathbf{v}$ at P_1 to produce $\mathbf{v}$ at P_2?

(a)   (b)   (c)   (d)

Fig. 5.6. Vector addition and subtraction. Two vectors (such as $\mathbf{v}_x$ and $\mathbf{v}_y$) may be added geometrically by the parallelogram method, as in (b), or by the triangle method, as in (c). In both cases their sum $\mathbf{v} = \mathbf{v}_x + \mathbf{v}_y$ is the same. In (c), $\mathbf{v}_y = \mathbf{v} - \mathbf{v}_x$; in (d), $\Delta \mathbf{v} = \mathbf{v}$ at $P_2 - \mathbf{v}$ at P_1.

In our previous analysis of vector algebra (Sections 3.3 and 3.6), we found that two velocity components $\mathbf{v}_x$ and $\mathbf{v}_y$ could be added to obtain the total velocity $\mathbf{v}$ by the parallelogram method shown in Figs. 3.8 or 5.6(b); but in the latter case we could just as well have added the components by the triangle method shown in Fig. 5.6(c). The vector sum $\mathbf{v}$ is obtained by adding the two arrows representing $\mathbf{v}_x$ and $\mathbf{v}_y$ head-to-tail, and drawing a third arrow from the tail of the first to the head of the second. We may symbolize this geometric method in an algebraic representation by the vector equation $\mathbf{v}_x + \mathbf{v}_y = \mathbf{v}$.

It follows that $\mathbf{v} - \mathbf{v}_x = \mathbf{v}_y$, since $\mathbf{v}_y$ is the quantity which must be added to $\mathbf{v}_x$ to obtain $\mathbf{v}$. If we now regard $\mathbf{v}_y$ in Fig. 5.6(c) as $\mathbf{v} - \mathbf{v}_x$, we see how to subtract two vectors in general: a difference between two vectors represented by arrows is found by placing their tail ends together and drawing the connecting arrow from the tip of the first to the tip of the second; this arrow then represents the vector quantity that must be added to the first vector to obtain the second.

In the present case (Fig. 5.5), we obtain the difference between vectors $\mathbf{v}$ at P_2 and $\mathbf{v}$ at P_1 by drawing an arrow from the terminus of the arrow representing $\mathbf{v}$ at P_1 to the terminus of $\mathbf{v}$ at P_2 [Fig. 5.6(d)]; this arrow represents $\Delta \mathbf{v}$, *the change in velocity from point P_1 to point P_2 during the time interval t.* Thus from a graphical construction like Fig. 5.6(d), by measurement with ruler and protractor, a value for $\Delta\mathbf{v}$ in any specific case can be obtained. The acceleration $\bar{\mathbf{a}}$ would then be $\Delta\mathbf{v}/t$.*

EXAMPLE 5.4. The velocity of an automobile changes from $\mathbf{v}_1 = 30$ mi/hr north to $\mathbf{v}_2 = 30$ mi/hr west in 2 min. Find the average acceleration.

Solution. In Fig. 5.7 the arrows representing the velocities show the change in velocity. Either by measurement or by geometric computation we find that the magnitude of the change is $\Delta v = 42$ mi/hr and its direction is 45° south of west (southwest). The average acceleration is therefore $\bar{\mathbf{a}} = \Delta\mathbf{v}/t = (42 \text{ mi/hr SW})/2 \text{ min} = 21 \text{ mi/hr·min SW} = 0.35 \text{ mi/min}^2 \text{ SW}$.

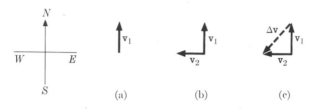

(a)   (b)   (c)

FIGURE 5.7

PROBLEM 5.6. A car on a circular racetrack of radius 200 m is moving with a constant speed of 25 m/sec. (a) How much does its velocity change in one second? (b) What is the average acceleration during that second? (Draw the necessary vector diagrams.)

But even without graphical construction, we can find the magnitude of $\Delta\mathbf{v}$ in terms of the speed of the body and the radius of its circular path. In Fig. 5.8 the entire problem has been represented. Part (a) shows the circular path, the points P_1 and P_2, and the arrows representing the velocities at those points. In part (b) the same arrows have been redrawn, carefully preserving their lengths and directions, and the difference between them, $\Delta\mathbf{v}$, has been constructed. Note that the vector triangle in (b) and the triangle OP_1P_2 in (a) are similar (satisfy yourself that this is the case). Adopting the symbol v for the magnitude of $\mathbf{v}$ and Δv for the magnitude of $\Delta\mathbf{v}$, and making use of the property of similar triangles that their corresponding sides are proportional, we can write

$$\frac{\Delta v}{v} = \frac{x}{r} \quad \text{or} \quad \Delta v = \frac{vx}{r}.$$

(Here italic type has been used, for we are interested solely in the lengths of the sides and not in their directions.) We now substitute this value for Δv into the equation for the average acceleration (Eq. 5.9).

---

*The general procedure for vector addition and vector subtraction is presented in Appendix G.

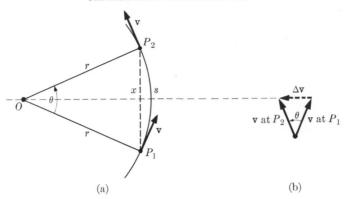

(a)   (b)

FIG. 5.8. If θ were very small, $\Delta\mathbf{v}$ would be nearly perpendicular to $\mathbf{v}$ both at P_1 and P_2; $\Delta\mathbf{v}$ is directed toward the center of the circle at all times.

Since we know only the magnitude of Δv, we can obtain only the magnitude of the average acceleration:

$$\bar{a} = \frac{\Delta v}{t} = \frac{vx}{rt} = \frac{v}{r} \cdot \frac{x}{t}.$$

Recall that Eq. (5.9) defines the average acceleration over the path from P_1 to P_2, whereas we are seeking an expression for the *instantaneous* centripetal acceleration a_c at any *point* of the path. In analogy to our discussion of instantaneous speed, we imagine the two points P_1 and P_2 to be brought very close together, so that the time t needed for the object to move from one point to the other is made very small, the angle P_1OP_2 becomes very small, and the chord x and the arc s connecting the two points attain essen tially equal values. Then the average acceleration $\bar{a}$ over this exceedingly small interval can be identified with the instantaneous acceleration a_c at any point within the interval. We can now substitute a_c for $\bar{a}$ and s for x in our last equation, obtaining

$$a_c = \frac{v}{r} \cdot \frac{s}{t}.$$

But s/t is simply the speed v of the object. Hence

$$a_c = \frac{v^2}{r}. \tag{5.10}$$

For uniform circular motion the speed v and the radius r have constant values. Therefore the centripetal acceleration a_c evidently does not change in magnitude from point to point. But what about the direction of this acceleration? It will coincide with the direction of $\Delta\mathbf{v}$. To determine this direction, think of the distance P_1P_2 and of the angle θ as being extremely small. Then, in Fig. 5.8(b) $\mathbf{v}_1$ and $\mathbf{v}_2$, which are each tangent to the circular path in (a), are very nearly parallel; therefore the vector $\Delta\mathbf{v}$ is essentially perpendicular to both $\mathbf{v}_1$ and $\mathbf{v}_2$. So $\Delta\mathbf{v}$, and therefore the acceleration $\mathbf{a}_c$, is perpendicular to the direction of motion at every point in its path; that is, the vector $\mathbf{a}_c$ points at every moment along the radius directly toward the center of the circle. This is what justifies calling it a *centripetal* acceleration.

EXAMPLE 5.5. Find the centripetal acceleration of an object on the earth's equator owing to the earth's rotation about its own axis.

Solution. Take the radius r of the earth at the equator to be 6.4×10^6 m. In one day, or 8.6×10^4 sec, the object moves in a circular path of length $s = 2\pi r = 2\pi \times 6.4 \times 10^6$ m. Hence the speed of the object is $v = s/t = (2\pi \times 6.4 \times 10^6 \text{ m})/(8.6 \times 10^4 \text{ sec}) = 4.7 \times 10^2$ m/sec. The centripetal acceleration then has a magnitude of $a_c = v^2/r = (4.7 \times 10^2 \text{ m/sec})^2/(6.4 \times 10^6 \text{ m}) = 3.5 \times 10^{-2}$ m/sec^2. The direction of this acceleration is toward the center of the earth.

Equation (5.10) can be put into several other useful forms when we recall that the circumference of a circle is $2\pi r$ and that the object traverses this circumference in the period T, with frequency $n \, [\equiv 1/T]$ and with angular speed $\omega \, [=v/r]$. The resulting forms are

$$a_c = \frac{v^2}{r} = \frac{4\pi^2 r}{T^2} = 4\pi^2 n^2 r = \omega^2 r. \tag{5.11}$$

PROBLEM 5.7. Derive the foregoing Eqs. (5.11).

On first encounter, one may feel that there is something implausible about the concept of centripetal acceleration. The difficulty is to convince oneself that a circular motion at *constant speed* is nevertheless accelerated, that in a uniform motion on a circle the acceleration is truly, at every instant, perpendicular to the direction of motion. But this merely is another way of saying that there is no change in speed, but only in the direction of motion from moment to moment. If the object had no centripetal acceleration, it would move not on a circle but along a straight line.

PROBLEM 5.8. (a) What is the centripetal acceleration of a particle on the rim of a 10-in. phonograph record rotating at 78 rev/min? (b) A test sample in a good ultracentrifuge may whirl at a distance of about 0.6 cm from the axis of rotation and at 60,000 rev/min. Find its centripetal acceleration.

PROBLEM 5.9. Calculate the centripetal acceleration of the artificial satellite described in Problem 5.3.

PROBLEM 5.10. Compute the centripetal acceleration of the earth as a whole with respect to the sun on the assumption that the earth moves about the sun in an annual circular orbit of radius 1.5×10^{11} m.

PROBLEM 5.11. A pilot dives his plane with a speed of 200 m/sec and then curves back into a climb (Fig. 5.9). Assume that, during the turning, the plane

moves in the arc of a circle with unchanged speed and with a centripetal
acceleration whose value is 3 times
that of the acceleration due to gravity.
Find the radius R of the circle.

PROBLEM 5.12. Find the magnitude
and direction of the centripetal acceleration of an object in Washington,
D. C. (latitude 39° north) owing to the
rotation of the earth about its own axis.
Note the difference between your result
and that obtained in Example 5.5.

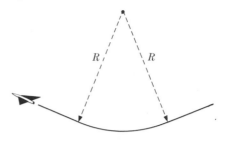

FIGURE 5.9

5.5 Centripetal force. Accelerations, including centripetal ones, do not occur except through the action of forces. For centripetal accelerations, Newton's second law of motion necessarily leads to the following conclusion: for a body of mass m to be in uniform circular motion with a centripetal acceleration a_c, it must be acted on continuously by a net force of magnitude ma_c, directed in the same sense as a_c, that is, toward the center of rotation at every moment. This force, whatever its origin in specific cases, is called a *centripetal force*, F_c. Newton's discussion in the *Principia* of 1687 speaks for itself:

DEFINITION: A centripetal force is that by which bodies are drawn or impelled, or in any way tend, toward a point as a center.

Of this sort is gravity, by which bodies tend to the center of the earth; magnetism, by which iron tends to the lodestone; and that force, whatever it is, by which the planets are continually drawn aside from the rectilinear motions, which otherwise they would pursue, and made to revolve in curvilinear orbits. A stone, whirled about in a sling, endeavors to recede from the hand that turns it; and by that endeavor, distends the sling, and that with so much the greater force, as it is revolved with the greater velocity, and as soon as it is let go, flies away. That force which opposes itself to this endeavor, and by which the sling continually draws back the stone toward the hand, and retains it in its orbit, because it is directed to the hand as the center of the orbit, I call the centripetal force. And the same thing is to be understood of all bodies, revolved in any orbits. They all endeavor to recede from the centers of their orbits; and were it not for the opposition of a . . . force which restrains them to, and detains them in their orbits, which I therefore call centripetal, would fly off in right lines, with a uniform motion. . . . nor could the moon without some such force be retained in its orbit. If this force were too small, it would not sufficiently turn the moon out of a rectilinear course; if it were too great, it would turn it too much, and draw down the moon from its orbit toward the earth. It is necessary that the force be of a just quantity and it belongs to the mathematicians to find the force that may serve exactly to retain a body in a given orbit with a given velocity; . . .

To paraphrase one of Newton's concrete examples, when a stone on a string is made to revolve (Fig. 5.10), it clearly is *not in equilibrium*, but instead is acted upon by a centrally directed force F_c, namely, a tensile force in the string, traceable in turn to the pull of the hand. If the string were to break, F_c would cease, and with it also the centripetal acceleration. Now there would be no force to change the stone's velocity and to maintain the circular path; consequently the stone, now in equilibrium (if we may forget the gravitational pull on it), would move in a straight line tangent to the circle at the point where the stone was when the string broke.

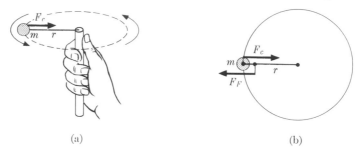

(a)   (b)

FIG. 5.10. A centripetal force F_c acts on the stone, while a centrifugal force F_F acts on the string and hand.

By Newton's third law, the force F_c on the rotating stone (while the string is still unbroken) is attended by a reaction, a contrary force of equal magnitude exerted by the stone on the string and ultimately on the hand at the center of rotation. This reaction is named the *centrifugal* or center-fleeing force F_F. Like any other action-reaction pair, F_c and F_F do *not* act on the same body, but on two different ones, here on the stone and on the string, respectively, as indicated in Fig. 5.10(b). Both forces disappear simultaneously when the string breaks.

The physical origins and means for providing a rotating object with the necessary centripetal force vary greatly. A rotating flywheel is held together by the strength of the material itself, which can supply the necessary tensile force, at least up to a point. A car rounding a curve on a level road is kept from moving off the road tangentially in a straight line by friction between the roadbed and the tires, which supplies the centripetal force acting sideways on the tires. The moon, as Newton was the first to explain, is kept captive in its orbit about the earth by the gravitational pull continuously exerted on it by the earth. But in each case, insofar as the motion is circular and uniform, $F_c = ma_c$ or, to clothe this expression in all its alternative forms,

$$F_c = ma_c = \frac{mv^2}{r} = m\frac{4\pi^2 r}{T^2} = m \cdot 4\pi^2 n^2 r = m\omega^2 r. \qquad (5.12)$$

PROBLEM 5.13. Derive, step by step, from first principles, the relation $F_c = m(4\pi^2/T^2)r$, and explain at each step what physical law, concept, approximation, etc., has been introduced.

PROBLEM 5.14. Assuming that the earth moves uniformly about the sun in a circular orbit, compute the centripetal force exerted on the earth by the sun. What centrifugal force is exerted on the sun by the earth? (The mass of the earth is 6×10^{24} kgm; if additional data are needed, see Appendix A.)

PROBLEM 5.15. A flywheel of diameter 3 m and mounted on a horizontal axis has a rim consisting of a band of metal of mass 10^3 kgm. The spokes are of such strength as to supply tensile force up to 10^6 new. Predict at what speed of rotation the wheel will burst. Make a drawing to show the paths of the flying pieces.

PROBLEM 5.16. Cite some examples of rotational motion other than those we have already mentioned, and explain in each case (a) how centripetal force is supplied to the rotating body, and (b) what body experiences the centrifugal force.

Surveying our total progress to this point, we recall that the initial problem in Chapter 1 was simply to describe uniform motion in a straight line; then followed composite (projectile) motion in a plane. When we considered the forces needed to produce such motions, Newton's laws supplied us with concise yet very general answers. Lastly, in the present chapter we extended our horizon still further by including some of the kinematics and dynamics of rotational motion. Although there will be occasion to add to this basic store of information on mechanics, we are now ready to apply our analysis to the specific problem of planetary motion—a *case study* as it were, one that lies at the borderline of physics and astronomy, illuminating both while revealing also a little more concerning the origins of modern science.

ADDITIONAL PROBLEMS

5.17. When he wrote the *Principia*, Newton knew that in 1672 Jean Richer had taken a pendulum clock from Paris to Cayenne, French Guiana, to help in astronomical observations; there the clock lost $2\frac{1}{2}$ minutes each day. Furthermore, from Huygens' work it was then known that the period T (in seconds) for a pendulum of given length was proportional to $1/\sqrt{g}$. If g for Paris is 9.809 m/sec^2, outline a procedure for computing the value of g at Cayenne. (It was this observation that drew general attention to the distinction between the concepts of mass and weight, until then largely undifferentiated.)

5.18. An automobile is moving with a constant velocity of 20 m/sec along a straight road. A piece of gravel is lodged in one of the tire treads, 35 cm from the center of the wheel. What is the magnitude and direction of the acceleration experienced by the piece of gravel?

5.19. A carousel rotates twice a minute. (a) What is the centripetal acceleration of a boy sitting on a horse 4 m from the center? (b) What centripetal force must the horse exert on the boy if the boy's mass is 30 kgm?

5.20. A train goes around a curve at 110 km/hr. (a) If the curve is an arc of a circle of radius 0.30 km, what is the centripetal acceleration? (b) Why are train roadbeds and automobile roads banked?

5.21. (a) In view of the result in Example 5.5, what fraction of one's true weight at the equator is needed to supply the centripetal force? Sketch the forces on a man standing on a spring-operated pan balance. What fraction of his true weight (gravitational pull to the earth) is indicated on the dial of the balance? (b) How fast would the earth have to spin about its axis for the man at the equator to register "no weight" on the balance? (c) Why does a living organism in an artificial earth satellite feel as if it were in gravitation-free space?

5.22. (a) Moving ships cannot turn quickly, and sometimes move forward as much as a mile in turning 90°; explain why. (b) Suggest how a spaceship might be made to change its direction of motion in interplanetary space.

5.23. A certain pendulum consists of a 1.0-kgm bob supported by a cord 1.0 m long. If the bob passes through its lowest point with a speed of 8.0 m/sec, (a) what is the centripetal force on the bob at this point? (b) What is the total force on the cord?

5.24. A daredevil rides a motorcycle inside a spherical cage of radius 4 m. If he travels in a vertical circle, what must his speed be if he is not to fall when at his highest point? (*Hint:* He will fall if there is a net downward force on him in excess of the necessary centripetal force. Compute the downward force due to his weight mg and compare it with the necessary centripetal force. Make a sketch of all the forces on the man.)

5.25. A boy whirls a stone in a horizontal circle 1.0 m above the ground by means of a string 1.2 m long. The string breaks and the stone flies off horizontally, striking the ground 10 m away. What was its centripetal acceleration while in circular motion? (*Hint:* Once the string breaks the stone is a projectile.)

5.26. A jet plane flying 750 mi/hr makes a turn in a circle of radius 1800 m. (a) Find the centripetal acceleration a_c of the pilot, and (b) express it in multiples of g. (c) If a pilot without special equipment "blacks out" when the centripetal acceleration is above $4.5g$ for any appreciable time, what is the smallest safe turn radius for a plane at the speed given?

SUPPLEMENTARY READING

MAGIE, W. F., *A source book in physics* (McGraw-Hill, 1935), pp. 27–30. Huygens' theorems on centripetal force.

SEARS, F. W., and M. W. ZEMANSKY, *College physics* (Addison-Wesley, 1948, and later printings), Chap. 9 on circular motion.

STACY, R. W., *et al.*, *Essentials of biological and medical physics* (McGraw-Hill, 1955), Chap. 12 on the effects of rotational motion on living matter.

TAYLOR, L. W., *Physics: the pioneer science* (Houghton Mifflin, 1941), Chaps. 5 and 6 on resolution and composition of vectors.

Part III

THE STUDY OF PLANETARY SYSTEMS

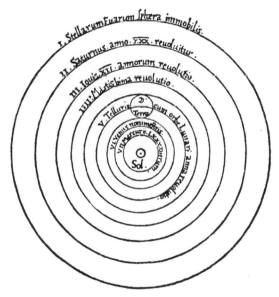

THE HELIOCENTRIC SYSTEM
A diagram from Copernicus' *De Revolutionibus* (1543).

THE STUDY OF PLANETARY SYSTEMS

One of man's most persistent and revealing preoccupations has been his attempt to fashion for himself an adequate conceptual model of the universe. This search has always been of intense interest to students of the physical sciences, for a number of reasons. In the first place, the development of many of the methods of science began when man attempted to reduce the chaotic motions of the stars, sun, moon, and planets to an orderly system. Second, we shall see that a continuum of ideas leads from the early speculations about planetary motion right to 20th-century beliefs, paralleling the expanding view of our universe from the early notion of a sky that seemed near, to that of a large rotating celestial sphere, then to the concept of our solar system as only a small part of a huge galaxy, and finally to the present-day universe of innumerable galaxies scattered throughout unbounded space.

Third, many of the great thinkers responsible for the strength and content of present physical theory have been involved in the development of the concept of this world system; their place in science is part of our story. Fourth, these achievements of physical science—the emerging model of our solar system and the conception of universal gravitation—have had profound effects on Western culture. For example, without an understanding of the 17th-century Newtonian revolution and its background, we cannot hope to comprehend fully the history of 18th-century Europe, the roots of modern economic and political theory, or the philosophy of a Locke, a Berkeley, or a Hume. And finally, this case study gives us the opportunity to watch the rise and fall of physical theories, to analyze their structures, and to sharpen our faculties of discrimination between useful theories and unfruitful ones. Thus a close examination of this one topic not only will reveal new and significant physical laws, but will also give us a brief chance to examine various other aspects of physical science that have helped to shape our cultural heritage.

CHAPTER 6

THE ASTRONOMY OF ANCIENT GREECE

6.1 Plato's problem. Many of the earliest developments in science can be traced to the imaginative minds of the great Greek thinkers. Although optical instruments of precision were still 2000 years away, simple observation of the night sky had by about 400 B.C. provided sufficient data and interpretations to nourish several world-theories. The stars and the Milky Way were commonly thought of as fixed with respect to one another on the surface of a very large sphere, and enclosed by this celestial sphere was the rest of the universe—the sun, the moon, the earth, and the five planets prominently visible to the unaided eye. The motion of these bodies within the celestial sphere was among the important concerns of philosophy at the time.

It is related that Plato (4th century B.C.) set a problem for his students along these lines: The stars—regarded as eternal, divine, unchanging beings—move around the earth once each day, as we can see, in that eminently perfect path, the circle. But there are a few heavenly bodies which, if watched throughout the year, appear to wander rather disturbingly across the sky, tracing out yearly paths that are perplexingly irregular. These are the *planets* (from the Greek word for *wanderer*). Surely they too must "really" somehow move in ordered circles or combinations of circles. Such circular motion being assumed axiomatically, how can we account for the observations on planetary motion or, to use the contemporary phrase, "save the phenomena"? Plato's important problem can be paraphrased as follows: "Determine what *uniform* and *ordered* (*circular*) motions must be assumed for each of the planets to account for its apparently irregular yearly paths."

6.2 The bases of Greek science. The very formulation of Plato's historic problem strikingly summarizes for us two main contributions of Greek philosophers to the topic of our discussion, namely, that physical theory arises out of prior metaphysical conceptions and that it is concerned with finding geometric and other mathematical relationships between observable physical quantities. Let us look more closely at these two characteristics of Greek science.

(1) Physical theory (say a theory of planetary motions) is intelligible only in the context of prior specific metaphysical* conceptions, for example,

---

*The term *metaphysics* is used here in a specific sense: it refers to the discipline in which principles of knowledge or of being are investigated in terms of intuitive, self-evident concepts, of concepts of direct "everyday" experience, and of analogies.

the postulate that heavenly bodies must execute "perfect," circular motions. It is much clearer to us than it was in antiquity that postulates of this kind are useful only insofar as they are held tentatively, subject to modification in the light of further experience and usefulness. We shall see how less attention to axiomatic *a priori* arguments and more to experience eventually proved to be of considerable importance in the development of a "new experimental science."

(2) The second implication in Plato's problem was that physical theory is concerned with observable and measurable phenomena, such as the apparent motions of the planets, its aims being to discover uniformities of behavior underlying the apparent irregularities and to express them in the language of number and geometry. This conviction that mathematics should be the language of science was derived in part from the Greek philosopher Pythagoras and his followers. Although not extended by Plato to areas of science other than astronomy, it was a treasured hint that reappeared in Europe in the late medieval period and eventually came fully into its own with Galileo and his contemporaries.

Let us now see how the successors of Plato tried to construct a system of the world in accordance with the postulate of "uniform and ordered motion," that is, a system in which the celestial objects have only uniform (constant) circular motions or combinations of several such motions. We shall find that their attempt was not fully successful, but had deeply significant consequences for our intellectual history.

6.3 The Aristotelian cosmological scheme. In attempting to rationalize the motions of celestial objects, certainly the most immediately obvious and simplest approach is to regard our earth as the center of the universe and to construct a *geocentric*, or earth-centered, system contained in a celestial sphere carrying the firmament or fixed stars, as in Fig. 6.1. The observed daily (diurnal) motion of these fixed stars is immediately accounted for in terms of our model if we require the large celestial sphere to rotate uniformly on a north-south axis once a day. We may then attempt to explain the apparent motions of the sun, the moon, and the five visible planets about the fixed earth by letting each be carried on a transparent sphere of its own, one within the other, all seven enclosed by the celestial sphere of fixed stars, and with the earth at the center of the whole scheme. But then we remember that the seven celestial bodies do not rise and set always at the same points on the horizon or always at the same times. Moreover, the planets are seen to travel during the year along complicated paths against the background of the fixed stars, sometimes even temporarily reversing their directions of motion—a planetary phenomenon known as *retrograde motion* (Fig. 6.2). So we proceed to give to the sphere that carries each of these bodies a set of simultaneous rotations about different axes and, by assigning various speeds and directions to each rotation, and

FIG. 6.1. A geocentric cosmological scheme in the Aristotelian tradition. The earth is fixed at the center of concentric rotating spheres. The sphere of the Moon (*lune*) separates the terrestrial region (composed of concentric shells of the four elements Earth, Water, Air, and Fire) from the celestial region. In the latter are the concentric spheres carrying Mercury, Venus, Sun, Mars, Jupiter, Saturn, and the stars. To simplify the diagram, only one sphere is shown for each planet. (From the DeGolyer copy of Petrus Apianus' *Cosmographie*, 1551.)

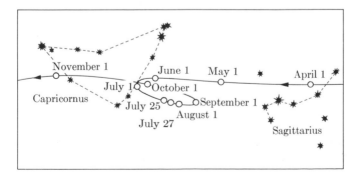

FIG. 6.2.   Retrograde motion of Mars.

various inclinations to each axis, try to obtain a model that will duplicate the actually observed paths. To cite an analogy, we might, on visiting a fairground at night, notice a light in the distance undergoing very complex but periodically repeating motions, and we might postulate that the light is that of a lamp fastened to the rim of a wheel of a bicycle being ridden on a merry-go-round. Even though we could see nothing but the light, we might be able to account for its observed motion by the trial-and-error method of assigning various orbits, speeds, and directions of motion to the several rotating objects which we suspect to be involved.

In the cosmological scheme developed by Plato's successors, the outermost sphere carried the fixed stars in their diurnal motion about the earth. Next there was a smaller, transparent sphere that turned about an axis embedded in the stellar sphere and on the surface of which the outermost planet, Saturn, was considered to be fixed. Since this sphere turned upon its own axis with a definite speed while being carried around simultaneously with the outer sphere, the motion of Saturn was a combination of two circular motions, which accounted for the observation that its path differed from the paths of the stars. However, it was soon found that the position of the axis and the speed of rotation of this second sphere could not possibly be adjusted to produce a motion of Saturn that would agree in its details with the observations. Consequently, a third sphere was added, within the first two and turning about an axis fastened to the intermediate sphere (Fig. 6.3). With Saturn fixed to the surface of this sphere, its motion was now a combination of three circular motions, at different speeds and about different axes.

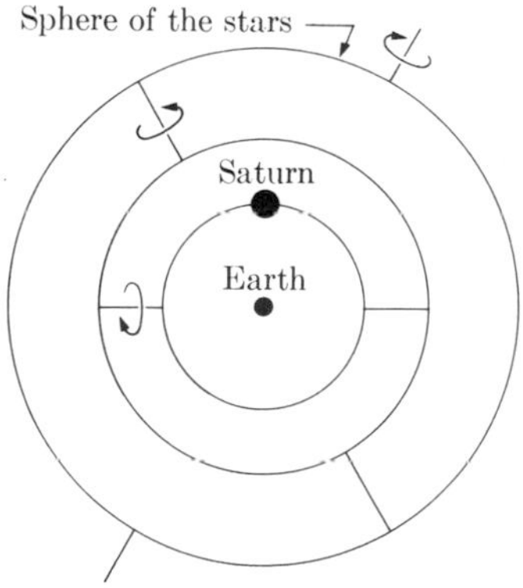

This process of adding spheres was continued until a model had been constructed that would faithfully account for the observed motion of Saturn. But the solution of the problem was barely begun: now it was necessary to introduce a set of spheres within Saturn's to reproduce the motion of Jupiter; and of course still more were needed for Mars, Venus, Mercury, the sun, and the moon.

Here the mathematical genius of the Greeks was indeed put to the test! The sun and the moon were relatively simple problems, but some

FIG. 6.3. A system of concentric spheres to account for the observed motion of Saturn.

of the planets offered much difficulty. Plato's pupil Eudoxus thought that 26 simultaneous uniform motions would do for all seven celestial bodies. In

Aristotle's work are prescribed 29 additional uniform motions, partly to account for some of the most obvious discrepancies between Eudoxus' system and the observed paths.*

As time went on and more and more observations of planetary positions were amassed, it was found that the movements of the spheres could be adjusted to meet them, although sometimes it became necessary to add more spheres to the system.   Yet there remained one easily observed feature of the sky that was unexplained by the system of concentric spheres: the planets appear brighter at some times than at others.   One explanation is that they are simply changing in brightness, but this would have been in conflict with the Greek idea of immutability of the heavens. Another, and more acceptable, explanation was that they appear to be brighter when they are closer to us.   But for the planets to come closer to or to recede from the earth is impossible if they are attached to spheres that are *concentric* with the earth.   Here is a difficulty of which Aristotle was aware, yet he discounted the importance of the simple but eventually fatal argument against the fundamental hypothesis of his system.   For it was then, as it is now, incomparably easier to ignore the testimony of a few contrary observations than to give up a whole world scheme that at the time was useful and seemed otherwise conclusive.   This does not at all mean that Aristotle was proposing a theory he knew to be false.   The scheme seemed necessary from the points of view of both his philosophy and his physics.   Remember our discussion of the problem of freely falling bodies in Chapter 2, where it was emphasized that the original Aristotelian science was not simply bad modern science but an activity fundamentally different from it.

Perhaps we may also see here an example of an important human trait that colors all scientific work and that even the greatest thinkers can never hope to overcome entirely: we all tend to deny the importance of facts or observations not in accord with our convictions and preconceptions, so that sometimes we ignore them altogether, even though, from another point of view, they stand before our very eyes.   Moreover, even the most general and modern scientific theory does not hope or even seriously attempt to accommodate every single detail of every specific case.   One is always forced to idealize the observations before attempting a match between "facts" and theory—not only because there are usually unavoidable experimental uncertainties in observation, but because conceptual schemes are consciously designed to apply to *selected* observations rather than to the totality of raw experience.   As a consequence, the history of science is studded with cases in which it was found that the neglected

---

*See *A source book in Greek science* by Morris R. Cohen and I. E. Drabkin (McGraw-Hill, 1948) for illuminating translations from the original sources.

part of a phenomenon eventually had to be considered its most significant aspect. Yet if we were to allow no tentative or plainly incomplete theories in science, we should probably never see more satisfactory ones evolving at all. Since the task cannot humanly be accomplished in one jump, we must be satisfied with successive approximations.

6.4 The heliocentric theory of Aristarchus. The problem of planetary motion, of course, persisted after Aristotle. There were two different major types of attack—heliocentric theories and modified geocentric theories. Let us first discuss an early form of the heliocentric or sun-centered scheme. Aristarchus of Samos (3rd century B.C.) suggested that a simple world system would result if the sun were put at the center of the universe and if the moon, the earth, and the five then known planets revolved around the sun with different speeds and in orbits of different sizes. We do not have many details of his theory, for it is known to us only through references in other ancient writings. Apparently he assumed that the earth has a daily rotation on its north-south axis, as well as a yearly revolution in the orbit around the sun; and he placed the whole system inside the sphere of fixed stars, which thereby could be considered at rest with respect to the center of the universe.

This heliocentric picture has at least one immediate advantage. It permits the planets to be nearer to the earth at times and farther away at other times, thus providing an explanation for the otherwise troublesome observations that the planets vary in brightness throughout the year. But the ancient world saw three serious flaws in Aristarchus' suggestion:

First, it did violence to contemporary philosophic doctrine, for example, to the view that the earth is differentiated from the "celestial bodies" by its very "immobility" and position, that its natural "place" is at the center of the universe. Indeed, Aristarchus' contemporaries considered him impious "for putting in motion the hearth of the Universe." Moreover his new picture of the solar system contradicted common sense and every-day observation; did not the very words used in astronomy—sunrise, progression of planets, and so on—reflect the intuitive certainty that the earth is at rest?

PROBLEM 6.1. List some of the everyday observations and common-sense notions that seem to lead naturally to a geocentric theory. In doing this, be careful not to *assume* the existence of any particular theory, geocentric or otherwise.

Second, so far as we know, Aristarchus did not fortify his system with calculations and quantitative predictions of planetary paths; his work seems to have been purely qualitative, although in some other accomplishments he showed considerable mathematical ability.

Third, the Greek thinkers offered a sound and ingenious bit of reasoning to refute Aristarchus. If the earth were to move around the sun, there would be points on its large circular orbit where it would be comparatively near a given fixed star on the celestial sphere, and other points where it would be farther away from this star. Thus the direction in which we would have to look for the star should be different when the earth is at different points in its annual sweep. This phenomenon, called the *annual parallax* of the fixed stars, should occur on the basis of Aristarchus' heliocentric hypothesis, but it was not observed by the Greek astronomers.

To explain the failure to observe the stellar parallax, we may say either (a) that the predicted shifts in directions to the stars are so small as to be unobservable with the unaided eye—which in turn requires the fixed stars to be unimaginably distant compared with the diameter of the yearly orbit of the earth, or (b) that Aristarchus was wrong and the earth does not move around within the celestial sphere. It seems natural that the ancients, predisposed to reject the heliocentric system and also loath to consider an infinitely extensive universe, chose the second of these alternatives.

PROBLEM 6.2. The annual parallax of a star (Fig. 6.4) is very small and difficult to measure, but by making observations six months apart (when the earth is at E_2 and E_4) the angle α can now be measured. Assume that before the 17th century astronomers could measure angles as small as $\frac{1}{2}°$. Since they did not detect any parallax, what must be the minimum distance to the nearest star? Use as your unit of length the mean distance from the earth to the sun, called the *astronomical unit*. (*Note:* The annual parallax of the nearest star is actually less than 1 sec of arc; it was first measured in 1838.)

The heliocentric theory of Aristarchus apparently had so little influence on Greek thought that it might seem unwarranted for us to give any time to it. Yet it was these speculations that helped to stimulate the crucial work of Copernicus 18 centuries later. Ideas, it is evident, are not bound by time or space; they can never be evaluated with *final* certainty.

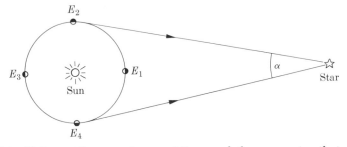

FIG. 6.4. If the earth moves in an orbit around the sun, a star that appears in a certain direction when the earth is at E_2 will be seen in a different direction (greatly exaggerated in this diagram) when the earth is at E_4. The annual parallax is given by $\alpha/2$.

6.5 Ptolemy's geocentric system. We now turn to another and, at the time, more vigorous offshoot of early astronomical thinking, namely, a modified geocentric system. The modifications introduced were often ingenious and served to eliminate some of the weaknesses of the earlier geocentric system of concentric spheres; for instance, it was found possible to alter the geocentric model so as to allow the planets to have variable distances from the earth, but with the earth still considered as immovable. Several astronomers made these contributions, foremost among whom was Hipparchus of Nicaea (2nd century B.C.) who is said to have erected an observatory at Rhodes. His important works are no longer extant, but astronomers in antiquity clearly held him to be the father of their science. His great contributions included the development of trigonometry, work on mathematical geography, the preparation of an extensive catalog of star positions, and the discovery that the position of the sun with respect to the background of fixed stars at the equinoxes (on about March 21 and September 21) slowly changes over the years (*precession of the equinoxes*). Hipparchus formulated concepts of planetary motion which were developed and extended with great success by the astronomer and geographer Claudius Ptolemy of Alexandria (2nd century A.D.). Ptolemy represents the culmination of all the effort of antiquity on the geocentric system, and it is upon this that we shall concentrate.

Ptolemy's important book on astronomy, like the rest of ancient knowledge, was transmitted to Western Europe by the Arabs, who so valued the work that they gave it the name by which it has been known ever since: *Almagest*, a contraction of an Arabic phrase meaning "The Greatest of Books."

The devices adopted by Ptolemy to represent planetary motion included *eccentric motion, epicyclic motion,* and *the equant.*

(1) *Eccentric motion.* If the stationary earth were not exactly at the center of the circular path of a celestial object, the latter would move along an *eccentric* path as seen from the earth, thus varying in distance from the earth as time progresses (Fig. 6.5). This scheme not only supplies a reason for the changes in brightness of the planets throughout the year, but accounts fairly well for the observations that the sun appears larger at noon in our winters than in our summers. Note that by introducing the notion of eccentric motions these astronomers really were violating the old doctrine that required that the circular motions of the planets be about the center of the earth.

(2) *Epicyclic motion.* In Fig. 6.6 a celestial body P, such as the sun or a planet, is pictured as having two simultaneous motions, one a uniform circular motion of P about a point D in space, the other a uniform circular motion of the point D about the earth E as a center. The smaller circle, with the moving center, is called an *epicycle,* the larger circle the *deferent.*

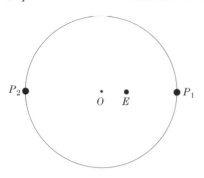

FIG. 6.5. In eccentric motion, the planet (or the sun) is assumed to move in a circular orbit whose center O is not at the stationary earth E. To an observer on the earth the planet then appears to be closer when at P_1 than when at P_2. The distance OE is here exaggerated.

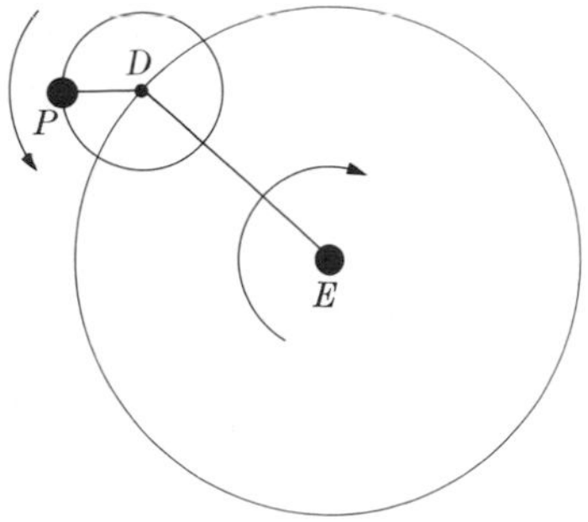

FIG. 6.6. An example of epicyclic motion of a planet P (not to scale). The planet moves uniformly about the point D, which in turn moves uniformly about the earth E.

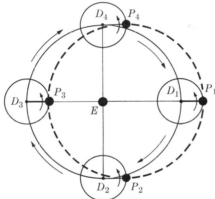

FIG. 6.7. One of the many types of planetary paths (dashed line) that can be obtained with epicyclic motion.

The values of the radii DP and ED of the epicycle and deferent and of the angular speeds of motion in these two circles could be adjusted as required. This gave the model-maker considerable freedom in assigning values that would give to the point P a motion closely duplicating the one actually observed for the celestial object from the earth. Thus in Fig. 6.7 the epicycle turns rather slowly as it moves around the deferent, bringing the planet closest to the earth at P_3 and farthest at P_1; by having the body P in Fig. 6.8 make several revolutions about the point D while D moves once around the earth E, the complicated motion indicated by the dashed line connecting 24 successive positions of P is obtained.

PROBLEM 6.3. What is the ratio of the angular speeds assigned to the epicycles and the deferent in Fig. 6.7? In Fig. 6.8?

The type of epicyclic scheme illustrated by Fig. 6.8 does, in fact, exhibit most of the observed complications in the paths of planets as seen from the earth against the background of the fixed stars. Note particularly the reversals in the direction of motion, or retrograde motions, of the planet in the regions of positions P_4, P_{11}, and P_{18}. The number of loops depends on the ratio of the angular speeds for the two circles, epicycle and deferent. To picture Jupiter's motion, 11 loops were needed, for this is the number of reversals observed in this planet's complete path around the earth, which it covers in approximately 12 years.

In passing we should note that the epicyclic device violated the same ancient doctrine as did eccentric motion, for the notion that a celestial body P moves about a point D on the deferent is, strictly speaking, incompatible with the original postulates, just as is any scheme that permits a planet to move around the earth in a path centered on some point other than the earth's center.

PROBLEM 6.4. Construct as well as you can with compass and ruler the path of P (similar to that in Fig. 6.7) for the case where P makes two revolutions about D while D makes one revolution about E.

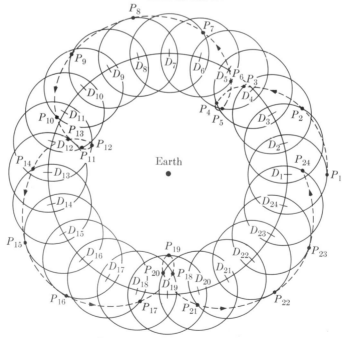

FIG. 6.8. An epicyclic motion of P that yields retrograde motions near three places, P_4, P_{11}, P_{18}, during each complete revolution.

In Ptolemy's adoption of the epicyclic and eccentric devices, note what has been retained from Plato and Aristotle and what has been amended. Use is still made of *circular* motion, of *uniform* motion, and of a *stationary* earth. No longer emphasized is the scheme of rotating spheres all concentric with the earth and serving as carriers of the sun, moon, and planets. Vanished is the requirement that every rotation be earth-centered; this change is even more strikingly evident when we see that Ptolemy found it necessary to add still another device, the *equant*, in order to represent more faithfully certain features of celestial motion.

(3) *The equant.* Figure 6.9 shows an object P in cyclic motion around a point D, while D simultaneously moves in a circle centered at O. If this scheme were purely epicyclic, the earth would be at O; if it were a mixture of epicyclic and eccentric motions, the earth might be anywhere along the line AA', say at the position E. So far, the motion of D has been specified as uniform with respect to O. But for Ptolemy's system to represent faithfully certain planetary motions, it was necessary in some cases to let D revolve uniformly with respect to a point Q, called the *equant;* that is, it had to be assumed that the angle DQA changes at a constant rate while D makes its circular sweep. With the adoption of this new device, there is no single point with respect to which the motion of D is both uniform *and* circular. Its motion is *uniform* as seen from Q and *circular* as seen from O.

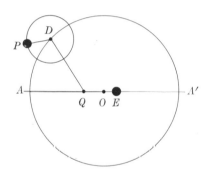

FIG. 6.9. Motion of P with respect to equant at Q.

6.6 The success of the Ptolemaic system. Ptolemy's *Almagest* set forth a system of the world utilizing the devices that we have just described and involving the following preliminary assumptions:

(1) that the heaven is spherical in form and rotates as a sphere;
(2) that the earth, too, viewed as a complete whole, is spherical in form;
(3) that it is situated in the middle of the whole heaven, like a center;
(4) that by reason of its size and its distance from the sphere of fixed stars the earth bears to this sphere the relation of a point;
(5) that the earth does not participate in any locomotion.

PROBLEM 6.5. What is the significance of Ptolemy's fourth preliminary assumption?

By adjusting the respective axes, directions of motions, rates and radii of rotations, the number of epicycles, eccentrics, and equants, by fitting his devices to the observed paths in a cut-and-try fashion, Ptolemy assembled the system that was still to prove useful to astronomers and navigators more than 14 centuries later. It was an answer to Plato's original question, and represents a magnificent piece of work carried out by a man of tremendous ability. One striking feature is that the centers of the epicycles of both Mercury and Venus fell on a line connecting the earth and the sun (Fig. 6.10).

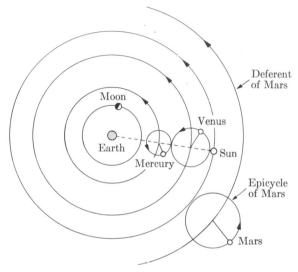

Fig. 6.10. Partial and schematic diagram of the Ptolemaic system of planetary motion.

But the complexity of the whole scheme was considerable, and subsequent observations required modification of some features of the model from time to time (for example, a change of an assigned equant, or the addition of an epicycle having its center on an epicycle, and so on). By the time of Copernicus, in the early part of the 16th century, this geocentric system required more than 70 simultaneous motions for the seven celestial bodies. Nevertheless, the system was generally accepted wherever it became known, for five powerful reasons:

(1) The Ptolemaic system gave an accurate enough description of what could be observed with the instruments of the times.

(2) It served well for predicting future positions of the celestial bodies, although only after cumbersome calculations; and when a serious discrepancy between predictions and observations occurred, it was often resolved by tampering a little with the "wheels" of the flexible apparatus.

(3) It provided a natural explanation of why the fixed stars showed no annual parallax.

(4) In most respects it was in accord with Greek philosophic and physical doctrine concerning the nature of the earth and the celestial bodies. Later, when reintroduced to Europe by the Arabs, the Ptolemaic system was given theological significance by medieval churchmen.*

(5) It had and still has "common-sense appeal." It is difficult not to feel that we actually can "see" the sun and stars moving around us, and it is both comforting and reasonable to think of ourselves on a stable, immovable earth. Indeed, for many practical purposes, an earth-centered picture is the simplest one, and it is still preferred for calculations in navigation.

But for all that, Ptolemy's geocentric theory was eventually displaced by a heliocentric one. Why did this happen? What were the most significant deficiencies in Ptolemy's picture? When is a scientific theory, from our present point of view, successful or unsuccessful? We shall want to discuss these questions in some detail after we have looked next at an outline of the great rival scheme of planetary motion.

Supplementary Reading

CLAGETT, M., *Greek science in antiquity* (Abelard, 1956).

COHEN, M. R., and I. E. DRABKIN, *A source book in Greek science* (McGraw-Hill, 1948). A wealth of source material and penetrating comments. See pp. 90–143 for astronomy.

CROMBIE, A. C., *Augustine to Galileo* (Falcon Press, London, 1952), Chap. III, (1) and (2).

DREYER, J. L. E., *History of the planetary systems from Thales to Kepler* (Cambridge University Press, 1906); republished as *A history of astronomy from Thales to Kepler* (Dover Publications, 1953).

FARRINGTON, B., *Greek science* (Pelican Books A142 and A192, 1944, 1949).

FARRINGTON, B., *Science in antiquity* (Oxford University Press, 1936, 1947).

HEATH, SIR THOMAS, *The Copernicus of antiquity* (*Aristarchus of Samos*), (Society for Promoting Christian Knowledge, 1920).

HEATH, SIR THOMAS, *Greek astronomy* (J. M. Dent, London, 1932).

MUNITZ, M. K., ed., *Theories of the universe* (The Free Press, Glencoe, Illinois, 1957), pp. 61–138. Discussion, with lengthy excerpts, of the work of Plato, Aristotle, Ptolemy, and medieval astronomers.

SARTON, G., *A history of science* (Harvard University Press, 1952).

TAYLOR, F. S., *A short history of science and of scientific thought* (W. W. Norton, 1949), Chap. III.

---

*In connection with our study of the Ptolemaic system it will be a most rewarding experience to read that great excursion through the medieval universe, the *Paradiso* of Dante (for example, in the 1944 edition of the Modern Library).

CHAPTER 7

THE HELIOCENTRIC THEORY OF COPERNICUS

7.1 The revival of learning in Europe. The Roman influence in Western Europe tended to cut off the West from Greek knowledge. The culture that we call Western Christendom grew up in ignorance of Greek science until the 12th century, when Greek scientific writings were acquired by the West from Islam. In the 13th century Thomas Aquinas (1225–1274) merged Greek philosophy and Christian theology into a single philosophy, Thomism, that took its philosophical roots in the writings of Aristotle, and as the knowledge of antiquity was absorbed in the West, the authority of Aristotle increased. Yet the finest astronomical system available was the Ptolemaic, not the earlier Aristotelian.

By the 15th century European scholars had become thoroughly aware of alterations that had been made in Greek writings by the Arabs, through whose hands those writings had passed, and an intensive search was undertaken for manuscripts in the original Greek. By the end of the century Greek editions of Aristotle's works had been printed. The *Almagest* of Ptolemy was printed, in the original Greek, in 1538. Already astronomers were bothered by differences between Aristotle's theory of homocentric spheres and Ptolemy's more complicated and more useful system of eccentrics, equants, deferents, and epicycles. Aristotle offered a whole cosmology, a coherent theory sweeping across all branches of science, including astronomy; Ptolemy offered an astronomy that achieved vast superiority over Aristotle's largely by abandoning the simplicity of the Aristotelian system. Such discordances often stimulate important scientific work; this was the case here.

7.2 The Copernican system. The development of the modern conception of the solar system now brings us to Nicolaus Copernicus (1473–1543), who was a young student in Poland when the New World was discovered. During his exciting life he witnessed in the world around him the gathering of great cultural changes. And on the very day of his death he saw the first printed copy of his great treatise, called *De revolutionibus* or the *Revolutions*, which gave us a whole new universe. His life and works reveal him as a humble and compassionate man who was not only a most remarkable astronomer and mathematician, but also a churchman, administrator, diplomat, physician, and able student of the classics and of economics.

One of Copernicus' motivations for criticizing the Ptolemaic system was the dissatisfaction he and many other astronomers felt with the accuracy

118

Fig. 7.1. Nicolaus Copernicus (1473–1543).

of prediction attainable by contemporary astronomical methods of calculation. Although the Ptolemaic system had been immensely useful for over thirteen centuries, there were now some considerable discrepancies between observation and prediction of planetary positions. Even the exact length of the year was in doubt, and consequently there was a widely felt need for reform of the calendar.

But there was also another influence at work in Copernicus' thinking. The clue lies in the full title of Copernicus' main work, *Six books concerning the revolutions of the heavenly spheres,* with its reminder of the Aristotelian idea of concentric spheres. Copernicus was indeed concerned with Plato's old problem, the construction of a planetary system by combination of the fewest possible uniform circular motions. In great part, Copernicus postulated his heliocentric system because it avoided the assumption, inherent in the Ptolemaic geocentric theory as taught at the time, that the notion of the equant could be used freely. Let us examine his own arguments on these points:

... the planetary theories of Ptolemy and most other astronomers, although consistent with the numerical data, seemed ... to present no small difficulty. For these theories were not adequate unless certain equants were also conceived; it then appeared that a planet moved with uniform velocity neither on its deferent nor about the center of its epicycle. Hence a system of this sort seemed neither sufficiently absolute nor sufficiently pleasing to the mind.

Having become aware of these defects, I often considered whether there could perhaps be found a more reasonable arrangement of circles, from which every apparent inequality would be derived and in which everything would move uniformly about its proper center, ... After I had addressed myself to this very difficult and almost insoluble problem, the suggestion at length came to me how it could be solved with fewer and simpler constructions than were formerly used, if some assumptions ... were granted me [foremost that of the motion of the planets around the sun]. (*The Commentariolus*)*

To Copernicus, any type of celestial motion other than uniform circular motion was "obviously" impossible: "the intellect recoils with horror" from any other suggestion; "it would be unworthy to suppose such a thing in a Creation constituted in the best possible way." These arguments are of the same type as those of the supporters of Aristotle, except that to them the immobility of the earth was equally "obvious."

Reading the classics, Copernicus reported in his preface to the *Revolutions* that he had found that:

... according to Cicero, Nicetas had thought the earth moved, ... according to Plutarch certain others [including Aristarchus] had held the same opinion ... when from this, therefore, I had conceived its possibility, I myself also began to meditate upon the mobility of the earth. And although it seemed an absurd opinion, yet, because I knew that others before me had been granted the liberty of supposing whatever circles they chose in order to demonstrate the observations concerning the celestial bodies, I considered that I too might well be allowed to try whether sounder demonstrations of the revolutions of the heavenly orbs might be discovered by supposing some motion of the earth ... I found after much and long observation, that if the motions of the other planets were added to the motions of the earth [daily rotation, and yearly revolution about the sun], ... not only did the apparent behavior of the others follow from this, but the system so connects the orders and sizes of the planets and their orbits, and of the whole heaven, that no single feature can be altered without confusion among the other parts and in all the Universe. For this reason, therefore, ... have I followed this system.

Thus, in essence, Copernicus proposed a change of point of view to the representation of celestial motions along the lines of Aristarchus' heliocentric system. By highly gifted calculations Copernicus then proved what Aristarchus had failed to prove: that the motion of celestial objects

*From *Three Copernican treatises*, tr. by Edward Rosen (Columbia University Press, 1939).

as then known could indeed be represented by a combination of uniform circular motions in a sun-centered system. All planets, now including the earth, could be visualized as moving on concentric spheres, with relatively fewer, small epicycles and eccentrics needed to account for the finer details of motion.* Moreover, the *same direction* of motion along almost all deferents and epicycles could be assumed, which had not been true for the geocentric model. But above all, the odious equant could be discarded; all motions were now truly circular and uniform with respect to their own centers. Plato's question was answered again, in an alternative way.

Copernicus' diagram (Fig. 7.2) shows the main concentric spheres carrying the planets around the sun. His accompanying text in the *Revolutions* explains the outlines of the system and, incidentally, gives us an important insight into what may have been his two deepest motivations:

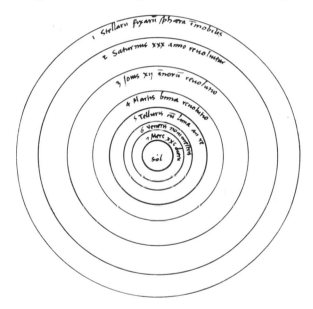

FIG. 7.2. Copernicus' diagram of his heliocentric system. (From his manuscript of the *Revolutions*, 1543.) This simplified representation omits the many epicycles actually used in the system.

The ideas here stated are difficult, even almost impossible, to accept; they are quite contrary to popular notions. Yet with the help of God, we will make everything as clear as day in what follows, at least for those who are not ignorant of mathematics ... The first and highest of all the spheres is the

---

*The common center of the main spheres actually had to fall a little to one side of the unmoving sun, so that this system is not *quite* heliocentric, just as Ptolemy's earth-position did not coincide with the center of the sun's motion.

sphere of the fixed stars. It encloses all the other spheres and is itself self-contained; it is immobile; it is certainly the portion of the universe with reference to which the movement and positions of all the other heavenly bodies must be considered. If some people are yet of the opinion that this sphere moves, we are of a contrary mind; and after deducing the motion of the earth, we shall show why we so conclude. Saturn, first of the planets, which accomplishes its revolution in thirty years, is nearest to the first sphere. Jupiter, making its revolution in twelve years, is next. Then comes Mars, revolving once in two years. The fourth place in the series is occupied by the sphere which contains the earth and the sphere of the moon, and which performs an annual revolution. The fifth place is that of Venus, revolving in nine months. Finally, the sixth place is occupied by Mercury, revolving in eighty days.

In the midst of all, the sun reposes, unmoving. Who, indeed, in this most beautiful temple would place the light-giver in any other part than that whence it can illumine all other parts? Not ineptly do some call the sun the lamp of the world, or the spirit of the world, or even the world's governor. Trismegistus calls it God visible; Sophocles, Electra, the All-seeing. Indeed, the sun, reposing as it were on a royal throne, controls the family of planets which surrounds him . . .

In this orderly arrangement there appears a wonderful symmetry in the universe and a precise relation between the motions and sizes of the orbs which is impossible to obtain in any other way.

So Copernicus sees the sun as the central, fixed, light- and life-giving surveyor of the universe, analogous to the Deity itself, which the sun indeed represents. And it is the internal consistency, the esthetic quality of relationships in this solar system, which so persuasively convinces him that his model is necessary and right.

7.3 Bracing the system. Knowing well that to many his work would seem absurd, "nay, almost contrary to ordinary human understanding," Copernicus attempted to fortify it against anticipated critisicm in three ways.

(1) He tried to make plausible the assertion that his assumptions agreed with dogma at least as well as did Ptolemy's. In many passages, of which we have seen samples, he remarked on the deficiencies of the Ptolemaic system, on how harmonious and orderly his own seemed, and on how pleasingly and evidently it reflected the mind of the Divine Architect. To Copernicus, as to most men, the observable world was but a symbol of the working of God's mind; to be able to find symmetry and order in the apparent chaos of sense data was to him an act of reverence, a renewed proof of the workings of an intelligent and intelligible Deity. He would have been horrified if he had known that his theory was ultimately responsible for the sharp clash between science and the church a century later. Copernicus, we must not forget, was a highly placed and honored church dignitary. In matters of church doctrine he might well have

regarded himself as a conservative who was objecting to current Scholastic teaching only to the extent of wishing to make it more consistent with Aristotle's principles of astronomy.

(2) Copernicus prepared enough quantitative material to put his book mathematically on the same footing as Ptolemy's, that is, he calculated the relative radii and speeds of the various components of his system so that tables of planetary motion could be made. Thus his work was in this respect on a better footing than the more qualitative approach of Aristarchus. However, on looking into Copernicus' treatise, we must not expect to find a mathematical treatment of the type found in modern texts. Much of our simplest mathematical notation did not come into use until long after Copernicus' time.

(3) With considerable ingenuity and success, Copernicus anticipated several objections that were as certain to be raised against his heliocentric system as they had been, long ago, against Aristarchus'. To the argument that his earth, rotating so rapidly about its own axis, would surely burst like a flywheel driven too fast, he countered, "Why does the defender of the geocentric theory not fear the same fate for his rotating celestial sphere —so much faster because so much larger?" To the argument that birds in flight and clouds should be left behind by the rapidly revolving and rotating earth,* he answered that the atmosphere moves along with the earth.

As to the old question of the absence of parallax among the fixed stars, he, like Aristarchus, gave the reasonable answer:

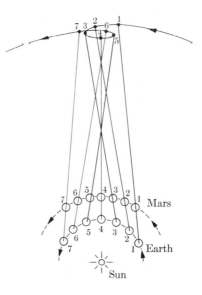

> ... the dimensions of the world are so vast that though the distance from the sun to the earth appears very large compared with the size of the orbs of some planets, yet compared with the dimensions of the sphere of fixed stars, it is as nothing.

This distance to the fixed stars, he said elsewhere, is "so immense as to render imperceptible to us even their apparent annual motion . . ." As we now know, the ratio of the distance of the nearest stars to the diameter of the earth's orbit is of the order of 10^5 to 1.

FIGURE 7.3

---

*The orbital speed around the sun is about 70,000 mi/hr, and the speed of west-east rotation alone of an object at the equator exceeds 1000 mi/hr.

Although Copernicus cited other arguments in support of his system, those we have mentioned will suffice to illustrate how he prepared for criticism of it. However, Copernicus' hope for acceptance of his system was not to be fulfilled quickly.

PROBLEM 7.1. Figure 7.3 shows the apparent motion of Mars against the background of the fixed stars on the heliocentric theory. Copy the figure and write a legend for it which explains the observed retrograde motion of Mars. Then construct a companion figure to show how the same observation can be explained on the geocentric theory.

7.4 The opposition to Copernicus' theory. Although many astronomers began to use the new system almost immediately because of the greater ease of computation afforded, it took more than a century for the heliocentric picture to receive full acceptance even by scientists. In the meantime the theory and its champions were faced with powerful opposition, some of it of the very same character as had appeared against those Greek philosophers who had suggested motion of the earth. The three most important opposing arguments will now be summarized:

(1) First came the argument concerning the immobility and central position of the earth. For all his efforts, Copernicus was in general unsuccessful in persuading his readers that the heliocentric system was at least as close as the geocentric one to the mind and intent of the Deity. The religious faiths of Europe, including the newly emerged Protestantism, found Biblical support for the belief that the Divine Architect had worked from a geocentric blueprint. Martin Luther branded Copernicus a fool and a heretic. The Roman Catholic Church eventually put the *Revolutions* on the *Index Librorum Prohibitorum* as "false and altogether opposed to Holy Scriptures," withdrawing its approval of an earlier outline of Copernicus' work. Some Jewish communities forbade the teaching of the heliocentric theory. It was as if man's egocentric philosophy demanded the middle of the stage for his earth, the scene of his daily life and of his aspirations in a world created especially for his use, and of the drama of special salvation with the expected eventual coming of the Saviour or Messiah.

It was granted by many that the Ptolemaic system was more complicated mathematically and in this respect might indeed be the less useful. And even Thomas Aquinas had grave misgivings about the Ptolemaic system because some of its features were not in strict conformity with the Aristotelian principle that required all motions of celestial bodies to be uniform and circular about the earth as a center. Yet to abandon the geocentric hypothesis seemed "philosophically false and absurd," fantastic, and dangerous.

And in all truth, what other reaction could one have expected? Copernicus provided somewhat greater mathematical simplicity, which was of no direct advantage to anyone except the practicing scientists, and in doing so relegated man from his central position to a place on one of many planets flying about the sun. And for this he offered not new evidence compelling to common sense, but only technical arguments. Even many scientists had grave doubts whether the Copernican system was anything more than a convenient artifice for use in astronomical calculations.

PROBLEM 7.2.   Read Joshua 10:13 and interpret the astronomical event referred to therein (a) in terms of the geocentric system, and (b) in terms of the heliocentric system.

(2) A further explanation for the resistance which the Copernican theory had to overcome is to be sought in the damage that it did to the accepted *physics* of the day. As the historian H. Butterfield has said:

> . . . at least some of the economy of the Copernican system is rather an optical illusion of more recent centuries. We nowadays may say that it requires smaller effort to move the earth round upon its axis than to swing the whole universe in a twenty-four hour revolution about the earth; but in the Aristotelian physics it required something colossal to shift the heavy and sluggish earth, while all the skies were made of a subtle substance that was supposed to have no weight, and they were comparatively easy to turn, since turning was concordant with their nature. Above all, if you grant Copernicus a certain advantage in respect of geometrical simplicity, the sacrifice that had to be made for the sake of this was nothing less than tremendous. You lost the whole cosmology associated with Aristotelianism—the whole intricately dovetailed system in which the nobility of the various elements and the hierarchical arrangement of these had been so beautifully interlocked. In fact, you had to throw overboard the very framework of existing science, and it was here that Copernicus clearly failed to discover a satisfactory alternative. He provided a neater geometry of the heavens, but it was one which made nonsense of the reasons and explanations that had previously been given to account for the movements in the sky. (*The origins of modern science: 1300–1800*)

(3) A third opposition to the Copernican theory arose from the oft-mentioned lack of observable parallax among fixed stars. Copernicus' reply (p. 123) was held to be unacceptable because it involved expanding the celestial sphere to practically an infinite distance away from the earth. This is to us no longer intellectually difficult, but it was a manifestly absurd notion at the time, one among many reasons being, perhaps, that the mind of the period could not be comfortable with a threatening Hell so close below the ground and a saving Heaven so infinitely far above. Indeed, even if someone could have observed an annual parallax of one of the stars at that time, this would have not necessarily settled the dispute in favor of Copernicus, for the Ptolemaic system could have been made to

explain away this parallax simply by superimposing on the great daily rotation of the fixed stars a yearly epicyclic motion.

7.5 Historical consequences. Although it did not enter the argument at the time, it was pointed out later that the Copernican system was, after all, not significantly superior to the Ptolemaic in its power to predict planetary motions. The two systems, in the form they assumed in the middle of the 16th century, were about equally able to predict future planetary positions within the then current error of observation of at least $\frac{1}{6}$ degree of arc. As Francis Bacon wrote in the early 17th century: "Now it is easy to see that both they who think the earth revolves and they who hold the *primum mobile* and the old construction are about equally and indifferently supported by the phenomena."

How, then, shall one decide the old question, which picture of the universe is the "true" one? In our modern terminology we would say that the rival systems differed mainly in the choice of the coordinate system used to describe the observed movements. When measurements are made with respect to the earth as the frame of reference, the sun and stars *do* move, and the earth, of course, is at rest. On the other hand, when measurements are made with respect to the sun, the earth is not at rest. Any other system of reference, for instance one placing the moon at the origin of the coordinate system and referring all motions to that new "center of the universe," is quite conceivable and equally "correct," although the resulting system might be tremendously complex. We hold today that the acceptance of a particular frame of reference should depend mainly on whether it will yield the simplest solution for a given problem. *Therefore we should not speak of such a choice as "true" or "false," but rather as convenient or inconvenient.*

Every newly discovered peculiarity of planetary motion could have been accommodated in some geocentric representation as certainly as in a heliocentric one. Neither Aristarchus nor Copernicus could have hoped to convince people to whom the beauty of simplicity and ease of application of a theory were, understandably, less important than their own meaningful and by no means unesthetic and unworkable systems.

Of course, eventually the vision of Copernicus did triumph. Later we shall follow the course of events leading to the universal acceptance of the heliocentric theory, although we shall find that his specific *system* of uniform circular motions had to be sacrificed along the way. We shall see that the real scientific significance of Copernicus' work and the reason for its ultimate glorification lie in a circumstance that could not have been foreseen or understood in his day, namely, that a heliocentric formulation opens the way to an explanation of planetary motion in terms of the science of mechanics developed during the following 150 years. The result was the synthesis of two sciences, even of two methods, achieved through Newton's theory of universal gravitation. Thus it was on the supposition that the earth revolves and rotates that it eventually became possible to explain such diverse phenomena as the diurnal and annual apparent motion of the stars, the flattening of the earth at its poles, the behavior of gyroscopes, tides, tradewinds, tornadoes, and much else that could not have been bound together so simply in a geocentric scheme.

But apart from this historic triumph, the memory of Copernicus is hallowed for two reasons of broad cultural significance. First, he was one of those giants of the 15th and 16th centuries who challenged the contemporary world picture and thereby gave life to the new and strange ideas which later were to grow into science as we now know it. Second, his theory proved to be a main force in the gathering intellectual revolution that broke a path through the medieval science that had been new and vigorous in the 14th century but had stagnated by the 15th century. The culmination was the Scientific Revolution which, to use the words of A. N. Whitehead, was the most intimate change in outlook that the human race had yet encountered.

Having seen the conflict of two scientific theories dealing with the same set of observable phenomena, we may now ask: *By what standards shall we more generally decide between rival scientific theories?* An important purpose of the study of planetary motion to this point has been to prepare us for the following discussion before returning to our main topic.

Supplementary Reading

ARMITAGE, A., *Sun, stand thou still* (Henry Schuman, 1947); also published under the title *The world of Copernicus* (Mentor Book M65). The life and work of Copernicus.

BOYNTON, H., *The beginnings of modern science* (Walter J. Black, 1948), pp. 5–11. Brief excerpt from writings of Copernicus.

BUTTERFIELD, H., *The origins of modern science: 1300–1800* (G. Bell, London, 1949; Macmillan, 1951 and later), Chap. 2.

COMMINS, S., and R. N. LINSCOTT, *Man and the universe: the philosophers of science* (Random House, 1947), pp. 43–69. Excerpts from writings of Copernicus.

HALL, A. R., *The scientific revolution 1500–1800* (Longmans, Green, 1954; Beacon Press, 1956), Chap. II.

KNICKERBOCKER, W. S., ed., *Classics of modern science* (Knopf, 1927), Chap. 2. Excerpts from Copernicus.

KNEDLER, J. W., *Masterworks of science* (Doubleday, 1947), pp. 49–72. Excerpts.

KUHN, T. S., *The Copernican revolution* (Harvard University Press, 1957).

MILTON, JOHN, *Paradise lost*, Book VIII, lines 1–202. Published in 1667, this work of the great poet contains a discussion of the geocentric and heliocentric systems from a classic point of view that mirrored the general opinion of educated Englishmen until the full impact of Newton's work was established.

MUNITZ, M. K., ed., *Theories of the universe* (The Free Press, Glencoe, Illinois, 1957), pp. 141–173. Discussion, with excerpts, of the work of Nicolas Cusanus and Copernicus.

ROSEN, E., *Three Copernican treatises* (Columbia University Press, 1939).

SHAPLEY, H., and H. E. HOWARTH, *A source book in astronomy* (McGraw-Hill, 1929), pp. 1–12. Excerpts.

CHAPTER 8

ON THE NATURE OF SCIENTIFIC THEORY

On the question of standards by which to appraise scientific theories—for example, the rival planetary theories—it should first be said that we cannot pretend to lay down criteria by which a working scientist should check his own progress during the construction of a theory, any more than we can construct a scientific method for his use. However, we shall attempt to clarify how the student of science and its development can evaluate a particular theory, past or present.

8.1 The purpose of theories. The task of science, as that of all thought, is to penetrate beyond the immediate and visible, to formulate connections, and thereby to place the observable phenomena into a new and larger context. For, like a floating iceberg whose bulk is largely hidden in the sea, only the smallest part of the physical world impresses itself upon us directly. To help us grasp the whole picture is the supreme function of *theory*. Thus, for example, we see some pinpoints of light in the night sky, and we develop from this a picture of the planetary system as it might appear from a point outside it.

On a simple level, a theory helps us to interpret the unknown in terms of the known. It is a conceptual scheme that we invent or postulate in order to explain to ourselves, and to others, observed phenomena and the relationships between them, thereby bringing together into one structure the concepts, laws, principles, hypotheses, and observations from often very widely different fields. These functions may equally well be claimed for a hypothesis itself. In truth, we need not lay down a precise dividing line, but might regard theory and hypothesis as differing only in degree of generality. Therefore we find at one extreme the *limited working hypothesis* by which we guide our way through a specific experiment, and at the other extreme the *general theory* which guides the design and interpretation of all experiments in that field of study.

Examples of general theories suggest themselves readily, even if we decide, perhaps rather arbitrarily, to use the word "theory" only for such few historic and general schemes of thought as the theories of planetary motion, of universal gravitation, of the nuclear atom, and the like. Galileo's theory of projectile motion welded together the descriptions of motions with constant velocity or with constant acceleration, including free fall, thereby producing one conceptual scheme, one over-all method of describing and predicting the motions of projectiles moving near the surface of the earth.

PROBLEM 8.1. Examine from the foregoing point of view the Ptolemaic and the Copernican theories. For each theory differentiate as clearly as you can between the factual *data* available to each theorizer and the *hypotheses* he developed to coordinate these separate data.

PROBLEM 8.2. Examine in a similar way some theory discussed in another field of knowledge that you have studied—perhaps Mendel's theory of heredity, the Marxian theory of society, Sigmund Freud's theory of the unconscious, or a theory of "business cycles."

8.2 Further characteristics of theories. If we inquire more deeply into the purposes of theories, we find that they have, in general, three main functions, each of which involves a number of interesting characteristics.

(1) *A theory generally serves to correlate many separate facts in a logical and more easily grasped structure of thought.* By such correlations, by putting in juxtaposition and order previously unrelated observations, we can understand and explain them; for we often explain by pointing to a relationship. Early Greek mythology explained the motions of the celestial bodies in terms of certain "necessary" attributes of the deities associated with the planets. Ptolemy and Copernicus explained them in terms of suitably chosen combinations of uniform circular motions. Such attempts to subordinate individual events to more inclusive schemes seems to be a mental necessity. It may be a matter of economy of thought, for a suitable theory enables us to grasp, remember, and deduce a large number of otherwise elusive facts; think, for example, of the wealth of separate facts summarized by the Copernican theory.

At the same time, a fruitful theory will also indicate its limits. For example, Galileo's theory of projectile motion served to explain why a very long trajectory cannot be expected to be parabolic, since air friction and the curvature of the earth are then no longer negligible factors.

It is striking how often we resort to mechanical models to provide a basis for explanatory schemes. In encountering some new and intriguing mechanical device, we find ourselves almost automatically attempting to explain its various observed motions as due to some single mechanism familiar to us although completely hidden within the gadget. Similarly, many theories in physical science have been based on mechanical models. Lord Kelvin once said, "If I can make a mechanical model then I can understand; if I cannot make one, I do not understand." Doubtless this is true of most people. However, not all scientific problems are easily or most usefully explained in terms of mechanical models; furthermore, there are several famous instances in the history of physical science which show that too firm a belief in a mechanical model may be a serious impediment to progress. Recent developments have shown that such models, like all analogies, while often helpful as guides to the imagination, can also lead it into dangerous traps. For example, it undoubtedly was, and is, easier to think of a beam of sunlight as a mechanical vibration transmitted through a material "aether" filling all space rather than as disembodied energy propagated through a vacuum, but the inescapable fallacies of the aether model eventually came to the surface and forced adoption of the less obvious and less "common-sensical" alternative.   Similarly, we owe modern chemistry in large part to the simple pictorial representation that John Dalton used to order his thoughts about atoms and molecules; but much of the early trouble experienced with his atomic theory can be traced to his too concrete and prematurely complete mental picture, as we shall see in the chapters on the chemical atom.

It has been suggested that physical science among the ancients, who relied frequently on analogies involving the behavior and drives of living beings, was *organismic*, whereas with Newton science became *mechanistic*. In our present century it is turning more and more to conceptual schemes involving abstract, *mathematical* sets of mental imagery. Even this mathematical type of model is not free from many of the dangers inherent in a mechanistic science.   But our thoughts proceed, as it were, on crutches, and so depend at any stage of development on these schemes and pictures no matter how incomplete they may be.

(2) *A theory or hypothesis, whether general or limited, is expected to suggest new relations*, to start the imagination along hitherto unsuspected connecting paths between old and new facts, to extend old horizons. The Ptolemaic theory of astronomy, the phlogiston theory of chemistry, the caloric theory of heat, the aether theory of light—all these played a vital and positive role in the life of science, for at the time they tended to pose problems, to reveal new relations, and to direct the attention and effort of many scientists along the same lines rather than in random directions.   As Francis Bacon remarked, truth will sooner come out of error than out of confusion.

PROBLEM 8.3.   This problem will illustrate how a theory can put separate, initially "unrelated" observations into a scheme of satisfying order.   The Copernican planetary system gives the following values for the periods of revolution of the planets about the sun and the distances from planets to the sun (the latter in astronomical units, 1 AU being the distance from the earth to the sun):

	Mercury	Venus	Earth	Mars	Jupiter	Saturn
Period	88 days	225 days	365¼ days	687 days	12 yr	30 yr
Distance from sun (in AU)	0.39	0.72	1.0	1.5	5.2	9.5

At the time of Copernicus the current Ptolemaic system yielded the following values for the periods of revolution of the points *D* (Fig. 6.7) in the deferents about the earth and the average distances from the planets to the earth (in multiples of the earth's radius):

	Sun	Mercury	Venus	Mars	Jupiter	Saturn
Period in deferent	1 yr	1 yr	1 yr	687 days	12 yr	30 yr
Distance from earth	1200	170	1100	8800	14,000	20,000

(a) Examine these values, and attempt to explain why Copernicus felt that there was exhibited a greater measure of order and harmony in his scheme, "a precise relation between the motions and sizes of the orbs which is impossible to attain in any other way." (*Hint:* One way to approach this problem is to make a graph of period *vs.* distance from each of the two tables of data.)

(b) On the basis of the Copernican planetary system, at what orbital distance from the sun would you look for a new (hypothetical) planet reported to have a period of 590 days?

(3) The foregoing pages hint at a further purpose of theories: *the prediction of specific new observable phenomena and the solution of practical problems.* In Shakespeare's great tragedy, Hamlet's theory of his uncle's guilt yields him a prediction of how the suspect will react to the little play-within-the-play; conversely, when the predicted reaction is actually obtained, this indicates to Hamlet that his theory very likely is valid, and that he has the solution to the problem of the old king's death. In astronomy and physics, where numerical data can usually be obtained, the theories can be so phrased as to make quantitative predictions possible. The problems to be solved may be quite abstract or general—for instance, why the planets sometimes seem near and at other times far. Or they may be very specific and practical; for example, just as some of the most ancient astronomical speculations seem to have been prompted by the need to predict the comings of the seasons and such portentous events as eclipses, so one of the problems that the Copernican theory helped to solve was the determination of the precise length of the year and of the lunar month, data needed at the time of Copernicus for a revision of the calendar.

PROBLEM 8.4. (a) Using Figs. 6.10 and 7.2, compare and describe the orbits of Venus as predicted by the two rival theories. (b) As is well known today, Venus is not self-luminous, but is visible because of the sunlight it reflects; therefore Venus exhibits phases, as does the moon, these being visible through a telescope from the earth. What does each of the rival theories suggest concerning the appearance of the phases of Venus? (*Hint:* Where would the sun have to be with respect to Venus and the earth when we see Venus fully illuminated? Make sketches of planetary positions.)

8.3 Criteria for a good theory in physical science. When we examine why scientists as a whole, in the historical development of science, have favored or rejected a given theory, we discern a number of criteria that seem to have implicitly dominated the slowly evolving process of decision. But by no means should we suppose that a theory is necessarily ever rejected solely because it fails to satisfy completely one or another of the criteria in the listing that follows.

Three qualifications have already been cited: (1) A fruitful theory *correlates many separate facts*, particularly the important prior observations, in a logical, preferably easily grasped structure of thought. (2) In the course of continued use it *suggests new relations* and stimulates directed research. (3) The theory permits us to *deduce predictions* that *check with experience* by test, and it is useful for clearing up puzzling difficulties and solving practical problems.

Einstein's theory of relativity is a good illustration of these three points. Einstein first showed that those observations already explained by pre-relativity physics were in accord with his brief set of postulates, and he demonstrated that a large variety of other facts from previously separate fields could also be deduced from these postulates, thereby gathering them into one structure. Second, he showed that his theory suggested several hitherto unlooked-for relations and effects (for instance, that a beam of light should be deflected when passing close to a body of very large mass) and he urged the experimental astrophysicist to search for these phenomena, for he knew that the theory depended for its validity on such verification. And lastly, Einstein not only used the new theory to clear up some old, previously unexplainable puzzles (for example, a systematic discrepancy in the expected motion of the planet Mercury in its path about the sun), but he also saw his work find amazingly fruitful applications in almost all branches of physics, from optics to nuclear physics.

The history of science has shown that a good theory frequently has, in addition to the three attributes above, one or more of the following three:

(4) When the smoke of initial battle has lifted, the more successful of two rival theories often turns out to be the one that is simpler in the sense that it involves *fewer basic assumptions or hypotheses*. Such a theory tends to survive because of the economy of thought that it affords. A theory that needs a separate mechanism or assumption for each fact to be explained is nothing but an elaborate and sterile tautology.

(5) A theory is more readily acceptable to contemporary scientists if its *postulates or assumptions are plausible*. If the whole tenor of the theory is not compatible with current ideas, the theory may be faced with a stormy and hostile reception, and may have to submit to long and careful scrutiny before its general acceptance. But this criterion of plausibility has its limitations. Common-sense ideas sometimes are a block to progress, and

assumptions lacking plausibility may be necessary. As the works of Copernicus and of Galileo have already shown us, and as will become even more evident in subsequent discussions, major advances in scientific theories often depend on the daring and persistence of one investigator who questions the obvious and stubbornly upholds the unbelievable.

This problem of the plausibility of new theories is difficult and subtle. Truly great ideas often seemed somewhat absurd when first proposed. Perhaps we call them *great* ideas because it took an unusual mind to break through the pattern of contemporary thought and to discern the value of what to contemporaries seemed implausible or absurd.

Why then do we not drop the tentative requirement of conformity? Why have almost all great innovators in science, from Copernicus to Einstein, initially met with skepticism, or worse, from most of their colleagues? Is it just unreasoning conservatism on the part of the scientific fraternity? Not at all. It must be remembered that in our discussions here we have mainly emphasized revolutionary ideas, and this must not be allowed to distort our perceptions; great *revolutionary* ideas arise only very rarely, compared with the large number of workable and fruitful ideas conceived within *traditional* settings. So the individual scientist is naturally predisposed to favor the traditional type of advance which he knows and believes in from personal experience. He, like the critics of Copernicus and Galileo, quite rightly must tend to oppose any large-scale destruction of his conception of nature, particularly at the earlier stages of the controversy, when the innovator has not yet been able to present many convincing results and confirmations of his new ideas. Indeed, the discoverer himself may be so strongly committed to traditional ideas, so startled by the implications of his own work, that he not only anticipates the storm of condemnation (as Copernicus did) but may decide to withhold his ideas or may even fail to draw the most important conclusions. A now famous instance of this sort appears in a scientific report published in 1939 by O. Hahn and F. Strassmann, who are usually credited with the experimental discovery of nuclear fission. At that time it was still axiomatic in the thinking of all scientists that heavy atomic nuclei were indivisible, that bombarding them with small particles, for example neutrons, would at best change their internal atomic structure only superficially or slightly. Yet these two men, after firing neutrons into pure uranium, were left with material which by chemical tests was proved to contain barium and other elements whose atoms have about half the mass of uranium atoms. "Evidently," we would say now, "the uranium atoms have been split." But in an almost agonized expression of the pains attending the birth of all great recognitions, Hahn and Strassmann could not quite dare to accept the evidence of their own chemical tests, and so they wrote: "As 'nuclear chemists,' in many ways closely associated with physics, we cannot yet bring ourselves to make this leap in contradiction to all previous lessons of nuclear physics. Perhaps, after all, our results have been rendered deceptive by some chain of strange accidents."

Later, after we have more thoroughly developed our view that science has laws of evolution similar to those describing the evolution of biological species (Chapters 13–15), we shall appreciate more fully the significance of the bitter and long struggles that new theories may create within science. *The fitness of theories is most advantageously shaped and most convincingly demonstrated in vigorous contest.* The situation is, after all, not so very different in other fields of human activity. None of the predominant religious and social concepts of our time have developed quietly or been accepted spontaneously. If the recent struggles in the rapidly developing physical sciences sometimes have been comparatively short, this may be credited largely to the emergence, from the 17th century onward, of a more or less tacit agreement among scientists as to the standards to be used in judging a new conceptual scheme—above all, of course, the pragmatic test of predictions.

Even so, a really new and startling idea may in retrospect clearly have fulfilled all these requirements without being widely accepted, for scientists as a group are not gifted more than other people in recognizing the full long-range potentialities of new and unconventional proposals. Max Planck, with perhaps a little too much bitterness about the early struggles over one of his own great contributions said, "An important scientific innovation rarely makes its way by gradually winning over and converting its opponents: it rarely happens that Saul becomes Paul. What does happen is that its opponents gradually die out, and that the growing generation is familiarized with the ideas from the beginning."

(6) Successful theory is flexible enough to grow, and to *undergo modifications* where necessary. But if, after a full life, it eventually dies, it dies gracefully, leaving a descendant of greater power and a minimum of wreckage among the old concepts.

Let us consider this important point. In any field of knowledge a prediction is no more than a guess unless it is deduced from some theory. And just as the nature and meaning of a prediction depend on a theory, so does the validity of a theory depend on the correctness of the predictions. Like the very laws it correlates, a theory must be based on a finite and perhaps small number of observations; yet to be useful it may have to predict correctly a very large number of future observations. Thus the Ptolemaic theory was built on a finite number of separate observations of planetary positions, yet it yielded enough reasonably correct predictions of the future positions of these planets to be still useful more than 1400 years later. Yet we see at once one reason why no physical theory is likely to last forever. Sooner or later observations are likely to be made that are not in accord with the predictions. Such observations usually lie in a region for which the predictions had to be extrapolated from the original range of the theory: for example, to the region of very small or of very large quantities, or of much more precise measurements than had served initially as a basis for the theory.

With ingenuity, ways can usually be found to modify the old theory so as to make it apply also to the new phenomena. As with an apple tree in an orchard, we keep a theory for the sake of its fruits; when the apple crop becomes poor, we then try to save the tree by judicious pruning and the like. In the endangered theory, perhaps a reformulation of some assumptions or concepts will save the scheme. If such attempts fail, the old theory still may be saved by retaining it in its original form but with the clear understanding that it applies only to a certain restricted range of phenomena; in this case an attempt must be made to develop a separate theory to take care of the new range. If, however, the flaws appeared within the proper jurisdiction of the old theory and the assumptions stand challenged beyond repair, then the only alternative is to abandon it as soon as a new, better one can be contrived.

These three eventualities—expansion, restriction, or replacement—appear in the history of theories and of laws generally. The schemes that we tend to remember and to honor most are those that provided a solution in a crisis, or pointed to the theory that replaced them. In the words of Niels Bohr, "The utmost any theory can do [is] to be instrumental in suggesting and guiding new developments beyond its original scope."

Finally, lest our brief discussion of these six criteria of good theories be mistaken for scientific dogma, we should echo the very humble opinion of Einstein on this same topic. He distinguished between two main criteria, (1) the *external confirmation* of a theory, that is, the experimental checks which assure us that the theory is valid, and (2) the *inner perfection* of a theory, which is measured by its degree of internal consistency, its "logical simplicity" or "naturalness." He then qualified these remarks as follows: "The meager precision of the [foregoing] assertions [(1) and (2) above] . . . I shall not attempt to excuse by lack of sufficient printing space at my disposal, but confess herewith that I am not, without more ado, and perhaps not at all, capable to replace these hints by more precise definitions."

ADDITIONAL PROBLEMS

8.5. (a) Summarize our six criteria for a good theory in physical science. (b) Discuss the relative advantages of the Ptolemaic and Copernican theories of celestial motion by comparing them in the light of each of the six criteria.

8.6. Was the geocentric theory as set forth by Ptolemy *false?* Was it *true?* Give reasons for your answers.

8.7. Using our six criteria, investigate the "death" of a theory from another field with which you are well acquainted (such as the phlogiston theory in chemistry or the theory of spontaneous generation in biology). What were the predictions that failed to come true, or the phenomena that contradicted the assumptions of the theory? Could it have been modified to serve for a time? Did a new theory rise directly from the old?

8.8. P. W. Bridgman writes in *Reflections of a physicist* (Philosophical Library, 1950), p. 252, that in the current flux in ideologies, moral ideas, and other social concepts the intelligent scientist sees ". . . an exemplification of what his physical experience has taught him: namely, ideas are to be inspected and re-examined when the domain of application is extended beyond that in which they arose. In one very important respect he recognizes that the present epoch differs from former epochs in that the enormous increase in invention, bringing peoples nearer together and increasing their command over forces more advantageous to man, effectively provides just that extension in the domain of application of social concepts which he is prepared to expect would demand fundamental revision." Write a short essay on your opinions about this quotation, and also examine what other guiding ideas, if any, you think may be transferred to the field of social studies from the study of physical theories.

SUPPLEMENTARY READING

Consult the bibliography at the end of Chapter 15.

CHAPTER 9

KEPLER'S LAWS

9.1 The background to Kepler's work. We have reached the years around 1600 in our study of the theory of planetary motion; from that point on the story developed with gathering momentum. The era of the Renaissance and the Reformation was passing. While mathematicians and astronomers were using the Copernican system because astronomical computations were easier with it than with the more cumbrous Ptolemaic system, many of them doubted whether the new picture was "really true" —anything more than a mere computational device. As for nonscientists, to whom the question of mathematical simplicity was of little interest, the objections to any system different from the geocentric seemed sufficient to rule out the Copernican system.

A few voices nevertheless were beginning to speak up for the heliocentric theory. In England, William Gilbert (1544–1603), physician to Queen Elizabeth I, published his *On the magnet (De magnete)*, which aided Copernicans in their claim that the heliocentric Copernican system is physically plausible. (Galileo's possession of a copy of *On the magnet* was considered by the Inquisition as additional evidence of his heresy.) The antiorthodox pantheist Giordano Bruno was traveling through Europe, announcing that the boundaries of the universe are infinitely far away and that our world is one of infinitely many.

Now the seeds of a new approach to science were sprouting vigorously. Gilbert wrote in the preface to his book:

> To you alone, true philosophers, ingenuous men who not only in books but in things themselves look for knowledge, have I dedicated these foundations of magnetic science—a new style of philosophizing.

A few years later Francis Bacon (1561–1626) expounded this "new philosophy" with great effectiveness. Galileo made the astronomical observations that struck so fatally at older ideas on the nature of the heavens. And at Copenhagen, Tycho Brahe (1546–1601), the first man since the Greeks to bring real improvements into astrometry, spent nearly a lifetime in patient observation and recording of planetary motion with till then unheard-of precision (Fig. 9.1). The sighting instruments which he developed and constructed were of great size and carefully and rigidly mounted on solid foundations, so that observations made years apart might be compared with one another. His measurements of planetary positions, made before the invention of the telescope, were often accurate to better than half a minute of arc, more than twenty times better than those of Copernicus.

FIG. 9.1. Tycho Brahe in his astronomical observatory. By means of the big brass quadrant, the assistant at F observes, to within 10 sec of arc, the altitude angle of a celestial object seen through the slit. Simultaneously, the assistant at Q reads the time of transit on a clock; a second clock is available, to check against the first. (From Brahe's *Astronomia instauratae mechanica*, 1598.)

FIG. 9.2. Johannes Kepler (1571–1630).

After Tycho's death, his German colleague Johannes Kepler (Fig. 9.2) continued the observations and especially the analysis of the voluminous data. Whereas Tycho had developed a geocentric system of his own, Kepler was a Copernican. The announced purpose of his labors was the construction of better astronomical tables of planetary motion than were then available on the basis of the more inaccurate data of Copernicus' own period. But Kepler's motivation and main preoccupation was the perfection of the heliocentric theory, whose harmony and simplicity he contemplated "with incredible and ravishing delight." From the outset of his career he was strongly influenced by Pythagorean and neo-Platonic metaphysics. To Kepler even more than to Copernicus, the clue to God's mind was in geometric order and mathematical relationships, expressed in the features of the simple heliocentric scheme. Among his earliest publications we find, typically, an enthusiastic attempt to link the six known planets and their respective distances from the sun with the relationships among the five regular solids of geometry.

In the preface to the *Mysterium cosmographicum* (1596) Kepler explained his program: "There were three things in particular, namely the *number*, the *distance*, and the *motion* of the heavenly bodies, concerning which 1 searched zealously for reasons why they were as they were, and not otherwise." His solution, as he explained later, was "a sort of combination of astronomy and Euclid's geometry . . . I took the dimensions of the planetary orbits according to the astronomy of Copernicus, who makes the sun immobile in the center, and the earth movable both round the sun and upon its own axis; and I showed that the differences of their orbits corresponded to the five regular Pythagorean figures . . . " (Fig. 9.3).

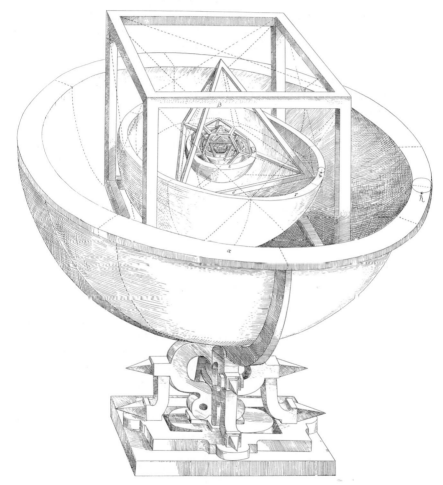

FIG. 9.3. Kepler's model (1596) of the plan by which the six planets were placed in the heliocentric system. The outermost sphere, corresponding to Saturn's path, is circumscribed around a cube. A sphere inscribed in the cube corresponds to Jupiter's orbit, and in turn encloses another of the five regular bodies, namely a tetrahedron. A sphere erected inside the latter gives Mars' orbit; and so forth.

What Kepler had found was that the observed relative distance between the six known planets corresponded, in most cases within less than 5%, to the relative spacing between the six concentric spheres which one can construct around and inside the five regular solids of classical geometry (tetrahedron, cube, octahedron, dodecahedron, and icosahedron) if these solids are first stacked one in the other like a Chinese puzzle. This geometric correspondence, he felt, revealed the master plan on which the solar system had been constructed, and hence provided the *reason* for the number of known planets and their observed orbital diameters. So convinced was he of the correctness of the scheme that he expected the remaining discrepancies to be due to previously unsuspected errors in the observational data then in use. This conviction was a main factor in Kepler's important decision to join Tycho Brahe, for he hoped to obtain better and more favorable data from this most skilled astronomical observer of the time.

9.2 Kepler's first law. In attempting to fit Tycho's new data on the orbit of Mars to a Copernican system of simple uniform circular motion (*even* if equants were used), Kepler found after four years' labor that he could not do it! The new data placed the orbit just eight minutes of arc outside the scheme of Copernican devices. Copernicus would not have noticed this, because he knew his observational data to be inaccurate by more than this margin. But Kepler could trust Tycho's unfailing eye and superb instruments, which yielded data with a margin of error less than one-fourth of these eight minutes.

With an integrity that has come to be regarded as the characteristic attitude of scientists in the face of stubborn quantitative facts, Kepler would not allow himself to hide this significant difference between the predictions of the theory and the observations by making convenient assumptions. To him, these eight minutes meant simply that the Copernican scheme involving a limited number of concentric spheres, epicycles, and eccentrics failed to explain the actual motion of Mars when the observations of that motion were made with sufficient accuracy. The scheme might have been modified by adding more epicycles, but then it would have lost its advantage over the Ptolemaic system. In a sense both systems were failing: the Ptolemaic was breaking under its own weight, and the Copernican, in original form, was clearly not quite accurate enough.

Kepler must have been stunned by this discovery, for after all he was a convinced Copernican. There followed years of continual labor, a search for a means of amending the Copernican theory to make it applicable to the new observations as well as to the old. This Kepler finally accomplished by dropping the one assumption that bound the Copernican system most explicitly to the doctrines derived from ancient Greece. While Kepler was studying planetary paths on the basis of a heliocentric representation, it occurred to him that they corresponded to a simple type of figure whose properties had been known to mathematicians since the 3rd century B.C., the ellipse (Fig. 9.4). Now he saw that if one considers the shape of the orbits themselves instead of trying to interpret these paths as combinations of different circles, if the ellipse were recognized as the "natural" path of a planet, a geometric world scheme of vastly greater simplicity was obtained: *all planets move in elliptical paths, with the sun at one focus of each ellipse.*

This "law of elliptical paths" is one of Kepler's three great laws of planetary motion, usually called his first law.

We are reminded of one of the passages in Galileo's work on projectile motion, where he explained that all projectiles followed paths known to mathematicians as parabolas. Kepler's work in astronomy, like Galileo's in mechanics, heralds the change toward the modern scientific attitude, namely, to regard phenomena of a wide variety as explained when they can all be described by a simple, preferably mathematical, pattern of behavior.

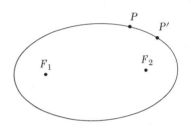

FIG. 9.4. The ellipse is that curve for which the sums of the distances of any two points on the curve from two fixed points, the foci (F_1 and F_2), are equal. Thus $F_1P + F_2P = F_1P' + F_2P'$, where P and P' are any two points on the curve.

Kepler's first law, by amending the Copernican heliocentric theory, gives us a wonderfully simple mental picture of the solar system. Gone are all epicycles, all eccentrics; the orbits are simply ellipses. Figure 9.5 is a schematic representation of the present general conception of the solar system—in essence Kepler's, but with the addition of the planets Uranus, Neptune, and Pluto, discovered much later. Note that all the ellipses are quite nearly circular. All orbits are almost in the same plane, except for a pronounced tilt of the plane of Pluto's orbit (which means that Neptune's and Pluto's paths do not cross at any point in space, even though Fig. 9.5 may give that impression).

PROBLEM 9.1. The equation for an ellipse with the origin of coordinates at the center is

$$\frac{x^2}{a^2} + \frac{y^2}{b^2} = 1,$$

where a and b denote, respectively, half the major and half the minor axis

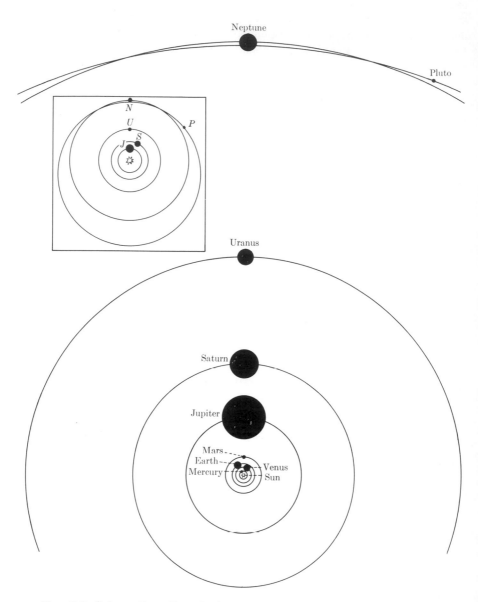

FIG. 9.5. Schematic outline of solar system, showing relative sizes of the orbits and, to a different scale, the relative sizes of the planets. The inset traces Pluto's full orbit.

(Fig. 9.6). On graph paper, construct a large ellipse by deciding on some constant values for a and b, for example 7 cm and 5 cm, and then solving for a few values of y corresponding to $\pm x$ values. The distance c from the origin of the coordinates to one or the other focus (F_1 or F_2) is given by

$$c = \sqrt{a^2 - b^2}.$$

Compute c and mark the positions of the foci on your ellipse. The eccentricity* e is a quantity that indicates how much an ellipse differs from a circle; by definition,

$$e = c/a = \sqrt{1 - (b^2/a^2)}.$$

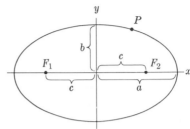

FIGURE 9.6

(Note from Fig. 9.6 that if $a = b$ the ellipse is a circle; hence a circle may be regarded as that special case of an ellipse for which the eccentricity e is zero.) Compute e for the ellipse you have drawn. Test by measurements made on the graph that for a point P *anywhere* on the ellipse, $PF_1 + PF_2 = $ a constant. Lastly, note that, for a given set of coordinates, an ellipse in a given plane is completely defined (that is, can be drawn) if only its values for a and b are given; these two data suffice.

PROBLEM 9.2. (a) Determine an approximate value of e for Pluto's orbit around the sun from measurements on Fig. 9.5. (Incidentally, for Mercury's orbit e is about 0.2, and for the other planets it is even smaller.) (b) The first artificial earth satellite went into an elliptical orbit which carried it initially 560 mi above the earth at the farthest point (*apogee*) and 155 mi at the nearest point (*perigee*). Compute the eccentricity of its orbit around the earth.

We can understand Plato's predisposition for uniform circular motions, but we cannot readily comprehend why planets should select elliptical paths. The satisfactory answer to this question came only some 80 years after Kepler's work, when Newton showed the law of elliptical paths to be one of the many logical consequences of a much more far-reaching set of postulates which we shall examine in Chapter 11.

Kepler's first law affords no information about *when* a planet will be at any specific position; it specifies the shape of the orbit in which the planet moves, but says nothing about the speed with which it moves in that orbit. This makes the law by itself rather useless for an astronomer who wishes to know where he should look for a planet at a given time. Kepler seems to have sacrificed the possibility of astronomical prediction for the sake of simplicity of path. Less than nothing has been gained, because the older theories at least yielded fairly good predictions of a planet's positions *and* of its time of appearance at each possible position.

---

*Do not confuse with the word "eccentric" as used in Section 6.5.

9.3 Kepler's second law. Kepler was perfectly aware that the first law alone is not sufficient to justify a jubilant overthrow of the apparatus of epicycles and eccentrics. He also needed a rule that would relate the speed of a planet at any point of its orbit to its speed at any other point. If such a relation could be found, then the motion of any one planet could be specified by just a few separate data: two data to specify the ellipse (for instance, the lengths of the major and minor axes, as in Problem 9.1), a third to give the speed at some particular point of the path (for instance, at *perihelion*, where the planet is nearest the sun), and a few additional data to specify how much the plane of this ellipse is tilted with respect to the planes of the other planets. Thus a simple relation between speed and position, if it could be found, would summarize the features of any one planet's motion in a compact and elegant way.

But so far there had been nothing to indicate that such a relation could be found. Consequently Kepler is said to have been in ecstasy when by sheer labor and ingenuity he finally was able to create the needed law out of the voluminous records available to him. Well might he have been ecstatic; his whole labor would have been of little use without this discovery.

Figure 9.7 illustrates what he found. We are here looking down on the plane of a planetary path, the sun S being at one focus of the ellipse. The planet may be our earth. During some selected time interval t, say two weeks in our winter, the planet is found to move from position A to position B. During an *equal* time interval t in the spring, it proceeds from M to N, and in the summer, from P to Q. In other words, as the drawing indicates, the speed is larger when the planet is near the sun, smaller when more distant. (For the earth the maximum and minimum values of the speed are 18.8 mi/sec at perihelion, and 18.2 mi/sec at aphelion.)

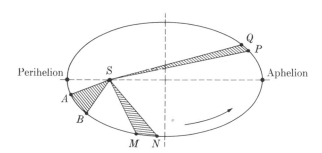

Fɪɢ. 9.7. Elliptical path of any one of the planets about the sun, illustrating Kepler's second law. The distances AB, MN, and PQ are covered in equal time intervals. (All planetary orbits are much more nearly circular than shown here.)

This qualitative finding became a precise quantitative expression with Kepler's recognition that the areas SAB, SMN, and SPQ (shaded areas in Fig. 9.7) all have the same value. *During any given time interval, the imaginary line connecting planet and sun sweeps out the same area anywhere along the elliptical path.* This is Kepler's second law of planetary motion, or *law of equal areas;* it applies to each of the planets and also to satellites in their paths about their own planets.

9.4 The meaning of the second law. To simplify the mathematical discussion showing that Kepler's second law actually does provide the desired relation between planetary positions and speeds, we shall confine ourselves to those planetary ellipses that are almost circular in shape. This is actually a good approximation for most of the orbits. The positions A and B, M and N, P and Q have been so selected that the time needed to move from A to B, from M to N, and so forth, is always the same. Let us symbolize this time interval by t, and let t be short, so that the distance SA and the speed at A differ very little from the corresponding values at B, those at M differ little from those at N, and so on. Then each of the shaded areas in Fig. 9.7 is approximately a circular sector. From plane geometry we know that the area of a sector of a circle is $\frac{1}{2} \times$ radius $\times$ arclength. Therefore, since $SB \doteq SA = R_1$ and $SN \doteq SM = R_2$, the two areas concerned are $\frac{1}{2}R_1(\overset{\frown}{AB})$ and $\frac{1}{2}R_2(\overset{\frown}{MN})$. Although these values for the areas are only approximate, we may improve them as much as we wish simply by taking a smaller time interval t and therefore shorter arclengths. Now Kepler's second law tells us that on the basis of actual measurement of planetary positions the aforementioned areas are equal; therefore

$$\tfrac{1}{2}R_1\overset{\frown}{AB} = \tfrac{1}{2}R_2\overset{\frown}{MN}. \tag{9.1}$$

When each member of this equation is multiplied by 2 and divided by t, we obtain

$$R_1 \frac{\overset{\frown}{AB}}{t} = R_2 \frac{\overset{\frown}{MN}}{t}. \tag{9.2}$$

But $\overset{\frown}{AB}$ is the distance moved in time t, and so $\overset{\frown}{AB}/t$ is simply the average speed $\bar{v}_1$ along the arc $\overset{\frown}{AB}$. Moreover, since we may take A and B to be extremely close together, the average speed $\bar{v}_1$ is indistinguishable from the instantaneous speed at any point between A and B. Similarly, in the right member of Eq. (9.2), the ratio $\overset{\frown}{MN}/t$ is the speed v_2 at any point between M and N. Thus we may rewrite Eq. (9.2) as

$$R_1v_1 = R_2v_2. \tag{9.3}$$

To generalize this result, we can say that, for any point on a nearly circular planetary orbit, the distance R from sun to planetary position multiplied by the speed v at this point is a constant quantity, or

$$Rv = \text{a constant.} \qquad (9.4)$$

Equation (9.4) is the desired relation between planetary positions and speeds and has been deduced from Kepler's second law. Suppose that we know the values of the distance R_1 and speed v_1 for one position, and want to compute the speed v_3 when the planet has moved to a later position where its distance from the sun is R_3. Applying Eq. (9.4), we have

$$R_3 v_3 = R_1 v_1, \quad \text{or} \quad v_3 = \frac{R_1 v_1}{R_3}.$$

In short, if it is known from observation that a planet has a speed v_1 when at a distance R_1 from the sun, we can predict its speed v_x for any other distance R_x. Moreover, since we now know how to find the speed for each point on the ellipse, we can predict either how long it will take the planet to reach a specified point or how far it will have gone in a given time interval. Even though the argument becomes more complex if we desire a completely rigorous deduction, the important conclusion is the same*. Kepler's second law therefore re-establishes the possibility of astronomical prediction, and does so in a simpler manner than through the multiplicity of geometric devices of the previous theories of planetary motion.

9.5 Kepler's third law. Kepler's first and second laws were published together in 1609 in his *New astronomy* (*Astronomia nova*). But he was still dissatisfied with one aspect of his achievement: it had not revealed any connection between the motions of the *different* planets. So far, each planet seemed to have its own elliptical orbit and speeds, but there appeared to be no over-all pattern for all planets. Nor was there any good reason why one should expect such a relationship. Kepler, however, was convinced that on investigating different possibilities he would hit on a simple rule linking all motions in the solar system. This conviction was so strong that it seems to us like an obsession, but it also was an indication of a deep undercurrent that has run through the whole history of science: the belief in the simplicity and uniformity of nature. This belief has always been a source of inspiration, helping scientists over the inevitable unforeseen obstacles, and sustaining their spirit during periods of long and fruitless labor. For Kepler it made bearable a life of heartbreaking personal

---

* For any point on any elliptical orbit, Eq. (9.4) becomes $Rv_\perp$ = constant, where $v_\perp$ is that component of the orbital speed v which s perpendicular to the radius R at that point.

misfortunes, so that he could write triumphantly, upon finally arriving at the third great law of planetary motion:

> ... after I had by unceasing toil through a long period of time, using the observations of Brahe, discovered the true distances of the orbits, at last, at last, the true relation ... overcame by storm the shadows of my mind, with such fullness of agreement between my seventeen years' labor on the observations of Brahe and this present study of mine that I at first believed that I was dreaming ... (*Harmony of the world,* 1619)

The law itself, in modern terminology, states that if T is the period of any given planet (that is, the time for one complete orbital revolution about the sun) and $\overline{R}$ is the *mean* radius of the orbit of that planet,* then

$$T^2 = k\overline{R}^3, \qquad (9.5)$$

where k is a constant quantity that has the *same value for all planets.*

We can at once compute the value of k, since we know that, for the earth, T_E is 1 yr (by definition) and $\overline{R}_E$ is 9.3×10^7 mi. Thus $k = T^2/\overline{R}^3 = 1 \text{ yr}^2/(9.3 \times 10^7 \text{ mi})^3 = 1.2 \times 10^{-24} \text{ yr}^2/\text{mi}^3$. If we prefer to use the mean radius of the earth's orbit $\overline{R}_E$ as the unit of length, that is, the astronomical unit (AU), then $\overline{R}_E = 1$ AU and

$$k = 1 \text{ yr}^2/\text{AU}^3.$$

When we know k, we can compute either T or $\overline{R}$ for any planet, given one of these two quantities. Kepler's third law establishes a beautifully simple relationship among the planets. Appropriately, it is often called the *harmonic law* of planetary motion.

EXAMPLE 9.1. We know from observation that the period of Jupiter is 12 yr. What value for the mean distance from the sun is predicted on the basis of Kepler's third law?

Solution.

$$\overline{R}_J^3 = T_J^2/k = 144 \text{ yr}^2/(1 \text{ yr}^2/\text{AU}^3) = 144 \text{ AU}^3,$$

or

$$\overline{R}_J = \sqrt[3]{144 \text{ AU}^3} = 5.2 \text{ AU}.$$

PROBLEM 9.3. Compute the values of $\overline{R}$ from the sun to two other planets, using the values for the periods listed in the quotation from Copernicus' *Revolutions* in Section 7.2.

PROBLEM 9.4. Kepler's third law, in the form of Eq. (9.5), applies also to the motion of satellites around planets, but the constant $T^2/\overline{R}^3$ has a value char-

---

* More precisely, $\overline{R}$ is the semimajor axis a (Fig. 9.6).

acteristic for each system. Knowing that the mean distance between the centers of earth and our moon is about 239,000 mi and that the moon's period is 27.3 days, calculate the constant ($\equiv k'$) for this system. Then compute the expected period for an artificial earth satellite at a mean distance of 1000 mi above the earth's surface.

9.6 The new concept of physical law. Kepler, using Tycho's observations and his own powerful three laws, proceeded to construct the accurate tables of planetary motion that had been needed for so long and were to remain useful for a century. We honor him for his accomplishments in astronomy, yet these are only a few of the achievements of this prodigious man. Especially to be singled out is a feature of his work, briefly mentioned before, that had a profound effect on the development of all the physical sciences. It is the rather new attitude to *observed facts*, evidenced by the change in Kepler's work from an earlier insistence on a geometric model and form as the main tool of explanation to an emphasis on the mathematical relationships underlying the planetary movements. His successful attempt to formulate physical laws in mathematical form helped to establish the *equation* as the prototype form of laws in physical science.

In this sense, Kepler's science was truly modern; he more than anyone before him bowed to the relentless and supreme arbiter of physical theory, namely, the evidence of *precise* and *quantitative* observation. Moreover, in the Keplerian system the planets no longer were considered to move in their orbits because of their divine nature or influence, as in Scholastic teachings, or because their spherical shapes themselves served as a self-evident explanation for their circular motions, as in Copernicus' thoughts. Rather, Kepler felt a need for backing up mathematical descriptions with physical mechanisms, and was in fact the first to look for a universal physical law based on terrestrial mechanics to comprehend the whole universe in quantitative detail. He early expressed his guiding thought as follows:

> I am much occupied with the investigation of the physical causes. My aim in this is to show that the celestial machine is to be likened not to a divine organism but rather to a clockwork . . . , insofar as nearly all the manifold movements are carried out by means of a single, quite simple magnetic force, as in the case of a clockwork all motions [are caused] by a simple weight. Moreover, I show how this physical conception is to be presented through calculation and geometry. (Letter to Herwart, 1605.)

The world as a celestial machine driven by a single force, in the image of a clockwork—this was indeed a prophetic goal! Intrigued by the recent work of William Gilbert on magnetism, Kepler's rich imagination could picture magnetic forces emanating from the sun to "drive" the planets in their orbits.

It was a promising and reasonable hypothesis; as it turned out, the fundamental idea that a single force determines the operations of the whole planetary system was correct, but it is not a magnetic force. In the end, therefore, Kepler does not find the physical cause, and he leaves us without a physical agency that explains in quantitative detail the reason for the planetary motions. These motions, however, are well described in his three empirical laws, and Kepler recognizes that a good mathematical description constitutes a triumph even when the physical causes are not yet understood. We are here reminded of Galileo's similar way of dealing with the "why" of motion in free fall, expressed at about the same time. It was left to Newton to show why magnetic forces would not account for the quantitative observations, and to adopt *gravitational* force as the physical mechanism, thereby tying Kepler's three laws together with a heliocentric conception and the laws of terrestrial mechanics in a monumental synthesis, to which we shall devote Chapters 11 and 12.

A final word about the place of Kepler's laws in present-day science. Three centuries of telescopic observations have shown that the laws of planetary motion hold except for some small deviations that are well understood. Moreover, these laws have also been found to have a much broader scope; for example, in atomic physics we can use them to describe the motion of electrons around nuclei under the action of electrical forces. Fruitful ideas may have applications far beyond the area for which they were created.

Supplementary Reading

Baker, R. H., *Astronomy* (Van Nostrand, 1930, and later editions). Excellent introduction.

Burtt, E. A., *The metaphysical foundations of modern science: a historical and critical essay* (Routledge and Kegan Paul, 1924, and later; the Humanities Press, 1951), Chaps. 1 and 2.

Caspar, M., *Johannes Kepler* (Kohlhammer, Stuttgart, 1950).

Dreyer, J. L. E., *History of the planetary systems from Thales to Kepler* (Cambridge University Press, 1906); republished as *A history of astronomy from Thales to Kepler* (Dover Publications, 1953), Chaps. XV, XVI.

Holton, G., "Johannes Kepler's universe: its physics and metaphysics," *American Journal of Physics*, v. 24 (1956), pp. 340–351.

Johannes Kepler, 1571–1630, edited by the History of Science Society (Williams and Wilkins, Baltimore, 1931).

Kepler, Johannes, "Epitome of Copernican astronomy," Books 4 and 5, "Harmony of the world," Book 5, in *Great books of the Western World* (Encyclopedia Britannica, Chicago, 1952), v. 16.

Newman, J. R., *The world of mathematics* (Simon and Schuster, 1956), v. 1, pp. 220–234.

RUSSELL, H. N., R. S. DUGAN, and J. Q. STEWART, *Astronomy* (Ginn, 1926, and later printings), v. 1, particularly Chapter 9.

SHAPLEY, H., and H. E. HOWARTH, *A source book in astronomy*. (McGraw-Hill, 1929), pp 13–19 and 29–40. Excerpts from Tycho Brahe and Kepler.

WHIPPLE, F. L., *Earth, moon, and planets* (Blakiston, 1941, and later printings).

CHAPTER 10

GALILEO'S CONTRIBUTION TO ASTRONOMY

There are more things in heaven and earth, Horatio,
Than are dreamt of in your philosophy . . .
Hamlet, Act I

One of the friends and fellow-scientists with whom Kepler corresponded and exchanged news of the latest findings was Galileo Galilei. Although the Italian's contributions to quantitative planetary theory were not so well developed as that of his friend across the Alps, Galileo nevertheless became a key figure in the field of astronomy. In a sense, Kepler and Galileo complemented each other in preparing the world for the eventual complete acceptance of the heliocentric viewpoint—the one laying the scientific foundation with his astronomical work, the other fighting objections with wit and eloquence and, in his work on mechanics, helping to overturn the whole structure of Scholastic physics with which the old cosmology was entwined.

Galileo's insistence on expressing his results in the concise language of mathematics, so clearly expressed in his work on freely falling bodies, is now accepted as his central achievement, re-enforcing the same trait then emerging from the work of Kepler. But perhaps the greatest difference between the work of Galileo and that of his Scholastic contemporaries was his orientation, his viewpoint, the kind of question he considered important. To most of his opponents, Galileo's specific problems were not general enough, since he excluded the orthodox philosophic problems. Indeed, his whole approach to the study of natural phenomena seemed to them fantastic, his conclusions preposterous, haughty, often impious. There is a strikingly close parallel between these objections to Galileo's point of view and the outraged and even violent derision initially heaped on discoverers of new ways of viewing the world in the arts, for instance Manet and the early impressionists.

10.1 The telescopic evidence. Galileo, like Kepler, was a Copernican in a Ptolemaic world. His specific contributions to the development of heliocentric theory were three: the first use of a telescope specifically for the purpose of astronomical observation, the new phenomena that he observed with the aid of the telescope, and the vigorous battle that he waged on behalf of the Copernican theory.

The old doctrines that were still being advanced in support of the geocentric system required that the celestial objects be "perfect," meaning spherical, unblemished, and unchanging. Yet Galileo reported in 1610 in his *Sidereus nuncius* (*Starry messenger*), that through his telescope he saw dark spots on the sun and details of the moon's surface that he interpreted as mountains and seas (Fig. 10.2). He noted that Venus went through phases, like the moon. Saturn seemed to exhibit bulges, instead of being spherical. Most surprisingly, Jupiter had four (of its twelve now known) satellites, or subplanets, thus adding in a catastrophic manner to

SIDEREVS
NVNCIVS
MAGNA, LONGEQVE ADMIRABILIA
Spectacula pandens, fuspiciendaque proponens vnicuique, præfertim verò

PHILOSOPHIS, *atq*, *ASTRONOMIS*, *quæ à*

GALILEO GALILEO
PATRITIO FLORENTINO
Patauini Gymnafij Publico Mathematico

PERSPICILLI
Nuper à se reperti beneficio funt obferuata in LVNÆ FACIE, FIXIS IN- NVMERIS, LACTEO CIRCVLO, STELLIS NEBVLOSIS, Apprime verò in

QVATVOR PLANETIS
Circa IOVIS Stellam difparibus interuallis, atque periodis, celeritate mirabili circumuolutis; quos, nemini in hanc vfque diem cognitos, nouiffimè Author depræhendit primus; atque

MEDICEA SIDERA
NVNCVPANDOS DECREVIT.

VENETIIS, Apud Thomam Baglionum. M DC X.
Superiorum Permiffu, & Priuilegio.

FIG. 10.1. The title page of the *Sidereus nuncius* (*Starry messenger*), the book in which Galileo first reported the use of the astronomical telescope (1610). This copy was given by Galileo to his friend the lyric poet, Gabriel Chiabrera; it is now in the DeGolyer Collection of the University of Oklahoma library.

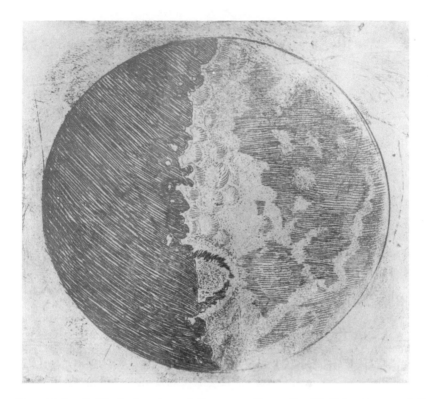

FIG. 10.2. Galileo's drawing of the moon (from the DeGolyer copy of the *Sidereus nuncius*).

the traditional seven nonstellar bodies of the heavens, and offering to plain view a miniature "Copernican" system with a center of revolution clearly at Jupiter and not at the earth (Fig. 10.3). The Milky Way resolved into aggregates of individual stars. The stars themselves, now visible in much greater numbers, appeared still as pinpoints of light, thus aiding the Copernican argument that they are extremely distant.

10.2 Galileo's arguments. We must understand that these suggestive observations were to Galileo illustrations of a truth that seemed to him compelling even without invoking the support of observations. In his work *Dialogue on the great world systems* (Fig. 10.4) he points out that observations alone do not decide uniquely between a heliocentric and a geocentric hypothesis, "for the same phenomena will appear in the one case as in the other." Tycho Brahe's compromise system, in which all

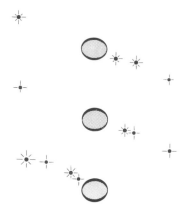

FIG. 10.3. Jupiter and its satellites, as they may appear through the telescope if observed a few days apart; drawn in the manner of Galileo's notebook.

planets except the earth went around the sun while the sun and the planets went around the fixed earth, was still another successful scheme, widely used at the time. Galileo's realization of the equivalence of these various possible systems is close to our modern view; but where we would make a choice between the hypotheses mainly on the basis of convenience in use, without regarding one as true and the others as false, Galileo thought of the earth's motion as "real," just *because* it simplified the picture to him and seemed inescapably reasonable.

Let us listen to the main arguments Galileo sets forth in the *Dialogue* in favor of the Copernican system, largely following those given by Copernicus himself:

> *First*, if we consider only the immense magnitude of the starry sphere compared to the smallness of the terrestrial globe, and weigh the velocity of the motions which must in a day and a night make an entire revolution, I cannot persuade myself that there is any man who believes it more reasonable and credible that it is the celestial sphere that turns round, while the terrestrial globe stands still.

As a *second* point Galileo reminds his readers that in the geocentric model it is necessary to ascribe to the planets a (slow) motion opposite in direction to that of the daily motion of the celestial sphere, again an unreasonable or at least inharmonious or unesthetic assumption. *Third*, Jupiter's four satellites were found by him to move in accord with the rule that the larger the orbit of the revolving body, as reckoned from the center of the orbit, the longer the period of revolution. That this rule holds for the planets had been pointed out long before by Copernicus, and Kepler's third law gives it quantitative expression. Even in the Ptolemaic system there is a sequential order in the periods, but with this disharmony:

as the size of the planetary orbit about the earth increases, the characteristic period of revolution around the earth increases from the shortest
one, $27\frac{1}{3}$ days, for the moon, to the largest then known period, 30 years, for
Saturn, and then drops back to 24 hours for the celestial sphere. But in the
heliocentric system, says Galileo,

> . . . the order of the periods will be exactly observed, and from the very slow
> sphere of Saturn we come to the fixed stars which are wholly immovable and
> so avoid a *fourth* difficulty we would have if the starry sphere be supposed
> movable. That is the immense disparity between the motions of those stars
> themselves, of which some would come to move most swiftly in most vast
> circles, others most slowly in circles very small, according as the former or
> the latter should be found nearer or more remote from the Poles.

DIALOGO
D I
GALILEO GALILEI LINCEO
MATEMATICO SOPRAORDINARIO

DELLO STVDIO DI PISA.

E Filofofo, e Matematico primario del

SERENISSIMO

GR.DVCA DI TOSCANA.

Doue ne i congreſſi di quattro giornate ſi diſcorre
ſopra i due

MASSIMI SISTEMI DEL MONDO
TOLEMAICO, E COPERNICANO;

*Proponendo indeterminatamente le ragioni Filofofiche, e Naturali
tanto per l'vna, quanto per l'altra parte.*

CON PRI VILEGI.

IN FIORENZA, Per Gio:Batiſta Landini MDCXXXII.

CON LICENZA DE' SVPERIORI.

Fig. 10.4. The frontispiece of Galileo's *Dialogue on the great world systems*
(1632). (From the copy in the DeGolyer Collection.)

Fifth, the precession of the equinoxes makes it appear that the positions of the "fixed" stars on the celestial sphere change slowly over the centuries; this observation makes improbable or at least unreasonable the claim of the geocentric theory that it is based on the immutable, ideal, eternal characteristics of the heavenly bodies. The heliocentric theory, however, easily explains the apparent changes as a consequence of the slightly changing tilt of the earth's axis.

> The absurdity is further increased (which is the *sixth* inconvenience) in that no thought can comprehend what ought to be the solidity of that immense sphere, whose depth so steadfastly holds fixed such a multitude of stars, which are with so much concord carried about without ever changing site among themselves with so great disparity of motions. Or else, supposing the heavens to be fluid, as we are with more reason to believe, so that every star wanders to and fro in it by ways of its own, what rules shall regulate their motions, and to what purpose, so that, seen from the Earth, they appear as though they were made by one single sphere? It is my opinion that they might so much more easily and more conveniently do that, by being constituted immovable, than by being made errant, as it is easier to number the blocks in the pavement of a piazza than a rout of boys which run up and down upon them.

Last, as a *seventh* point, although the geocentric system requires that the heavens must have great force and efficacy to carry along the many and large stars in their daily motion about the earth, yet "the little globe of the Earth contumaciously and pertinaciously stands unmoved against such an impulse. This in my thinking is very difficult; . . . "

The Scholastic opponent of Galileo's views, Simplicio, answers to these points:

> It seems that you base all you say upon the greater simplicity and facility of producing the same effects. To this I reply that I am also of the same opinion if I think in terms of my own not only finite but feeble power; but, with respect to the strength of the Mover, which is infinite, it is no less easy to move the Universe than the Earth, yea, than a straw. And if his power be infinite, why should he not rather exercise a great part of it than a smaller? Therefore, I hold that your discourse in general is not convincing.

Salviati replies for Galileo:

> If I had at any time said that the Universe did not move for want of power in the Mover, I would have erred, and your reproof would have been seasonable; and I grant you that to an infinite power it is as easy to move a hundred thousand as one. But what I did say does not concern the Mover; it refers only to the bodies, . . . As to what you say in the next place, that of an infinite power it is better to exercise a great part than a small, I answer that one part of the infinite is not greater than another, if both [parts] are finite . . . If a finite power is necessary to move the Universe, though it is very great in com-

parison to that which suffices to move the Earth alone, yet it does not involve a greater part of the infinite power, nor is that part less infinite which remains unemployed.

Since, Salviati points out, less power can be used in the one case than in the other to achieve the same end, "and, moreover, having an eye to the many other abbreviations and aptnesses that are to be obtained only in this way," it is reasonable to assume the simpler and easier method. Turning the weapon of authority against Simplicio, he concludes:

> ... a most true maxim of Aristotle teaches us that *frustra fit per plura, quod potest fieri per pauciora,* "that is done in vain by many means which may be done with fewer." This renders it more probable that the diurnal motion belongs to the Earth alone, rather than to the whole Universe with the sole exception of the Earth.

PROBLEM 10.1. Examine each of Galileo's telescopic observations (Section 10.1) separately to determine whether it strengthened or weakened the case for (a) the geocentric theory as an astronomical system, (b) the heliocentric theory as an astronomical system, (c) the philosophic doctrines behind the geocentric theory. In particular, note Galileo's observations for Venus, and refer to your answers to Problem 8.4. It should be clear that the Ptolemaic system, without some revision, cannot account for all of Venus' moonlike phases; propose a modification of the Ptolemaic system that would remove this difficulty, while retaining the *geocentric* feature.

10.3 The opposition to Galileo. In his characteristic enthusiasm, Galileo thought that his telescopic discoveries would make everyone see, *as with his own eyes,* the absurdity of the assumptions that had been standing in the way of a general acceptance of the Copernican system. But men can believe only what they are ready to believe. The Scholastics, in fighting the new Copernicans, felt convinced that they themselves were surely "sticking to facts," that the heliocentric theory, in addition to its theological errors, was obviously false and in contradiction with both sense-observation and common sense. They had made Scholastic science their exclusive tool for understanding facts, just as today most people depend for their understanding of physical facts on their ability to visualize them in terms of simple mechanical models operating according to Newtonian laws.

But at the roots of the tragic position of the Scholastics was the circumstance that the recognition of the Copernican system as even a *possible* theory would have had to be preceded by a most far-reaching re-examination and re-evaluation of their personal beliefs. It would have required them to do what is humanly almost impossible: to discard their common-sense ideas, to seek new bases for their old moral and theological doctrines, and to learn their science anew. Of course this is what Galileo himself had done to an amazing degree, and although we call him a genius for this very reason, many of his contemporaries called him a fool, or worse. Because they were satisfied with their science, the Scholastics were for the most part oblivious to the possibility that coming events would soon reveal the relative ineffectiveness of their point of view in man's quest to understand nature.

Galileo's concrete observations meant little to them. The Florentine astronomer Francesco Sizi argued in this manner why there could not, *must* not be any satellites around Jupiter:

> There are seven windows in the head, two nostrils, two ears, two eyes and a mouth; so in the heavens there are two favorable stars, two unpropitious, two luminaries, and Mercury alone undecided and indifferent. From which and many other similar phenomena of nature such as the seven metals, etc., which it were tedious to enumerate, we gather that the number of planets is necessarily seven ... Besides, the Jews and other ancient nations, as well as modern Europeans, have adopted the division of the week into seven days, and have named them from the seven planets: now if we increase the number of planets, this whole system falls to the ground ... Moreover, the satellites are invisible to the naked eye and therefore can have no influence on the earth and therefore would be useless and therefore do not exist.

A year after making his telescopic discoveries, Galileo had to write to Kepler:

> You are the first and almost the only person who, after a cursory investigation, has given entire credit to my statements ... What do you say of the leading philosophers here to whom I have offered a thousand times of my own accord to show my studies, but who, with the lazy obstinacy of a serpent who has eaten his fill, have never consented to look at the planets, or moon, or telescope?

However, before we too thoroughly condemn those "leading philosophers" of an earlier day, we should note a forceful comment on this point made by Sir Oliver Lodge in 1893:

> ... but I have met educated persons who, while they might laugh at the men who refused to look through a telescope lest they should learn something they did not like, yet also themselves commit the very same folly ... I am constrained to say this much: Take heed lest some prophet, after having excited your indignation at the follies and bigotry of a bygone generation, does not turn upon you with the sentence *"Thou art the man."*

10.4 Science and freedom. The tragedy that descended on Galileo is described in many places;* it is impossible to do justice to the whole story without referring to the full details. Briefly, he was warned in 1616

---

*For example, in de Santillana's historical introduction to the *Dialogue on the great world systems,* or in his book *The crime of Galileo.*

by the Inquisition to cease teaching the Copernican theory, for it was now held "contrary to Holy Scripture." At that time Copernicus' book itself was placed on the *Index Expurgatorius,* and was suspended "until corrected." But Galileo could not suppress what he felt deeply to be the truth. Whereas Copernicus had still invoked Aristotelian doctrine to make his theory plausible, Galileo had reached the new point of view where he urged acceptance of the heliocentric system on its own merits of simplicity and usefulness. This was the great break.

In 1623, Cardinal Barberini, a friend of Galileo's, was elevated to the Papal throne, and Galileo seems to have considered it safe now to write again on the controversial subject. In 1632, after making some required changes, he obtained consent to publish the treatise that we have been discussing, the *Dialogue on the great world systems,* setting forth most persuasively the Copernican view in what pretended to be an impartial discussion of the relative merits of the Ptolemaic and Copernican systems. After the treatise appeared it was realized that Galileo may have tried to circumvent the warning of 1616. Moreover, Galileo had made himself conspicuous to some ecclesiastical factions by maintaining that the phenomena and laws of nature, open to all eyes, are proofs and direct revelations of the Deity quite as valid and grandiose as those recorded in the Bible. "From the Divine Word, the Sacred Scripture and Nature did both alike proceed . . . Nor does God less admirably discover himself to us in Nature's actions than in the Scripture's sacred dictions." These opinions are not only held now by many present-day scientists, but also have become official Church doctrine since 1893; however, at that time, they could be taken for symptoms of heresies for which Galileo's contemporary, Giordano Bruno, had been burned at the stake in 1600. Nor did Galileo help his case by his forthright and tactless behavior.

These factors, and the Inquisition's decision to freeze educational patterns and hence to avoid disturbing changes in the state of knowledge, made it necessary, in the minds of influential men, to challenge Galileo. He was called to Rome and went, although Church authorities could not have forced his appearance before the tribunal of the Inquisition. This voluntary appearance is another reflection of Galileo's faith in the validity of his astronomical views. From the still partly secret records of the proceedings we gather that he was induced to make an elaborate formal renunciation of the Copernican theory and was held a technical prisoner of the Inquisition in his home, near Florence. None of Galileo's friends in Italy dared to defend him publicly. His book was placed on the *Index* (where it remained along with Copernicus' and one of Kepler's until 1835). Galileo's famous *Abjuration,** written for him to recite on his knees and later ordered to

---

*Reprinted in full in Chapter 15 of de Santillana's *The crime of Galileo.*

be read from the pulpits throughout Italy, contains this abject promise:

> I swear that in the future I will never again say or assert, verbally or in writing, anything that might furnish occasion for a similar suspicion regarding me; but, should I know any heretic or person suspected of heresy, I will denounce him to this Holy Office, or to the Inquisitor or Ordinary of the place where I may be.

To scientists today this famous facet of the story of planetary theories is not just an episode in passing. Not a few scientists and scholars in our time have had to face powerful enemies of open-minded inquiry and of free teaching. The fight for freedom in science is waged not only because in the long run science itself is threatened if freedom of inquiry is lost, but also because all intellectual freedom is threatened whenever any facet of it is attacked. Even Plato, realizing that his projected authoritarian state would be threatened by intellectual nonconformists, recommended for the latter the now time-honored treatment: "re-education," prison, or death. Our age saw geneticists in one of the totalitarian countries being expected to reject well-established theories, not on grounds of persuasive new *scientific* evidence, but because of doctrinal conflicts. The 1930's witnessed the working of racist metaphysics within the ranks of science itself when a prominent Nazi physicist asserted that "Natural science, properly so-called, is of completely Aryan origin." In fact, an organized attempt was made to eliminate Einstein's contributions from German physics texts.

The warfare of authoritarianism against science, like the warfare of ignorance against knowledge, has not diminished since Galileo's days. Yet scientists and nonscientists alike can take a good deal of comfort from the verdict of history, for less than 50 years after Galileo, Newton's monumental *Principia* had appeared, integrating the work of Copernicus, Kepler, and Galileo so brilliantly with the principles of mechanics that the long-delayed triumph of those pioneers of science was irrevocable. And, as we shall see in the next chapter, the eventual triumph of these embattled contributors was far more extensive and significant than they themselves could have hoped.

ADDITIONAL PROBLEMS

10.2. Prepare a brief summary of Galileo's seven points in favor of the Copernican system. Comment on the persuasiveness of each argument.

10.3. List the astronomical observations which Galileo made, and comment on the persuasiveness of each in supporting the heliocentric theory.

10.4. In J. B. Conant's book, *On understanding science* (Yale University Press, 1947) are summarized "Certain principles of the tactics and strategy of science" which have been illustrated here. These principles are: (1) "New concepts evolve from experiments or observations and are fruitful of new experiments and observations." (2) "Significant observations are the result of 'controlled experiments' or observations; the difficulties of experimentation must not be overlooked." (3) "New techniques arise as a result of experimentation and influence further experimentation." (4) In addition, Conant emphasizes the important aspect of scientific work that may be called "The interaction between science and society."

Examine the development of planetary theory in terms of each of the above four points (preferably after reading at least pages 101–109 in Conant's book).

SUPPLEMENTARY READING

BOYNTON, H., *The beginnings of modern science* (Walter J. Black, 1948), pp. 27–43. Excerpts from Galileo.

BURTT, E. A., *The metaphysical foundations of modern physical science: a historical and critical essay* (Routledge and Kegan Paul, 1924, and later; the Humanities Press, 1951), Chap. 3.

BUTTERFIELD, H., *The origins of modern science: 1300–1800* (G. Bell, London, 1949; Macmillan, 1951, and later), Chap. 4.

CROMBIE, A. C., *Augustine to Galileo* (Falcon Press, London, 1952), Chap. VI, (1) and (2).

DE SANTILLANA, G., *The age of adventure: the Renaissance philosophers* (Houghton Mifflin and Mentor Book MD184, New American Library, 1956). Discussion, with source materials, of the work of Copernicus, Kepler, Galileo, and Bruno.

DE SANTILLANA, G., *The crime of Galileo* (University of Chicago Press, 1955).

DRAKE, S., *Discoveries and opinions of Galileo* (Doubleday, 1957; Anchor book A94). Includes Galileo's *Starry messenger* (1610) and *Letter to the Grand Duchess Christina* (1615).

GALILEO GALILEI, *Dialogue on the great world systems*, edited by G. de Santillana (University of Chicago Press, 1953). In particular, read the historical introduction and the "Second day."

HALL, A. R., *The scientific revolution 1500–1800* (Longmans, Green, 1954; Beacon Press, 1956), Chap. IV.

KNICKERBOCKER, W. S., ed., *Classics of modern science* (Knopf, 1927), Chap. 4. Excerpt from Galileo.

KOYRÉ, A., *From the closed world to the infinite universe* (Johns Hopkins Press, 1957).

MOULTON, F. R., and J. J. SCHIFFERES, *The autobiography of science* (Doubleday, Doran, 1945, 1951). Brief condensations. See pp. 63–77 (Galileo).

MUNITZ, M. K., ed., *Theories of the universe* (The Free Press, Glencoe, Illinois, 1957), pp. 174–201. Discussion, with excerpts, of the work of Bruno, Galileo, and Kepler.

SHAPLEY, H., and H. E. HOWARTH, *A source book in astronomy* (McGraw-Hill, 1929), pp. 41–57. Excerpts.

TAYLOR, F. S., *Galileo and the freedom of thought* (Watt, 1938). An appraisal of Galileo's work and tribulations.

CHAPTER 11

THE THEORY OF UNIVERSAL GRAVITATION

11.1 The seventeenth century. From the 13th century on, science drew the attention of increasing numbers of scholars. As we have seen, by the 16th century European science was shaking loose from close adherence to the science of antiquity and entering a highly creative stage—and not only in astronomy and mechanics. Vesalius' great treatise on the structure of the human body, Agricola's writings in mineralogy, Fabricius' discovery of the valves in the veins, and Gilbert's book on magnetism are only a few of the noteworthy 16th-century contributions to science. This explosive growth continues into the 17th century. To Galileo's writings on mechanics and astronomy are joined, in related fields, the work on vacuums and pneumatics by Torricelli, Pascal, Guericke, Boyle, and Mariotte; Wallis' work in mathematics; Descartes' great studies on analytic geometry and on optics; Huygens' work in astronomy and on centripetal force, his development of the pendulum clock, and his book on light; the improvement of microscopes and the invention of reflecting telescopes; Newton's work, including that on optics and his further development of the calculus; the opening of the famous Greenwich observatory; Roemer's measurement of the speed of light; Hooke's work, including that on elasticity; and work in geogony by Leibniz and Descartes.

The men of science in this period are finding better means for communicating with one another. They have formed scientific societies in Italy, England, and France, among them the Royal Society of London, founded in 1662. The members of the Royal Society hold regular meetings, they cooperate and debate, write copiously, and sometimes quarrel healthily. As a group, they solicit support for their work, combat attacks by antagonists, and have a widely read scientific journal. Science is clearly becoming a well-defined activity, vigorously pursued.

What is behind this sudden blossoming? Even a partial answer would lead us far away from science itself to an examination of the whole picture of quickening social, political, and economic changes in the 16th and 17th centuries. One aspect is a pyramiding effect of centuries of work, now coming to fruition; another is that both craftsmen and men of leisure and wealth are beginning to turn to science, the one group for improvement of methods and products, the other for a new and exciting hobby. But the need for science and the availability of money and time do not alone explain or sustain such a thriving enterprise. Even more important are three further elements: *the turning of the interest of men of ability and curiosity toward science; well-formulated problems; and good mathematical and experimental tools.*

Men of ability and curiosity were indeed at hand. Some, like Newton, were well-educated scholars, often in the great universities; others, like Newton's friends Edmond Halley and Christopher Wren, were gifted amateurs, also largely university graduates.

There were abundant illustrations of how to achieve well-formulated problems in the writings of Galileo. His work represented the new way of viewing the world of fact and experiment, and it was he, above all others, who had directed attention to mathematics as the fruitful language of physical science. His scorn of sterile introspection and blind subservience to dogma echoed through all fields of science. And the old Platonic question, "By the assumption of what uniform and ordered motions can the apparent motions of the planets be accounted for?" had lost its original meaning in the new science; the new preoccupation is illustrated by what may be called the two most critical problems in 17th-century physics: "What forces act on the planets to explain their observed paths?" and "How are the observed effects of terrestrial gravitation to be explained now that Aristotelian doctrines have failed us?"

Good mathematical and experimental tools were also being created. With mathematics now finding wide application in physics, the two fields cross-fertilized and gave rich harvests. The increasing sea trade, exploration, and world expansion of the 16th century quickened interest in problems of navigation, geography, and cartography; instrument makers and mapmakers turned to mathematics and astronomy for assistance in their problems. Borelli, a pupil of Galileo, applied mechanics to the study of muscular physiology and established the field of experimental biology. The simple microscope was put to use by Leeuwenhoek to explore hitherto unseen worlds, even while Newton was doing the important work in optics that was to provide a firm foundation for better compound microscopes as well as new astronomical telescopes.

At last there were many men with similar attitudes working in the same fields. They could communicate more freely and had better access to the accumulated achievements of their predecessors, partly through the still relatively young art of printing. They had become impatient with qualitative reasoning and began to be more and more intrigued with the quantitative approach. To use a modern analogy, the critical mass was reached, and the chain reaction could proceed.

This, from the point of view of science, was the new age in which Newton lived. But before we enter upon his work on gravitation, a brief word of caution. The history of ideas, in science as in any other field, is not simply an account of visits with the most important scientists. The work of each genius is made possible, is stabilized, and is connected with the whole structure of science only through the labors of lesser-known men, just as the bricks in a wall are surrounded by fortifying mortar. Science cannot be made by giants alone. As Lord Rutherford said: "It is not in the nature of things for any one man to make a sudden violent discovery; science goes step by step, and every man depends on the work of his predecessors . . . Scientists are not dependent on the ideas of a single man, but on the combined wisdom of thousands of men." Therefore, properly, we should trace in each man's contribution the heritage of the past, the influence of his contemporaries, and the meaning for his successors. This is the exciting and rewarding task of the scholar concerned with the history of science, but here we can touch only on the barest outlines.

11.2 Newton: biographical note. Isaac Newton was born in the manor house of Woolsthorpe in Lincolnshire in 1642. He was a quiet and frail boy who is said to have loved to build and tinker with mechanical gadgets. Through the fortunate intervention of an uncle, Newton was allowed to go to Trinity College at Cambridge University in 1661, where he proved an eager and excellent student. By 1666, at twenty-four, he had quietly made profound discoveries in mathematics (binomial theorem, differential calculus), optics (theory of colors), and mechanics. Referring to this period, Newton wrote later:

> All this was in the two plague years of 1665 and 1666, for in those days I was in the prime of my age for invention, and minded Mathematicks and Philosophy [physical science] more than at any time since.

From Newton's writings one may conclude that during those years, having left Cambridge to study in isolation at his home in Woolsthorpe, he had developed a clear idea of the first two laws of motion and of the formula for centripetal acceleration, although he did not announce the latter until many years after the appearance of Huygens' equivalent statement.

This too must have been the time of the famous incident of the falling apple. One of the sources for this story is a biography of Newton written by his friend William Stukeley in 1752, which records that on one occasion Stukeley was having tea with Newton in a garden under some apple trees, when Newton told him that "he was just in the same situation, as when formerly, the notion of gravitation came to his mind. It was occasion'd by the fall of an apple, as he sat in a contemplative mood . . ." However, one must not of course interpret this remark of Newton's to mean that the progress of science depends upon such an accidental occurrence as an apple falling. We have seen that the concept of gravitation had been developing for nearly a century, and the apple merely served as a focus of attention: the key element in Newton's remark is "contemplative mood," rather than the apple. At any rate, this was perhaps the trigger that turned Newton's mind to the subject of gravitation.

PHILOSOPHIÆ

NATURALIS

PRINCIPIA

MATHEMATICA

Autore *J S. NEWTON*, *Trin. Coll. Cantab. Soc.* Mathefeos
Profeffore *Lucafiano*, & Societatis Regalis Sodali.

IMPRIMATUR·

S. P E P Y S, *Reg. Soc.* P R Æ S E S.

Julii 5. 1686.

L O N D I N I,

Juffu *Societatis Regiæ* ac Typis *Jofephi Streater*. Proftat apud
plures Bibliopolas. *Anno* MDCLXXXVII.

FIG. 11.1. Title page of Newton's *Principia* (1687).

After his return to Cambridge, Newton did such creditable work that he succeeded his teacher as professor of mathematics. He lectured, and contributed papers to the Royal Society, at first particularly on optics. But his "Theory about Light and Colors," when finally published in 1672, involved him in so much bitter controversy with rivals that the shy and introspective man even resolved not to publish anything else.

Newton now concentrated mainly on an extension of his early efforts in celestial mechanics, the study of planetary motions as a problem of physics. In 1684 his devoted friend Edmond Halley sought his advice in a dispute with Christopher Wren and Robert Hooke concerning the force that must act on a body to make it move in an elliptical orbit in accordance with Kepler's laws. Newton told him that he had some time ago found the rigorous solution to this problem and "much other matter." Halley persuaded his reluctant friend to complete and publish this work dealing with some of the most debated and intriguing scientific questions of the time. In less than two years of incredible labors the *Principia* was ready for the printer; its appearance in 1687 established Newton's reputation as one of the greatest scientists of all time (Fig. 11.1).

A few years afterward, Newton, who had always been in delicate health, appears to have had what we would now call a nervous breakdown. On recovering, and until his death 35 years later, he did very little further work in science, turning more and more to theology. During those years he received honors in abundance. In 1699 he was appointed Warden of the Mint and later its Master, and he helped materially in re-establishing the currency of the country. In 1689 and 1701 he represented his university in Parliament. He was knighted in 1705. From 1703 until his death, in 1727, he was president of the Royal Society. He was buried in Westminster Abbey.

11.3 Newton's "Rules of Reasoning." In Newton's preface to the *Principia*, probably the most famous book in the history of physics, we find a brief outline of the work:

> Since the ancients (as we are told by Pappus) esteemed the science of mechanics of greatest importance in the investigation of natural things, and the moderns, rejecting substantial forms and occult qualities, have endeavored to subject the phenomena of nature to the laws of mathematics, I have in this treatise cultivated mathematics as far as it relates to philosophy [we would say "physical science"] . . . for the whole burden of philosophy seems to consist in this—from the phenomena of motions to investigate [by induction] the forces of nature, and then from these forces to demonstate [by deduction] the other phenomena, and to this end the general propositions of the first and second Books are directed. In the third Book I give an example of this in the explication of the System of the World; for by the propositions mathematically demonstrated in the former Books, in the third I derive from the

celestial phenomena the forces of gravity with which bodies tend to the sun and the several planets. Then from these forces, by other propositions which are also mathematical, I deduce the motions of the planets, the comets, the moon, and the sea [tides] . . .

The treatise proper begins with a set of definitions: mass, momentum, inertia, force, centripetal force. Then follows a section on *absolute* and *relative* space, time, and motion. Immediately thereafter we find the famous three Axioms or Laws of Motion and the principles of addition of vector quantities.

In Book Three there is a remarkable and important passage on Newton's "Rules of Reasoning in Philosophy" which are implicitly used throughout his work. These rules are the essence distilled from the previous five centuries of study in scientific methodology. They are intended to guide the scientist in constructing hypotheses, and for that purpose they are still up-to-date. The rules, which are four in number, may be paraphrased as follows:

RULE I. Nature is simple, therefore we should not introduce any more hypotheses than are necessary to explain the observed phenomena. "Nature does nothing in vain, and more is in vain when less will serve." This is almost a paraphrase of Galileo's axiom "Nature . . . does not that by many things which may be done by few," which in turn reflected the opinion of Aristotle and others back to the very dawn of science.

RULE II. "Therefore to the same effects we must, as far as possible, assign the same causes: as to respiration in man and in a beast; the descent of stones in Europe and in America; . . ."

RULE III. Those properties of bodies that are both unchanging and common to all bodies within reach of our experiments are to be considered the universal properties of all bodies whatsoever. (For example, since every object available to the experimenter exhibits the property of inertia, this rule leads to the hypothesis "every object has inertia.")

RULE IV. In "experimental philosophy," those hypotheses or generalizations which have been formulated in the light of experience are to be regarded as "accurately or very nearly true, notwithstanding any contrary hypotheses that may be imagined," and they are to be so regarded until such time as other phenomena are discovered with which they are not in accord, thus necessitating their modification.

PROBLEM 11.1. Compare Newton's four "Rules of Reasoning in Philosophy" with the criteria for a good theory set forth in Section 8.2, (3) through (5).

PROBLEM 11.2. As a review of Newton's three laws of motion, find what is *wrong* with the following argument. Imagine a large rock of mass m_R falling with acceleration g toward the earth, of mass m_E. The only force acting on the rock is the gravitational pull $m_R g$. An observer located on the rock would see the earth approaching the rock with an acceleration $-g$, from which he concludes that the gravitational force exerted by the rock on the earth is $-m_E g$. But, by Newton's third law, the gravitational force exerted by the earth on the rock is equal in magnitude and opposite in direction to that exerted by the rock on the earth. Hence $m_R g = -(-m_E g)$, or $m_R = m_E$. Thus the observer concludes that all rocks have the same mass as the earth. (*Hint:* To prove that the argument is wrong, note that the laws of motion have attached to them a lengthy text which, among other things, specifies a system of coordinates with respect to which the acceleration is to be measured.)

11.4 Toward the principle of universal gravitation: The direction of the planetary force. In the *Principia* Newton not only set forth the system of terrestrial mechanics that we have examined in Chapter 4, he also showed that motions in the solar system were explainable by postulating that *all bodies in the universe exert forces of gravitational attraction on one another*. Thus he extended his mechanics to the heavens. For some time there had been a feeling that there were forces acting upon the planets to regulate their motions, and Gilbert, Kepler, and Descartes had drawn attention to the sun as the origin of this force. But it was Newton's work that utterly destroyed the old dichotomy between terrestrial and celestial science and firmly established the heliocentric system. It also produced a flood of adulation from Newton's contemporaries, the two most famous examples being Alexander Pope's lines

> Nature and Nature's laws lay hid in night:
> God said, Let Newton be: and all was light,

and Edmond Halley's ode to Newton, which ends

> Nearer to the gods no mortal may approach.

As we now examine some of the important steps in the formulation and verification of the law of universal gravitation, we shall find that they afford splendid illustrations of the interplay between established laws, new hypotheses, experiments, and observations, and of the role of mathematical deduction in physical science.

In retracing the road by which Newton arrived at his world picture, we first encounter the realization that the planets must not be regarded as being in equilibrium. No longer is an explanation of their "natural" motion to be sought in terms of their "natural" places. Instead, each planet is seen to be undergoing continuous acceleration toward a point near the center of the planetary orbit and therefore, by Newton's first and second laws of motion, each planet is being continuously acted on by a net force. The first question is: what is this force?

In the First Book of the *Principia* Newton plunges directly into this problem and shows that, whatever the source or nature or magnitude of the net force acting on any planet or satellite, its *direction* must at every instant be toward a point as the "center of motion" of the orbital path. It must be what we may call a *central force*. Let us follow Newton's thoughts as set forth in the *Principia* as far as we can; they surely deserve our attention in detail.*

(1) Suppose that a body was at rest at a point Q [Fig. 11.2(a)] when, either by a sudden pull on a string connected to it or by means of a blow, we apply to it a force of short duration directed toward O, as in Fig. 11.2(b). The body will be accelerated during the blow, quickly acquire a velocity toward O, and in some definite time interval Δt will move a definite distance QQ'.

(2) Now suppose that, instead, the body is not acted upon by a force but is moving along the line $PQRS$ with constant speed [Fig. 11.2(a)]. It traverses equal distances PQ, QR, RS in equal time intervals Δt.

(3) In Fig. 11.2(c), we combine situations (1) and (2). A body moving initially with constant speed from P to Q along $PQRS$ experiences a blow directed toward O when it reaches Q, at a time Δt after leaving P. After another equally long time interval Δt, the original motion alone would have carried the body to R; the effect of the blow alone would have carried it to Q'. The combined motion is along the line QR', so that the body reaches point R' after a time interval Δt. The point R' may be located by drawing line RR' through R parallel to QQ' and drawing $Q'R'$ through Q' parallel to QR; this is effectively the addition of the two components of the displacement QR'.

(4) The imaginary line connecting the body and O has first swept across

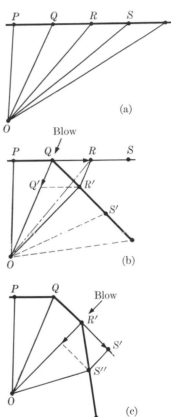

(a)

(b)

(c)

FIG. 11.2. If an object experiences a centrally directed force, it will move in accordance with Kepler's second law.

---

*It is significant to note that Newton's argument is cast in the traditional deductive pattern of Euclid, as, for that matter, was the work of Thomas Aquinas and Spinoza.

the area OPQ in a time interval Δt and then has swept across the area OQR' in the second, equal time interval Δt [Fig. 11.2(b)]. These two areas are equal, as we shall prove by showing that they both are equal to the area OQR. First, triangles OPQ and OQR have equal bases, since $PQ = QR$ from (2), and they have the same height OP; therefore they have equal areas. Triangles OQR and OQR' also have the same area because they have the same base OQ and equal heights, for the heights are the perpendicular distances of the vertices R and R' from the base OQ and, since RR' is parallel to QQ', every point on RR' is the same perpendicular distance from the base OQ. Thus, the area OPQ swept out during the first time interval Δt is equal to the area OQR' swept out in the next, equally long, time interval Δt.

Suppose that the body does not go on to point S', but experiences another brief application of force at the end of the second time interval, that is, when it is at R', as shown in Fig. 11.2(c). If this force is again directed toward O, precisely the same argument will show that $OR'S''$, the area swept out in a third equal time interval Δt, is again the same as OQR' and OPQ.

(5) Let us imagine that we take a shorter time interval Δt between successive blows, so that the blows come closer together and the changes in direction of motion are more frequent than before. Newton showed that we are completely justified in carrying this process on *ad infinitum*, without losing validity of the proof concerning the areas. Thus, as the blows come so close together that they blend into a continuously acting force, always centrally directed toward O, and as the path of the body blends into a smooth curve, the line from O to the body continues to sweep out equal areas in equal times. In other words, *if a body is continuously acted upon by a central force, it will move in accordance with Kepler's second law.*

(6) Now in Proposition II of the *Principia* Newton reverses the argument. Consider a body moving along the line $PQR'S''$ [Fig. 11.2(c)] so that the areas swept out in equal time intervals Δt are equal. The body must experience a force at Q (and at R' and S''), for if it did not, the first law of motion tells us that it would move to R in time interval Δt, whereas actually it moves to R'. Hence the blow at Q must produce a component of displacement RR' which, added to the displacement QR due to the original motion, displaces the body to R'. But RR' is parallel to QO, that is, the displacement due to the blow is in the direction from Q to O. The blow must therefore have been toward O. Again, on taking smaller and smaller time intervals, we make the transition from the broken-line path to the motion along a smooth curve, and reach the conclusion that if any body *is* moving so that a line from a fixed point O to the body sweeps out equal areas in equal times, it must be continuously subjected to a net force directed toward O. In other words, *any body moving in accordance with Kepler's*

second law must be acted upon by a central force. The point toward which this "central" force is directed is, for motion on an ellipse, one of its foci, and for a circle it is its center.

The extension into the physical world is clear. We know that each planet moves in accordance with Kepler's second law; therefore the net force on each planet must be directed toward one focus of its elliptical orbit. It is worth pausing to note that Newton's derivation was a considerable achievement. Earlier scientists had proposed all sorts of agencies that might be acting on the planets of the heliocentric system in their orbits about the sun. Newton, sensing the heart of the problem of celestial mechanics, focused his attention upon the *net force* acting on these planets. He showed that the observations of planetary positions demand as a logical consequence that no matter how many forces are simultaneously acting on a planet, or what their nature or their magnitude, the (vector) sum of all forces must be a net force directed toward a fixed point, and this point, this center of motion, is just where the sun is located.

PROBLEM 11.3. Summarize Newton's argument to this point in brief outline form.

11.5 The magnitude of the planetary force. We turn now to the next big question: what is the magnitude of the net force acting on a planet, and how does it vary as the planet moves from point to point along its elliptical path? Newton was able to show (and he was the first to do this with mathematical rigor) that if the path of an object is a conic section whether this be an ellipse, a circle, a parabola, or a hyperbola—and if the force on that object always is directed to one focus, then the force *must be inversely proportional to the square of the body's distance from the focus of the conic section.* In short, any body moving in accordance with Kepler's first law of elliptical paths is acted on by a net force F that at any instant is given by the proportionality

$$F \propto \frac{1}{R^2},\qquad(11.1)$$

which may also be written in equation form as

$$F = \frac{C}{R^2},\qquad(11.2)$$

where C is a constant quantity for a particular body and R is the distance measured from the focus of the ellipse to the center of the body. For a body that is spherical in shape and homogeneous in makeup, the "center of the body" to which R must be measured is the center of the sphere. Equation (11.2) is referred to as an "inverse-square law."

Historically, Newton's demonstration that elliptical planetary paths imply an inverse-square law for the force came at a time when the notion of such a relationship was generally "in the air." In fact, Halley had come to Newton in 1684 for the express purpose of asking whether the latter could supply the proof others were looking for in vain.

It is clear that Eq. (11.2) is somewhat unsatisfactory in its present form, for it does not allow calculation of the numerical value of the net force acting on the planet, since the value of the constant C is undetermined. Unlike the constant k in Kepler's third law, $T^2 = k\overline{R}^3$ (Eq. 9.5), which could be computed by substituting observed values of T and $\overline{R}$ into Eq. (9.5), the constant C in $F = C/R^2$ cannot be found in this manner because F cannot be directly measured.

It would look as though we had come to a dead end. We know the *direction* of the planetary force, we know the *form* of the relation between the force and the distance, but we cannot find the *magnitude* of the force.

11.6 The origin and nature of the planetary force. Faced with the difficulty of finding the value of C in Eq. (11.2), Newton attacked the problem from an entirely different direction, by investigating the physical nature of the force F. This was not a new problem, for Kepler's speculation that some magnetic force reached out from the sun to move the planets, while not in itself a fruitful hypothesis, helped to call attention to the sun as a relevant factor in explaining planetary motion. Another picture had been proposed by the great French philosopher and mathematician René Descartes (1596–1650), who held that all space was filled with a subtle, invisible fluid consisting of contiguous material corpuscles, and that the planets were caught in a huge vortex-like motion of this fluid about the sun. This mechanism was attractive to the minds of the day and was widely accepted for a time, but Newton showed that it could not account for the quantitative observations on planetary motion as summarized, for example, in Kepler's laws.

At this point Newton proposed a dramatic solution: *All objects in the world attract one another with a gravitational force like that existing between a falling stone and the earth; consequently the central force on a planet is nothing but a gravitational attraction toward the sun,* and similarly, the central force on a satellite revolving about a planet is accounted for by the gravitational pull exerted on it by the planet.

Only a century or two earlier it would have been generally considered impious or foolish to suggest that one type of force, gravitation, extends throughout the whole universe, that the forces controlling the motions of the heavenly bodies were of the same nature as those that explained the free fall of bodies toward the earth, but now the postulate of universal gravitation seemed natural. This was the culmination of a movement that had been going on for several centuries, namely, a steady attack upon the Aristotelian dichotomy between terrestrial and celestial regions. In flat contradiction to Aristotle's teachings, Newton proposed that the same mechanics applies to both terrestrial and celestial motion. Newtonian mechanics, valid for terrestrial motion, could now be extended to planetary motion, and the laws of planetary motion which Kepler had discovered could be considered simply as a consequence of the same all-pervading mechanics. This merging of the mechanics of the heavens and the mechanics of the earth is often called the *Newtonian synthesis*.

As Newton told Stukeley (Section 11.2), it was the sight of a falling apple that focused his attention upon this subject. The fall of the apple straight down indicates that the earth exerts a force of attraction. It is reasonable that the power to attract matter may extend far beyond the branches of the tree and indeed probably as far as the moon. Further, by the third law of motion, it would be a mutual effect: the apple draws the earth and the earth draws the apple; the moon experiences a gravitational force due to the earth, and the earth experiences just as large a force in the opposite direction. Drawing perhaps on a suggestion made by William Gilbert, nearly a century earlier, that the effect of a magnet is proportional to the *mass* of the magnet, Newton decided that the gravitational force between two objects that attract each other is proportional to the mass of each. Thus the gravitational force on the apple due to the earth (Fig. 11.3) is proportional to the mass of the apple ($F_{grav} \propto m_A$) and also to the mass of the earth ($F_{grav} \propto m_E$). Putting these two proportionalities together yields $F_{grav} \propto m_A m_E$. The force on the earth due to the apple, which is just as large in the opposite direction, is given by the same proportionality.

Similarly, the magnitude of the gravitational pull experienced by the moon or by the earth owing to their mutual attraction would be given by the proportionality $F_{grav} \propto m_E m_M$. And if gravitation is a force linking *any* two objects (of masses m_1 and m_2) in general, we may expect that

$$F_{grav} \propto m_1 m_2. \quad (11.3)$$

In particular, for a planet of mass m_P experiencing a force of attraction to the sun (mass m_S),

$$F_{grav} \propto m_P m_S.$$

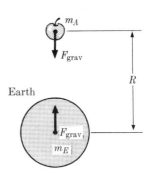

FIG. 11.3. The force of mutual attraction between the earth and an apple is proportional to m_A, m_E, and the inverse square of the distance between them.

At this point of the argument, these proportionalities are untested but plausible suggestions. Moreover, they show how the interaction between two "gravitating" bodies may depend on the masses, but do not take into account the separation R between them. But on this point we recall that Newton showed, as a result of Kepler's first law, that all planets must be acted upon by a net force proportional to $1/R^2$ (Eq. 11.1). Confident that this net force will prove to be the gravitational attraction which the sun exerts on each planet, and in the expectation that the laws of mechanics found in any part of the universe apply universally, Newton again generalized this finding. He postulated that the force between *any* two masses, m_1 and m_2 or m_P and m_S, is proportional to the inverse square of the distance between them:

$$F_{\text{grav}} \propto \frac{1}{R^2}. \tag{11.4}$$

Combining (11.3) and (11.4), we obtain

$$F_{\text{grav}} \propto \frac{m_1 m_2}{R^2} \tag{11.5}$$

or, putting in a constant of proportionality G to convert the proportionality into an equation,

$$F_{\text{grav}} = G\,\frac{m_1 m_2}{R^2}. \tag{11.6}$$

This equation, if verified, would amount to a *principle of universal gravitation*. According to it, a planet at distance R_{PS} from the sun should experience an attraction whose magnitude is given by

$$F_{\text{grav}} = G\,\frac{m_P m_S}{R_{PS}^2}. \tag{11.7}$$

We have arrived at the last two equations by making a great many assumptions. Obviously, we must now test whether the result of our derivation corresponds to facts, otherwise Eq. (11.7) cannot answer the question raised at the end of the last section, namely, how large the planetary force may be. But the attempt to test the last two equations directly involves us immediately in apparently insurmountable problems. For example, a calculation of the gravitational force of the sun upon the earth with the help of Eq. (11.7) is impossible because, at this point, we do not know the values of the constant G and the masses of the planet earth or of the sun. Applying Eq. (11.6) to the case of the apple, we can consider the mass of the apple and its weight (F_{grav}) to be known by observation; but what is the value of G and the mass of the earth? And how is R, the distance between the apple and the earth, to be determined? Part of the earth is only a few feet away from the apple, other parts are up to 8000 miles away. Similarly, applying Eq. (11.6) to the moon and the earth, what is the distance R to mean here? In surmounting these obstacles, Newton achieved his greatest triumph.

First, Newton proved that if the two objects attracting each other are spherical and homogeneous, or made of spherical shells each of which is homogeneous, *the distance R to use in Eq. (11.6) or (11.7) is the distance between the centers of the spheres*. The proof was given as follows. Newton imagined any two spherical objects to be composed of very many small particles, each of which attracted each of the particles in the other sphere with a force given by Eq. (11.6). Because the particles are so small, the distances between them can be considered definitely determinable, in principle. Then the mutual gravitational force between the spheres is the sum of all the individual gravitational forces between the constituent particles, and this was shown to be proportional to the product of the total masses of both spheres divided by the square of the distance between their centers.

Another hurdle remains before the way is clear for testing the principle of universal gravitation. The earth, the apple, and the moon are not homogeneous spheres and hence, strictly speaking, Eq. (11.6) may not apply to gravitational forces between them. However, two saving factors enable us to consider the equation applicable: (1) if the object is small compared with the distance involved (for example, the apple compared with the distance from it to the center of the earth), lack of homogeneity and sphericity is unimportant; and (2) the moon and the earth are approximately spherical and homogeneous, as is the case for all other planets and satellites, and for the sun itself.

11.7 The moon problem. Now we are ready to test the proposed principle of universal gravitation by applying it to the observed motion of the moon, following what may have been Newton's own procedure. If the principle of universal gravitation is correct, the moon experiences a gravitational pull toward the earth given by Eq. (11.6) in the special form

$$F_{\text{grav}} = G \, \frac{m_M m_E}{R_{ME}^2}, \tag{11.8}$$

where R_{ME} stands for the distance between the centers of moon and earth (a quantity known on the basis of astronomical observation). While the individual quantities G, m_M, and m_E are not directly known, the product Gm_E can be evaluated by the following surprisingly simple consideration. If a spherical object of mass m is at the surface of the earth, the distance from it to the center of the earth is the radius of the earth itself, namely, r_E. The gravitational force on it is given by the expression $G(mm_E/r_E^2)$ and, of course, also by mg:

$$mg = G\,\frac{mm_E}{r_E^2}.$$

Consequently,

$$Gm_E = gr_E^2. \tag{11.9}$$

Thus Eq. (11.8) for the gravitational attraction experienced by the moon at distance R_{ME} becomes

$$F_{\text{grav}} = m_M g\,\frac{r_E^2}{R_{ME}^2}. \tag{11.10}$$

The direction of this gravitational force on the moon is, of course, toward the center of the earth.

But if this gravitational force is the only force tending to pull the moon to the earth, it must have the same value as the centripetal force $m_M(v^2/R_{ME})$ acting on the moon in its (nearly) circular orbit about the earth (Eq. 5.12). Therefore we write

$$\frac{m_M v^2}{R_{ME}} = m_M g\,\frac{r_E^2}{R_{ME}^2}.$$

The speed v of the moon is just the circumference of the orbit, $2\pi R_{ME}$, divided by the period, T_M, of the moon's motion, so that our last equation becomes

$$\frac{m_M 4\pi^2 R_{ME}^2}{T_M^2 R_{ME}} = m_M g\,\frac{r_E^2}{R_{ME}^2}$$

or

$$T_M^2 = \frac{4\pi^2 R_{ME}^3}{gr_E^2}, \qquad T_M = \frac{2\pi}{r_E}\sqrt{\frac{R_{ME}^3}{g}}. \tag{11.11}$$

Equation (11.11) predicts a value for the period of the moon's orbital motion in terms of other, measurable quantities.

Here, at last, is a result of the theory that can be put to a direct test, for each factor in Eq. (11.11) is known from independent, prior observations. In Newton's day, these known values were: local gravitational acceleration $g =$ approximately 32 ft/sec^2, radius of earth $r_E = 4000$ mi, radius of moon's orbit $R_{ME} = 60$ times the earth's radius. Therefore, on converting to consistent units,

$$T_M = 27 \text{ days.}$$

This is a remarkable result, for the *observed* value of T_M, the period of the moon for making one complete 360° revolution about the earth (corrected, of course, for the rotation of the earth on its own axis, which makes the apparent period of the moon a couple of days longer) is about $27\frac{1}{3}$ days. The empirical and theoretically predicted values of T_M do coincide within a reasonable margin of error! Our faith in the inverse-square law for gravitational force, in the hypothesis that the net force on the moon is indeed this gravitational force, and in the assumption that the laws of terrestrial mechanics are applicable also for objects at least as far away as the moon is thus strengthened.

This was the calculation that Newton found to "answer pretty nearly" (see Problem 11.8 below), probably within a few percent. His assumption of a strictly circular path for the moon, and his use of the rough values of r_E and g then available, made it clear to him from the start that no "perfect" agreement between theory and observation could be expected. Indeed, if the phrase "perfect agreement between theory and observation" is to be used at all, it should be defined as correspondence of the respective values within the expected margin of error.

PROBLEM 11.4. (a) Summarize, in brief outline form, the argument leading to this point in the establishment of the principle of universal gravitation. (b) Have we established the validity of Eq. (11.6)?

PROBLEM 11.5. Equation (11.10) can be written in the form $F_{\text{grav}}/m_M g = (1/R_{ME})^2/(1/r_E)^2$. Put this expression into verbal form, and give it a physical interpretation.

PROBLEM 11.6. Note that the expression for the period of the moon in a circular orbit around the earth, Eq. (11.11), does not depend on the mass of the moon. What must be the period of a "space platform" orbiting around the earth 2000 mi above its surface? Use consistent units, but make only a rough "order-of-magnitude" calculation, i.e., express all data as the nearest whole multiple of 1, or 10, or 100, etc.

PROBLEM 11.7. (a) Given Eq. (11.9) and the fact that the average density (mass/volume) of the earth is likely to be above 1 (water) and below 11 (lead), compute a plausible order-of-magnitude value of G, the constant of proportionality in the principle of universal gravitation. (b) Equation (11.6), if universally applicable between any two bodies, leads to the expectation that two billiard balls on a flat table should move toward each other by mutual gravitational attraction. In the light of the answer to (a), explain why this is not observed.

PROBLEM 11.8. Speaking of the prolific year 1666, Newton later said:

> And the same year I began to think of gravity extending to the orb of the Moon, and . . . from Kepler's Rule [Third Law] . . . I deduced that the forces which keep the Planets in their orbs must [be] reciprocally as the squares of their distances from the centers about which they revolve: and thereby compared the force requisite to keep the Moon in her orb with the force of gravity at the surface of the earth, and found them to answer pretty nearly.

Retrace Newton's steps. Begin by assuming, for simplicity, that the planets move in circular orbits, with the sun at the center. Then the speed, orbital radius, and period are related by Eq. (5.3). Using that equation, together with Kepler's third law, Eq. (9.5), and the expression for centripetal force, Eq. (5.12), show that the centripetal force is inversely proportional to the square of the orbital radius. Finally, compare the centripetal force and the gravitational force on the moon.

11.8 Extension of the principle of gravitation to planetary motion. The preceding section was concerned solely with the force between earth and moon, and not with the larger problem of the sun and the planets. But the digression to the moon problem served a purpose: if gravity does account for the motion of the moon, we feel encouraged to propose tentatively that forces of gravitation extend through the entire solar system, that the sun does for the planets what the earth does for the moon. In Newton's words:

> The force that retains the celestial bodies in their orbits has been hitherto called centripetal force; but it being now made plain that it can be no other than a gravitational force, we shall hereafter call it gravity. For the cause of that centripetal force which retains the moon in its orbit will extend itself to all planets, by Rules I, II, and IV.

We must remember, however, that such rules (Section 11.3) are intended simply for guidance and are not prescriptive. They suggest, but do not prove; this task, as Newton well knew, still remained to be done.

If we assume that the planetary orbits around the sun are practically circular, the centripetal force F_c on any particular planet with period T_P and mass m_P is, by Eq. (5.12),

$$F_c = \frac{m_P v^2}{R_{PS}} = \frac{m_P 4\pi^2 R_{PS}}{T_P^2}, \tag{11.12}$$

where R_{PS} is the radius of the orbit. Is the value of F_c given by Eq. (11.12) equal to the gravitational attraction exerted by the sun on the particular planet? If the value of the gravitational acceleration of an object falling freely toward the surface of the sun were known we could obtain an answer by using the same method as in the preceding section; but of course there is no way to obtain this value by direct experiment, and so we must seek another method to test whether a gravitational force explains the motion of planets around the sun.

With the confidence gained by his success with the moon problem, Newton boldly proposed here *to adopt the principle of universal gravitation*, as in Eq. (11.6), for any two particles in the universe. The tentative and speculative use of the principle now gives way to its systematic and general use as a basic law. Since the celestial bodies are very likely to be constructed of nearly homogeneous, nearly spherical shells, and since in any case the distances between the sun and the planets are large compared with their sizes, Eq. (11.7) can be used to determine the mutual gravitational attraction:

$$F_{\text{grav}} = G \, \frac{m_P m_S}{R_{PS}^2}. \tag{11.7}$$

Substituting this value of F_{grav} for F_c in Eq. (11.12), we obtain

$$G \, \frac{m_P m_S}{R_{PS}^2} = \frac{m_P 4\pi^2 R_{PS}}{T_P^2},$$

or

$$T_P^2 = \left[\frac{4\pi^2}{m_S G} \right] R_{PS}^3. \tag{11.13}$$

The expression in brackets involves only the proportionality constant G, the mass of the sun m_S, and a numerical factor; since G has been assumed to be a universal constant, the term in the brackets is also a constant. Thus Eq. (11.13) can be written as

$$T^2 = KR^3, \tag{11.14}$$

where $K = 4\pi^2/m_S G$, and so has the same value no matter to which planet T and R refer. In words, for all planets, the square of the period is proportional to the cube of the orbital radius. *But this is precisely the content of Kepler's third empirical law (Eq. 9.5); here we have deduced it from Newtonian mechanics.* We are thus led to believe more firmly in the assumption on which this deduction is based, namely, the principle of universal gravitation. To be sure, we have so far not shown that the numerical value of K in Eq. (11.14) is the same as the empirical value for k in Eq. (9.5), but at least the *form* of the two equations is the same.

Our deduction involved the simplification that planetary orbits are taken to be circular, and this is nearly true. Newton, however, actually carried out the derivation for elliptic orbits, with the same result as given here.

Newtonian theory also accounts for the facts summarized in Kepler's *first* and *second* laws. If each planet is acted upon by a gravitational force directed always toward the sun, it fits the case (Section 11.5) of an object moving under the influence of a centrally directed net force, which necessarily sweeps out equal areas in equal times. Moreover, a central force described by an inverse-square law, as Newton showed, makes the path a conic section, with the center of the force at one of the foci. Thus the predictions made from Newtonian theory agree with Kepler's laws and hence with astronomical observations. By Newton's Fourth Rule of Reasoning we may therefore regard the law of gravitation as "accurately or very nearly true, notwithstanding any contrary hypotheses that may be imagined."

It may come as a disappointment to learn that Newton was unable to put observed values into Eq. (11.13) so as to have a test of its quantitative validity, in addition to the correspondence of its *form* with Kepler's third law as expressed in Eq. (9.5); this test had to await independent determinations of m_S and G with the help of methods that were not available in Newton's time. However, once Newtonian theory, and particularly the conception of gravitational forces extending throughout our solar system, had been made plausible by the arguments just presented, sufficient additional confirmation came in two ways: through a set of astonishingly fruitful consequences along unexpected lines, and through the fact that a unifying explanation for so many separate existing puzzles was provided. The lack of a more direct test was therefore of no immediate commanding interest.

11.9 The synthesis of celestial and terrestrial mechanics. Newtonian mechanics accounted for the observed motions of the heavenly bodies, but what about terrestrial motions? Newton showed, to be sure, that the weight of the moon and the weight of a terrestrial object are compatible concepts. However, could his mechanics account also for, say, the motion of projectiles? We saw in Chapter 2 that Galileo succeeded in describing projectile motion by postulating that any freely falling body undergoes constant acceleration downward. Sagredo asked, "What is the *cause* of the acceleration of . . . heavy bodies . . . ?" But Galileo's spokesman, Salviati, emphatically refused to discuss the question at that point.

With the aid of Newtonian mechanics we can now treat this problem. The force acting on a freely falling object of mass m_O near the earth's surface, according to the law of gravitation, is

$$F_{grav} = G \, \frac{m_E m_O}{r_{EO}^2} ,$$

where G is the constant of gravitation, m_E is the mass of the earth, and r_{EO} is the distance between the centers of object and earth. But the force on the falling object is, of course, also given by Newton's second law of motion:

$$F_{net} = m_O a = m_O g,$$

where g is the local acceleration due to gravity. If the effects of air and the rotation of the earth can be neglected, $F_{net} = F_{grav}$.

Therefore

$$m_O g = G \frac{m_E m_O}{r_{EO}^2},$$

or

$$g = \frac{G m_E}{r_{EO}^2}. \tag{11.15}$$

Since G and the mass of the earth remain the same, no matter what object is dropped, we can conclude that, on the assumption that we may neglect the effects of nonsphericity, inhomogeneity, and rotation of the earth, the gravitational acceleration g varies only with the distance r_{EO} of the object from the center of the earth. Moreover, for objects falling to the ground from moderate heights, r_{EO} and consequently g change so little that for most practical purposes they can be regarded as constant. For example, if an object falls from a height of 600 ft to the surface of the earth (at which place r_{EO} is simply the earth's radius, or about 4000 mi), the change in r_{EO} is only about 1/300 of 1 percent, which is why in most problems g is assumed constant for all objects in free fall. Newton's mechanics yields Galileo's "reasonable" postulate. Now we can answer Sagredo: "The cause of the acceleration of heavy bodies" is the virtually constant gravitational force between them and the earth.

Thus we see that Newtonian mechanics explains Galileo's laws of projectile motion as well as Kepler's laws of planetary motion. By "explains" we mean simply that from certain basic axioms which have proved to yield reliable deductions, namely Newton's laws of motion and the principle of universal gravitation, the results of Kepler and Galileo can be derived. Celestial and terrestrial mechanics are thus brought together into a single unified system; this is the central point of the Newtonian synthesis.

PROBLEM 11.9. Use Eq. (11.15) to obtain an equation for the gravitational acceleration g' at a distance r'_{EO} from the center of the earth in terms of g (the value on earth) and the radius of the earth. What is the difference (in percent) between the values of g and g' for an object taken 1000 mi above the surface of the earth?

PROBLEM 11.10. A planet of mass m_P and radius r_P has a moon of mass m_M and radius r_M. How far from the center of the planet is the point P where the gravitational pulls on an object due to m_P and m_M would balance? First derive the general formula, then find the numerical distance for the case of our earth and moon.

PROBLEM 11.11. Newton considered how one might launch a projectile "from the top of a high mountain" so that it does not fall to the earth (Fig. 11.4). He went on to "imagine bodies to be projected in the direction of lines parallel

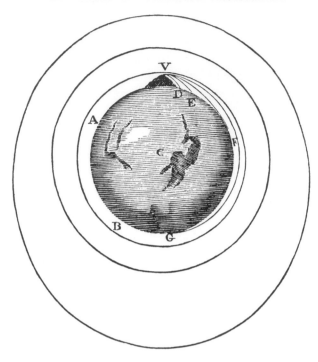

FIG. 11.4. Newton's presentation of the paths of projectiles launched horizontally from various heights above the earth's surface.

to the horizon from greater heights," i.e., "1000 or more miles," which would "go on revolving through the heavens in those orbits just as the planets do in their orbits." What conditions must be fulfilled for these motions to be possible?

PROBLEM 11.12.   State the principle of universal gravitation in its most general form.   Under what conditions is it presumed to apply?

11.10 Some influences on Newton's work. After our detailed consideration of Newton's work on universal gravitation, it is interesting to reexamine his personal attributes and beliefs.   What were the main intellectual tools, concepts, and attitudes that influenced him?   To deepen our insight into his achievements, we should at least summarize these influences, some of which we have already mentioned.

(1) Newton was a man of his time and not a "hardboiled" scientist of the 20th-century type.   He was not free from considerable traces of what we would today regard as pseudosciences.   In addition to some early interest in astrology, he seems to have spent much time in his "elaboratory," cooking potions that to us would smell more of alchemy than of chemistry—although the aim there, as in all of his activities, seems to have been the search for underlying general principles, rather than quick

practical gains. His belief in "absolutes" and his anthropomorphic conception of a Creator appear, by our present standards, to have very deeply affected some of his scientific writings. But here we touch on the secret of motivation for his scientific work, about which little is known.

(2) The decisive attitude throughout Newton's work was that the mechanics of celestial phenomena is explainable in terms of terrestrial concepts and laws.

(3) Fundamentally, Newton put his faith in the proximity and accessibility of natural law. We must add a word about his methodology. His debt to the pioneers of the new experimental science is clear; for example, he constructed ingenious pieces of equipment and performed experiments when the theory needed verification. But he also successfully combined this approach with the postulational-deductive method developed so well by Galileo and prominently employed by Descartes. With his mathematical powers enriching the experimental attitude, Newton set a clear, straight course for the methods of physical science.

(4) Not just Newton's attitude toward physical concepts but many of the concepts themselves, such as acceleration and force, had been developing for centuries; and the older ideas of force had recently been clarified by Robert Hooke and Christiaan Huygens. Galileo's work had firmly established the concept of inertia and had paved the way for the formulation of the first law of motion.

. (5) Apart from his own experiments, Newton took the necessary observational data from a great variety of sources. For example, Tycho Brahe was one of several astronomers, old and new, whose observations of the moon's motion he consulted. When he could not carry out his own measurements he knew whom to ask, and he corresponded widely with men like Flamsteed and Halley, both Royal Astronomers. There is evidence that he searched the scientific literature very carefully when he was in need of exact data, for example, on the radius of the earth.

(6) Lastly, we must not fail to note how fruitfully and exhaustively Newton's own specific contributions were used repeatedly throughout his work. The laws of motion and his mathematical inventions appear throughout his other work. But he was modest about his own achievements, and maintained that if he had seen further than others *"it is by standing upon the shoulders of Giants."*

SUPPLEMENTARY READING

BERLIN, I., *The age of enlightenment: the 18th century philosophers* (Houghton Mifflin and Mentor Book MD172, New American Library, 1956).

BURTT, E. A., *The metaphysical foundations of modern physical science: a historical and critical essay* (Routledge and Kegan Paul, 1924, and later; the Humanities Press, 1951). Especially Chapters 4, 5, and 7.

BUTTERFIELD, H., *The origins of modern science: 1300–1800* (G. Bell, London, 1949; Macmillan, 1951, and later), Chap. 8.

CLARK, G. N., *Science and social welfare in the age of Newton* (Oxford University Press, 1937, and later).

HAMPSHIRE, S., *The age of reason: the 17th century philosophers* (Houghton Mifflin and Mentor Book MD158, New American Library, 1956).

KEYNES, J. M., *Essays in biography* (Rupert Hart-David, London, 1951). Also reprinted in J. R. Newman's *The world of mathematics* (Simon and Schuster, 1956), v. 1. The great economist presents the picture based on Newton's own papers, of Newton as a Faust, a searcher for the key to *all* knowledge in science, theology, and magic.

KOYRÉ, A., *From the closed world to the infinite universe* (Johns Hopkins Press, 1957).

MAGIE, W. F., *A source book in physics* (McGraw-Hill, 1935), p. 92.

MUNITZ, M. K., ed., *Theories of the universe* (The Free Press, Glencoe, Illinois, 1957), pp. 202–224. Discussion, with excerpts, of the work of Newton and Huygens.

NEWTON, ISAAC, *Philosophiae naturalis principia mathematica*, trans. by A. Motte, revised by F. Cajori (University of California Press, 1934, and later printings). See particularly the beginning of Book Three, the General Scholium, and the Notes.

NUSSBAUM, F. L., *The triumph of science and reason, 1660–1685* (Harper, 1953), Chap. 1.

ORNSTEIN, M., *The role of scientific societies in the seventeenth century* (privately printed, 1913; University of Chicago Press, 1928, and later printings).

RANDALL, J. H., *The making of the modern mind* (Houghton Mifflin, 1926, and later), Chaps. 10–15.

SHAPLEY, H., and H. E. HOWARTH, *A source book in astronomy* (McGraw-Hill, 1929), pp. 74–93. Excerpts from the *Principia*.

Sir Isaac Newton, 1727–1927 (Williams and Wilkins, Baltimore, 1928). A collection of essays.

STIMSON, D., *Scientists and amateurs* (Henry Schuman, 1948). An account of the Royal Society and its members.

WOLF, A., *A history of science, technology and philosophy in the XVIth and XVIIth centuries* (Macmillan, 1935, 1950).

CHAPTER 12

SOME CONSEQUENCES OF NEWTON'S WORK

12.1 The numerical value of G. What amazed Newton's contemporaries and further increases our own admiration for him was not only the range and genius of his work on mechanics and the originality and elegance of his proofs, but also the detail with which he developed each idea to its fullest fruition. It took almost a century for science fully to comprehend, verify, and round out his work, and at the end of a second century an important scientist and philosopher still had to confess that, since Newton's time, no essentially new principle in mechanics had been stated, that everything which had been accomplished in mechanics since Newton's day had been a deductive, formal, mathematical development on the basis of his laws.

But one important problem left by Newton was the determination of the numerical value of G, the constant in the principle of universal gravitation. Solution of Eq. (11.6) for G yields

$$G = F_{\text{grav}} \frac{R^2}{m_1 m_2}. \qquad (12.1)$$

Evidently G could be computed if we had a way to measure the gravitational force F_{grav} between two objects of known masses m_1 and m_2 placed at a known distance R apart.

We might suspend two massive spherical objects from fixed points and then try to use spring balances to measure the force F_{grav} tending to pull them together (Fig. 12.1). However, for the relatively small masses that can be used in a laboratory experiment, the attracting force F_{grav} is so exceedingly small that delicate instruments and special techniques are needed even to detect its presence. Newton realized these difficulties and indeed suggested the two types of experiment that have since yielded reliable values of G.

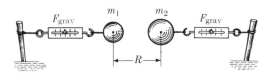

Fɪɢ. 12.1. The gravitational force between m_1 and m_2 might be measured by this method if it were not so small for objects of ordinary size.

The most serious technical problems of measurement were solved by Henry Cavendish (1731–1810) over 100 years after the publication of the *Principia*. He employed a *torsion balance* (Fig. 12.2), an instrument that had been devised somewhat earlier for precisely this purpose by his friend John Michell. In essence, the usually unnoticeably small forces of gravitation between objects of ordinary size can here be measured in terms of the known forces applied through the suspension to balance the mutual attraction of the neighboring spheres. Since each of the quantities on the right side of Eq. (12.1) is either known or measurable, G can be computed. Subsequent experimenters have progressively improved on the details of experimentation and on the results obtained by Cavendish, and today the accepted value of G is

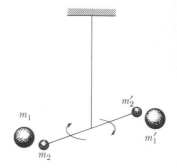

Fig. 12.2. Schematic diagram of the torsion balance used by Cavendish. When the large lead balls m_1 and m_1' were brought close to the small balls m_2 and m_2', their mutual gravitational attraction caused the vertical suspension to be twisted by a measurable amount. Then external, known forces could be applied to balance out and thereby measure the gravitational forces.

$$G = 6.67 \times 10^{-11} \text{ new·m}^2/\text{kgm}^2.$$

Once a value has been determined for G, it can be used to make a most revealing computation, often called "weighing the earth."

EXAMPLE 12.1. Compute the mass m_E of the earth.

Solution. If an object of mass m is at the earth's surface, the gravitational force F_{grav} on it is its weight, mg; and the distance between the object and the center of the earth is simply the earth's radius r_E, the mean value of which is 6.37×10^6 m (Appendix A). According to the principle of gravitation,

$$F_{\text{grav}} = G \frac{m m_E}{r_E^2}.$$

Solving for m_E and substituting known values, we have

$$m_E = \frac{F_{\text{grav}} r_E^2}{G m} = \frac{m g r_E^2}{G m} = \frac{g r_E^2}{G} = \frac{(9.80 \text{ m/sec}^2)(6.37 \times 10^6 \text{ m})^2}{(6.67 \times 10^{-11} \text{ new·m}^2/\text{kgm}^2)}$$

$$= 5.96 \times 10^{24} \text{ kgm} \doteq 7 \times 10^{21} \text{ tons.}$$

PROBLEM 12.1. What assumptions were made in solving Example 12.1? How accurate would you expect the result to be?

PROBLEM 12.2. (a) Two ships, each of mass 2×10^7 kgm, are 500 m apart. What is the gravitational attraction between them? (b) What is the gravitational attraction between you and your neighbor in the classroom? (c) How does this force compare with the gravitational pull which the earth exerts on you?

PROBLEM 12.3. Suppose that we are exploring the possibility of determining G with an arrangement similar to that shown in Fig. 12.1. The error inherent in the force-measuring devices available to us is about 2×10^{-4} new. If we were to use two similar, solid lead spheres placed almost in contact with each other, what is the smallest value that the radius of each sphere could have if G is to be determinable? (Density of lead is 1.132×10^4 kgm/m^3.) The foregoing computation is fairly representative of the sort that one must make while designing apparatus for experimentation.

PROBLEM 12.4. If by chance our unit of mass were not 1 kgm but a unit 3.88 times larger (call it 1 um), what would be the value of G in terms of this unit and the meter and the second? Does this result seem to teach any particular lesson?

Cavendish's results, and all the more accurate ones since, have shown that the value of G does indeed depend only on the units used, and not at all on the composition of the attracting objects; it is the same even for those of meteoric origin. Being disposed to apply terrestrial laws to celestial bodies, we extend our findings and maintain that in the absence of evidence to the contrary *all materials in the world, including the sun, planets, and satellites, are subject to the same principle of gravitation, involving the universal gravitational constant G.*

12.2 The mass of the celestial bodies. Once a value of G was at hand, the mass m_S of the sun could be computed by using the expression that had been found for the constant of proportionality K in Eq. (11.14), where $K = 4\pi^2/Gm_S$. We know that in Kepler's third law, $k = 1$ yr^2/1 AU^3 and that 1 AU $= 1.49 \times 10^{11}$ m, 1 yr $= 3.16 \times 10^7$ sec. If the theory of universal gravitation is correct, the empirical constant k and the derived constant K must have the same value, or $k = K$. Accordingly, $K = 4\pi^2/Gm_S$, or

$$m_S = \frac{4\pi^2}{Gk}$$

$$= \frac{4\pi^2}{(6.67 \times 10^{-11}\ \text{new·m}^2/\text{kgm}^2) \cdot [(3.16 \times 10^7\ \text{sec})^2/(1.49 \times 10^{11}\ \text{m})^3]}$$

$$= 2.0 \times 10^{30}\ \text{kgm} \doteq 2 \times 10^{27}\ \text{tons}.$$

The same sort of argument applies to a planet having a satellite of mass m_{St} moving about it in an orbit of average radius R_{St}. The gravitational force between planet and satellite is

$$F = G \frac{m_P m_{St}}{R_{St}^2}.$$

The centripetal force on the satellite is $F_c = m_{St} a_c$, and since the orbit is very nearly circular, the centripetal acceleration is v_{St}^2 / R_{St}. Just as in the case of the moon, we write $v_{St} = 2\pi R_{St} / T_{St}$, so that

$$F_c = m_{St} a_c = m_{St} \frac{v_{St}^2}{R_{St}} = m_{St} \frac{4\pi^2 R_{St}}{T_{St}^2}.$$

Equating these two expressions for the force, we have

$$G \frac{m_P m_{St}}{R_{St}^2} = m_{St} \frac{4\pi^2 R_{St}}{T_{St}^2},$$

or, upon solving for T_{St}^2,

$$T_{St}^2 = \left[\frac{4\pi^2}{G m_P} \right] R_{St}^3 = k' R_{St}^3. \tag{12.2}$$

This equation has precisely the same form as that for Kepler's third law, with the mass of the planet replacing the mass of the sun in the constant factor enclosed in brackets. A planet with its satellites does indeed form a miniature solar system, as Galileo had earlier pointed out for the case of Jupiter. Moreover, Eq. (12.2) permits calculation of the mass of any planet from observations of the motion of its satellite. (Other methods must be used to get the masses of planets that have no satellites.)

The masses of some of the celestial bodies are listed in Table 12.1.

Table 12.1. Mass relative to earth ($1.00 = 5.98 \times 10^{24}$ kgm).

Sun	333,000	Jupiter	318.4
Moon	1/81.3	Saturn	95.3
Mercury	0.054	Uranus	14.6
Venus	0.81	Neptune	17.3
Earth	1.00	Pluto	<0.1
Mars	0.107		

PROBLEM 12.5.   The innermost of Saturn's nine satellites, Mimas, has a fairly circular orbit of radius 187,000 km and a period of about 23 hr. Find the mass of Saturn.

EXAMPLE 12.2.   Book III of the *Principia* contains a summary of the observed periods and orbital radii of planets and satellites. For the first satellite of Jupiter, Newton lists a period of 1 day, 18 hr, 27 min, 34 sec, and gives four observations for the orbital radius: $5\frac{2}{3}$, 5.52, 5, and $5\frac{2}{3}$ (the unit of length being the radius r_J of Jupiter itself—not, of course, of its orbit). Compute the constant k' in the relation $T^2 = k'R^3$ for Jupiter's satellites.

Solution.   The average of the four observations of the orbital radius R_{St} is $5.5\,r_J$. Although the period is known with great precision, it is useless to employ this precise value when the orbital radius is known to not more than two significant figures. Thus, 1 day, 18 hr, 27 min, 34 sec $\doteq$ 1.8 days $= T_{St}$. Then

$$k' = \frac{T_{St}^2}{R_{St}^3} = \frac{(1.8\text{ day})^2}{(5.5r_J)^3} = \frac{0.019\text{ day}^2}{r_J^3}.$$

PROBLEM 12.6.   In the *Principia* Newton gives the periods of the 2nd, 3rd, and 4th satellites of Jupiter as 3 days, 13 hr, 13 min, 42 sec; 7 days, 3 hr, 42 min, 36 sec; and 16 days, 16 hr, 32 min, 9 sec. (a) Using the value of k' obtained in Example 12.2, compute the radii of the orbits of these three satellites in terms of Jupiter's own radius r_J. (b) The radius of Jupiter itself is 7.18×10^7 m; find the mass of Jupiter.

PROBLEM 12.7.   Describe, in quantitative detail, a possible method for obtaining the mass of our moon by sending to it an observable projectile which will be caught by the moon's gravitational pull and remains in an orbit around the moon as its satellite.

PROBLEM 12.8.   (a) Using the value of k' computed in Problem 9.4, compute the distance from the earth's center to an artificial satellite having a period of one day in its motion around the center of the earth. How far would the satellite be from the surface of the earth? (b) A satellite with this period could effectively stay always directly above one city on the equator. Why could it not be expected to remain directly above a city that is *not* on the equator?

12.3 Perturbations.

For the masses of the satellites themselves (including our own moon), and of the planets that boast of no satellites (Mercury, Venus), the calculations are not so simple. In the absence of a plan like that in Problem 12.7, these masses must be deduced from the relatively minor although complicated effects that we have neglected until now, namely, the gravitational interactions between one planet and another, or between one satellite and another. Because of such interactions, the path, say, of a planet differs slightly from the regular path it would have if the sun were the only attracting body. These slight deviations due to the pulls of bodies other than the central, parent body are called *perturbations*. Except for the purpose of mass determinations and the computation of accurate astronomical and nautical tables, these perturbations and other similar complications can usually be ignored. However, from the analysis of the perturbations, the moon's mass, to cite one example, was found to be about $\frac{1}{81}$ of the earth's.

We may be tempted to marvel that these secondary effects, which are so important in the long run, were too small to be observed earlier and thus perhaps to confuse the original investigators. Newton, for example, did not have to consider perturbations in his initial calculations. Extreme accuracy of observation, although axiomatic in experimental science, sometimes does not become fruitful and important until the more elaborate theory for handling the fine detail of data is developed. But in the present instance there is an extra twist: if the perturbations were appreciably larger, this would not merely have handicapped the work of Copernicus, Kepler, and Newton, but we might well have no solar system to contemplate at all; it probably would not have lasted these billions of years without catastrophic collisions among its members.

PROBLEM 12.9. Using the computed values for the masses of the earth, moon, and sun, the distances of moon and sun from the earth, and the fact that the angle subtended at our eye by the diameter of either the moon or the sun is about 0.5°, find the average densities of the earth, the moon, and the sun. (The density of most rocks is about 3×10^3 kgm/m^3.)

PROBLEM 12.10. The diameter of the moon, as computed from observations, is about 3500 km. Its mass is given in Table 12.1. (a) Compute the gravitational acceleration at the surface of the moon. (b) If a man weighs 160 lbf (= 712 new) on the earth, what would he weigh on the moon? (c) If his jump on earth can be up to 5 ft high, what is the corresponding figure on the moon?

12.4 Comets. These celestial objects, whose dreaded appearance had been interpreted as sure signs of disaster as late as Newton's era, were now shown to be nothing but passing clouds of material that are subject to gravitational forces. They become visible by reflected light while near the sun. One of the most famous comets is Halley's, named after Edmond Halley, who studied it carefully when it appeared in 1682 (Fig. 12.3). He identified it with the comets of 1607 and 1531 and, realizing that its orbit and hence its period might be somewhat perturbed by the gravitational attractions of planets, went on to identify it with comets observed in 1456, 1301, 1145, and 1066. Later astronomers have found historical records of every return to perihelion back to the year 87 B.C. Halley predicted its return early in 1759, and more precise computations by Clairaut in the 18th century fixed the date of perihelion passage within a month of the actual event as subsequently observed. This was heralded as another significant triumph of Newtonian science. There have been two returns since then, and the next is expected in 1986.

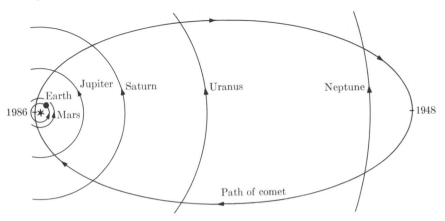

FIG. 12.3. Path of Halley's comet.

12.5 The shapes of planets and satellites.

12.5 The shapes of planets and satellites. Newton reasoned that the shape assumed by each planet or satellite during its formation should be spherical, because the mutual gravitational attractions of the separate parts would tend to pull the initially dispersed or fluid material into a compact sphere. Furthermore, although a nonrotating body might then indeed form a perfect sphere, he saw that a body rotating about an axis ought to assume the shape of an oblate spheroid; that is, it ought to bulge at the equator and flatten at the poles. This prediction has been amply verified by telescopic observations (see Fig. 12.4 for the case of Jupiter). Indeed, from the relative magnitude of the equatorial bulge, the period of rotation about the axis can be calculated.

FIG. 12.4. The planet Jupiter.

For the earth, Newton predicted the same effect of flattening at the poles, and later, accurate measurements showed that the diameter of the earth from pole to pole actually is 27 mi less than across the equatorial plane. As one consequence, an object weighs somewhat less at the equator than at the poles, owing to the greater distance between the center of the earth and the equator.*

PROBLEM 12.11.   Draw an exaggerated diagram of a flattened sphere to represent the rotating earth. Show that when an object, for example a bob on a plumb line, hangs freely from a spring balance at latitude 45°, the balance does not register the true gravitational pull F_{grav} on the body, and the plumb line does not point to the precise center of the earth. (These discrepancies are, in usual practice, small enough to be neglected.)

PROBLEM 12.12.   According to one of the speculative theories on the origin of our moon, it may have been formed of material thrown off by the spinning earth. How fast would the earth have had to rotate at that time to make this picture plausible?

If we descend below the surface of the earth, as into a deep mine, g is found to become progressively *smaller*. This does not mean that the law of gravitation fails to hold for objects that are below the earth's surface. Instead, the law predicts that there should be just this reduction in the gravitational attraction because the earth overhead is now attracting any object upward, decreasing the downward force. Newtonian mechanics predicts that, at least in the idealized case, all portions of the earth *farther from the center* than the object may be disregarded, since collectively they produce a net force of zero.

PROBLEM 12.13.   By how much would you expect the weight of an object to decrease if it could be placed (a) halfway between the surface and the center of the earth? (b) at the center of the earth? (c) halfway between the earth and the moon (full distance $\doteq 4 \times 10^8$ m)?

12.6 The tides.   The phenomenon of the tides of the sea, so important to navigators, tradesmen, and explorers through the ages, had remained a puzzle despite the efforts of such men as Galileo to discover their cause. Newton, by applying the law of gravitation, was able to explain at least the main features—the diurnal high tide and the semimonthly spring tide (maximum high tide). He recognized that the moon, and to a lesser extent the other celestial bodies, would pull on the ocean and tend to "heap up"

---

*This difference is small, but another effect joins in to diminish still more the observed acceleration of a freely falling body at the equator, namely, the large velocity of any object in that region (about 1000 mi/hr) owing to the rotation of the earth about its axis (see discussion on centripetal force, Section 5.5, and Problem 5.21).

the waters. Newton showed that the bulge of water is raised at the same time on *both* sides of the globe, and does not stay directly under the moon; instead, owing to the rotation of the earth, the bulge is always a little ahead of the moon (Fig. 12.5). Thus high tide occurs a few hours after the moon's passage across the local meridian. The sun is responsible for a similar though smaller effect, which either increases or decreases the tide level depending on the relative positions of the sun and the moon.

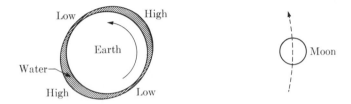

FIG. 12.5. Tides caused by the moon. The earth is to be imagined as rotating in this (much exaggerated) envelope of water, causing the bulge of water to be displaced. The high tide thus stays a little ahead of the moon.

The exact and detailed features of this complex phenomenon depend to a great extent on the topography of shore line and ocean floor. Long series of actual observations establish the rules for predicting exact times and levels of the tides at each locality. In passing, we should note that the "solid" earth has similarly explained tides, large enough so that they must be allowed for in certain astronomical and other refined experiments. It is just such a tidal effect that offers one of the methods for the approximate calculation of the mass of the moon.*

12.7 The discovery of additional planets. One of the most intriguing aspects of Newton's work still remains to be told, namely, the role played by his law of gravitation in the discovery of new planets long after Newton's death. Sir Oliver Lodge wrote:

> The explanation by Newton of the observed facts of the motions of the moon, the way he accounted for precession and nutation and for the tides, the way in which Laplace [whose mathematical work extended Newton's calculations] explained every detail of the planetary motions—these achievements may seem to the professional astronomer equally, if not more, striking and wonderful; . . . But to predict in the solitude of the study, with no weapons other than pen, ink, and paper, an unknown and enormously distant world, to calculate its orbit when as yet it had never been seen, and to be able to say to a practical astronomer, "Point your telescope in such a direction at such a

---

*For further details on the forces generating tides, see the references in the Supplementary Reading list at the end of this chapter.

time, and you will see a new planet hitherto unknown to man"—this must always appeal to the imagination with dramatic intensity ... (*Pioneers of science*, 1910)

The events leading to just such a development began one night in 1781 when William Herschel (1738–1822) of Bath, England, an extraordinarily energetic mixture of professional musician and gifted amateur astronomer, was searching the sky with his homemade, 10-ft telescope. For years he had patiently looked at and re-examined every corner of the heavens, and he was becoming well-known among astronomers for his discoveries of new stars, nebulae, and comets. On that particular night he observed a hitherto uncatalogued object of such "uncommon appearance" that he suspected it to be a new comet. Through the Royal Society the news spread. As observations continued night after night, it became evident that this was not a comet but a previously undiscovered planet, more than 14 times larger in mass than the earth, requiring some 84 years to move once around the sun. It was about twice as far from the sun as Saturn, considered until then the outermost member of the solar family. Thus, quite without reference to theoretical physics, Uranus was discovered. It provided an unsuspected and sensational widening of the ancient horizon. John Keats mirrored the impact of this announcement on Herschel's contemporaries when, seeking to describe his emotions on first looking into Chapman's *Homer*, he wrote:

> Then I felt like some watcher of the skies,
> When a new planet swims into his ken.

At the time of Herschel's discovery, it was known how to compute the elliptic orbit of a planet from a few widely separated observations of its varying positions. Also, the expected small deviations from the true ellipse owing to the perturbing force of the other planets were accurately predictable on the basis of Newton's law of gravitation. The expected orbit of Uranus was thus mapped out, and all went well for many years. But by 1830 evidence was accumulating that Uranus was misbehaving, that the assumptions on which its schedule had been worked out were in need of revision.

Some astronomers suggested that Newton's law of gravitation perhaps did not hold precisely for distances as large as that between Uranus and the sun, but they had nothing better to offer (and, as has been pointed out, a useful theory generally is not overthrown when it fails to account for isolated facts, but only when there is a more satisfactory theory to replace it). Others thought that a hitherto undiscovered comet or a more distant planet might be producing additional perturbations in Uranus' orbit; they too were merely guessing and offered no concrete quantitative predictions.

The idea of an undiscovered planet beyond Uranus intrigued John C. Adams, a young undergraduate at Cambridge University. He undertook the immensely difficult mathematical task of calculating the positions of this suspected perturbing body from the observations of Uranus' motion and the assumption that Newton's law of gravitation applied to the interaction between the hypothetical planet and Uranus. The calculations were completed in 1845, two years after his graduation. For the necessary confirmation, Adams wrote to the Royal Observatory at Greenwich, asking that its powerful telescope be used to search for the hypothetical new planet beyond Uranus. Since Adams was an unknown mathematician, his request was at first not taken seriously; it would have meant interrupting current work to undertake a search that might well have been long and fruitless.

A few months later, another young man, J. J. Leverrier in France, published the result of similar, independent calculations, that placed the suspected planet in nearly the same positions as those deduced by Adams. Leverrier sent his own prediction to the head of the observatory at Berlin, who, having in hand a new star map to aid in the search, on the very evening of the letter's arrival himself looked for the new planet and found it at very nearly its predicted position. Thus *Neptune* was added to the solar system in 1846. This, coming more than a century after Newton's death, was indeed a triumph of the law of gravitation! And incidentally, these circumstances also sufficed to keep disputes about priority of discovery alive for many decades between partisans for Adams and for Leverrier.

Neptune, in turn, was closely watched. Its mean orbital radius is about 30 AU, and therefore its period as given by Kepler's law is 164 years. But in time, as astronomical observations became more refined, additional perturbations were observed for both Neptune and Uranus that could not be accounted for in terms of known forces; this led naturally to the hypothesis that there was still another undiscovered planet. An arduous 25-year long search yielded the discovery of *Pluto* in 1930, announced on the double anniversary of Herschel's discovery of Uranus and also the birthday of Percival Lowell, whose calculations had led to the search for Pluto and who had founded the observatory in Arizona at which the discovery was made.

Another astronomer, W. H. Pickering, had made independent calculations and predictions of Pluto's position as far back as 1909, and had initiated a telescopic search for the planet at Mount Wilson Observatory in California. Nothing was found then; but after the discovery at the Lowell Observatory in 1930, the old Mount Wilson photographs were re-examined, and they showed that Pluto would have been discovered in 1919 if its image had not fallen directly on a small flaw in the photographic emulsion! This story dramatizes the frequently forgotten possibility that for every overpublicized discovery which is made by "accident," without elaborate preparations, there may well be an equally important discovery which, also by accident, *failed* to be made despite careful research.

12.8 The Bode-Titus law. The result of Kepler's long search for regularity in the solar system, his laws of planetary motion, showed that there exists a simple relation between the speed and the orbital radius of each planet, but it left unanswered the question why a given planet does not move in some other possible orbit with a correspondingly different speed. Why, for example, is the earth not in a larger orbit, closer to that of Mars, with a correspondingly smaller speed than its present one? Nothing in Kepler's or Newton's work predicted that the observed orbit was in any way unique or necessary. To find an explanation for the observed spacing of the orbits was a challenging problem, and it eventually led to the discovery of an empirical rule by J. E. Bode (1747–1826), following a suggestion by his friend J. D. Titus. This strange and perplexing rule, known as "Bode's law" or as the "Bode-Titus law," either describes an extraordinary set of coincidences or else represents an entirely new regularity in the solar system, symptomatic of a possible physical mechanism responsible for the spacing of the planetary orbits.

In the statement of this law, each planet is identified by a number n that represents its ordinal position with respect to the sun: $n = 1$ for Mercury, $n = 2$ for Venus, $n = 3$ for the earth, etc. Then, according to the Bode-Titus law, the mean radius $\overline{R}$ of a planet's orbit is given by

$$\overline{R} \text{ (in AU)} = 0.4 + (0.3 \times 2^{n-2}). \tag{12.3}$$

But this equation is found to work *only if* (1) for Mercury, the term in parentheses is made zero, and (2) the number 5 is skipped in assigning values of n to the different planets (i.e., n for Jupiter is not 5 but 6). Some observed and predicted values for $\overline{R}$ appear in Table 12.2; the correspondences are certainly striking.

Because the number $n = 5$ could not be used for any known planet, Bode boldly suggested that the disproportionately large space existing between Mars and Jupiter might harbor an unnoticed planet for which $n = 5$ and which, *according to this rule*, would have a mean orbital radius of 2.8 AU.

PROBLEM 12.14. Verify that the Bode-Titus law yields 2.8 AU for the mean orbital radius of a hypothetical planet with $n = 5$.

Here was a chance to confirm whether the rule was anything more than coincidence and fantasy! Bode was convinced that a search would reveal the suspected planet, and he wrote, in a manner which reminds us of

Table 12.2. Distances of the first six planets from the sun.

Planet	Assigned value of n	Mean distance $\bar{R}$ from the sun (AU)	
		Observed value	Value from Bode-Titus law
Mercury	1	0.39	0.4
Venus	2	0.72	0.7
Earth	3	1.0	1.0
Mars	4	1.5	1.6
Jupiter	6	5.2	5.2
Saturn	7	9.5	10.0

the motivations of many scientists, "From Mars outward there follows a space . . . in which, up to now, no planet has been seen. Can we believe that the Creator of the world has left this space empty? Certainly not!"

At first no one discovered anything in that seemingly forsaken gap, and interest in the law must have lagged; one might say it did not fulfill the criterion of stimulation of further discoveries. Then, nine years after Bode's announcement, came Herschel's discovery of distant Uranus, beyond Saturn. With $n = 8$ as a logical number to assign to Uranus, the law predicted a mean orbital radius of 19.6 AU, and this was within about 2% of the value based on subsequent observation!

This agreement directed attention to the other predictions inherent in Bode's law, and the search for the "missing" planet with $n = 5$ was renewed with vigor. In time, the first result came, but, as so often in science, only as the by-product of other research. In 1801, the Sicilian astronomer G. Piazzi, while compiling a new star catalog, was looking in the sky for a star which, as it turned out later, had been entered upon an old star map through a printer's error. On the first night of the 19th century he noticed a new "star." Within a few days he detected a displacement of it relative to the fixed stars, which was evidence that the new celestial object was in the solar system. In the exciting months that followed, astronomers and mathematicians joined forces to compute the orbit of the foundling, now christened *Ceres*. It was a disappointingly puny object (less than 500 miles in diameter), but the calculated orbital radius was 2.77 AU, within about 1% of the value predicted by the Bode-Titus law for the "missing planet" in that region between Mars and Jupiter!

Even while Ceres was being hailed as the long-sought planet, another, smaller one was discovered with about the same orbit, and then still others, all smaller than Ceres. Today, the paths of almost 2000 of these minor planets (*planetoids* or *asteroids*) have been plotted; some orbits are very eccentric, and nearly all lie in the region between Mars and Jupiter. Evidently all or most of them spring from one family with a common history. Perhaps they are fragments that were forming into one planet when its evolution was somehow interrupted, or possibly they are the shattered remnants of a larger planet. We might speculate that two or more planets in the process of establishing orbits near each other eventually collided "because," according to the Bode-Titus law, only one orbit is permissible in that region. This line of reasoning would put the empirical law into a new light; we might be tempted to search for other indications that the law expresses simply the series of dynamically possible, stable orbits for single planets.

The discovery of these planetoids bore out Bode's ideas so strikingly that it was natural to apply his rule when the suspicion of a planet beyond Uranus first arose. The next value for n being 9, the corresponding orbital radius would be $0.4 + 0.3 \times 2^{9-2}$ AU, that is, 38.8 AU. With this lead, Adams and Leverrier had proceeded to calculate the orbital position of the hypothetical planet. When Neptune was found and its observed course plotted, the orbital radius turned out to be some 20% smaller than the Bode-Titus value—the first marked deficiency in the law, but luckily not so serious as to invalidate the calculations that led to Neptune's discovery. Later, when Pluto was found, its orbital radius of 39.46 AU was much more seriously at variance with the value of 77.2 AU obtained when 10 is substituted for n in Eq. (12.3). Either we must accept the Bode-Titus law as having a more limited role than was initially hoped for it, or we must search for a reason why it does not hold for the outermost planets, and for a modification to make it serviceable there also.

The latter alternative would seem to be the more fruitful one, but it must remain unfulfilled until we can explain this empirical, we might almost say numerological, law on some broader basis. Unless we know *why the Bode-Titus law holds for the planets up to Uranus*, we cannot know *why it breaks down beyond Uranus*. A solution to this problem has been sought for a long time and may now be forthcoming, for recent work on astronomical theory has given hope that the law can be explained (derived from) the laws of mechanics. As noted before, the mutual perturbations of planets over billions of years would leave only a few orbits as stable possibilities, and some cosmologists and astrophysicists at present seem to be near the proof that the laws of mechanics predict such stability for the orbits that are actually observed. But this is a most difficult problem in theoretical astrophysics which from time to time has challenged some of the greatest scientists during the past 100 years.

PROBLEM 12.15. (a) What can the Bode-Titus law predict concerning a hypothetical planet between the sun and Mercury? (On the basis of some rather doubtful observations made about a century ago it was thought that there was a planet in this region; it was given the name *Vulcan*, but has not been found since.)   (b) Suppose it were announced that an additional small planet had just been observed between Jupiter and Saturn. Can you suggest a way to recast the Bode-Titus law into some other form so as to take this new planet into account?   (c) Recently it has been suggested that the planet Pluto originally was a moon of Neptune, but was wrenched into its present orbit by perturbations. Comment on this hypothesis on the basis of Bode's law. (d) Is the Bode-Titus law true? Is it false?

PROBLEM 12.16. Assume that there is somewhere a planetary system other than our own, in which the distances from the central star to the four nearest planets are as follows:

$$\text{Ordinal number of planet } (n): \quad 1 \quad 2 \quad 3 \quad 4$$
$$\text{Radius of orbit, in AU } (R): \qquad 3 \quad 6 \quad 11 \quad 18$$

(a) Formulate a rule or "law," analogous to Eq. (12.3), that will relate R to n for each planet of this system. (b) At what distance R would you expect the next, or fifth, planet to be? Comment on your "law" if this expectation is fulfilled, and if it is not.

12.9 Beyond the solar system.

Turning now to a very ambitious problem, we ask: Do Newton's laws, so serviceable and fruitful within the solar system, continue to apply beyond, among the "fixed" stars?

To Copernicus or Galileo this question would have been meaningless, for it was not until Newton's time that relative motions among the stars were noticed (by Halley). In fact, our whole solar system was found to be moving with respect to the distant stars. This motion is not the annual parallax of the stars, owing to motion of the earth around the sun, but is a *proper motion* of the entire solar system. In 1803, William Herschel discovered that some star neighbors rotate about each other ("double stars"), and his son, John, showed that their motions are compatible with the assumption that the gravitational forces between them are the same as those between members of the solar system.

This new picture of a moving universe places our solar system in the uncrowded company of billions of other stars (suns) and their possible attendants. A whole cloud of stars forms our *galaxy*, a roughly lentil-shaped region about 10^5 light-years* across and some 1500 light-years thick, though not sharply defined (Fig. 12.6). Our own planetary system, located at a distance of about 30,000 light-years from the galactic center, is rather lost in the whole structure.

---

*One light-year is the *distance* over which light can travel in one year, i.e., 9.5×10^{12} km, or 5.9×10^{12} mi. The values cited for the galactic dimensions give only the general order of magnitude.

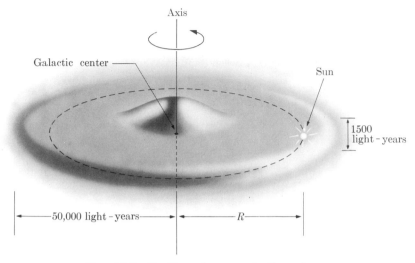

FIG. 12.6. Position of our sun in the galaxy.

Such a picture evokes the thought that the mutual gravitational attractions of the stars should cause our galaxy slowly to gather together and coalesce into one solid mass at the center. This does not happen; the stars are not moving toward a common center, and consequently two explanations have been advanced: either the law of gravitation is not applicable beyond our solar system or, in analogy with the solar system itself, the whole galaxy is spinning about its axis, "distracting" the threatening gravitational attractions by making them do the chores of centripetal forces. On examination, the second explanation actually seems to hold.* Our own solar system is revolving about the galactic center with a speed of about 150 mi/sec. According to our present view, the edge of the whole galaxy, whose framework we see as the Milky Way, completes one revolution about the center in perhaps a quarter-billion years.

Now let us sketch out a bold computation. If Newton's laws hold on such a scale, we should be able to compute the approximate mass m_G of the whole galaxy from the rate of revolution of our own sun about the galactic center. We shall neglect the effect upon our sun of those parts of our galaxy that are farther from the galactic center than the sun is (Fig. 12.6). Then we may say that the centripetal force F_c on the sun is, by Eq. (5.12),

$$F_c = m_S \frac{4\pi^2 R}{T^2},$$

*For modern views of the structure of our galaxy and the universe beyond, see the Supplementary Reading list at the end of this chapter.

where m_S is the mass of the sun, R is the radius of the sun's orbit about the galactic center, and T is its period of revolution. The gravitational pull exerted on the sun by the mass m_G of that part of the galaxy closer to the center than the sun and acting approximately as if all this mass were located at the center, is, by Eq. (11.6),

$$F_{\text{grav}} = G \, \frac{m_S m_G}{R^2}.$$

If it is this force F_{grav} that supplies the centripetal force F_c, then we write

$$m_S \, \frac{4\pi^2 R}{T^2} = G \, \frac{m_S m_G}{R^2},$$

or

$$m_G = \frac{4\pi^2 R^3}{GT^2}.$$

Thus the galactic mass can be computed, for we know, as the result of other arguments based on experimental observation, that the distance R is about 3×10^4 light-years, and the period T is about 2×10^8 yr.

PROBLEM 12.17. Show that the mass of our galaxy, on the basis of the afore-mentioned assumptions, is approximately 10^{43} kgm.

It turns out that this calculated mass is more than twice that of all the stars which our galaxy is likely to hold, even on the most generous estimate. Either our assumptions are poor, or there is a large amount of matter in the galaxy in addition to that in the stars. Our assumptions were rather crude, but short of abandoning the principle of gravitation, no amount of tinkering with those admittedly qualitative details will explain the excess in calculated mass. So we turn to the alternative; and it is rewarding, for there is much evidence that our galaxy does contain matter not consolidated into suns and attendant planets, namely, nebulae, interstellar dust, and rarefied gases.

There are many such clues to the presence of this tenuous matter that would rescue the Newtonian laws, one being its effect on starlight. The density of interstellar matter is inconceivably small, perhaps only a few atoms per cubic centimeter, far less than for the best vacuums obtainable in the laboratory. But a galaxy represents an enormous volume, and an estimation of the total distributed material supplements the known star masses by about the missing amount. Thus our confidence in the principle of universal gravitation is extended to galactic proportions.

Beyond our galaxy, starting at a distance of about 30 times its diameter, we find other galaxies scattered through space, as far as our biggest telescopes can reach. These island universes seem to be comparable in size

FIG. 12.7. A spiral nebula, M-51 in Canes Venatici, about a million light-years from our own. (Photographed with the 200-inch telescope on Palomar Mountain.)

to ours, and often have the appearance of a spiral or pinwheel (Fig. 12.7), which is probably the shape of our own galaxy. These distant galaxies appear to be receding from us and from one another with a speed of 100 to 1000 mi/sec. At the same time, they are spinning at rates close to our own, and hence may be assumed to have similar masses and to be describable by the same laws of mechanics. With this extension of the principle of gravitation to the expanding Universe, "to all the distance of nature's infinitude," we find ourselves near to the limit of our imagination, and at the height of admiration for so universal a principle. There have been few products of human genius to match its ambitious promise and its exciting consequences.

12.10 "I frame no hypotheses." Newton's work not only explains Kepler's empirical laws, but predicts and explains a wealth of other phenomena, both terrestrial and celestial. Since the main purposes of any theory are to predict, explain, and summarize, Newton's work appears to us today as eminently satisfactory. However, there remained one feature which gravely bothered Newton's contemporaries and indeed Newton himself. How could one account for gravitation itself? Is there not some intervening medium between objects that somehow transmits their mutual pull in a mechanical fashion?

The very raising of these questions reflects how firmly the mind is committed to physical models and mechanical explanations, and how unsatisfied we are at first with mathematical, abstract arguments. Rather than accept "action at a distance" (the conception of one object exerting a force on another without the agency of a medium between them), most scientists at and after Newton's time came to think of all space as filled with some kind of omnipresent fluid; and this fluid, apart from being so tenuous as to be undetectable by any experiment, still had to be strong and versatile enough to communicate all gravitational forces, and incidentally perhaps also serve to propagate light and electric and magnetic effects.

The search for some such medium was long and the arguments loud. At the end of Book III of the *Principia*, Newton put his often misinterpreted remarks:

> But hitherto I have not been able to discover the cause of those properties of gravity from phenomena [observation and experimentation], and I frame no hypotheses . . . And to us it is enough that gravity does really exist and act according to the laws which we have explained, and abundantly serves to account for all the motions of the celestial bodies, and of our sea.

This is a famous statement, clearly an echo of Galileo's admonition in very similar circumstances (Section 2.6). By saying in essence "I propose no hypotheses concerning the cause of gravitation," Newton flatly rejected any responsibility for making intuitively plausible a theory that had already amply proved its worth in a wealth of predictions. He was wary of introducing into the *Principia* hypotheses (for example, that of a mechanical ether) beyond those needed to derive the laws and observations. The mathematical law of gravitation explained and predicted a wide range of observations; that had to be enough justification for accepting it. Newton agreed that it was an important problem whether the law of gravitation might eventually be explained in terms of something still more fundamental, but this, Newton suggested, he could not show at that time. Nor did he feel that his theory suffered by this inability. The purpose of physical theory *per se* is not to find ultimate causes but to explain observables in terms of a consistent and fruitful scheme of concepts and derivations based on observation, and *that* he had done.

Newton's refusal, in the absence of experimental clues, to propose a mechanism by which two bodies separated in space might be physically linked together does not mean that he reverted to another earlier device, namely, dismissal of the question by inventing some principle of gravity innate in matter, such as might well have satisfied a medieval scholar. This is brought out in another connection in a passage in Query 31 of his treatise on *Opticks*, written by Newton half a century after he had completed most of his work on gravitation:

> And the *Aristotelians* gave the name of occult qualities, not to manifest qualities, but to such qualities only as they supposed to lie hid in bodies, and to be the unknown causes of manifest effects: such as would be the causes of gravity, and of magnetick and electrick attractions, and of fermentations, if we should suppose that these forces or actions arose from qualities unknown to us, and uncapable of being discovered and made manifest. Such occult qualities put a stop to the improvement of natural philosophy, and therefore of late years have been rejected. To tell us that every species of things is endow'd with an occult specifick quality by which it acts and produces manifest effects, is to tell us nothing: but to derive two or three general Principles of Motion from phænomena, and afterwards to tell us how the properties and actions of all corporeal things follow from those manifest principles, would be a very great step in philosophy, though the causes of those principles were not yet discover'd: And therefore I scruple not to propose the Principles of Motion above-mention'd, they being of very general extent, and leave their causes to be found out.

Nevertheless, the question of how one body can interact with another across empty space has an obstinate appeal for our picture-seeking minds. This helps to explain the great following commanded by Descartes' vortex theory; it provided a picture of a universe completely filled with a whirlpool of material corpuscles acting on one another and on the planets by simple physical contact (Fig. 12.8). Here we have a conceptual scheme that was plausible and easy to grasp. However, as was fully appreciated by Newton though not by the majority of his contemporaries, it failed to agree quantitatively with observations; specifically, Kepler's laws of planetary motion were derivable consequences of Newtonian mechanics but not of Descartes' theory. In the second edition of the *Principia*, in 1713, Newton found it necessary to add a few sentences to show that the vortex theory contradicted Kepler's laws.

Yet the inherent appeal of Descartes' picture to common sense growing out of muscular experiences made Newton's lack of an intuitive "reason" for planetary motion stand out glaringly. Newton had to spend much time in upholding his system against the Cartesians and also in resisting demands within his own camp for a metaphysical or theological postulate concerning the "cause" of gravitation. He declared again and again that he was neither able nor willing "to adjudge natural causes" of gravitation. This large step toward the modern conception of what is required of

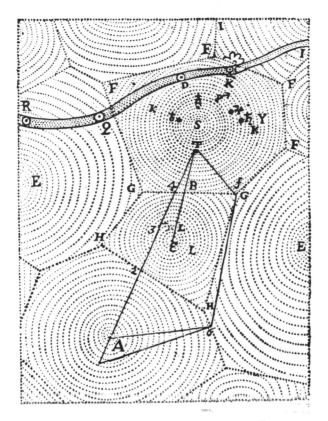

Fig. 12.8. A drawing by which Descartes illustrated his theory, in which all of space was presumed to be filled with matter. A comet, passing among the vortices, is briefly carried along by the general motion in the solar system around S.

physical theory is all the more remarkable because Newton, who later regarded himself as much theologian as scientist, might have been led here to introduce an explicit theistic hypothesis.

12.11 Newton's place in modern science. So impressive were the victories of Newtonian mechanics that, in the early part of the 18th century, there spread a mechanistic world view which asserted that man's confident intellect could eventually reduce *all* phenomena and problems to the level of mechanical interpretations. The development of this new view through the extrapolation of the findings of science to philosophy was carried out mainly by philosophers, and it had important effects on economics, the "science of man," religion, and political theory. Everywhere the success of the work of Newton and the Newtonians was one of the strong influences on the concerns and methods of the time.

One consequence of the mechanistic attitude, lingering on to the present day, was a widespread belief that Newton's laws (and other fundamental physical laws developed later) made possible the determination of the whole future of the universe and each of its parts if only the several positions, velocities, and accelerations of all particles at any one instant were given. It was a veiled way of saying that everything worth knowing was understandable in terms of physics, and that all of physics was essentially known. Today we honor Newtonian mechanics for less all-inclusive but more valid reasons. The *Principia* historically provided the basis of most of our physics and no small part of our technology, and Newton's methods were the most fruitful in guiding the work in the physical sciences in the subsequent two centuries.

Today we also recognize that Newton's mechanics, despite its breathtaking scope of applicability, holds in its stated form only within certain definable regions of nature. For example, although the principle of universal gravitation may be applicable *within* each galaxy, it is possible that the gravitational forces operating between galaxies are repulsive rather than attractive; this was one explanation advanced for the larger speeds with which the more distant systems are receding from our own. Even within the solar system, there are a few small discrepancies between predictions and facts. The most famous concerns the position of Mercury at perihelion, that is, at its position of closest approach to the sun; the observed position shifts progressively from the predicted position by some 43 seconds of arc per century. Similar small failures of Newtonian mechanics exist for the paths of recurring comets that come close to the sun. And, as we shall see in Part VIII, at the other end of the scale, among atoms and subatomic particles, it has been necessary to develop a whole set of non-Newtonian concepts for these submicroscopic realms.

These various difficulties, it must be noted, cannot be traced to small inaccuracies in the algebraic law of gravitation, for example, to the possibility that the exponent in the expression Gm_1m_2/R^2 might not be exactly 2, but slightly larger or smaller. On the contrary, as in the case of Kepler's finding that the system of Copernicus did not account accurately for the detail and "fine structure" of planetary motion, we are here again confronted with the necessity for scrutinizing our fundamental assumptions. Such studies have so far brought no single revision that can account for all the deviations from classical predictions. At each extreme of scale, Newtonian science blends into other conceptual schemes specifically designed for these regions. At present it is joined at one end with relativistic mechanics which, among many other achievements, provides relationships holding for objects moving with extremely high speeds or passing close to other bodies of very large mass. At the other end Newtonian science borders on quantum mechanics, which gives us a physics of atoms and molecules. As for the middle domain, Newtonian mechanics still describes the world of ordinary experience and of "classical" physics as accurately and satisfyingly as it did always.

Additional Problems

12.18. Would Newton's laws of motion, as usually stated, hold in a geocentric system like Ptolemy's? (*Hint:* The term "motion along a straight line" in Newton's first law refers to a line in space such as might be drawn from one relatively "fixed" star to another.) If they do not, explain why not and whether it is plausible that equivalent postulates might be formulated to describe motions in a geocentric system.

12.19. To what man (or men) do each of the following phrases apply? (a) Attempted to deduce the relative orbital radii of planets merely from the properties of numbers or of geometric forms. (b) Made use of epicycles. (c) Made use of equants. (d) Made use of the ellipse to represent planetary orbits. (e) Believed in the heliocentric (sun-centered) planetary system. (f) Could not account for the change in apparent brightness of planets. (g) Knew the numerical value of the universal gravitational constant G.

12.20. Turn to page 104, where five objectives for all of Part III are listed. Examine each objective and illustrate how it was developed in Part III.

Supplementary Reading

Bok, B. J., and P. F. Bok, *The milky way* (Harvard University Press, 1957).

Boynton, H., *The beginnings of modern science* (Walter J. Black, 1948), pp. 104–117 on Cavendish and Herschel.

Brinton, C., *The shaping of the modern mind* (Mentor Book M98, New American Library, 1953), Chaps. 3 and 4.

Butterfield, H., *The origins of modern science: 1300–1800* (G. Bell, London, 1949; Macmillan, 1951, and later).

Cassirer, E., *The philosophy of enlightenment* (Princeton University Press, 1951; Beacon Press, 1955).

Kemble, E. C., *An introduction to physical science* (Wiley, in preparation), Chaps. 7 and 9. Includes discussion of tides and consideration of dynamics of elliptical orbits.

Kline, M., *Mathematics in western culture* (Oxford University Press, 1953).

Knickerbocker, W. S., ed., *Classics of modern science* (Knopf, 1927), Chap. 15 on Herschel.

Koyré, A., *From the closed world to the infinite universe* (Johns Hopkins Press, 1957).

MATHER, K. F., and S. L. MASON, *Source book in geology* (McGraw-Hill, 1939), pp. 103–107. Cavendish experiment.

MUNITZ, M. K., *Space, time and creation: philosophical aspects of scientific cosmology* (The Free Press, Glencoe, Illinois, 1957).

MUNITZ, M. K., ed., *Theories of the universe* (The Free Press, 1957), pp. 271 ff. Modern theories of cosmology, discussed with long excerpts from the works of foremost contributors.

NEWMAN, J. R., *The world of mathematics* (Simon and Schuster, 1956), pp. 820–839 on the discovery of Neptune.

PAYNE-GAPOSCHKIN, C., *Introduction to astronomy* (Prentice Hall, 1954).

RANDALL, J. H., *The making of the modern mind* (Houghton Mifflin, 1926, and later), Chaps. 10–15.

RUSSELL, H. N., R. S. DUGAN, and J. Q. STEWART, *Astronomy* (Ginn, 1926, and later printings), v. 1, particularly Chapter 10 on tides.

SHAPLEY, H., *Galaxies* (Blakiston, 1943).

SHAPLEY, H., and H. E. HOWARTH, *A source book in astronomy* (McGraw-Hill, 1929), pp. 140–151 (Herschel), 180–182 (Bode), 245–248 (Adams), 249–254 (Leverrier).

SHAPLEY, H., H. WRIGHT, and S. RAPPORT, *Readings in the physical sciences* (Appleton, 1948), pp. 122–128.

WIENER, P. P., and A. NOLAND, ed., *Roots of scientific thought; a cultural perspective* (Basic Books, 1957). Valuable essays by E. Rosen, M. Nicolson, A. Koyré, E. W. Strong, L. Thorndyke, M. Boas, F. R. Johnson, E. Zilsel, and others on 16th- and 17th-century science.

Part IV

ON STRUCTURE AND METHOD
IN PHYSICAL SCIENCE

13 On the Nature of Concepts
14 On the Duality and Growth of Science
15 On Scientific Discovery

As in Mathematicks, so in Natural Philosophy, the Investigation of difficult Things by the Method of Analysis, ought ever to precede the Method of Composition. This Analysis consists in making Experiments and Observations, and in drawing general Conclusions from them by Induction, and admitting of no Objections against the Conclusions, but such as are taken from Experiments, or other certain Truths. For Hypotheses are not to be regarded in experimental Philosophy. And although the arguing from Experiments and Observations by Induction be no Demonstration of general Conclusions; yet it is the best way of arguing which the Nature of Things admits of, and may be looked upon as so much the stronger, by how much the Induction is more general. And if no Exception occur from Phænomena, the Conclusion may be pronounced generally. But if at any time afterwards any Exception shall occur from Experiments, it may then begin to be pronounced with such Exceptions as occur. By this way of Analysis we may proceed from Compounds to Ingredients, and from Motions to the Forces producing them; and in general, from Effects to their Causes, and from particular Causes to more general ones, till the Argument end in the most general. This is the Method of Analysis: And the Synthesis consists in assuming the Causes discover'd, and establish'd as Principles, and by them explaining the Phænomena proceeding from them, and proving the Explanations.

Newton on methods in scientific work.
(From *Opticks*, 2nd English ed., 1717)

ON STRUCTURE AND METHOD
IN PHYSICAL SCIENCE

As long as there has been science, there has also been commentary on the tasks and procedures of science. From Aristotle to Galileo, from Francis Bacon to the present, almost all major scientists and philosophers have contributed their varying views and opinions. The literature on the subject is voluminous; presentations from every point of view can be found. What we shall do here, now that we have studied several important cases in physical science, is to discuss, in an informal manner, representative opinions held by some of the men who have prominently influenced scientific thought, and so attempt to reach a plausible point of view from which to analyze the progress and procedures of science—not for the sake of a technical exposition of the problems raised, but for increased understanding and enjoyment of the scientific enterprise.

These three chapters in Part IV carry on and complete the cycle begun with Chapter 8, "On the Nature of Scientific Theory."

CHAPTER 13

ON THE NATURE OF CONCEPTS

13.1 Introduction. When you ask "What is science?", you are in effect asking mainly "What do scientists now do at their desks and in their laboratories, and what part of their past work is still useful to men in a given field?" Because the physical scientist over the last three centuries has removed himself more and more from direct communication with non-scientists, let us first visualize his tasks in terms of an analogy involving his youthful and more immediately approachable colleague, the cultural anthropologist, whose laboratory is perhaps a comparatively isolated community of primitive people. The anthropologist immerses himself in the life of the community to observe it, to study its pattern—but, of course, the eye cannot see, the mind cannot grasp, meaningful patterns within the chaos of movement and sound until the necessary concepts with which to discover, think about, and describe relationships in the community life have been crystallized out of experience. One set of concepts, such as *family, ruler, in-group, mental ability,* and so on, belongs to the prior "common-sense" background of our investigator; this corresponds in the physical sciences to such notions as *space, time, distance,* and *speed.* Another and to us more interesting set of concepts comes out of the particular phenomenon under study. The anthropologist will learn the language and customs of the people and will discover and invent new mental constructs important to the organization of his observations and his understanding of the community, for instance the terms "uso" and "taupo," which in Samoa denote respectively a sibling of the same sex and the ceremonial princess of the house. Similarly, the physical scientist must invent such new guiding ideas as *mass, gravitational field,* and *valence.*

Significantly, our anthropologist may find that the group he is studying lacks the manifestation of many concepts without which our own society seemingly could not operate, for example, some elements of the moral code of the West, the knowledge of one's own exact age, or even the simple recognition and naming of most colors; and again science, too, had to learn, often the hard way, that there are no useful equivalents in inanimate nature for such common-sense terms as mutual longing or absolute simultaneity.

The formulation or creation of new concepts helps the anthropologist gradually to reinterpret what originally appeared to be the meaningless, aimless, or "primitive" life of the village, and a complex, perhaps rigid pattern emerges. His own early common-sense concepts themselves may undergo profound changes. The word *law*, for example, has quite different connotations in different cultures, just as the idea of *force* in physics (and, in fact, every technical concept that grew out of the vocabulary of common sense) is now at variance with the original meaning of the same word as still used outside the sciences.

In the end, our anthropologist may succeed in finding the answer to the original problem, bringing back an account of that people's political and family organization, personal esthetic values, religious beliefs and practices, economic methods, and so on. Perhaps he will also be able to reconstruct the history of that people, or even to illuminate the behavior of another group, his own, in relation to that culture. At any rate, it is evident in this example that his job was not finished when he had collected the initial direct observables; on the contrary, that was the barest beginning, the stimulus for the really important part of his work. We shall find it useful to keep this example in mind as we pass on to the analogous picture of physical scientists as explorers in a universe of observables, attempting to find its pattern and meaning.

13.2 Science and nonscience. Science is an ever-unfinished quest to discover facts and establish relationships between them. But let us go beyond this. While not trying to propose a one-sentence definition of the whole complex concept "science," we may perhaps agree at the outset that *the main business of science is to trace in the chaos and flux of phenomena a consistent structure with order and meaning*, that is, to interpret and to transcend direct experience. "The object of all sciences," in Einstein's words, "is to coordinate our experiences and to bring them into a logical system." And Niels Bohr agrees when he says "The task of science is both to extend the range of our experience and to reduce it to order."

Probably you will think these statements too all-inclusive; the same aim might well be claimed by art or by philosophy. Thus T. S. Eliot has said, "It is the function of all art to give us some perception of an order in life by imposing an order upon it," and A. N. Whitehead defined speculative philosophy as "the endeavor to frame a coherent, logical, necessary system of general ideas in terms of which every element of our experience can be interpreted." Indeed, in science, as in art and philosophy, our most persistent intellectual efforts are directed toward the discovery of pattern, order, system, structure, whether it be as primitive as the discernment of recurring seasons or as sweeping as a cosmological synthesis. In this sense, science is but one facet of the great intellectual adventure, the attempt to understand the world of experience in each of its aspects. The search for constancies in the flux of experience is so fundamental and so universal a preoccupation of intelligent life itself that, in common with many of the Greek philosophers, we may regard mind as the principle that produces order. We note without astonishment among the great early men of science an artist, Leonardo da Vinci, and a churchman, Copernicus; indeed, the very origin of the word *science* (Latin *scire*, to know, to learn) indicates the extent of its appeal and the depths of its roots.

Of course, the fundamental and distinct differences separating the sciences from the nonsciences must not be denied. There are obvious points which set one apart from the other, for example, the motivations of the investigators, to be discussed in more detail in Chapter 14. To predict nature and so to control her, to understand nature and so to enjoy her, these are the main motivations for the examination of nature through science, whereas understanding of nature through art is motivated by an effort toward self-realization, the proclamation and ennoblement of man's own spirit.

But these motivations in science and in art are in a sense complementary, not contradictory, and they illuminate the two sides of man. Both coexist to some degree within each individual. It would indeed be artificial to distinguish between the triumph of the scientist and that of the artist within Johannes Kepler as he writes in the *Harmony of the world* on the occasion of publishing his third law of planetary motion:

> What I prophesied 22 years ago, as soon as I found the heavenly orbits were of the same number as the five [regular] solids, what I fully believed long before I had seen Ptolemy's Harmonies, what I promised my friends in the name of this book, which I christened before I was 16 years old, I urged as an end to be sought, that for which I joined Tycho Brahe, for which I settled at Prague, for which I have spent most of my life at astronomical calculations—at last I have brought to light, and seen to be true beyond my fondest hopes. It is not 18 months since I saw the first ray of light, 3 months since the unclouded sun-glorious sight—burst upon me. Let nothing confine me: I will indulge my sacred ecstasy. I will triumph over mankind by the honest confession that I have stolen the golden vases of the Egyptians to raise a tabernacle for my God far away from the lands of Egypt. If you forgive me, I rejoice; if you are angry, I cannot help it. This book is written; the die is cast. Let it be read now or by posterity, I care not which. . .

Much more clear-cut than the first is a second point of difference between science and nonscience; it lies in the kind of concepts and rules the scientist uses, and the type of argument which will cause him to say, "Yes, I understand and I agree." This will occupy our attention to some degree, as will a third point of difference: the observation that in the course of time, despite great innovation and revolutions, there accumulates in science a set of internationally acceptable, basic, and fairly enduring conceptual schemes, whereas this can hardly be said for many other human endeavors.

At once the question arises how man, so short-lived and so fallible, can penetrate such complexities to construct lasting patterns and obtain general agreement. For the scientist's work, like that of any other explorer, involves the whole man, demanding as it does reflection, observation, experimentation, imagination, and a measure of intuition. Being human, he fails far more often than he succeeds, and even his successes and failures may in the light of further progress reverse positions. He often cannot fully explain his reasons for dedicating himself to his work and the steps by which he progresses; and if he is vocal on such matters, he very likely is contradicted by the testimony of some of his colleagues. And yet, the *result* of this uncertain human activity, namely, the growing body of science itself, is undeniably a successful, vigorous enterprise, bountiful in discoveries, in distinct contrast to the frailties and confusions of its human creators. We shall explore this paradox in this group of chapters, for it is the key to an understanding of the activities of the scientist and of the successful features of his work.

13.3 The lack of a single method. All too often the suggestion is made that the successes of science are the results of applying "the scientific method." But if by "scientific method" we mean the sequence and rule by which scientists now and in the past have actually done their work, then two things soon become obvious. First, as for every task, there are here not one but many methods and uncountable variants and, second, even these different methods are usually read into the story after the work has been completed, and so reflect the actual working procedures only in a rather artificial and debatable way. The ever-present longing to discover some *one* master procedure or set of rules underlying all scientific work is understandable, for such a discovery might enormously benefit all fields of scholarship; but like the search for the philosopher's stone, this hope has had to be abandoned. In the time of Francis Bacon and Descartes, early in the 17th century, it was still quite reasonable to hope that this all-powerful key to knowledge could be found, but the verdict of subsequent centuries has been plainly negative. As early as 1776 the chemist Joseph Priestley warned "how little *mystery* there really is in the business of experimental philosophy, and with how little *sagacity*, or even *design*, discoveries (which some persons are pleased to consider as great and wonderful things) have been made."

Priestley's words, even though presenting an extreme view that does not do justice to his own carefully prepared researches, are nevertheless a proper antidote to the other extreme of opinion which would present science to us as a special, infallible scheme relentlessly progressing from success to success with the precision of a smoothly moving machine. For upon looking into the history of scientific discoveries, we are soon overwhelmed by evidences that there is no single well-defined procedure, no logical system of discovery. By temperament and by characteristics of performance, scientists have always differed from one another as widely as, say, composers. Some proceeded from one step to the next with the certainty and restraint of a Bach, others moved among ideas with the abandon of a Schumann. Among the great scientists there have been adventurers and recluses, self-taught artisans and aristocrats, saints and villains, mystics and businessmen, reactionaries and rebels. In *The study of the history of science*, George Sarton said about them:

> Their manners and customs, their temperamental reactions, differ exceedingly and introduce infinite caprice and fantasy into the development of science. The logician may frown but the humanist chuckles.
>
> Happily such differences are more favorable to the progress of science than unfavorable. Even as all kinds of men are needed to build up a pleasant or an unpleasant community, even so ·we need all kinds of scientists to develop science in every possible direction. Some are very sharp and narrow-minded, others broad-minded and superficial. Many scientists, like Hannibal, know how to conquer, but not how to use their victories. Others are colonizers rather than explorers. Others are pedagogues. Others want to measure everything more accurately than it was measured before. This may lead them to the making of fundamental discoveries, or they may fail, and be looked upon as insufferable pedants. This list might be lengthened endlessly.

The process of discovery itself has been as varied as the temperament of the scientists. While individual research projects are as a rule unspectacular, each investigation being fairly routine and logically consistent within its prescribed scope, it is precisely the most important results that have depended on an illogical conclusion drawn from dubious hypotheses, or on the misinterpretation of a bad experiment. Occasionally a simple experiment yielded unexpected riches, and sometimes the most elaborately planned experiment missed the essential effect by a small margin.

A historic conceptual scheme may first capture the mind in *seemingly* the most casual or unpredictable way. To cite two famous examples, Darwin said he got "a theory by which to work" while reading "for amusement" Malthus' treatise on population. One of Kekulé's fundamental contributions to chemistry came to him suddenly during a reverie. Similar things have happened to scientists in every field. On the other hand, competent men at times had all the "significant facts" for an important finding in their hands and yet drew conclusions that were trivial or proved to be unfruitful. Others devised useful theories that seemingly were in violent contradiction with some facts before their very eyes.

In Chapter 15 we shall read the opinions of the men of science themselves concerning methods of investigation; but even the present superficial recital is enough to establish a feeling that the success of science lies not so much in some single method of work, but perhaps rather in some peculiar mechanism mediating between two factors—the scientist's individual contribution, and the body of science in which the contributions of the individuals are brought together after supplementing and modifying, cooperating and competing with one another. A crude analogy may help here. If we compare the structure of science to that of an anthill, the successful construction of that astonishingly complex and yet highly functional habitation surely must be explained not by the diverse, almost erratic behavior of the individual insects, but in large measure by a marvelous coordination of innumerable individual efforts. The mechanism of coordination among these social insects is still largely a mystery, but in the analogous case of science something positive might be said. We approach it by turning our attention to the extraordinary power possessed by the concepts that scientists devise and use.

13.4 Physical concepts; operational definitions. All intelligent endeavor stands with one foot on observation and the other on contemplation. But scientists have gradually come to specify certain *types* of observations and of thought processes. One distinctly striking specification arises from the tacit desire among scientists to assure that in a given argument they are in fact discussing the same concepts. The desire for clarity is, of course, a general one, but here we find a particularly successful scheme of meeting it, even though at the cost of some sacrifices.

Consider a much-simplified example. Suppose the task is to find the length of a certain wire. If four men were asked to make this measurement, they would all appear to understand clearly what is wanted because they all would independently go through quite similar manual and mathematical operations to arrive at their answers, even though these answers might not completely coincide. (If the word *similar* is disturbing in the previous sentence, we may go so far as to claim that these men will, on mutual consultation, very probably all agree to follow *exactly* the same operations.) Suppose that their respective independent determinations of the length of the wire are 5.01 cm, 5 cm, 4.99 cm, and 5.1 cm. The impressive point here is not that they disagree on the numerical value obtained or on the accuracy desired, but that they do agree on the type of answer to give. They do not, for example, say "as long as a sparrow in spring," "five times the width of my finger," "much longer than it is wide," and "pretty short." Evidently the phrase "length of a wire" means the same thing to all four experimenters, and we may be fairly sure that on consultation all four would convince themselves of the acceptability of one single result, say 5.03 ± 0.04 cm. Much of the success and rapid growth of the sciences depends on simple agreements of this sort, for it is clear that in such circumstances the energies of investigators are not continually drained off by fruitless arguments about definitions and rules of procedure. Thus the labors of many men over centuries of time can combine in one advancing stream.

There are, of course, large areas of possible disagreement among scientists, but these disagreements can be settled, often by recourse to some one series of measurements that both disputants (rightly or wrongly) acknowledge at the time to be decisive. One of the impressive features of modern physical science is the rapidity with which most major differences of opinion in the field usually disappear, a state of affairs that is noticeably in contrast with that of some other disciplines, where the hard core of agreement is necessarily much narrower than in the sciences.* The secret of this successful harmony and continuity in physical science (which were idealized only a little in the previous paragraph) lies to a large degree in the *nature of concepts and their definitions*. For example, the concept "length of an object" as *used* in physical science is ultimately defined by the very *operations* involved in making the measurement. The question "What is the length of a certain object?" is for all practical purposes identical with the question "What is the difference between the two numbers stamped on a specific measuring stick at the two marks which coincide with the ends of the objects?"

This last sentence affords an abbreviated example of what we shall call an *operational definition*, here of length; and our four experimenters who are measuring the length of the wire can regard it as the *meaning of length*, available for examination if any dispute should arise. In principle, each of the concepts used in the physical sciences can be made clear in terms of some such operational definition. This is one of the most important mechanisms whereby mutual understanding among scientists is made possible, for there is less chance of misinterpreting action than words. As the American physicist and philosopher of science P. W. Bridgman has said, "The true meaning of a term is to be found by observing what a man does with it, not what he says about it."†

If you were tempted to object that the operational definition of length given here is far from the common-sense meaning of the term, you would

---

*In this sense, science is a simpler subject than the social studies and humanities. Science limits itself largely to solvable questions, whereas the others generally direct themselves to those ancient problems and preoccupations which are worthy of engagement precisely because they have endured over the centuries.

†In addition to manual operations, there are also mathematical and other mental operations that lie at the base of many physical concepts; each such definition becomes a fairly unambiguous set of directives to all scientists who have worked in the field, which explains why their vocabulary is not regularly the subject of dispute.

have touched on an important point. Everyday notions seem clear and scientific terms seem mysterious. However, a little thought shows the opposite to be the case. The words of daily life are usually so flexible and ill-defined, so open to emotional coloring and misunderstanding, that our task here is to get used to the special vocabulary of the sciences and to the insistence on its *rigorous* use, an exceedingly useful habit that scientists inherited from Scholastic logicians.

Then again, we are likely to have the uncomfortable feeling that such a definition of length merely shows us how to measure according to some man-made convention, and does not tell us what length "really is." Once more this is correct, and once more we must try to make our peace with the limitations of modern science; it does not claim to find out "what things really are." This is a question that eventually we must explore thoroughly; we are touching here again on a problem that is at the very core of science, namely, what reality means to a man in a laboratory. For the moment let us take the answer of that great French mathematician and philosopher of science, Henri Poincaré, who half a century ago illustrated the operational attitude toward physical concepts in this manner: "When we say force is the cause of motion we talk metaphysics, and this definition, if we were content with it, would be absolutely sterile. For a definition to be of any use, it must teach us to *measure* force; moreover, that suffices; it is not at all necessary that it teach what force is *in itself* nor whether it is the cause or the effect of motion."

Lastly, you may be puzzled that a simple quantity such as length cannot be determined with "perfect" exactness, and may question why we should have to say "the length of this object is 5.03 ± 0.04 cm." The term ±0.04 cm is called the *probable error;* it means that the chances are fifty-fifty that the next measurement of the object will read between 4.99 and 5.07 cm. All measurements, except for simple counting, must contain some error or uncertainty, no matter how carefully the job is done. But even though this error may be slight, can we hope to build an *exact* science on concepts defined by necessarily uncertain measurements?

This paradox is resolved by two recognitions. First, the word "error" does not have in science the connotations "wrong," "mistaken," and "sinful" which it so often has in everyday speech; a measured value can be regarded as "exact" only if we know also just what range of values to expect on repeating the measurement. To put it succinctly, *a science is exact if the practitioner knows the approximate magnitude of the error in his quantitative conclusions.* Second, and this must be repeated frequently, science is not after absolute certainties, but after relationships among observables. We realize that the observables can be defined and measured only with some uncertainty; and we shall not demand more than that of the relationships between them, thus leaving the search for absolute truths, even if regretfully, to other fields of thought.

13.5 Physically "meaningless" concepts and statements. The consequence of even such a trivial-sounding operational definition as that of length may be quite startling. In the modern theory of relativity, rigorous definitions of this type directed the course of thought to unexpected results, one being that the measured length of an object depends on how fast the object moves with respect to the observer, a finding that accounted for some observations that had previously been most perplexing. A result of this work of Einstein's was an increasing awareness on the part of scientists that to be generally acceptable in physical sciences concepts should in principle have meaning in terms of possible operations. It was then seen that certain tacitly accepted ideas were leading to serious contradictions in parts of physical theory because, by their very formulation, they could not be connected with any possible activities or operations in the laboratory. The concepts of time and space that were modified by Einstein's theory, for example, previously had generally been defined not by specific and exclusive reference to manipulations with meter sticks, light signals, clocks, and the like, but in some absolute, intuitive sense.

The classic references here are two statements of Newton in the first pages of the *Principia:*

> Absolute, true, and mathematical time, of itself, and from its own nature, flows equably without regard to anything external, and by another name is called duration . . .

Note the phrase "without regard to anything external," that is, without necessary relation to the rotation of a second hand on a clock. With this definition of "true" time, one could not hope to measure it. Again,

> Absolute space, in its own nature, without regard to anything external, remains always similar and immovable.

Today, statements such as these, which are inherently without operational meaning, are sometimes called "meaningless," perhaps a drastic term but accurate in this limited sense.*

Galileo, while much nearer than Newton to that science of the Scholastics which he helped to displace, saw quite clearly that science should be based on concepts that have meaning in terms of possible observations. Recall again his preface to the definition of acceleration: "We however have decided to consider the phenomena of freely falling bodies with an acceleration such as actually occurs in nature, and to make our definition of accelerated motion exhibit the essential features of this type of natural accelerated motion."

---

*You may well ask whether Newton's own physics was invalidated by such meaningless basic postulates. The answer is no, simply because Newton did not make explicit use of them in his physical work. His reasons for stating them at all are complex and can be traced to his philosophic tenets.

If we regard as "meaningless" any concept not definable by operations, it follows that even whole statements and many intelligent-sounding, deeply disturbing questions may turn out to be meaningless *from the standpoint of the physical scientist.* Here are a few examples: "Which is *really* at rest, the sun or the earth?" "Will this table cease to exist while it is not being observed?" "What is length in itself, apart from measurements?" "Are there natural laws that man can never hope to discover?"

If the roots of science as an established enterprise are the operationally meaningful concepts, then there must be a large range of experience that is being neglected by science. This is indeed the case. In a sense one may compare a scientist to a man who is looking at the night sky with a powerful telescope and is thus able to examine a small region with extreme penetration while, however, holding in abeyance the chance to watch a whole world at one glance. Examining the number of stars, their relative brightness, and the like, does not disqualify us from scanning the skies for the sheer experience of the grand display that so impresses the casual observer. On the contrary, one activity can only enrich the other. But the two are different, and each has its own limitations.

The scientist must limit his attention along certain lines. It was Galileo who drew the distinction between those experiences and concepts which might safely serve as the foundation stones of physical science and those which, having a measure of more *subjective* meaning, should from the point of view of physical science be regarded as sources of illusion and debate. He regarded as the foundation stones the direct observables that could be measured and mathematically symbolized, such as position and velocity, the very elements that at the time had, to use the modern phrase, simple operational significance. These he distinguished from more subjective experiences and notions that were not then amenable to instrumental measurement. This distinction between what he called "primary" and "secondary" quantities impressed and was accepted by such followers of Galileo as Newton, and by and large it is still acknowledged in the physical sciences.

We might say that Galileo's decision reduced the extent of the scientist's *admissible* experience to a small fraction of his total experience, but to precisely that fraction which he could quantify or by other means share fairly unambiguously with his fellows. The ideas of physical science sometimes seem so stylized simply because they have been devised to describe those features of experience which are likely to be of least interest from a common-sense point of view—measurement, mathematical manipulation, numerical prediction, precise communicability—and hence are not helpful in describing and interpreting those important everyday experiences involving our feelings, emotional reactions, and social relationships.

13.6 Mathematical law and abstraction. Insistence on quantitative concepts may seem unwarranted until we recognize that the work of the physical scientist is based on a faith as ancient as it is astonishing, namely, that the phenomena of nature which we observe are describable in terms of axioms or postulates that are mathematical, and that such observations are *explained* when we find mathematical expressions relating them. Galileo, to whose work we shall refer for examples in these three chapters where appropriate, expressed it in this manner:

> Philosophy [we should call it science now] is written in that great book which ever lies before our eyes—I mean the universe—but we cannot understand it if we do not learn the language and grasp the symbols in which it is written. This book is written in the mathematical language, and the symbols are triangles, circles, and other geometrical figures [we should now add all other mathematical devices] without whose help it is impossible to comprehend a single word of it, without which one wanders in vain through a dark labyrinth.

To Galileo, as well as to some of his contemporaries and to modern physical scientists, mathematical methods provide the technique *par excellence* for ordering and comprehending nature. To logic, which for the Scholastics was the main tool of investigation, is now primarily delegated the task of establishing the consistency of the scheme of mathematical demonstration, hypotheses, and observations. While Galileo and Kepler still felt compelled to announce this faith loudly and often, and Newton could not persuade many of his contemporaries that the algebraic formulation of the principle of gravitation itself served as an acceptable explanation without having to have a physical mechanism to account for it, by now, through the fruitfulness of this view, it has become a fundamental, unexamined attitude among physical scientists.

By the phrase "mathematical relations between observables," we mean, of course, that our general descriptions are usually stated in the form "variable x is related to variables y, z, . . . by such and such a mathematical function"; for example, for a heavy object falling from rest, $s = \frac{1}{2}gt^2$. Some postulates state that some expression, say, $(x/y) + z$, tends to attain a maximum or a minimum value under given conditions. For projectile velocities, the superposition principle asserts that the two velocity components v_x and v_y in projectile motion are independent. Above all others in usefulness is that type of relationship that says in effect "this function of these variables under given conditions is *always constant.*" The Galilean postulate of the constancy of the acceleration of free fall is of this kind. Kepler's second and third laws are similar examples. There will be numerous others, such as the principles of conservation of mass and of energy. Clearly, postulates of this kind are so highly prized because they combine the most successful features of physical science with its most persistent preoccupation—the mathematical formulation of concepts and the discovery of unchanging patterns in the chaos of experience.

Mathematical formulations impose several conditions upon the form and content of scientific work. For instance, those who were formerly prone to think of a postulate as a relation between cause and effect must instead come to regard it as a relation between variables. Thus in an expression of the type $x = yz$, we can just as well write $y = x/z$, or $z = x/y$, and there is no way of telling whether x or y or z is a cause or an effect. In other words, it is on the whole more fruitful to think of an *interaction* rather than a simple *causation*, and to ask to what factors x is *related* instead of asking what *causes* x.

The mere fact that mathematically formulated ideas can be expressed symbolically in equations like the above is a great aid to speedy understanding and manipulation of concepts, once the necessary mathematics has been learned. Consider the mere *convenience* of writing an equation like $s = \frac{1}{2}gt^2$, instead of expressing this generalization in rhetorical form. Note how extraneous word colorings disappear, how easy it is to communicate results to others, and how such equations invite the drawing of further conclusions about the relationships between the quantities involved. There is a good parallel here in the field of chemistry, which was immeasurably advanced in the early 19th century by the simple expedient of expressing reactions by means of chemical formulas.

Still other consequences follow from the decision of scientists to restrict and direct their attention toward measurable phenomena and the mathematical relations between them. If the important thing about a rolling ball on an inclined plane is no longer its composition, its history in the workshop, its color, or its usefulness for the sport of bowling, if all that really matters to the particular group of investigators is the relationship $s \propto t^2$, then this ball ceases to be an individual entity—it might equally well have been any other smooth sphere. In the long run the actual ball seems totally forgotten, its place being taken by "an object," "a body," or even "a particle," idealizations abstracted from the experimental situation. In this sense the laws of science, such as those for motion on an inclined plane, do not directly deal with actual bodies but with abstractions moving in a hypothetical space with properties of its own, in a world that we can manipulate at will, now thinking away all air resistance, now regarding the inclined plane as perfectly smooth and straight, now changing only one aspect, perhaps the angle of inclination, and leaving all other parameters unvaried. This world, rendered in an esoteric language of its own and filled with simplifications and exaggerations, is in some important aspects analogous to that of the modern painter, poet, or composer.

Thus all the features of science conspire to transform actual objects in beautiful Pisa into undistinguished particles moving in Euclidean space.

Much would be lost by this transposition if that were the end of the scientific process, although even this much, the first part, yields the unique and absorbing satisfaction of being able to reduce, order, and so to begin to understand raw sense-experience. But there is more: at no point is the contact with observables completely broken; the same rules by which the transition in one direction was made are also applicable on the return trip from the world of abstraction to that of observables. This is guaranteed by the operational character of the concepts employed in the abstract world. For example, while deriving the equation $v^2 = v_0^2 + 2as$ from the other equations of motion, you may have felt out of touch with the observable world of moving bodies; yet the equation you finally derived could be tested by referring it to actual motions. In fact *the hypothetical world to which our mathematical manipulations apply is justified and taken seriously only insofar as it does yield new knowledge about the world of observables.* If it were to fail in this function, we should have to rearrange the rules within the abstract world until they finally do give a useful harvest. As it happens, the abstraction from a real ball to a particle did give us laws of motion applicable not only to this ball but to all other balls, to all simple round and sliding objects, and the like.

This is indeed making a good profit in return for sacrificing temporarily the identity of the real spherical object. The philosopher Rudolph Carnap has suggested a neat analogy in this regard. The symbols and equations of the physicist bear the same relation to the actual world of phenomena as the written notes of a melody do to the audible tones of the song itself. The written notes, of course, do not make sounds by themselves, and yet the sounds are not altogether lost in them. At any time one can retranslate the marks on paper into the audible melody, provided one knows the convention which relates notes to tones. Correspondingly, we might now visualize science as an arch resting on two pillars, observation and experience, with conceptualization and abstraction supported in between. The security of the arch depends on the firmness of the pillars.

A whole view of science can be developed along these lines. It is expressed succinctly by James B. Conant's definition of science: "Science is an interconnected series of concepts and conceptual schemes that have developed as the result of experimentation and observation and are fruitful of further experimentation and observations."

13.7 Explanation. Any discussion concerning the nature of concepts in physical science must come to grips with a criticism of the axiomatic proposition that the physical scientist finds *explanations* by formulating mathematical relations between observables. Our critic may be saying, "I can see that this convention works in the sense that it permits us to formulate expressions for, say, projectile motion by means of which we can accurately direct missiles. However, I do not agree that anything is *explained* thereby. True, when Galileo pointed out that the paths of projectiles coincide with the type of geometric curve called a parabola, he did discover a simple and elegant description applicable to a large number of separate cases and useful for predicting actual missile trajectories. But I want to know the *ultimate reason why* projectiles move along parabolic paths."

Now it is simple enough to explain why trajectories are parabolic, as we did in Section 3.4, but only in terms of the laws of Newtonian mechanics. Our interrogator, on the other hand, does not want more of that. He might well find satisfaction with the explanation current prior to Newton (Section 2.3), or perhaps with some other picture, say one in which the projectiles are imagined to be guided by invisible curved tubes or tracks in an invisible fluid supposedly filling all space.

If pushed far enough, our interrogator will have to make a startling concession: his only tools for understanding physical phenomena are pictures, allusions, and analogies involving the primitive mechanical events of everyday life. We might say he thinks predominantly with the concrete common sense of his muscles. For example, the gravitational or electrical effect of one body on another across a vacuum is incomprehensible to him unless we allow him to imagine between those two bodies some invisible medium that somehow transmits an actual mechanical pull or push from one to the other.

This feature of the human mind, this thirst for concreteness, characterizes not only the frequent preoccupation with mechanical models within science itself, but also the most primitive type of common-sense explanation. This has always been so. Thus the people of ancient India pictured the earth as supported in space on the backs of gigantic elephants, and the early Egyptians believed that Osiris weighed human souls in a handheld balance. It would indeed be surprising if the imagery of religion, poetry, and even of early science had not found its original raw material predominantly in our ordinary, direct, everyday experiences. Moreover, some of the greatest scientific contributions were made by men whose physical intuitions were just so directed. But as modern physical science has turned to problems more and more removed from the realm of common experience, it also has become necessary to enlarge the kit of conceptual tools with which to grasp and comprehend phenomena. Our discussion of atomic physics will later serve as a particularly striking example of the breakdown of naive types of understanding that insist on intuitive, visualizable explanations; early statements of this theme are to be found in Galileo's insistence that motion was to be explained in terms of a particular mathematical formulation abstracted from experience, and Newton's unwillingness to postulate "causes underlying" gravitation, expressed in his statement: "To us it is enough that gravity does really exist and act according to the laws which we have explained, and abundantly serves to account for all the motions of the celestial bodies, and of our sea."

To take one more specific example, from modern physics, consider the phenomenon of radioactive decay of a particular isotope of radium. Experiment shows that a given pure sample containing initially the number N_0 atoms of this kind gradually changes into a different element, radon, which in turn gradually changes into still another element, and so on. After a time t only some number N_t of the original N_0 radium atoms are still unchanged, as is shown in the graph of Fig. 13.1. These numbers can be related by the postulate that this graph is, for all pure radioactive elements, an *exponential* curve, and that the equation for this curve is

$$N_t = N_0 e^{-0.693(t/T)}. \tag{13.1}$$

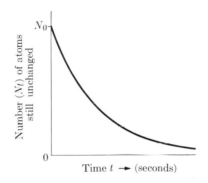

FIG. 13.1. Decay of a radioactive element.

Here e stands for the number 2.718, and T, the "half-life," is a parameter whose value depends only on the radioactive substance involved and affords a measure of the rapidity of the decay.

Since Eq. (13.1) describes and summarizes the facts neatly for all natural and artificial radioactive substances, we clearly may refer to it as a *law of radioactive decay*. Yet, while this empirical mathematical law is indispensable and enlightening, it does not in the least explain *why* atoms of radioactive elements explode and change into other elements. That is another and as yet largely unsolved problem. However, the solution will inevitably again be through some mathematically expressed postulate, such as a formula describing the fluctuation of the binding forces within atomic nuclei, so that ultimately the observations described by Eq. (13.1) will still be explained by means of mathematical formulations.

In its most general sense, "to explain" means to reduce the unfamiliar to the familiar, to establish a relationship between what is to be explained and our (correctly or incorrectly) unquestioned preconceptions. The preconceptions of the Scholastics were grandiose and sweeping— natural place, final causes, celestial perfections, and so on—and reflected the impressive but perhaps overly ambitious universality of their questions and explanations. The modern scientist has trained himself to hold somewhat more limited and specialized preconceptions, for instance, that nature is describable in terms of simple models or mathematical schemes. To him the algebraic law of gravitation, for example, is the satisfying explanation for a host of phenomena, whereas to many nonscientists the very same law would be regarded as an additional unexplained mystery. It requires training and repeated personal success in solving physical problems to be really satisfied with mathematical formulations and answers, just as it surely involves a strenuous program of orientation to be fully content with the rewards and the rules of behavior in any profession.

Having now examined the nature of concepts in physical science, we are ready to consider how these concepts are integrated in the advance of science.

Supplementary Reading

A guide to supplementary reading in connection with all chapters of Part IV is given at the end of Chapter 15.

CHAPTER 14

ON THE DUALITY AND GROWTH OF SCIENCE

14.1 The free license of creativity. Our discussion of the nature of physical concepts has shown that a main reason for formulating concepts is to use them in connection with mathematical laws. It is tempting to go one step further and to demand that the practicing scientist deal only with ideas that correspond to strictly measurables, that he formulate only those concepts which can be reduced to the least ambiguous of all data, namely, numbers and measurements. The history of science indeed furnishes numerous examples of great advances that followed from the formulation of strictly quantitative concepts, whether the measurements from which they grew were concerned with the time of descent of rolling balls, or the tabulation of population statistics, or the weights of compounds in chemical reactions, or, in the case of Pavlov's experiments, with the rate of flow of saliva in experimental animals. The 19th-century scientist Lord Kelvin commended this approach in the famous statement:

> I often say that when you can measure what you are speaking about, and express it in numbers, you know something about it; but when you cannot express it in numbers, your knowledge is of a meagre and unsatisfactory kind; it may be the beginning of knowledge, but you have scarcely, in your thoughts, advanced to the stage of *Science*, whatever the matter may be.

However, a stand like Kelvin's (which at present appears to be having a formidable influence on some thinkers in the social studies) does justice neither to the complexity nor to the fertility of the human mind, and certainly not to the needs of contemporary physical science itself—neither to scientists nor to science. Quite apart from the practical impossibility of demanding of one's mind that at all times it identify such concepts as "electron" only with the measurable aspects of that construct, there are specifically two main objections: first, this position mistakes how scientists as individuals do their work and, second, it mistakes how science as a system grows out of the contributions of individuals. Let us examine these important points rather closely.

It would have been a mistake to conclude from study of the earlier chapters that practicing scientists, while they are engaged in creative work, do, or even can, continually check the strict meaningfulness of their concepts and problems. As a rule an investigator is and should be unaware of such methodological questions until some obstinate trouble develops. The operational view, where successful, is almost instinctive, and should come into the open only as a therapeutic device. We are reminded of a

229

tightrope walker who undoubtedly is indifferent to an orderly inquiry into the physical laws by which he performs and survives; very likely he would fall off if he worried much about them. Many of us have seen, too, the deplorable results when certain artists became overly conscious of their media and methods. The point is that *while a scientist struggles with a problem, there can be little conscious limitation on his free and at times audacious constructions.* Depending on his field, his problem, his training and temperament, he may allow himself to be guided by a logical sequence based on more or less provisional hypotheses, by a "feeling for things," by likely analogy, by some promising guess, or he may follow a judicious cut-and-try procedure. The well-planned experiment, of course, is by far the most frequent one, and has generally the best chance of success; yet successful experimenters have often not even mapped out a tentative plan of attack, but have instead let their enthusiasms, their hunches, and their sheer joy of discovery suggest the line of work. Sometimes the discovery of a new effect or tool or technique is followed by a period of trying out one or another application in a manner that superficially seems almost playful.

Even the philosophic orientations of scientists are far less uniform than might be supposed. Roughly speaking, the choices open to them are of three sorts. Perhaps most people would defend the position that the experiences which come through their senses are directly occasioned by and correspond exactly to an external world, a "real" world which exists regardless of our interpretations. This view is called *realism*, and it is in opposition to two major philosophic systems (among a host of others): *idealism*, which maintains that our ideas and impressions are the only realities, and that we use those to construct convenient concepts such as chairs, meter sticks, and laboratories; and *positivism*, which does not speak of such "realities" at all, excludes speculation upon ultimate causes or origins, and regards nothing as ascertainable or meaningful beyond sense data (for example, pointer readings) and concepts that are referable to sense data. Now it might be supposed that because the established part of physical science ideally should be directly verifiable in terms of measurement, all scientists must be positivists. The truth, however, is that most scientists, while in agreement with positivism's practical consequences for their own work, do not actively participate in this philosophic controversy. As Einstein has said, the practicing scientist may appear to trained philosophers "as a type of unscrupulous opportunist":

> ...he appears as *realist*, insofar as he seeks to describe the world independent of the act of perception; as *idealist* insofar as he looks upon the concepts and theories as the free inventions of the human spirit (not logically derivable from that which is empirically given); as *positivist* insofar as he considers his

concepts and theories justified only to the extent to which they furnish a logical representation of relations among sense experiences. He may even appear as *Platonist* or Pythagorean insofar as he considers the viewpoint of logical simplicity as an indispensable and effective tool of his research.*

14.2 Private science and public science. The important problems of creative science necessarily differ in a number of ways from the science problems that a student may encounter in homework or laboratory exercises. Rarely does the scientist know at the outset whether a problem can be solved at all with the conceptions and tools initially available, or where new complications might lurk. Also, because all of science has a certain unity, the work of even a specialist may involve a large variety of different specific fields, sometimes in unexpected ways. An inquiry into the physical structure of liquids, for example, may have to call upon such diverse subjects as thermodynamics, physical chemistry, crystallography, acoustics, electronics, and even some practical metallurgy. Since the methods and relationships of one field frequently suggest analogous procedures in another, the working scientist is ever alert for the slightest hints of new difficulties and of their resolutions. He proceeds through his problem like an explorer through a jungle, sensitive to every sign with every faculty of his being. Indeed, some of the most creative of theoretical scientists have stated that during the early stages of their work they do not even *think* in terms of conventional communicable symbols and words.

Only when this "private" stage is over and the individual contribution is formalized and prepared for absorption into "public" science does it begin to be really important that each step and every concept be made meaningful and clear. These two stages of science, which we shall have occasion to call science-in-the-making and science-as-an-institution, must be clearly differentiated. Once an adequate distinction has been made between these levels of meaning in the term "science," one of the central sources of confusion concerning the nature and growth of science has been removed.

The American nuclear physicist H. D. Smyth has thus characterized the distinction: "We have a paradox in the method of science. The research man may often think and work like an artist, but he has to talk like a bookkeeper, in terms of facts, figures, and logical sequence of thought." For this reason we must not take at their face value either the chronology or the methods set forth in scientific papers and treatises, including those of Galileo and Newton. It is part of the game of science, simply because it promotes economy of thought and communication, to make the results

---

*P. A. Schilpp (ed.), *Albert Einstein, philosopher and scientist* (Library of Living Philosophers, Evanston, Illinois, 1949).

in retrospect appear neatly derived from clear fundamentals, until, in John Milton's phrase,

> ...so easy it seemed
> Once found, which yet unfound most would have thought
> Impossible!

A research worker may hide months of tortuous and often wasteful effort behind a few elegant paragraphs, just as a sculptor puts away his tools, preliminary studies, and clumsy scaffolds before unveiling his work.

A famous example shows how dangerous it is to refuse to accept provisional concepts into scientific work simply because they are not yet amenable to rigorous tests. Despite the large amount of indirect evidence for the hypothesis that matter is atomic in structure, a few prominent scientists, around the turn of this century, still rejected the atomic view stubbornly and vehemently as lacking "direct" confirmation. They eventually had to yield when all around them the atomic hypothesis led to an avalanche of testable conclusions and even to a revolution in classical science itself. Although perhaps an initial attitude of fundamental skepticism was justified, these men deprived themselves unduly long of a useful conceptual scheme (and the rest of science of their possible additional contributions) by waiting until the atomic picture had been fully fortified operationally. Today most scientists tacitly agree that their private creative activity must be unfettered by such preconceptions. "To set limits to speculation is treason to the future."

14.3 The natural selection of physical concepts. It begins to appear that there are no simple rules to lead us to the discovery of new phenomena or to the invention of new concepts, and none by which to foretell whether our contributions will turn out to be useful and durable. But science does exist and is a vigorous and successful enterprise. The lesson to be drawn from history is that *science as a structure grows by a struggle for survival among ideas*—that there are marvelous processes at work which in time purify the meanings even of initially confused concepts. These processes eventually permit the absorption into science-as-an-institution (public science) of anything important that may have been developed, no matter by what means or methods, in science-in-the-making (private science).

We have seen that those concepts which have contributed most to the growth of physical science have two general characteristics. First, each of these concepts (acceleration, force, energy, valence, etc.) has a core of meaning that is clear and unambiguous or that at least has attained tacitly understood and communicable operational meaning through continual application in experimental situations. Second, nearly all physical concepts are quantitative, that is, they can be associated with numbers by means of measurements or mathematical operations; thus we speak of a mass of 10 kgm, a temperature of 20°C, a space of 3 dimensions. This assertion holds even for many concepts that superficially appear to be devoid of such numerical significance. For example, although we cannot say that a body has 3, 4, or 5 *units* of equilibrium, we nevertheless define this concept by saying that a body is in equilibrium when its acceleration is zero. Although we define "melting" as the change of state of a substance from solid to liquid, this statement acquires precise physical meaning only when the change is described in terms of changes in the numerical values of the viscosity and hardness. A physicist may describe an electron as the smallest quantity of electricity known to exist independently, but when he uses this concept he deals with its numerical aspects: its electric charge of -1.6×10^{-19} mks units, its mass of 9.1×10^{-31} kgm, and so forth; in brief "electron" is primarily a summary term for this whole complex of measurables.

The above two characteristics of concepts are joined by a third, *general usefulness*, without which science would degenerate into a bewildering complex of data. The chaos of experience allows us to formulate infinitely many ideas, all of them having the first two characteristics. For example, we could arbitrarily invent some new concept X referring to observations of freely falling bodies, defining X, perhaps, by the equation $X = (v - v_0)/s$. At first glance, X appears worthy of a name of its own and of wide acceptance, like the quantity $a = (v - v_0)/t$. But pragmatically, X does not happen to appear prominently in simple laws of nature; unlike acceleration, X does not remain constant during free fall. Therefore X, though a possible, meaningful concept, actually falls by the wayside as useless and unwanted. (Incidentally, this X happens to be the very quantity that many medieval investigators erroneously suspected of being constant during free fall.)

What makes certain concepts important, therefore, is their recurrence in a great many successful descriptions and laws, often in areas very far removed from the context of their initial formulation. The electron, first discovered in attempts to explain phenomena in discharge tubes similar to those now used as "neon" signs, later reappeared prominently in the explanations for electric currents in wires and liquids, for photoelectricity, for thermionic phenomena (as in today's radio and television tubes), for radioactivity, for the emission of light from hot bodies, and much besides. Here we have the only reason and the full meaning behind the statement that scientists "believe in the reality" of electrons: the concept is needed so often and in so many ways. "The only justification for our concepts," said Einstein, "is that they serve to represent the complex of our experiences."

At the inception of an idea it is, of course, hardly possible to tell whether it will stand the test of wide applicability and so survive in the body of science. In this sense we may say that Galileo's work would have had far less stature without the successive growth of physical science. Galileo sensed, but could not have known, that his work on mechanics would turn out to be extremely important, and that his special methods and discoveries would (with Kepler's and Newton's work) find general significance by transcending the immediate. There is a challenge in this for each individual scientist: the science of tomorrow may well need or even depend on his own work.

The most spectacular case of such generally useful ideas, as we have seen, is that of the concepts of length, mass, and time. In terms of these almost all other physical concepts can be constructed or defined. We can never cease to marvel that nature should be so reducible—here must be either the basis or the result of the scientist's guiding preconception concerning the simplicity of nature. We shall meet an abundance of other important "derived" concepts which run like strong ropes through the maze of phenomena to give us support and direction in the most varied circumstances. Such concepts, usually defined initially in connection with a limited problem, have spread and become all-important over the years, and in this evolution have frequently changed or broadened in meaning as the context and the fields of application have widened; e.g., such ideas as *force, energy* and *element*. This possibility of change is again suggestive of the recurring discovery that the concepts of science are not absolute, but have meaning only in terms of what scientists can do with them.

We can now attempt a preliminary summing-up of the main points so far. We see the physical scientist as a seeker of harmonies and constancies in the jungle of experience. He aims at knowledge and prediction, particularly through discovery of quantitative laws. However, such individual contributions constitute only one part of the story, for science proceeds in two stages. One, which we have called private science or science-in-the-making, involves the speculative and creative elements, the continual flow of contributions by many individuals, each working at his own particular task without consciously examining his methods, each motivated in his own way and perhaps uninterested at the time in attending to the long-range philosophic problems of science. By contrast, public science, or science-as-an-institution, is the evolving compromise, a growing network synthesized from individual contributions that have proved to be meaningful and useful to generation after generation of scientists. The sober tables of physical and chemical constants, the bare equations in treatises and textbooks form the hard core of science, the residue distilled from individual triumphs of insight, checked and cross-checked by the multiple testimony of general experience.

This duality of science is one of its main sources of strength. To illuminate it in terms of concrete examples, let us consider several related questions, the first being that of motivation. These considerations will incidentally also prepare the way for bigger tasks that follow—examining the details of the process whereby "public" science grows out of "private" science, and explaining the vital role played by the contradictory elements that frequently exist within science.

14.4 Motivation. When Whitehead said, "Science can find no individual enjoyment in Nature; science can find no aim in Nature; science can find no creativity in Nature," he seemed to express a widespread opinion, and in his searching analysis even touched on the ambivalent feeling of the present age toward science—the simultaneous fear and reverence for this reputedly emotionless yet deeply exciting enterprise. Perhaps we can see now that the opinion expressed in this quotation refers to only one of the two aspects of science, the stable and not the transient one, to "public," not "private," science. "Public" science is successful just insofar as it is indifferent to human enjoyments and concerns, but the opposite is true of the "private" science of the individual investigator. His creativity depends on the interpenetration of his personal ideals and his work; he may be enchanted largely by unrationalized preoccupations, which include in a certain sense even the desire to *know*.

In other years, when scientists acknowledged their motivations more freely, they often openly confessed their nonrational, mystical, or religious convictions. Ever since the time of the Pythagoreans the faith reflected in the phrase "the world is divine because it is a harmony" has been a motivating theme. Galileo, a pious man, looked upon the laws of nature as works and evidences of the Deity equal in authority to the evidences of the Scriptures. Almost without exception, scientists as a group have at all times, including our own, manifested the same religious convictions or lack of convictions as have other contemporary groups of educated men. Until about a century ago, the typical scientist openly asserted that the physical world could not be understood without resort to fundamental theistic assumptions. Although the details of the argument have since changed considerably, its general form has never been put more beautifully or stated more sincerely than in Newton's retrospective description of his own scientific activity as a prelude to religious knowledge, specifically, that of the "first cause," the Deity:

> . . . the main Business of natural Philosophy is to argue from Phænomena without feigning Hypotheses, and to deduce Causes from Effects, till we come to the very first Cause, which certainly is not mechanical; and not only to unfold the Mechanism of the World, but chiefly to resolve these and such like Questions. What is there in places almost empty of Matter, and whence is it that the Sun and Planets gravitate towards one another, without dense Matter between them? Whence is it that Nature doth nothing in vain; and whence

arises all that Order and Beauty which we see in the World? To what end are Comets, and whence is it that Planets move all one and the same way in Orbs concentrick, while Comets move all manner of ways in Orbs very excentrick; and what hinders the fix'd Stars from falling upon one another? How came the Bodies of Animals to be contrived with so much Art, and for what ends were their several Parts? Was the Eye contrived without Skill in Opticks, and the Ear without Knowledge of Sounds? How do the Motions of the Body follow from the Will, and whence is the Instinct in Animals? Is not the Sensory of Animals that place to which the sensitive Substance is present, and into which the sensible Species of Things are carried through the Nerves and Brain, that there they may be perceived by their immediate presence to that Substance? And these things being rightly dispatch'd, does it not appear from Phænomena that there is a Being incorporeal, living, intelligent, omnipresent, who in infinite Space, as it were in his Sensory, sees the things themselves intimately, and throughly perceives them, and comprehends them wholly by their immediate presence to himself: Of which things the Images only carried through the Organs of Sense into our little Sensoriums, are there seen and beheld by that which in us perceives and thinks. And tho' every true Step made in this Philosophy brings us not immediately to the Knowledge of the first Cause, yet it brings us nearer to it, and on that account is to be highly valued. (*Opticks*, 2nd English ed., 1717)

In a letter written to a friend 25 years earlier, in 1692, Newton said of this motivation for writing the *Principia:*

When I wrote my treatise [the *Principia*, 1687] about our system, I had an eye on such principles as might work with considering men for the belief of a Deity; and nothing can rejoice me more than to find it useful for that purpose.

Consider another persistent trend in scientific thought, the preoccupation with integral numbers, of which we have seen one example in Bode's law and shall see others. Galileo, at the very outset of the discussion of the laws of free fall, in the *Two new sciences*, said: "... so far as I know, no one has yet pointed out that the distances traversed, during equal intervals of time, by a body falling from rest, stand to one another in the same ratio as the odd numbers beginning with unity." Throughout the development of physics and chemistry and to the present day we encounter this satisfaction with such simple numerical relations. In the atomic theory of today, relations involving series of integers play a fundamental role. Such examples can be multiplied. For example, the Swiss physicist Wolfgang Pauli, in telling of the work of his great teacher Arnold Sommerfeld in providing an explanation for the particular wavelengths found in the spectra of glowing gases, said,

Sommerfeld however preferred ... a direct interpretation, as independent of models as possible, of the laws of spectra in terms of integral numbers, following as Kepler once did in his investigation of the planetary system, an inner feeling for harmony.

When thus presented, the motivation of many scientists, just like the process of discovery itself, perhaps appears to be surprisingly "unscientific." But precisely because it involves irrational elements, the drive toward discovery is powerful even under the most adverse conditions. How shall we explain that in the sciences, just as in other creative fields of endeavor, much great work has been done under the handicaps of extreme poverty and severe ill-health, sometimes even under the threat of imminent death? Or that many scientists reject the ever-present lure of increased standards of living offered by uncreative positions, and instead follow their chosen, unrestricted work, often with fewer material rewards? We must recognize this symbiotic relationship: the progress of science has often depended on the almost unreasonable tenacity of its devotees and, on the other hand, scientific activity yields a unique exhilaration and deep fulfillment. In support of this point the words of Henri Poincaré are, as always, persuasive:

> The scientist does not study nature because it is useful; he studies it because he delights in it, and he delights in it because it is beautiful. If nature were not beautiful, it would not be worth knowing, and if nature were not worth knowing, life would not be worth living. Of course, I do not here speak of that beauty which strikes the senses, the beauty of qualities and of appearances; not that I undervalue such beauty, far from it, but it has nothing to do with science; I mean that profounder beauty which comes from the harmonious order of the parts and which a pure intelligence can grasp. This it is which gives body, a structure so to speak, to the iridescent appearances which flatter our senses, and without this support the beauty of these fugitive dreams would be only imperfect, because it would be vague and always fleeting. On the contrary, intellectual beauty is sufficient unto itself, and it is for its sake, more perhaps than for the future good of humanity, that the scientist devotes himself to long and difficult labors. (*Science and method*)

14.5 Objectivity. At this point we should face a question that surely must have been suggested by the preceding discussion. What of the much-vaunted objectivity of scientists? One hears of this so often that there is a tendency to regard any inquiry as "scientific" merely if it claims to be unbiased. For example, Bertrand Russell has said, "The kernel of the scientific outlook is the refusal to regard our own desires, tastes, and interests as affording a key to the understanding of the world." But how can the objective search for truth fail to be endangered by the large degree of personal involvement mentioned earlier? Or, since it patently has not endangered science, how can we account for the discrepancy between the nature of motivations and of results?

Here we have, by a second route, come back to the original dilemma, the apparent contradiction in function between "private" and "public" science. To resolve it we will begin with an extreme example, that of the theoretical physicist and astrophysicist Sir Arthur Eddington, who had such strong convictions on the subject that he once wrote a "Defense of Mysticism." Whether or not his persuasion was "meaningless" from the point of view of public science, it very likely was a mainspring, a deep cause, of his devoted search for truth. What is important here is that in his voluminous and distinguished articles on physics you will find no *overt* expression of his personal mysticism, nothing that might not equally well have been written by a gifted scientist with exactly the opposite metaphysical orientation, or even one belonging to the "hard-boiled" school who is quite indifferent to such questions. In modern science, personal philosophic persuasions do not intrude *explicitly* into the published work—not because they are nonexistent, *but because they are expendable.*

We may go a step further. In a free society, the metaphysical tenets of individual scientists, though often quite strong, are generally so varied, so vague, and technically so inept that in a sense they tend to cancel out, or to be ineffectual because of the lack of a basis for general acceptance and agreement of such tenets. Indirectly, this situation has the effect of assuring that science as a whole preserves the freedom to change rapidly and to move in any direction that seems interesting. Only where there exists one explicit and widely accepted set of dogmas, as in some of the Renaissance Scholastic universities or in some of the modern totalitarian states, will extraneous explicit metaphysics in a scientific publication be regarded as acceptable. The consequences are liable to be highly detrimental to the life of science in the long run.

As contrasted with the personal motivations and *implicit* metaphysical assumptions of the scientist, for which he does not have to (and probably could not) account to anyone, the intellectual disciplines imposed on a scientist, such as the form of publication of research papers, are now quite rigorously defined. He knows that the only points upon which he and his colleagues will agree are sound demonstrations and repeatable experiments —that his personal inclinations and theirs may well not coincide, that these inclinations and satisfactions should remain private and, from the point of view of public science, incidental. This severe convention, which is in such clashing contrast with the human side of the investigator, is a kind of sociological device for helping to ensure the rapid evolution of science. For when enthusiasm runs high, the chances for mistakes rise. Therefore, the investigator must force himself to the most searching re-examination before describing his work to that mercilessly impartial jury, his colleagues. Louis Pasteur gave us a good insight into this attitude:

> When you believe you have found an important scientific fact and are feverishly curious to publish it, constrain yourself for days, weeks, years sometimes; fight yourself, try and ruin your own experiments, and only proclaim

your discovery after having exhausted all contrary hypotheses. But when after so many efforts you have at last arrived at certainty, your joy is one of the greatest that can be felt by the human soul.

The development of this attitude is fairly recent. Francis Bacon, in attacking the subjective science of his day, held that the scientist, if he is to build on a sure foundation, must suppress as much as possible the human element, his prejudices, premature hypotheses, his guesses and wishes. To this end Bacon outlined a procedure which prescribed the structure of scientific work so rigidly that the human element would indeed be kept at bay even during the "private" stage of scientific work. In the historical context his proposal was not unreasonable; it might have worked, and it did seem to answer the question of how to remain objective. But as it turned out, scientists found another, less rigorous, less safe, but far more fruitful procedure for reducing human error, one that does so without stifling personal enthusiasm and motivation, the main source of both error *and* fruitful knowledge. This safeguard, which we have seen described so well by Pasteur, is *superposed* on the free creativity of the individual; his inquiry is not controlled in its progress as if it were confined in a train moving on rails, but rather as though it were a rider on a horse whose direction of progress is maintained by an occasional but firm tug on the reins.

14.6 Fact and interpretation. Why, one may ask, should there be any need for an imposed discipline? Is there not discipline in the very *facts* which the scientist observes? Are they not unambiguous in themselves? This raises another interesting problem, that of the relationship between fact and interpretation.

Our very life, as well as our science, continually depends on the observation and classification of facts, and yet there is nothing more deceptive than facts. It is impossible to make a *raw* observation, that is, to acquire knowledge solely of a "fact," without at the same time having some interpretation, some hypothesis, enter the mind, as careful cross-examination of witnesses in a courtroom often shows quite dramatically. If we pursued the matter far enough, we might have to agree that the only genuine or basic facts are those which impress our elementary senses—the fact that we see a black or a white splotch, feel hot or cold, hear a painful or a soft sound. Yet such basic facts, as Galileo pointed out, by themselves could not conceivably have given rise to our science; indeed, many animals must be able to transcend such raw observations. *Perception* must pass into thought and knowledge via *conceptualization*. Starting from vague impressions of "now-here-then-there," man had to invent, perhaps over a period of a thousand generations, such largely unanalyzed ideas as space, object, position, distance, time interval, motion, and speed, before he could even think about appearances.

Since facts cannot be discerned without the assistance of intellectual tools (for example, hypotheses) it follows that scientists do have preconceptions and do use unexamined associations, although these may be justified by a long history of successful results. This admission seems to contradict the popular opinion that the first step in science is to throw overboard all prejudgments. However, without preconceptions one cannot conceive new thoughts. Therefore, what is required in science, as in other phases of life, is the ability to become aware of one's preconceptions in an emergency, to discard those that have become meaningless, to use the others with caution, and, in the absence of knowledge, to have the courage "to pronounce that wise, ingenious, and modest sentence 'I know it not'," as Galileo counseled.

Without our almost axiomatic key concepts we should be largely deprived of intelligence and communication. Imagine a geologist trying to describe his observation of a mountain range solely in terms of "pure facts." He could not even begin to speak of the mountain range at all, for, strictly, all he sees is a change in the level of terrain. Even that implies several derived concepts, so instead of saying "the mountain" he would have to describe merely a pattern of light and darkness, and that his eyes had to focus differently upon the various features of the field of view. Again, "pattern," "focus," and so on, are themselves concepts that he would need before making even this halting beginning.

Thus our thoughts about observations and facts actually involve manipulation of concepts, constructs, and notions, with all their hidden dangers—dangers of erroneous classification, of unwarranted extrapolation and analogy, of too ambitious generalization or too timid specialization. No wonder science treasures such concepts as length, time, mass, and electric charge, which, by long experience, have proved reliable enough to provide a basis for its whole edifice.

Since the least ambiguous facts are those which involve only accounts of pointer readings and the like, physics should ideally start only with such descriptions. Even here there is room for quarrel, for we do have to decide in advance of the experiment what pointer readings are sufficiently significant and important to warrant their collection and description. In this sense, facts do not exist outside of the observer. Let a layman observe the sky through the 200-inch telescope at Palomar Mountain and he will see little of interest and understand little that he sees. But let a trained man examine a comet briefly a few times with relatively poor equipment, and he will call upon astronomical theories to tell us the speed of the comet at any moment, the material of which it is made, the time when it will return, and much else. In short, the pattern we perceive when we note "a fact" is organized and interpreted by a whole system of attitudes and thoughts, memories, beliefs, and learned constructs. It is thought that gives us eyes.

Not only do raw facts alone fail to lead to science, but a program of enthusiastic fact-gathering *per se* has more than once delayed the progress of science. As J. B. Conant has said, "Science advances not by the accumulation of new facts . . . but by the continuous development of new and fruitful concepts." The picture of the experimental scientist in his well-stocked laboratory, engaged in intensive, unbiased, and undirected observation, is absurd, though widespread. Particularly when instruments are to be used, even the initial "preliminary experiments" are preceded by study, thought, and planning. Without this nonexperimental activity, the expensively obtained facts are meaningless.

We conclude once more that individual scientists do not stand alone. To understand even the simplest observations each investigator must rely on the distilled wisdom of science as an institution. When Newton modestly pictured himself as surveying the world from the shoulders of giants, he described the position of every individual scientist.

14.7 How science grows. We may now coordinate several observations on the growth of science to gain one over-all view. The key point is the distinction between private and public science—if you like, the difference between the man Galileo Galilei and the statement $s \propto t^2$. This dual view of science has an analogy in the dual interpretation of the law, either as the ensemble of individual trials and juridical opinions, or as a complete *corpus juris*. Better still, compare the difference between private and public science with the difference in the interpretations one might give to the animal species, i.e., to exemplify it by the diverse living, struggling individuals which it contains, or as calmly catalogued and described in zoology texts at the present state of evolution.

The last analogy suggests a helpful approach to the question of how science grows. The evolution of science and of an animal species both appear to involve four similar mechanisms. First, in both cases our concept of *growth* presupposes a mechanism *that provides continuity*, for neither a species nor a science can persist unless there is some definite and stable means for handing on the structure from generation to generation. In biology the mechanism of continuity is found in the processes of heredity based on the highly specific nature of the genes. In science it is identifiable with our beliefs concerning the specific operational character of the important concepts. Without this measure of unambiguous continuity, scientists could not successfully communicate their work.

Second, a mechanism of *mutation* is superimposed on continuity, leaving open the constant opportunity for individual variations. In an animal species, mutations are produced by various chemical and physical influences on the genes and on chromosome partition and recombination. In a science we believe that they are assured by the essential democracy of the institution and the fertility of the free human mind.

A third mechanism is *multiplicity of effort*. To assure continuity and growth despite the low rate of occurrence of really important modifications, and in the absence of some master plan by which to proceed, a species and a science alike must rely on a large number of individual efforts, from which may ultimately come those few advances that are truly significant. The uncountable fossils of bygone members of the species, like the uncountable pages describing individual researches through the centuries, are mute testimonies of the unavoidable wastefulness of the process of evolution, both of a species and of scientific knowledge.

Finally, there is a *selection* mechanism whereby only certain of the seemingly innumerable contributions and unpredictable mutations are incorporated into the continuous stream of science—a conflict among ideas not greatly different from that fight for existence in nature which enables the species to adapt itself to a changing environment. The survival of a variant under the most diverse and adverse conditions is mirrored in science by the survival of those discoveries, concepts, and relationships that find usefulness in the greatest variety of further application, of those conceptual schemes that withstand the continual check against experience.

One might repeat that science has been so successful because its task is easy and clear-cut compared with that, say, of art or philosophy. In truth the patient search by any scientist for new facts and relationships is likely to have some measure of success. However, this is only a part of the whole picture; the limited amount of scientific knowledge that one person can produce would die with him if it were not for its communicability to others. Moreover, such knowledge would forever be limited by the frailties of individual minds if it were not for some selective growth. *Continuity or communicability, individual variability, multiplicity of free effort, and selective growth—these are the four related principles on which is based the successful growth of science.*

Now we can see still another relationship between private and public science. Each astronomer, or physicist, or chemist, or geologist, fulfills two functions, and it is the easy confusion of these two that commonly produces a distorted picture of him. On the one hand he is an unfettered creator of private science; on the other hand his mind, together with those of his colleagues, is the agency by which the public science is transmitted from one generation to the next. Thus public science, unlike the anthill built from the tiny contributions of individual insects, does not exist *by itself* merely in the form of books, periodical articles, and laboratory apparatus, but exists first of all in the minds of the scholars who work in the field. Consequently public science, or science-as-an-institution, in passing through the ages from one group of rational beings to the following, continually undergoes a twofold change: it is ever more sharpened toward communicability and unambiguity, and it is incessantly expanded by tests for continuing meaning and usefulness in the course of widening experience and deeper experiments.

In retrospect we can now see the signs of these mechanisms of evolution in the nature of physical concepts themselves. Recall the three characteristics of scientific concepts: their operational meaning, their preferably quantitative nature, and their reappearance in diverse fields of inquiry. All of these help to assure the continuation and expansion of the scientific enterprise. They aid in the unambiguous communication of problems and results, make possible unambiguous agreement (or disagreement) among different workers on facts and their interpretations, and knit together the efforts of many independent scientists, even when widely separated in subject interest, time, and locality.

14.8 Consequences of the model. Several generally accepted features of scientific inquiry are derivable from the view that science-as-an-institution is continually transmitted and modified in its flow through the minds of original creators, and that it is shaped by the processes of evolution. Here is a summary of a few such points.

(a) *Freedom of research and teaching.* Convenience and freedom of communication are vital to the very existence of science at each moment. The jealous secrecy with which the alchemists hid their results doomed their efforts to stagnation and helped to delay the rise of chemistry, just as today the imposition of secrecy on basic research has threatened to constrict the arteries of science. The right to pursue any promising lead and to publish purely scientific information must be vigorously defended if science is to thrive. This makes apparent the important role played by free, disinterested research in academic institutions, where an investigator may follow the unpredictable path of knowledge without serious constraint and interference. In science, as in society, truth can be found only in the free market place of ideas. Only the filter of years, not the regulations of men, can extract the real worth from each contribution.

(b) *Scientific organizations.* The rise of organizations among scientists reflects the realization that the continued growth of scientific knowledge depends upon communication among its practitioners. From the 17th century onward there has been a rapidly increasing multiplication of the channels of communication through scientific societies, institutes, periodicals, and symposiums. National and international meetings are held regularly by scientists. Some organizations exist for the sole purpose of summarizing (abstracting), indexing, and distributing accounts of the growing avalanche of scientific developments. Scientists work in committees and hold international congresses to decide on uniform nomenclature, definitions, and standards of measurement. They sponsor publication of monumental volumes of physical and chemical tables of constants. Above all, they are eager to share their latest findings and difficulties.

(c) *Variety of work.* Multiplicity of effort is not only a characteristic of all past work, it is a staggering reality in science today. Because here we have necessarily presented only some of the more spectacular and historic advances of science and so run the danger of distorting proportions, let us now look at a brief listing of some reports on current research, selected almost at random from a single issue of *Physics Abstracts*, an internationally distributed periodical that each month summarizes about a thousand technical papers in physics alone.

An American mathematical physicist reports on a new way of solving a difficult type of equation, and illustrates his work by an application to typical problems involving electric currents in complex circuits.

A Swedish engineer surveys the field of computing machines, and a scientific journal in South Africa is cited as having an article on the possible use of such machines in solving problems in statistics.

A British journal publishes a paper on astrophysics in which certain unsolved problems are reviewed and the conclusion is drawn that the desired solutions may hinge on the introduction of new physical concepts.

The French *Bulletin of Astronomy* presents a discussion by the British Astronomer Royal on the desirability of introducing a slight change into the present set of definitions of the *second of time* in terms of specific astronomical observations.

New measurements are available on the recently discovered high-frequency radiowaves, akin to "static," that occur during sunspot activity but which originate in various parts of our galaxy and beyond; one abstract reports, "The theories put forward to explain these effects are compared and it appears that a satisfactory theoretical explanation has not yet been found."

A Russian re-examines the problem of the origin of planets and their satellites in the light of recent findings in geophysics, geology, and geochemistry; and an American Nobel Prize chemist discusses the evidence for the presence of certain substances on Mars.

An eminent physicist has re-examined the effect of electric fields on the viscosity of liquids; since the effect is small, extremely refined experimental methods had to be devised.

A number of independent reports, including one from India and another from Germany, deal with the varied information on the structure of substances that is obtained by studying the propagation of sound through them. This fairly new field of research has been growing rapidly during the past few years, and is now finding application in biology and medicine; for instance, one abstract is entitled "Detection of intracranial pathology by ultrasound."

A new measurement, claimed to be accurate to one part in 10^6, has been made of the speed of light by means of apparatus originally developed in wartime laboratories for use in radar.

Two Americans have precisely determined the wavelengths of the light emitted by a new electric discharge tube containing the vapor of a single isotope of mercury; arguments are advanced in favor of adoption of one of these wavelengths as the primary standard of length.

Several advances in experimentation and theory are reported from the thriving field of low-temperature physics. Of particular interest is a brief account of contributions to competing theories, rivaling for the correct interpretation of the phenomenon of superconductivity.

Some hundreds of papers, including a considerable proportion from Japan and Italy, deal with the fundamental properties of subatomic particles—their electric charge, behavior in electric and magnetic fields or during collisions with one another, their characteristics in cyclotrons and other accelerators, and so forth. This is the field that is the focus of activity in physics at the moment.

And there is of course a great deal more; we have at this point not even reached those abstracts dealing with such topics as crystallography, cosmic rays, molecular structure, radioactivity, and so forth. What is most noticeable here is the variety of topics and interests, and the apparent importance of many of the papers. Yet no one would venture to predict which of these contributions will be best remembered and most used several decades hence. And also, it is clear that science is an international activity, regardless of cultural differences; the whole world is its stage and its concern, and the whole world provides its authors and its audience.

(d) *Simultaneous discoveries.* Our view of science as an organism describable by laws of evolution helps to explain the truism that "once a situation is ready" for a discovery, it frequently is made in several places at about the same time. When we say of some general advance that the time was ripe for it, we mean usually that at least three conditions obtained: there were *reasons* for looking into the problem, that is, it now made sense to ask such a question and it may in fact have been generally discussed; next, there were *means* for looking, that is, the needed experimental tools were obtainable; and there were mental schemes for *understanding*, that is, the needed concepts and conceptual systems were not too difficult to assemble. When all this happens at one time, several investigators may compete unknowingly or knowingly, for it is possible that they each have a similar heritage, have encountered and interpreted the problem in the same way, and thus, borne by the same wave, may reach the same shore.

(e) *Belated acceptance.* We have also had examples of the opposite phenomenon: the initial rejection or long neglect that is often experienced by precisely the most startling innovators, even though their contribution later may come to be widely accepted. If public science is not simply the sum of individual contributions, but exists, as we have asserted, within the minds of practicing scientists, then it follows that a contribution, to become part of public science, must find acceptance in the minds of many men. This takes time, especially if the innovation is seriously out of line with the existing climate of opinion in the field. As we have seen, some initial resistance to new ideas is desirable in the long run for the healthy evolution of science. But it can happen, though rarely, that the ideas of a man regarded as something of a crackpot by his contemporaries reappear, even though much modified, as an important contribution later on when the scientific horizon has widened in the course of evolution. The history of science clearly shows that there is need for the recluse of yet undisplayed ability just as there is need for widely acclaimed heroes and the army of competent foot soldiers.

(f) *The rapid emergence of science.* By the same token that freedom in science increases the chances for both multiplicity of effort and individual variation, so also does a free science, ever productive of its own tools for further advancement, tend to become not only self-perpetuating but self-accelerating. As knowledge begets knowledge, it increases as though in a geometric series.

It is a source of constant wonder that modern science, once it got its first real impetus in the 17th century, swept over Europe within a century. Although the issues were complex, as we have seen, one may speculate that two trends contributed materially: Western science, from the 14th century on, had expanded and progressed to the point where the principles of multiplicity of effort and of individual variations were finally in effective operation, and the work of Galileo and of his contemporaries now provided attitudes and concepts which, being quantitative and clearly meaningful, allowed the principle of continuity to operate more fully than before, thereby modifying the science of the time toward the self-sustaining character which it attained in the early 18th century.

(g) *The interconnection of all knowledge.* We have noted that one cannot foresee the course of science; only rarely can one evaluate a discovery at the time and predict how important its place in science will be. For the very same reasons, we cannot foresee whether some discovery will be applied for the benefit of mankind or put to evil uses by those who formulate or merely respond to the wishes of society. As an illustration of these several points, consider that the phenomenon of radioactivity was discovered rather casually by Henri Becquerel when a photographic plate become exposed to the rays from a nearby piece of uranium salt (he had put them together in a drawer in preparation for an experiment that actually had been inspired by a plausible but erroneous hypothesis). Consider further that Becquerel did not understand the meaning of his observations; that through the brave and arduous labors of the Curies the new radioactive elements were isolated and identified—an unsuspected widening of the horizon of physical science; that the resulting new knowledge then stimulated several generations of scientific workers and so directly and indirectly revolutionized our conceptual models of the atom, of radiation, and of chemical reactions. Then recall that today radioactivity is an integral part or indispensable tool of innumerable studies quite outside the field of discovery, notably in the medical treatment of certain dread diseases, and also in research in biology, geology, astrophysics, metallurgy, even archeology, and many others. Surely no one will dare prescribe limits to the process of discovery!

And then consider the great contemporary dilemma: the technological applications of nuclear energy, the lineal descendants of the discovery of radioactivity, may put the philosopher's stone into every man's pocket and lead us to the happy age for which we are hardly prepared, or they may help us end the short history of our species. All major nations are simultaneously engaged on the one hand in designing processes and engines for industry and commerce and, on the other, in planning for the possible destruction of one another's populations.

Frightened by the potential misapplication of the indirect fruits of science, some have suggested that the pursuit of science itself be halted. Quite apart from the bad logic and the impossibility of effective enactment of such proposals, they are also symptomatic of a poor understanding of the nature and role of science. Knowledge is like a great net; if one were to cut out the part which is labeled science, the rest of the net would be of little use. Moreover, although knowledge without deeper human wisdom may fail us, *less* knowledge hardly assures either wisdom or survival; indeed, one might at least question whether ignorance is now either possible or worth living for. Since salvation and disaster are not reached by separate roads, we may not simply choose one and avoid the other; they both lie at the end of the same path, the final choice being within ourselves. If we sought to resolve the dilemma by fiat, by some official control of science, we should all have to submit to a censorship that, because of its inability to predict the outcome of the results obtained by curious minds, essentially would have to rule out all intelligent speculation. Surely, this would mean the loss, along with science, of our basic freedoms, and of all hope for an enlightened future. These effects would be as destructive of our society as the vengeance of a savage conqueror.

If we look for an alternative solution, we might well try to emulate the lesson afforded by the growth of science itself: *the marvelous ability of men to arrive at fruitful agreement through the free and vigorous exchange of intelligence.*

CHAPTER 15

ON SCIENTIFIC DISCOVERY

Having examined the character of physical concepts and the relationships between scientists and their work, let us turn to the question whether anything positive may be said about the process of discovery in science. It will be fitting and revealing to consult first the opinions of active scientists, and then to suggest a model to represent the process of discovery.

15.1 Opinions on scientific procedure. We remember the warning not to expect uniformity of procedure. Although a representative feeling among scientists in general about the main elements of scientific procedure has never crystallized, there are nevertheless several types of opinions that have been held prominently, and five facets have reappeared frequently enough to be of interest. None of these by itself tells the whole story; none should be construed to be in rivalry with the others. Rather we shall consider them as five complementary aspects of the same general opinion on procedures, the emphasis depending on the particular problem and the particular scientist.

(a) The first view that we will consider is epitomized by a remark made by Joseph Priestley in 1776:

> More is owing to what we call *chance*, that is, philosophically speaking, to the observation of events *arising from unknown* [unsuspected] *causes*, than to any proper *design* or preconceived *theory* in the business.

Superficially one indeed cannot help but be impressed by the role of chance in scientific work. Remember Newton's remark that a falling apple directed his mind toward the principle of gravitation. The initial observations leading to the epochal discoveries of the battery, many of the elements, electromagnetism, radioactivity, and contemporary chemotherapy were all made more or less by chance. With reference to related sciences, W. I. B. Beveridge writes in his book *The art of scientific investigation* (1951), "Probably the majority of discoveries in biology and medicine have been come upon unexpectedly, or at least had an element of chance in them, especially the most important and revolutionary ones."

This dovetails with what has been said before concerning the irrational elements in the process of discovery. However, we must look at the whole picture. Most scientific work is unspectacular both in genesis and achievement; if chance enters at all, it is greatly outweighed by sheer hard work. Whatever else may be true of the methods of science, they are not short

248

cuts to knowledge; they operate within the matrix of a life spent in the laboratory, at the desk, or in field expeditions. Indeed, Priestley's own work in chemistry contradicts his insistence on the pre-eminent role of chance. Close examination of the work of other investigators usually reveals that they were operating with the benefit of hypotheses that had prepared their minds to accept the discoveries.

And at the very least there is the unassailable dictum, "chance favors the prepared mind." The great chance discoveries in science were made by people who distinguished themselves by other work as well. It is only the master of his subject who can turn to his advantage the irrational and the unsuspected. Chance observations usually become important if they trigger off trains of thought that from all evidences could have been arrived at more systematically by those minds. This trigger action of chance is not to be despised, but to interpret the stimulus correctly one must have had prior training and thought on the general subject of the discovery.

(b) We do not need to dismiss Priestley's viewpoint as erroneous if we permit other elements to enter more prominently into the process of discovery. One such ingredient has been described forcefully by P. W. Bridgman in a famous passage in his *Reflections of a physicist* (1950):

> I like to say that there is no scientific method as such, but that the most vital feature of the scientist's procedure has been merely to do his utmost with his mind, *no holds barred*. This means in particular that no special privileges are accorded to authority or to tradition, that personal prejudices and predilections are carefully guarded against, that one makes continued check to assure oneself that one is not making mistakes, and that any line of inquiry will be followed that appears at all promising. All of these rules are applicable to any situation in which one has to obtain the right answer and all of them are only manifestations of intelligence.

This statement clearly recalls and illustrates what has been said before about the lack of *a* method, about the variability among scientists and their methods.

(c) In much the same vein others (among them Max Planck, the discoverer of the quantum concept) regard their work simply as an extension and refinement of common sense. By itself, this view of science is also incomplete. We must admit that the primitive notions of science sprang from everyday experience, that much of science had its origins in the common-sense practices of early craftsmen and artisans, and that even today research often involves a kind of common-sense empiricism, particularly in engineering and technology. But when we examine modern physical science, then common sense is "common" only in the sense that the special training and endowments of the worker in a specific field allow him to find the way through his problems as naturally as the craftsman at his own task.

(d) A fourth opinion characterizes the essence of scientific procedure in the terse statement: "The scientific method consists in observing and experimenting." This view has a wide range of interpretations and misinterpretations. In the extreme case it may refer to a technique like that advocated by Bacon—an orderly experimental search for *facts* while carefully keeping one's mind free from the influences of prior notions. The facts so collected were to be interpreted or explained only at the very end by a process of "true" induction, that is, induction unspoiled by hypotheses prematurely formulated. Now sometimes a research project does reach a stage where for months or even years theorizing on a large scale is held in check, pending the collection of sufficiently comprehensive data. But we have already had reason to doubt that any productive scientist displays the Baconian attitude of complete commitment to observation and experimentation, and whether this procedure is even fruitful. We are supported in our doubt by history. Surely Galileo's experiments with the inclined plane were not the result of a simple desire to see what a rolling ball would do. On the contrary, Galileo quite certainly knew in advance what type of results the experiments would yield. Some foreknowledge or sense for the sort of solution to be expected is almost inseparable from the recognition even of the *existence* of a problem. Galileo confessed his conviction of the Aristotelian faith that nature acts in the simplest possible way, hence he expected some very simple relationship between distances, times, and speeds.

At the least, some criteria are needed to focus the observer's attention on certain aspects of the total experience to the exclusion of the rest; for example, measuring the distance and time in the inclined-plane experiment is valuable for an eventual solution only if these factors are dominant in the determination of the ball's motion. This is the case even though some aspects of a situation may initially appear promising and yet turn out to be irrelevant. Thus Galileo, like many before him, appears to have suspected initially that the material of which a body is made determines its velocity of free fall. In some instances long investigation is needed to determine which factors are most relevant.

On the whole, the problem here is similar to that of the craftsman who must have at least some conception of the final product before he decides on the medium and tools for rendering the work. The experimentalist, particularly, must design his apparatus and procedure with a fair idea of the type and magnitude of the effect to be expected, including the allowable errors and the masking secondary effects. In short, the scientist cannot just observe and experiment. He cannot just *search;* he has to search *for something,* and he must have some conception of what is to be expected—otherwise he may pass by the solution without recognizing it.

Now what still remains of the opinion that "the scientific method consists in observing and experimenting"? Much; above all, this: whether we put our theorizing at the beginning or at the end, and no matter by what mental procedure we arrive at our laws, *sooner or later we must submit our work to the test of experience.* Even work so purely theoretical in character as the theory of relativity originated in the contemplation of certain perplexing experimental information concerning the propagation of light and the motion of charged particles, and at the end of his theoretical exposition, Einstein returned to the experimental aspects of science by discussing several possible experimental tests of the theory. Of one such proposed test he said bluntly, "If the displacement of spectral lines toward the red . . . does not exist, then the general theory of relativity will be untenable." Here we have again the persistent and striking *leitmotif* in science, the appeal to *observation and experiment as last authorities.*

(e) Finally, a view of scientific procedure held in highest esteem by some of those responsible for the spectacular achievements in contemporary theoretical physics is typified by Einstein's statement, "there is no logical way to the discovery of the elemental laws. There is only the way of intuition, which is helped by a feeling for the order lying behind the appearances." We hear from these men that they immerse themselves completely in the problem at hand, and either speculatively or by unselfconscious induction try to reach postulates that will serve as a basis for resolving the problematic situation. Instead of going from step to step with conscious certainty, as some do, these men make large intellectual jumps as though borne by a guiding necessity. Sometimes they reveal that such solutions occur to them "in a sudden flash of insight" after long, even feverish study.

This type of inspired creativity is usually thought to be more common in *belle lettres* and the arts. It is close to the procedure advocated by Plato (for example, in the *Phaedo*) as well as by certain Scholastics. One can, and many contemporary historians of science do, defend the view that this was the main approach of Galileo—that he postulated that the acceleration $\Delta v/\Delta t$ of all freely falling objects is constant, and then deduced from this the experimentally confirmable behavior of falling and rolling bodies. A related fashion, encouraged by the method of presentation used by Newton in the *Principia* and favored particularly among French scientists in the last century, was to organize the presentation of scientific work along lines similar to those developed by the later Greek mathematicians, beginning with clearly stated postulates or hypotheses, then deducing theorems or laws from them rigorously and mathematically, and finally calling in experimental confirmations as though merely by way of illustration.

In this type of presentation, for which there sometimes is no alternative, the experiment may be replaced by the "thought" experiment, an argument which says in essence, "Let us imagine this or that plausible situation; surely you must agree that things will happen thus and thus exactly in accord with my deduction." Thus Galileo said that he did not need to determine by actual experiment whether a stone dropped from the mast of a ship moving with constant speed will strike at the foot of the mast no matter what the speed of the ship; he knew that this would follow as a consequence of the principle of superposition or composition (vector addition) of velocities, used and amply verified in his treatment of projectile motion.

But here again we are dealing with only one aspect of scientific procedure; for however important may be the role of inspired postulation or of the unexplainable appearance of a key principle in the exceptional mind, this does not by itself tell the whole story, particularly with regard to the experimental stages of scientific inquiry. In fact, we can now summarize the various characteristics for good scientific work which successful investigators emphasize in varying degrees: *an intuitive feeling for nature, particularly for its quantitative aspects; the sensitivity for recognizing a favorable though unexpected turn of events; a common sense deepened through special training; a habit of using one's intelligence to the utmost; and a reliance first and last on observation and experiment.*

This list is certainly far from being a magic formula for revealing *the* scientific method. The fact is, no such formula exists, and we may expect from the scientists themselves only the most general hints about their procedures; for in science, as in every field of creative endeavor, the most expert work is done by men who have passed beyond the need and the interest to rationalize each step. In the sense that each problem has its own difficulties and each scientist his own approach, we may say that the scientific inquiry has its art as much as its methods.

Perhaps the five views on procedure that we have discussed may be best brought together and characterized by some one phrase such as "scientific orientation," or "scientific outlook," or "scientific attitude." We may even venture to say that while scientific work is not characterized by any single method, to a considerable extent *scientists generally do share this complex of characteristic attitudes* toward their life occupation; this helps to make understandable why scientists can evaluate and complement one another's work, can usually adapt themselves to another field, to new problems and a new set of collaborators, and can sometimes make contributions to several widely separated sciences.

15.2 Some steps in the formulation of laws. Although the evidence presented dispels hope for an easy formula of discovery, we must not let ourselves fall into the extreme skepticism of Priestley. From our now suitably modest point of view, we may still analyze how scientific laws grow out of observations, concepts, and hypotheses. To be silent on this subject would be to disregard or dismiss the distinguished and varied testimony of numerous influential writers on the philosophy and methodology of modern science, such as Peirce, Duhem, Mach, Poincaré, Whitehead, Russell, Dewey, Cassirer, Reichenbach, Weyl, and a host of contemporary philosophers.

What we shall do is analyze in several steps a *hypothetical* case of the formulation of a law, without claiming that formulations *in general* do actually follow this specific pattern. Thus the scheme to be discussed is intended to be merely a mnemonic device that may be helpful in thinking about some recurring and related features of scientific procedure, either in the work of an individual or in the historical development of a generalization involving the contributions of several generations.

(a) Our first step surely must be to stress the importance in any inquiry of the *investigator's knowledge of contemporary science,* including the tested tricks of the trade and the more or less tacit assumptions embodied in every intellectual enterprise. Thus, Galileo was familiar with Scholastic mechanics and the relatively advanced work on projectile motion of Tartaglia and Benedetti. Sometimes such prior knowledge may ultimately prove unsatisfactory and the assumptions even misleading. But at the outset it is the existing conceptual scheme that gives direction to the inquiry; it represents the initial "common sense" from which the scientist may draw or perhaps eventually must break away. At later stages he may well have to go back to his books or instruments to supplement his knowledge in unfamiliar fields which turn out to touch on the developing situation, or, finding nothing helpful in existing disciplines, he may have to invent new instruments and techniques or new mathematical aids. For example, Copernicus had to invent some of his solid geometry, and Newton much of his calculus.

(b) A second element in the initial setting, even before a problem has suggested itself, is *an intimate acquaintance with natural phenomena through personal experience and observation.* Ideally, what is desired is a state of resonance between the investigator and nature. This is, of course, the setting in which "chance" observations occur. But, more importantly, immersion in nature provides the investigator with the raw material with which to construct his questions or problems, and enables him to acquire the necessary measure of nonrational insight. And it is observation that implants in him the almost intuitive feeling for the behavior of things in the field of his specialty, for the variables that may be significant, and for their interaction. To cite again the work of Einstein, because it was perhaps as far removed from personal participation in experimentation as is possible in physical science, we find in his autobiographical notes this interesting remark: "I really could have gotten a sound mathematical education [at the Polytechnic Institute in Zurich]. However, I worked most of the time in the physical laboratory, fascinated by the direct contact with experience."

(c) With the setting thus prepared, *the question or problem may present itself to the mind* during an "occasion of reflection" (to use John Dewey's happy phrase), arising perhaps from some surprising chance finding, but more probably as the result either of some dissatisfaction with the degree of consistency, generality, or accuracy of the current explanation, or of some "hunch" where the rewarding new field of study lies. There is no clear biographical account to tell us why and how Galileo first began his study of motion, but we may gather that one motivation was dissatisfaction with contemporary qualitative modes of description. Other men seemed to have been presented with the problem to be solved through imaginative pictorialization of physical processes, or by the desire to find symmetry or particular patterns in the operations of nature.

(d) Intimately connected with a recognition of the existence of the problem is a measure of more or less unformulated *foreknowledge of the type of solution to be expected*. Kepler's laws of planetary motion did not obtrude themselves upon a completely uncommitted investigator; they were found by a man who knew in his very soul that some such simple quantitative relations must exist. The ability to look in a particular direction before one can know what one will see appears to be a talent indispensable for consistently good work.

(e) This early stage of research may not only suggest new and interesting problems and some tentative hypotheses concerning the eventual solution of the problems, but it may also give rise to *specific concepts with which to analyze the problematic situation,* concepts often crystallized from earlier and vaguer ones. One illustration was Newton's early idea of a universal force of gravitation. Similarly, Galileo saw the need for the precise formulation of the concept "acceleration" in connection with his study of projectile motion. Another case is that of Wilhelm Röntgen, the discoverer of x-rays (1895), who found that the rays pass through objects, but that this transparency diminished appreciably with an increase in either the thickness or the density of the objects. It occurred to him that pieces of various metals for which the product of thickness and density is the same might have the same transparency. It so happens that this proved not to be the case; but evidently if this simple constancy had been found, the concept "thickness $\times$ density" soon would have been assigned a name of its own and equipped with a letter symbol, and doubtless would have figured prominently in the eventual solution of the problem of transparency of metals to x-rays.

But here it may be well to emphasize that the great concepts, like the great problems on which physics is built, generally do not spring ready-made from the minds of individual scientists. They change and develop during the inquiry or, as exemplified by such concepts as force, density, and energy, they may have behind them a long history of evolution, involving many men and many false starts. Even when we give Galileo credit for the definition of *acceleration*, we should not forget that he brought to fruition a notion that had existed in more or less crude form for centuries before his time.

(f) Along with the *preliminary experimentation* and the first guiding ideas, there may begin to grow in the researcher's mind a *working hypothesis*, for example Röntgen's idea that for x-rays there might be a simple relation between transparency, thickness, and density. This process of inducing a hypothesis or a postulate from a necessarily limited number of facts can be likened to the unpredictable experience one may have during a game of chess, when one suddenly "sees through" the whole arrangement on the board and in a single flash discerns the chain of moves that will bring about a successful ending. Although the mechanism of such sudden perception is not well understood, we can at any rate point to the essential part played by hypotheses in the scheme of scientific inquiry: they stimulate intelligent, directed activity, be it theoretical or experimental (Section 8.2). To provide this directive action, an initial hypothesis need not be directly fruitful. We have long ceased to be surprised about the large number of useful theories that have been developed with the temporary aid of a hypothesis that later failed.

We have frequently mentioned induction, which, for our purposes, may be defined as an attempt to arrive at a generalization (a hypothesis, or a postulate, or a law) that is more comprehensive than the facts upon which it is initially based. Heavy reliance on this "process" has always been necessary in science, since by induction we simply mean the obtaining of the postulates that serve to explain the phenomena. Nevertheless, we must be constantly sensitive to the fact that induction involves a leap of the creative mind, for there is no rigorous "logic of induction" comparable to the rules that constitute the logic of deduction. While we must often generalize from the particular to the universal, we can never know with certainty that we are generalizing rightly; a hypothesis can only be tested by a somewhat inconclusive method: we deduce its consequences and check them against experience. That is, we can say with confidence that *if* a given generalization is correct, then facts $a, b, c, \ldots$ must necessarily follow. But when, upon testing, these facts are actually observed, we can then do no more than conclude that the hypothesis is *perhaps* correct, for there may be numerous other hypotheses from which the same facts might equally well be deduced.

It is quite impressive how many wrong reasons there are which can make a particular generalization seem to be valid or invalid. Sometimes a hypothesis will be faulty and yet seem to be confirmed by experiment because the measurements or inferences from the experimental data are faulty, or because the errors have canceled one another. Again, the experiments may be valid but the hypothesis erroneous except for the single prediction which was tested. On the other hand, a *valid* hypothesis may fail to be borne out by experiment because the effect looked for is too small to be detected with the instruments at hand; or one may be deceived by masking disturbances from an unrecognized source, or by faults in the experimental method, or by misinterpretation of the test. In short, nature's full complexity and subtlety may be far greater than our imagination can grasp or our hypothesis can accommodate.

Although there are no substitutes for the precarious business of reaching generalizations by induction and of attempting to confirm them by tests, there are several tricks that in the long history of thought have proved to be helpful in dealing with hypotheses and with results based on them: *to try the simplest hypotheses first, to make several independent checks before accepting an experimental result of importance, never to regard a hypothesis as true beyond all possible doubt, and continually to re-evaluate and reformulate old knowledge in the light of the new.*

Ernst Mach said, "Let us early get used to the fact that science is unfinished, variable." If we are reconciled to the view that a poor hypothesis is better than none, that our thoughts may be grossly oversimplified and later may need drastic modification, that several useful hypotheses may coexist, then we shall not be tempted to regard all work of the past as foolish or all work of the present as certain. Furthermore, if we consider hypotheses as stimuli for action, we shall not demand that they be immediately and directly confirmable. Indeed, the large-scale explanatory postulate usually does not lend itself to direct experimental test (for example, the hypothesis that the agency by which the sun pulls on all planets is the same gravitational force that pulls a stone to the earth), but in any event we insist on testing its plausibility and usefulness by examining the degree of agreement between observed fact and the corresponding prediction deduced from the hypothesis (in the present example, various astronomical observations).

(g) As work progresses, the initial working hypotheses permit the scientist to *design and perform experiments that are more specific and better controlled.* Gradually insight will progress, as if on two crutches—now the hypotheses helping to interpret one experiment and suggesting the next, now the experimental result causing the investigator to modify the hypotheses, in continual interplay. *Thus the investigator may reach, by a process of successive approximations, the desired formulation of a satisfactory set of hypotheses or postulates.*

In retrospect, we can collect the stages cited in this purely hypothetical example. Basic to the setting is the knowledge of contemporary science, and possibly some prior unsystematic observation. The recognition of the problem focuses the attention of the investigator, and probably is also attended by some vague foreknowledge of the type of solution to be expected. Some preliminary experimentation might now be called for. A working hypothesis is formulated, and the need for new concepts may be recognized. Additional directed experimentation and observation modify the working hypothesis, and this in turn is reflected in the design of new experimental tests, or even in the reformulation of the original problem. Finally, the repeated interaction between hypothesis and experience leads gradually to the formulation of a general theory, a set of satisfactory postulates.

15.3 Types of physical laws. The appellation "law" is usually reserved in physical science for those postulates that have not only been found to be trustworthy but that can be expressed as mathematical relationships. However, laws are not all of one kind. Some are *empirical rules* which summarize in a simple and convenient manner a great amount of observational material, although the person who formulated the rule may have no idea *why* the rule should hold in nature. This was the case with Kepler's third law of planetary motion, Bode's law, and many others.

Other laws were formulated on the basis of an induction that is not seen to follow with any sense of compelling necessity from direct observation. Newton's laws of motion are examples; they are postulates providing definitions of and relations between the concepts force, mass, and acceleration, which are useful for dealing with an incredibly large variety of phenomena. Similarly, the essence of Galileo's laws of projectile motion is a postulate which cannot be "directly seen," namely, the principle of superposition of velocities or the independence of horizontal and vertical velocity components for trajectories in a plane. Newton's principle of universal gravitation shares many features of this type of law also, for it contains basically the postulate, far removed from direct observation, that there exists between any two particles in the universe a mutual attraction.

A third kind of law (although it is unnecessary and dangerous to imagine that there are definite lines of demarcation between these laws) is the type which is *deduced from a theory*, from a network of definitions, rules, postulates, and conceptual models. Here the examples include the law of multiple proportions in chemistry, deduced by Dalton on the basis of the atomic model of matter; the law of diffusion speeds in gases, which can be derived from the kinetic theory of gases; the law of the pendulum, which follows from the principles of mechanics; and many others.

This type of law, which we may name *derivative*, often seems the most satisfying of the three because, since it has been derived from some underlying theory, we are tempted to feel it is also somehow more fully "explained." Indeed, scientists continually seek to reduce purely empirical laws to derivative ones, thereby giving the empirical law a measure of additional "meaning,"* while at the same time extending and fortifying the theory itself. Thus Kepler's three empirical laws are deducible from the postulates of Newtonian mechanics.

There is here a kind of symbiotic relationship between law and theory. A theory becomes more and more respected and powerful the more phenomena can be derived from it, and the law describing these phenomena becomes more meaningful and useful if it can be made part of a general theory. Thus, Newton's theory of universal gravitation gained greatly in stature because it enabled derivation of the laws governing the moon's motion, which had been known by empirical rules since the days of the Babylonian observers. These rules in turn, now that they were "understandable" in terms of the theory, could be reformulated more accurately; in fact, the theory even enriched them, for example by calling attention to hitherto unnoticed peculiarities of the moon's motion. Another important example of this kind will be presented in the section on the nuclear atom, whose theory has been enormously important in modern science because it swallowed up whole textbooks full of isolated empirical laws from all branches of physics and chemistry, and reissued them as derivative laws springing from the unifying concept of the atom.

From this discussion we may perhaps draw some general conclusions valid beyond the physical sciences. *Empirical rules may be valid enough in a limited field, but they do not contain enough information to warn the unwary user when some particular new case is really outside the field of applicability of the empirical rule.* Not until the damage is done is it clear that the rule did not apply.

Most of our own everyday actions tend to be governed by this type of uncomprehended rule and plausible generalization. This is doubly unfortunate, since these rules, unlike those in science, are usually not even based on accurate, clear-headed observation. While our life thereby may become simpler, it also is made more brutal and senseless, and we open ourselves up to an invasion of pseudoscience, superstition, and prejudice, even in matters subject to test and measurement.

15.4 The limitations of physical laws. Clearly, the word "law" is inadequate, for it is used to designate so many different types of generaliza-

---

*This feeling appears somewhat fallacious if subjected to rigorous analysis. After all, the theory itself is acceptable only if its derived laws can be checked by experiment, and may in fact turn out to be incorrect *even if* the derived laws are verifiable; we shall see such an example when we come to deal with the theory of heat. Nevertheless, great theories are relatively stable for long periods, and laws derived from them are as secure as we have any right to expect.

tions: rules, postulates, principles, or theoretically derived relations. For our present purpose, however, we shall not need to keep careful distinctions between these differences in our terminology.

But the word "law" is also misleading in a more important sense. Being generalizations tested by experiments, laws can be no more trustworthy than are the terms used in expressing them or the accuracy and extent of the supporting experiments. Although the laws of nature are usually called inexorable and inescapable, probably because the word erroneously suggests analogies with divine and juridical law, they actually are humanly formulated generalizations that are neither eternally true nor unchangeable. They are, in the words of Karl Pearson, "descriptions," not "prescriptions." The most certain statement we can make about the laws of science is that sooner or later the advance of knowledge and experience will show their limitations in scope or accuracy. Each ultimately is the result of induction from a necessarily limited number of experiments or observations; yet if it is to be usefully employed, one must pretend, cautiously, that it applies to all situations of the same kind (see Newton's "Rules of Reasoning," Section 11.3). One example is the set of extensive tables that Galileo compiled for the range of projectiles. The experimental basis for this part of his work must have been quite limited, but once he had derived the parabolic trajectory, which is the essence of his theory of projectile motion, he could derive and accept further consequences that had never been anticipated or tested experimentally. But at the same time it is necessary to be constantly alert for a new situation in which this ancient theory will prove to be inadequate, not only because it involves idealizations, such as the assumption that the air resistance is negligibly small, but also because there is, for example, no logical necessity for assuming that the laws for low-speed cannon balls will be applicable to projectiles of high speeds and long ranges.

Here we must also remember the warning that the statement of any physical law carries a "hidden text" which defines and explains the symbols involved, specifies how these symbols are to be manipulated mathematically, gives the degree of accuracy and the range of experience supporting the law, and so forth. Thus the "text" not only helps to prevent misapplication of the law, but implies that sooner or later a limit may be encountered beyond which the law is no longer completely valid in its stated form. An analogy may be found in the awareness of a party of mountain climbers that there are limits beyond which they can put no demands on their ropes, their gear, and their own bodies. In both cases the limits usually cannot be clearly recognized or defined until some failure brings them to attention. But whereas the climbers naturally dread such a failure, scientists are not helpless or discouraged if occasionally a new phenomenon is not in accord with the established rules; for beyond the limits of the law may lie a hitherto undiscovered realm of science —new and important knowledge. Later we shall encounter several great theories, such as Planck's and Bohr's, that had their beginnings in the observation of new phenomena that seemed to lie beyond the range of contemporary physical laws.

Galileo's equations for projectile motion carried with them such "texts." We find in his work a careful examination of the major limitations involved. For example, he pointed out that the trajectory will not be parabolic for extremely long ranges because then the acceleration due to gravity, being always directed toward the center of our round earth, will no longer have exactly the same direction at different points on the path, as he had assumed in obtaining his equations for the trajectory. Strictly speaking, this same limitation holds even for short ranges, as Galileo well knew, but theory and test show it to modify the simpler treatment only negligibly for many purposes, just as it is often permissible to neglect such effects as those due to air resistance, rotation of the earth, and variations in the magnitude of g along the path. Of these limitations on the applicability of our laws we need not be ashamed. If forced to deal with projectile motions in which these secondary factors are not negligibly small, we are confident of being able to solve our problems either by finding laws that are more comprehensive or by finding correction factors that can be applied to our calculations.

When a law (or set of laws) does break down, it is often possible to rejuvenate and extend it, perhaps by redefining some of the concepts involved. But if it cannot be extended, it still is as useful as before in explaining and predicting the phenomena to which it originally was applicable. As we noted, Newton's laws of mechanics are still as valid as they ever were for describing the vast range of motions for which they were originally developed, even though they must be replaced by the laws of relativistic mechanics when dealing with certain subatomic and celestial phenomena. Here an analogy has been suggested. If we liken the facts to be explained to fish in a pond, then the law or set of laws is the net with which we make the catch. It may turn out that our particular net is not fine enough to haul in *all* fish, large and small, but it may still be quite satisfactory for supplying our ordinary needs. We may go even further and maintain that to be useful at all, our conceptual schemes, like our nets, *must* contain holes; if it were otherwise (if, so to speak, we were to go fishing with large buckets instead of nets), we should not be able to distinguish between the significant and the trivial, the fish and the water.

15.5 Summary of the constituents of science. In previous chapters we have dealt with the nature of theories and concepts, and in the present chapter with the process of discovery and the formulation of laws. Now we are in a position to summarize the three main elements that make up the established part of physical science.

First of all there are *concepts*—velocity, force, mass, chemical element, and so on—which provide the basic vocabulary and ideas of a science. Second, there are the *relationships* among the concepts. These relationships may be quite restricted in scope (for example, the statement that in free fall from rest, $s \propto t^2$), or they may be broad generalizations (for example, Newton's law of universal gravitation). Third, there is a part of science that we tend to take for granted, namely the *grammar*, which provides the means for expressing the definitions and relationships among concepts; it includes the logic of language itself (such as rules as to how to use the words *and*, *or*) and the logic of mathematics (how to use $+$ or $-$, how to add vectors, and so on).

These three parts of science are obviously so completely interrelated that any one taken by itself is quite meaningless. A concept is useless and cannot even be defined if it has no relation to other concepts. A law or other generalization means nothing unless there are linguistic and mathematical rules for relating the concepts involved in it. This tight interlacing of the parts of science explains why each particular scientific advance remains more or less tentative until it is absorbed into the science as a whole. For example, a newly discovered law may disturb the hitherto accepted relationships among concepts or even the usefulness of some old concept; and so there will be a period of rearrangement until the new discovery is fully incorporated into the ever-growing structure. The development of a law or set of laws may perhaps be likened to the flow of water down a slope, where there are eddies and back currents from the advancing front, and where also here and there a sudden surge reaches out to embrace and hold some territory far ahead of the main advance. How fortunate for the progress of science that individual investigators do not permit themselves to become discouraged by this prospect of lengthy struggle, that they find their reward in the day-to-day progress of their work and in the expectation of the unpromised light which may at any moment come over their horizon.

Problems

15.1. What are the main differences between a *law of physical science* (e.g., $s = \frac{1}{2}gt^2$ and the other equations for free fall) on one hand and, on the other, a *law of magic* (e.g., the belief of the Hopi Indian that the ceremonial handling of rattlesnakes increases the chances of rainfall), a *law of phrenology*, a *civil law* (e.g., highway traffic regulations), and a *moral* or *divine law* (the Ten Commandments)?

15.2. In a recent magazine article there appeared the following statement. Comment on its validity in a short essay.

"But the first thing to realize even about physics is its extraordinary indirectness. Physics appears to begin with very straightforward questions, but there are catches in it right from the start. For example: every high school student is told that according to Aristotle the heavier of two weights would fall faster, but that Galileo, by dropping two different weights from the leaning tower of Pisa, 'proved' that Aristotle was wrong, for the weights were found to fall in exactly the same time. And yet Aristotle was right. The heavier body does fall faster, because of air resistance, which slows up the lighter body more than the heavier. Only a very little faster, it is true, and the difference may not be detectable; but since scientists claim that they use words with such great precision, it is fair to hold them to it. If you press a physicist on this point, he will readily admit that what he means is that the two bodies would fall equally fast *in a vacuum*. If you press him further, he will very reluctantly admit that nobody has ever produced a complete vacuum. And so it turns out that not the physicist but Aristotle is talking about the actual world in which we live."

15.3. What are the *raw observations* concerning the sun, stars, planets, satellites, etc., which the theory of universal gravitation explains? Try to avoid the inclusion of theory in your statements of the observable facts.

15.4. Examine a law outside physical science with which you are *well* acquainted (e.g., a law of linguistics, biology, or economics) and decide whether or not one may trace its growth by the same type of analysis as was used for our hypothetical physical law (Section 15.2).

15.5. Comment on these definitions: (a) The mass of an object is the measure of its quantity. (b) The range of a projectile is the horizontal component of its displacement. (c) The "volage" of an object is its volume divided by its age. (d) The factor π is approximately equal to 22/7.

15.6. Comment on these statements from the point of view of physical science: (a) The Newtonian theory of gravitation is correct. (b) The speed of light is known within $\pm 0.003\%$. (c) The findings of physical science do not represent absolute truths.

15.7. Why do *you* believe that the earth is round? that the moon is spherical? that there was once a scientist named Isaac Newton? Of what facts are you certain beyond all possible doubt? Why?

15.8. Suggest some reasons why astronomy is one of the oldest and best-developed of the sciences.

15.9. Write a short essay on one of these topics: (a) The scientist as a creative investigator. (b) Science as an evolving organism. (c) Important factors in the process of scientific discovery. (d) The discovery of truths by free and vigorous exchange of intelligence. (e) The complementary aspects of scientific experience and poetic experience. (f) The power of operational definitions in physical science.

15.10. Write a short essay on the extrapolation of the operational view to fields other than physical science represented in the following statement by P. W. Bridgman (1927): "I believe that many of the questions asked about social and philosophical subjects will be found meaningless when examined from the point of view of operations. It would doubtless conduce greatly to clarity of thought if the operational mode of thinking were adopted in all fields of inquiry . . ."

Supplementary Reading

Beveridge, W. I. B., *The art of scientific investigation* (W. W. Norton, 1951).

Bridgman, P. W., *The logic of modern physics* (Macmillan, 1927), Chaps. I, II, and the first part of III.

Bronowski, J., *The common sense of science* (Harvard University Press, 1953).

Brown, G. B., *Science, its method and its philosophy* (W. W. Norton, 1950).

Cassirer, E., *Substance and function* (Dover, 1953), Chap. IV.

Cohen, M. R., and E. Nagel, *An introduction to logic and scientific method* (Harcourt, Brace, 1934).

Conant, J. B., *Science and common sense* (Yale University Press, 1951). Particularly Chapters 1–3.

Feigl, H., and M. Brodbeck, *Readings in the philosophy of science* (Appleton-Century-Crofts, 1953), Parts I, IV, and VIII.

Feigl, H., and W. Sellars, *Readings in philosophical analysis* (Appleton-Century-Crofts, 1949). Particularly pages 498–514.

Frank, P., *Modern science and its philosophy* (Harvard University Press, 1949; George Braziller, 1955).

Frank, P., *Philosophy of science* (Prentice-Hall, 1957), Chaps. 1–4.

Hadamard, J. S., *An essay on the psychology of invention in the mathematical field* (Princeton University Press, 1945; Dover, 1954).

Hutten, E. H., *The language of modern physics* (Allen & Unwin, London, 1956).

Johnson, D., "Mysterious Craters of the Carolina Coast," *American Scientist*, January 1944. An exercise in "scientific methods."

Langer, S. K., *Philosophy in a new key* (Harvard University Press, 1942).

Margenau, H., *The nature of physical reality* (McGraw-Hill, 1950).

Northrop, F. S. C., *Logic of the sciences and the humanities* (Macmillan, 1947). Particularly Chapters I and II.

Poincaré, H., *The foundation of science* (Science Press, 1929; Dover, 1952). Particularly Book I, Chapters 1 and 3 in "Science and Method."

Reichenbach, H., *The rise of scientific philosophy* (University of California Press, 1951).

Sarton, G., *The study of the history of science* (Harvard University Press, 1936), pp. 1–52.

Shapley, H., H. Wright, and S. Rapport, *Readings in the physical sciences* (Appleton-Century-Crofts, 1948), pp. 401–423.

Toulmin, S. E., *Philosophy of science* (Hutchinson, 1953).

Wertheimer, M., *Productive thinking* (Harper, 1945).

Whitehead, A. N., *Science and the modern world* (Macmillan, 1925; also Pelican Mentor Book M28, 1948), Chaps. I and IX.

Wiener, P. P., ed., *Readings in philosophy of science* (Scribner, 1953), Parts A and D.

Part V
THE CONSERVATION PRINCIPLES

JAMES PRESCOTT JOULE
(1818–1889)

THE CONSERVATION PRINCIPLES

Looking back at the structure which we have raised so far, we realize how greatly success in the pursuit of scientific knowledge is predicated on our ability to perform three closely interrelated tasks: to isolate the phenomenon from distracting or trivial other effects, to describe unambiguously what is happening, and to discern some specific permanence in the flux of events under observation. These tasks lie at the beginning of every scientific activity, and nowhere is their outcome more effectively exemplified than in the various *laws* or *principles of conservation*. These principles, perhaps the most powerful, certainly the most prized, tools of analysis in physical science, say in essence that no matter what happens in detail to a system of interacting bodies, there are certain measurable quantities (the total mass, or the total momentum, or the total energy, and so on) that can be counted on to remain *constant* under certain prescribed conditions.

There is a spectacular beauty about these principles. They can break through the clamor and confusion of appearances and point to an underlying constancy so convincingly that some particular situation may change at one stroke from chaos to ordered necessity. Moreover, so extensive is the range of application of these conservation principles that they serve to unify the various physical sciences within themselves and with one another. Indeed, these principles are no longer regarded as mere summaries of experimental facts, but instead have become, as it were, the starting points of scientific understanding itself, fundamental postulates from which a vast variety of laws can be derived.

We shall discuss here three principles of conservation: of mass, of momentum, and of energy.* This Part also serves as a logical and historical bridge between the study of universal gravitation and subsequent chapters on atomic theory.

---

*The principle of conservation of electric charge is dealt with in Chapter 26.

CHAPTER 16

THE PRINCIPLE OF CONSERVATION OF MASS

16.1 Prelude to the mass-conservation principle. In his great work *De rerum natura* (*On the nature of things*), the Roman poet Lucretius (1st century B.C.), contemporary of Julius Caesar and Cicero, recorded and embellished the nature-philosophy of Greece's Leucippus, Democritus (both 5th century B.C.), and Epicurus (4th century B.C.). He reiterated the view that "Things cannot be born from nothing, cannot when begotten be brought back to nothing," that everything now existing must have continuous existence in past, present, and future, although form, appearance, and the like may indeed change.

Yet, there is a very considerable span of thought from the panegyric of Lucretius to the modern principle of conservation of mass—that almost axiomatic basis of much in our science—which asserts that despite changes of position, shape, phase, chemical composition, and so forth, *the total mass of the material in a given enclosed region remains constant.* It is futile to search the writings of the Ancients for direct parentage of this modern principle of science. Lucretius' ultimate purpose, for example, was not to present a scientific text, but to reduce the contemporary burden of superstition and fear through an exposition of the Epicurean philosophy and the rational explanation of natural phenomena. Although he documented his thesis throughout with penetrating observations from nature, his concern was not primarily with a physical problem, but rather with the exposition of a particular philosophy, that of materialism.

16.2 Steps toward a formulation. Before the notion that the quantity of matter is indestructible could be reformulated in terms meaningful to modern science, three separate developments had to take place, each in itself a contribution of the greatest physical scientist of his generation. First there had to arise the concept of the *closed* or *isolated system.* Among the Greeks and the Scholastics the dominant view was one of a unified, completely integrated universe. In such a scheme, the behavior of any single object was regarded as determined by its relation to the rest of the cosmos, by the necessary role it must play in the whole drama. It was difficult, therefore, to think of events in isolation, for example, to concentrate attention on the behavior of a single object in a particular region rather than on events occurring in the universe as a whole.

From the early 17th century on, scientific thinking tended more and more toward a narrow limitation of attention in a given experimental situation, concentrating upon those few factors that seemed most relevant and decisive. The great success of this approach became evident in Galileo's work on mechanics. To investigate the behavior of a body freed "from its weight," he asked us to consider a ball placed upon a frictionless horizontal plane. The weight and the upward thrust of the supporting plane balance each other; we may then ignore both the earth and the plane as factors influencing the motion of the ball, and can focus our attention upon the ball alone, an *isolated object*. We are invited to map out in thought a region containing only the body in equilibrium, a region at whose boundaries all causal connections with phenomena on the outside are broken. (We discussed a similar case, in similar terms, when we considered the motion of one part of an Atwood's machine.)

In Newton's first law of motion the conception of the isolated system is most evident, for the postulate allows us to think about the behavior of a totally isolated object, one which in thought is removed altogether from the influence of other objects, as would be approximately true if the object were in interstellar space.

This conception of a closed or isolated system by which to define the region of attention was one prerequisite for the formulation of a conservation principle of mass. Such a closed system might be formed simply by a well-stoppered bottle containing the sample of matter; the system is *closed* inasmuch as no matter can leave or enter the experimentation space. A second requisite was the development of a quantitative definition for the *amount of matter* in any object. This was provided by Newton in the opening paragraph of the *Principia* where, speaking of the term "quantity of matter," he states, "It is this quantity that I mean hereafter under the name of body or mass." To know quantitatively the amount of matter in an object it is thus necessary to know only its inertia (or else its weight, for the inertia "is proportional to the weight, as I have found by experiments"). Here we have one of the basic tenets of Newtonian mechanics: there is something enduring and constant about any given object—not its color, shape, or volume, nor its position and motion, but rather its *mass* and therefore, in a given locality, its weight also.

Given the conceptions of a closed system and of quantity of matter or mass, the third step became possible: the formulation and experimental verification of the hypothesis that the *mass of an isolated body or system of bodies remains unchanged*, even if physical or chemical interactions occur within the system.

Nowadays, this hypothesis has become a matter of common sense. As a simple example, we know, of course, that a pound of sugar will continue to weigh a pound if it is in a closed container and is kept in a given locality, and since weight is proportional to mass in a given locality, we may conclude that the mass remains unchanged. To consider a more complicated example, suppose that we burn a piece of wood in a fireplace and examine whether the mass before and after burning is the same. If we compare the weight of the unburned wood and of the ashes, the weight and therefore the mass will be found to have decreased. But if we execute the same chemical reaction in a closed system, one that contains at the outset the wood and the air, then it will be found that the ashes and remaining gases at the end weigh neither more nor less than the original components of the system. In brief, the total mass of the system has not been changed by the process of burning.

This example shows how important it is to recognize and define the system that is to be regarded as isolated or closed in a particular problem. Chemists failed to do so until nearly a century after the appearance of Newton's *Principia;* they were hampered by other notions prevailing at the time. Indeed, the whole science of chemistry had to undergo a major revolution before it absorbed the conception of a closed system in which mass was conserved.

16.3 The problem of calcination. In the 17th century two classes of substances, called *calxes* and *metals*, were known to be related to each other, for, from a given calx, the corresponding metal could be produced, and from that metal the calx could again be obtained. For example, iron calx (which we shall later identify as iron oxide) can be made to yield iron, and a sample of metallic iron can be changed to an iron calx. Since any change from calx to metal usually required the application of heat, such changes came to be explained in terms of the participation of the ancient element "Fire," somewhat modified in 18th-century theory and given the name *phlogiston.* Thus when a particular calx was heated, it was presumed that phlogiston went into the calx, perhaps from the source of heat, and that the resulting metal was a combination of the calx and phlogiston, the latter being a metalizing "principle" that could produce the corresponding metal from each calx. We may briefly indicate the process by writing

$$\text{calx} + \text{phlogiston} \longrightarrow \text{metal.} \tag{16.1}$$

To explain the reverse process, it was assumed that a metal could be changed into a calx by removing phlogiston; that is,

$$\text{metal} - \text{phlogiston} \longrightarrow \text{calx.} \tag{16.2}$$

This latter process, known as calcination, was studied by a contemporary of Galileo's, Jean Rey, who noted that tin calx weighed more than the tin from which it was produced. To us this result would raise the serious question how "metal *minus* phlogiston" could weigh more than

FIG. 16.1.   Antoine Laurent Lavoisier (1743–1794) and Madame Lavoisier who acted as his assistant in his scientific work. From Jacques Louis David's portrait of 1788.   (Courtesy Metropolitan Museum of Art.)

"metal." But to 17th- and early 18th-century scientists this observed gain in weight on calcination was not so disturbing. They were finding the phlogiston theory very useful for explaining a large number of chemical phenomena. Moreover, not until the latter part of the 18th century, 150 years after Rey, did the conception come to the fore that the weights of substances in chemical reaction are of crucial significance. This conception was at the heart of the work of Antoine Laurent Lavoisier, often called the father of modern chemistry (Fig. 16.1).

16.4 The overthrow of the phlogiston theory. By making a number of improvements in apparatus for the study of gases, 18th-century chemists opened up the possibility for precise experimentation on chemical reactions in isolated or closed systems. Lavoisier's experiments with calcination and similar phenomena led him, in the 1770's, to put forward a new hypothesis to replace that of phlogiston. It was in a sense an inversion of the phlogiston hypothesis, for he suggested that the calx be viewed as a combination of the metal with some part of the air. When his contemporary, the English clergyman, schoolteacher, and scientist Joseph Priestley (1733–1804), discovered the gas oxygen, Lavoisier immediately realized that this was the part of the air that combined with a metal to produce the corresponding calx. The process of obtaining metal from calx, which we now call *reduction*, may thus be described as

$$\text{calx} - \text{oxygen} \longrightarrow \text{metal}, \tag{16.3}$$

while for the converse process, called *oxidation*, we may write

$$\text{metal} + \text{oxygen} \longrightarrow \text{calx}. \tag{16.4}$$

An illustration of this relationship is afforded by one of Lavoisier's many descriptions of experiments in his textbook *Traité elémentaire de chimie* (*Elements of chemistry*) in 1789 (Fig. 16.2):

> The following elegant experiment of Mr. Ingenhouz, upon the combustion of iron, is well known. [Then follows a description of this experiment, the burning of iron wire in a closed vessel of oxygen-enriched air.] As Mr. Ingenhouz has examined the change [in weight] produced neither on the iron nor upon the air by this operation, I have repeated the experiment under different circumstances, in an apparatus adapted to answer my particular views, as follows . . . [The modification is now given that permits accurate determination of weights.] If the experiment has succeeded well, from 100 grains [5.3 grams] of iron will be obtained 135 or 136 grains of ethiops [oxide of iron], which is an augmentation [of mass or of weight] of 35 percent. If all the attention has been paid to this experiment which it deserves, the air will be found diminished in weight exactly by what the iron has gained. Having therefore burnt 100 grains of iron, which has acquired an additional weight of 35 grains, the diminution of air will be found exactly 70 cubical inches: and it will be shown, in the sequel, that the weight of vital air [oxygen] is pretty nearly half a grain for each cubical inch; so that, in effect, the augmentation of weight in the one exactly coincides with the loss of it in the other.

In our mode of expression, Lavoisier found that

100 grains of iron + 35 grains of oxygen $\longrightarrow$ 135 grains of iron oxide,

TRAITE
ÉLÉMENTAIRE
DE CHIMIE,
PRÉSENTÉ DANS UN ORDRE NOUVEAU
ET D'APRÈS LES DÉCOUVERTES MODERNES;

Avec Figures :

Par M. LAVOISIER, de l'Académie des Sciences, de la Société Royale de Médecine, des Sociétés d'Agriculture de Paris & d'Orléans, de la Société Royale de Londres, de l'Institut de Bologne, de la Société Helvétique de Basle, de celles de Philadelphie, Harlem, Manchester, Padoue, &c.

TOME PREMIER.

A PARIS,

Chez CUCHET, Libraire, rue & hôtel Serpente.

M. DCC. LXXXIX.

Sous le Privilège de l'Académie des Sciences & de la Société Royale de Médecine.

FIG. 16.2. The title page of Lavoisier's *Elements of chemistry*, the book which laid the foundation for modern chemistry. (From the DeGolyer Collection copy.)

or, generalizing,

$$m \text{ grains iron} + n \text{ grains oxygen} \longrightarrow (m + n) \text{ grains of iron oxide.}$$

In other experiments, particularly with mercury, Lavoisier successfully decomposed a sample of calx, and obtained the metal and the oxygen in the same amounts by weights as had been originally used to form the calx; this corresponds to Eq. (16.3). In short, Lavoisier showed that the absorption of phlogiston in the earlier theory corresponded to the release of oxygen, and *vice versa*. Not only did Jean Rey's observation thereby receive a reasonable explanation, it also became obvious to Lavoisier that attention to weight relations is a key to the understanding of chemistry.

But it is worth noting in passing that such experiments do not furnish proof that the oxygen theory is "right" and the phlogiston theory "wrong." For example, by making the assumption that phlogiston has "negative weight" we could say that m grains of iron is really $(m + n)$ grains of iron calx compounded with phlogiston weighing $(-n)$ grains, that the phlogiston somehow buoys up the iron calx. When the iron releases this phlogiston, it would revert to iron calx of weight $(m + n)$ grains, and the air, having acquired the phlogiston and its buoyancy, would then weigh n grains less. In equation form,

$$m \text{ grains iron} = (m + n) \text{ grains iron oxide} - n \text{ grains oxygen}$$

is equivalent to

$$m \text{ grains iron} = (m + n) \text{ grains iron calx} + (-n) \text{ grains phlogiston.}$$

Thus the phlogiston hypothesis might be saved. Yet to save it we must assume that one substance, phlogiston, has negative weight and is therefore different from any other known substance. This assumption violates the first of Newton's Rules of Reasoning, one of the most fundamental rules of science, namely, to begin always with the simplest explanation available. And of course the oxygen hypothesis of combustion later turned out to be immensely fruitful in many other respects. Historically, the verdict in the dispute was very quickly given to Lavoisier; his experiments and his interpretations of them were decisive in the triumph of the oxygen hypothesis of combustion over that of phlogiston.

16.5 The principle of conservation of mass. We have examined only a single example of oxidation and reduction. Yet the oxygen theory applies to a vast variety of phenomena: burning is one; another is the breathing of animals. *And underlying the entire theory is the principle that the total* *quantity of matter in a closed, isolated system remains constant during chemical changes.* As Lavoisier wrote in 1789:

> We must lay it down as an incontestable axiom, that in all the operations of art and nature, nothing is created; an equal quantity of matter exists both before and after the experiment, . . . and nothing takes place beyond changes and modifications in the combination of these elements. Upon this principle, the whole art of performing chemical experiments depends.

From the accounts of his experiments, Lavoisier's meaning of "quantity of matter" is clearly *weight.* Since weight in any given locality is proportional to mass, we may rephrase Lavoisier's statement thus: "in all the operations of art and nature" *the total mass within a given isolated system remains constant.* We shall encounter this *principle of conservation of mass* again and again in both physics and chemistry. Moreover, of all the conservation principles, it is the one grasped most simply and directly by the modern mind.

PROBLEMS

16.1. Read Chapter 7 of Conant's *Science and common sense,* and discuss three chemical reactions (e.g., the burning of coal, the calcination of a metal, the reduction of a metallic ore) as each would be explained by (a) the phlogiston hypothesis and (b) the modern oxygen hypothesis.

16.2. Read pages 399 to 408 of *Readings in the physical sciences,* by Shapley, Wright, and Rapport; then discuss Lavoisier's experimental procedure, with special reference to the extent to which he made use of the principle of conservation of mass.

16.3. In Lavoisier's *Elements of chemistry* read the Author's Preface and Chapters III, V, and VII; then describe three of his chemical reactions that clearly demonstrate the principle of conservation of mass.

SUPPLEMENTARY READING

BONNER, F. T., and M. PHILLIPS, *Principles of physical science* (Addison-Wesley, 1957), Chap. 6.

BUCKLEY, H., *A short history of physics* (Methuen, 1927), Chap. III.

CONANT, J. B., *Science and common sense* (Yale University Press, 1951). See Chapter 7 on the development of the modern theory of combustion.

CONANT, J. B., *The overthrow of the phlogiston theory* (Harvard University Press, 1950); also in *Harvard case histories in experimental science* (Harvard University Press, 1957), v. 1, pp. 65–115.

FRENCH, S. J., *Torch and crucible* (Princeton University Press, 1941). A biography of Lavoisier.

KNICKERBOCKER, W. S., ed., *Classics of modern science* (Knopf, 1927), Chaps. 13 and 14. Excerpts from Priestley and Lavoisier.

LUCRETIUS, *On the nature of things* (Dutton, Everyman's Library edition No. 750A; Oxford University Press; Harvard University Press; Rutgers University Press).

McKIE, D., *Antoine Lavoisier; scientist, economist, social reformer* (Henry Schuman, 1952).

SHAPLEY, H., H. WRIGHT, and S. RAPPORT, *Readings in the physical sciences* (Appleton-Century-Crofts, 1948).

WILSON, M., and D. I. DUVEEN, "Priestley" and "Lavoisier," in *Lives in science* (Simon and Schuster, 1957), pp. 87–107.

CHAPTER 17

THE PRINCIPLE OF CONSERVATION OF MOMENTUM

17.1 The primitive notion of impetus. Even if everything has been done to describe the motion of bodies accurately, to analyze the path of projectiles and of the planets, and to specify the forces needed to account for such motions, there still remains a mystifying puzzle that does not seem in accord with common sense. While anyone can see intuitively that an object can be in motion while it is actually being pushed or pulled, it is far less clear to the untutored understanding why an object, once it is set in motion, will continue in motion when no net force continues to be applied to it by some external agent in immediate contact. The source of this feeling of difficulty is probably not far to seek; after all, we learned in childhood that in order to make objects move toward or away from us we must be prepared to supply some effort, and that the objects around us can be kept in motion only by having something act on them. Our intuitive conceptions are organismically oriented.

To the Greeks, and to the Aristotelian-Thomistic scholars of the Renaissance, the assertion that no net force, no agent is needed to keep an object moving with constant speed in a straight line would have been patently absurd. And to them even the *non*uniform progress of an arrow or a bullet was explainable only in terms of a propelling motion of the surrounding air acting continuously from the moment of projection. The maxim was: whatever moves is being kept in motion by something else. Significantly enough, even Newton could not free his physical universe from the need for constant association with a cause for the phenomena. Of course, in his thinking the planetary motions were no longer to be regarded as due to the incessant activity of God and the angels; yet in his cosmic philosophy, these motions were still thought of as proceeding in the sensorium of the Deity, by virtue, so to speak, of His continuous though passive attention to and knowledge of the happenings.

Actually, the attempt to liberate the idea of motion from the necessity of a mover goes back at least to a 5th-century Greek writer, John Philoponus, whose ideas were extended by the 14th-century English Franciscan friar, William of Ockam. Developed further by certain 14th-century Scholastics at the University of Paris, notably Jean Buridan and Albert of Saxony, the essence of this point of view lay in a concept called *impetus.* A projectile moving through the air was thought to possess an impetus, the amount of which depended on both the projectile's speed and the quantity of matter in it. The impetus was considered to be both an expression of the motion and at the same time its cause. If the body slows down, the impetus is less since the speed is less; and equivalently, having less impetus, the body cannot be expected to move as fast. It was further suggested that the agent used to launch the projectile somehow impressed upon it the impetus, and that this impetus was used up or slowly vanished in flight, so that "natural" fall to the ground then occurred.

Certainly by our present standards the notion of impetus was fuzzy. With the Newtonian concept of mass still lacking, there was no way to determine precisely how the amount of impetus varied with the quantity of matter. Yet the notion both focused attention upon speed and quantity of matter as important variables and encouraged a closer study of the details of motion. One could turn away from the question, "What keeps certain objects moving uniformly?" and instead ask the more fruitful question, "What keeps most objects *from* moving uniformly?" This is a restatement of the problem of motion from an entirely different point of view, and historically, by and large, such reformulations have been one of the most powerful methods toward progress in science. In the present case it resulted, as we know, in an entirely new conception: the net force on a body produces, not constant velocity as in the Aristotelian definition of force (Section 4.2), but *change* of velocity.

17.2 The concept of momentum. The 14th-century developments concerning the concept of impetus are of interest to us at this point because they were the forerunners of the concept called *momentum*. By definition, *the momentum of a body is the product of the body's mass m and its instantaneous velocity* **v**. To denote this product $m\mathbf{v}$, we shall employ the symbol **M**. Thus the defining equation for momentum is

$$\mathbf{M} = m\mathbf{v}.$$

Since it is the product of a scalar quantity (mass) and a vector quantity (velocity), **M** is a *vector quantity*, representable by an arrow pointing in the same direction as the one that represents the corresponding velocity. Note the use here of the boldface **v** to give emphasis to the fact that it is the velocity, not the speed, that enters into the definition of momentum; similarly, we have used the boldface **M** to emphasize the vectorial character of momentum. From now on we shall use boldface letters to denote vector quantities and continue to use italic letters for scalar quantities and for the magnitudes of vector quantities.

Newton defined momentum on the first page of the *Principia:*

> The quantity of motion [for which phrase we use the term *momentum*] is the measure of the same, arising from the velocity and quantity of matter conjointly.

He first applied the concept in his statement of the second law of motion. This statement may be rendered in modern terms as follows:

Law II. The net force acting on a body is equal to, and in the direction of, the time-rate of change of the momentum.

In symbols,

$$\mathbf{F}_{\text{net}} = \frac{m\mathbf{v}_2 - m\mathbf{v}_1}{t},\qquad(17.1)$$

where $m\mathbf{v}_2 - m\mathbf{v}_1$ is the *change* in momentum of a body of mass m, occurring during the time interval t.

EXAMPLE 17.1. A 1500-kgm car moving northward on a straight road increases its speed from 10 to 30 m/sec in 10 sec. Compute (a) the initial momentum, (b) the final momentum, and (c) the average net force producing the acceleration.

Solution. (a) The initial velocity $\mathbf{v}$ is 10 m/sec north, and so the initial momentum $m\mathbf{v}$ is 1500 kgm $\times$ 10 m/sec north, or 15×10^3 kgm·m/sec north. (b) Similarly, the final momentum is 1500 kgm $\times$ 30 m/sec north, or 45×10^3 kgm·m/sec north; note that the direction does not change here, therefore the vector subtraction $m\mathbf{v}_2 - m\mathbf{v}_1$ is simply a subtraction of magnitudes. (c) The average accelerating net force, from Eq. (17.1), is

$$\mathbf{F}_{\text{net}} = \frac{m\mathbf{v}_2 - m\mathbf{v}_1}{t}.$$

In magnitude,

$$F_{\text{net}} = \frac{(45 \times 10^3 \text{ kgm·m/sec}) - (15 \times 10^3 \text{ kgm·m/sec})}{10 \text{ sec}}$$

$$= 3.0 \times 10^3 \frac{\text{kgm·m}}{\text{sec}^2} = 3.0 \times 10^3 \text{ new,}$$

and the direction of F_{net} is the same as that of $m\mathbf{v}_2 - m\mathbf{v}_1$, namely to the north.

To say that Eq. (17.1) is a statement of the second law of motion may seem strange, for in Chapter 4 we asserted that Eq. (4.2), namely, $F_{\text{net}} = ma$, represents this law. However, Eqs. (17.1) and (4.2) are for our purposes equivalent statements. To see this, recall that in ordinary circumstances the mass m of a body does not change observably when the body's velocity changes. This means that Eq. (17.1) may be written in the form

$$\mathbf{F}_{\text{net}} = \frac{m\mathbf{v}_2 - m\mathbf{v}_1}{t} = \frac{m(\mathbf{v}_2 - \mathbf{v}_1)}{t} = m\mathbf{a},$$

for $(\mathbf{v}_2 - \mathbf{v}_1)/t$ is, by definition, the average acceleration $\mathbf{a}$ during the time interval t.

EXAMPLE 17.2. Use the equation $\mathbf{F}_{net} = m\mathbf{a}$ to compute the average accelerating force on the car of Example 17.1.

Solution. The acceleration $\mathbf{a}$ is $(\mathbf{v}_2 - \mathbf{v}_1)/t = (30$ m/sec north $- 10$ m/sec north)/10 sec $= 2.0$ m/sec^2 north; hence $\mathbf{F}_{net} = m\mathbf{a} = 1500$ kgm $\times 2.0$ m/sec^2 north $= 3.0 \times 10^3$ kgm·m/sec^2 north $= 3.0 \times 10^3$ new north. This is the same value as was obtained by using Eq. (17.1).

EXAMPLE 17.3. A 2-gm bullet is shot into a tree stump. It enters with a speed of 3×10^4 cm/sec and comes to rest after having penetrated 5 cm in a straight line. Compute the average force on the bullet during the impact, using Eq. (17.1).

Solution. Here m is 2×10^{-3} kgm, $\mathbf{v}_1 = 3 \times 10^2$ m/sec, and $\mathbf{v}_2 = 0$; so the change in momentum is $m\mathbf{v}_2 - m\mathbf{v}_1 = 2 \times 10^{-3}$ kgm $(0 - 3 \times 10^2$ m/sec$) = -6 \times 10^{-1}$ kgm·m/sec $= -0.6$ kgm·m/sec, the negative sign indicating a negative change, or decrease, of momentum. The time interval t needed for the bullet to slow down from 3×10^2 m/sec to rest while traveling 5 cm, or 5×10^{-2} m, may be found from $s = \frac{1}{2}(v_1 + v_2)t$, provided that uniform deceleration is assumed; this interval t is, by computation, $\frac{1}{3} \times 10^{-3}$ sec. Consequently,

$$\mathbf{F}_{net} = \frac{-0.6 \text{ kgm·m/sec}}{\frac{1}{3} \times 10^{-3} \text{ sec}} = -1.8 \times 10^3 \text{ new,}$$

where the negative sign indicates that the force on the bullet, due to the resistance of the wood, is in a direction opposite to that of the bullet's initial motion.

PROBLEM 17.1. A 1500-kgm car has stalled on a level road. The coefficient of rolling friction between tires and road is 0.03. Use the second law of motion in the form of Eq. (17.1) to find how long one would have to push horizontally on the car with a force of 1.3×10^3 new to impart to it a speed of 1 m/sec. What assumptions are you making?

PROBLEM 17.2. A man standing on the edge of a cliff of height 150 m dropped a 2.0-kgm stone. What total change of momentum did the stone undergo between the moments of release and of hitting the ground in the valley below?

PROBLEM 17.3. What would have been the change in momentum, in Problem 17.2, if the man had initially thrown the stone (a) vertically downward with a speed of 15 m/sec? (b) vertically upward with that same speed? (c) What would have been the amount of the increase in momentum if the man had thrown the stone horizontally outward with an initial speed of 15 m/sec?

PROBLEM 17.4. An elastic ball with a mass of 30 gm is thrown against a wall, hitting it horizontally at a speed of 20 m/sec and bouncing straight back with virtually the same speed. What is the momentum of the ball (a) before the collision and (b) after the collision? What is the *change* of momentum of the ball between the moment it approaches the wall in full flight and the moment it (c) has just been stopped and (d) has recoiled from the wall and is moving away at full speed?

17.3 The principle of conservation of momentum.

Up to this point the concept of momentum does not seem to have offered much that is new.

For instance, the forces in the preceding examples and problems could have been computed by using Eq. (4.2) rather than Eq. (17.1). The great usefulness of the concept is to be sought in the discovery, appearing gradually by 1670, that if two or more bodies collide or undergo mutual attraction or repulsion, the vector sum of their momenta does not change, however much the momentum of each body may change; as Newton put it, "the quantity of motion [total momentum] suffers no change from the action of bodies among themselves." *If we consider a closed or isolated system in which a number N of bodies act upon one another*, the individual motions may indeed change greatly, but *the vector sum of all N momenta remains constant throughout.* In symbols,

$$\mathbf{M}_A + \mathbf{M}_B + \cdots + \mathbf{M}_N = \mathbf{M}_A + \mathbf{M}_B + \cdots + \mathbf{M}_N, \quad (17.2)$$
(at any one time)   (at any other time)

or, more briefly,

$$\sum\mathbf{M} \text{ (at any one time)} = \sum\mathbf{M} \text{ (at any other time).} \quad (17.3)$$

(The symbol Σ, Greek sigma, is merely a brief way of indicating "sum of.") Equations (17.2) and (17.3) are equivalent statements of the same principle, the *principle of conservation of momentum.*

Actually, this principle follows immediately from Newton's laws of motion. To see this, recall that an essential conception in Newtonian mechanics is that all changes in the velocities of bodies are to be regarded as the results of interactions between pairs of bodies, and that the forces between any pair of bodies are related in the manner described by the third law of motion; that is, for any interacting pair of bodies A and B, the force $\mathbf{F}_A$ on A due to B is equal in magnitude but oppositely directed to the force $\mathbf{F}_B$ on B due to A, or

$$\mathbf{F}_A = -\mathbf{F}_B. \quad (17.4)$$

But according to the second law of motion, Eq. (17.1),

$$\mathbf{F}_A = \frac{m_A\mathbf{v}_{A2} - m_A\mathbf{v}_{A1}}{t}, \qquad F_B = \frac{m_B\mathbf{v}_{B2} - m_B\mathbf{v}_{B1}}{t}.$$

Substituting these expressions for $\mathbf{F}_A$ and $\mathbf{F}_B$ in Eq. (17.4) and taking account of the fact that the time interval t during which the interaction takes place must be the same for both bodies, we have

$$m_A\mathbf{v}_{A2} - m_A\mathbf{v}_{A1} = -(m_B\mathbf{v}_{B2} - m_B\mathbf{v}_{B1}). \quad (17.5)$$

In words, the changes of momentum of any two interacting bodies are equal in magnitude but opposite in direction. Evidently Eq. (17.5) may be rewritten in the alternative forms

$$m_A \mathbf{v}_{A1} + m_B \mathbf{v}_{B1} = m_A \mathbf{v}_{A2} + m_B \mathbf{v}_{B2}, \tag{17.6}$$

and

$$\underset{\text{(before interaction)}}{\mathbf{M}_{A1} + \mathbf{M}_{B1}} = \underset{\text{(after interaction)}}{\mathbf{M}_{A2} + \mathbf{M}_{B2}.} \tag{17.7}$$

Comparison with Eq. (17.2) or (17.3) shows that this is the principle of conservation of momentum for a system consisting, in this example, of two bodies. If we were to apply similar reasoning to a system of more than two bodies interacting simultaneously, we would obtain the more general formulation, Eq. (17.2). Thus, as asserted earlier, the principle of conservation of momentum is derivable from the postulates of Newtonian mechanics.

To appreciate the tremendous usefulness and generality of the momentum principle, one must see it used in a variety of specific examples. For example, for a swarm of gas molecules kept, say, at 20°C, the number of interacting molecules may be in the billions; yet, although each of the colliding molecules will be continually undergoing changes of velocity, we can assert with confidence that the *vector sum* of all the momenta at any one instant will be equal to that at any other instant (Fig. 17.1).

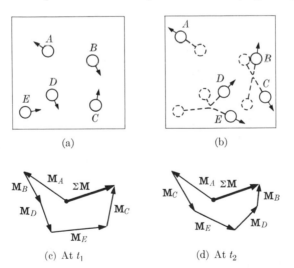

FIG. 17.1. Consider a gas at constant temperature. (a) Each gas molecule, at any instant t_1, has a certain velocity and hence a certain momentum. (b) A short time later, at t_2, the velocity and momentum of each particle have been changed by collision with other particles. (c) Yet the total momentum ($\Sigma\mathbf{M}$) of all particles at t_1 is the same as (d) the total momentum ($\Sigma\mathbf{M}$) at t_2.

It will be noticed that the momentum principle holds regardless of the character of the interactions: they may be collisions of any kind, for example, between lumps of clay or steel balls; or mutual attractions or repulsions of any origin, whether magnetic, electric, or gravitational; or frictional forces; or forces produced by means of springs or by explosions. Indeed, the single limitation on the momentum principle as formulated above is that it applies only to a closed system, that is, to a set of bodies that is not being acted upon by any motion-changing forces exerted by bodies which are outside the set.*

17.4 Collision phenomena.   The possibility of formulating the momentum principle was first suspected in connection with investigations of collisions of two bodies like those in the following two illustrations.

Illustration 1. Figure 17.2, adapted from a 17th-century treatise, illustrates the following sequence of events: a cannon ball A is fired horizontally toward a ball B *of equal mass* that is stationary on a table; the two balls are next shown at the instant of collision; finally, ball A remains at rest on the table while ball B is seen to move off with a velocity equal to the velocity of A before the collision.

This sequence of observations, which is familiar to everyone acquainted with the games of billiards or croquet, and to which we shall return in discussing the case of nuclear particle interactions, may be explained

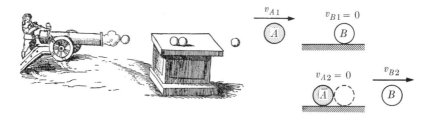

Fig. 17.2. An illustration of conservation of momentum. A moving cannon ball collides with a stationary one of equal mass and completely transfers its momentum. (After a drawing in Johann Marcus Marci's *De proportione motus*, 1648.)

---

*Descartes was familiar with an early form of the momentum principle and regarded it as a necessary consequence of the "evident" fact that God had "created matter with motion and rest in its parts, and . . . thereafter conserves in the universe by His ordinary operations as much of motion and of rest as He put in it in the first creation." It is revealing to note that the principle of conservation of *mass* can be traced to a *materialistic* assumption (Section 16.1), whereas here the principle of conservation of momentum is predicated on a *theistic* assumption.

directly in terms of Newton's laws of motion. The third law asserts that, during the brief time interval that the balls are in contact, the decelerating (stopping) force $\mathbf{F}_A$ on ball A is equal in magnitude though oppositely directed to the accelerating force $\mathbf{F}_B$ on ball B; and, by the second law, since the balls have the same mass the deceleration of A and the acceleration of B are equally large. Thus, owing to the collision, the velocity $\mathbf{v}_{B2}$ gained by B is equal to the velocity $\mathbf{v}_{A1}$ lost by A, or $\mathbf{v}_{B2} = \mathbf{v}_{A1}$. The full value of the velocity, and hence the momentum, is transmitted from A to B in this case.

Now let us show how simple it is, using the principle of conservation of momentum, to predict the magnitude of the velocity $\mathbf{v}_{B2}$ gained by ball B during collision, knowing that ball A is brought to rest. We shall use Eq. (17.3) or, since only two bodies are involved, the more special formulation of Eq. (17.7). We regard the two balls as forming a closed system; that is, we center our attention on the effects resulting from their collision and ignore the effects of all bodies that are outside the system, such as any frictional effects due to the table and the gravitational pull of the earth on the balls. We have for the two balls the data $m_A = m_B$; $\mathbf{v}_{A1}$ is given; $\mathbf{v}_{B1} = 0$; $\mathbf{v}_{A2} = 0$. We want to find $\mathbf{v}_{B2}$. Substituting the given data into Eq. (17.7), we obtain

$$m_A\mathbf{v}_{A1} + m_B \times 0 = m_A \times 0 + m_B\mathbf{v}_{B2}.$$

But $m_A = m_B$; therefore this equation reduces to $\mathbf{v}_{A1} = \mathbf{v}_{B2}$, which answers our question. Note that when all the vector quantities lie in the same line, as they do in this illustration, the vector addition reduces to simple algebraic addition.

PROBLEM 17.5. If the two colliding balls in Fig. 17.2 had different masses, then it would be observed that ball A would not come to rest; that is, $\mathbf{v}_{A2}$ would not be zero. Using Eq. (17.7), show that in this case

$$\mathbf{v}_{B2} = \frac{m_A}{m_B}(\mathbf{v}_{A1} - \mathbf{v}_{A2}) + \mathbf{v}_{B1}.$$

PROBLEM 17.6. Show that the result in Illustration 1 is a special case of the more general equation of Problem 17.5.

In all the discussion above, and in most of the following, the principle of conservation of momentum is applied over a very brief time interval; the situation just before a collision is compared with that obtaining just after the collision. This condition is chosen because if the time interval considered were longer, the second ball would begin to fall away from the horizontal level after collision, owing to its interaction with the earth, and the momenta of the ball and the earth would change more and more after the collision had taken place. Thus the earth becomes part of the system to be considered, and the conservation principle then leads not to Eq. (17.7), which presumed that the earth's momentum remains unchanged, but to the more general equation

$$\mathbf{M}_{A1} + \mathbf{M}_{B1} + \mathbf{M}_{earth,1} = \mathbf{M}_{A2} + \mathbf{M}_{B2} + \mathbf{M}_{earth,2}.$$
(before interaction)   (any time after interaction)

Illustration 2. In the preceding illustration, the collisions were assumed to be *elastic* in the technical sense of the word, that is, to have occurred, for example, between rigid bodies like billiard balls, or between good springs which have virtually no internal friction and no permanent deformation. Note now what happens in a perfectly *inelastic* collision, that is, when the colliding bodies do not separate afterwards but interpenetrate and so deform each other and travel off together. This would be the case, for example, if on an icy road a car of mass m_A and speed v_{A1} were to catch up with a truck of mass m_B going in the same direction with speed v_{B1} and, upon collision, became embedded in the rear of the truck. What is their common speed just after collision, assuming that the two bodies can be regarded as a closed system?

Here m_A, m_B, $\mathbf{v}_{A1}$, and $\mathbf{v}_{B1}$ are given, and $\mathbf{v}_{A2} = \mathbf{v}_{B2} = ?$ Thus Eq. (17.7) becomes

$$m_A\mathbf{v}_{A1} + m_B\mathbf{v}_{B1} = (m_A + m_B)\mathbf{v}_{B2},$$

$$\mathbf{v}_{B2} = \frac{m_A\mathbf{v}_{A1} + m_B\mathbf{v}_{B1}}{m_A + m_B}. \tag{17.8}$$

Suppose now that the car and the truck are moving toward each other, so that they hit head-on in inelastic impact. Equation (17.8) still holds in this case, for nothing was assumed concerning the direction of approach in the derivation from the general principle, Eq. (17.7). In actual calculation, we must simply take care to assign positive numerical values to velocities or momenta that are, say, in the right-hand direction, and negative numerical values to those in the opposite direction.

EXAMPLE 17.4. Suppose that the pendulum bobs in Fig. 17.3 are made of soft clay, so that they stick together after impact. Their masses are $m_A =$ 0.50 kgm and $m_B =$ 0.25 kgm, and their velocities at the moment just before impact are $\mathbf{v}_{A1} =$ 0.10 m/sec to the right and $\mathbf{v}_{B1} =$ 0.15 m/sec to

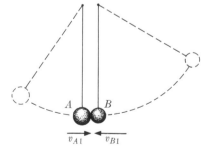

FIG. 17.3. Collision of pendulum bobs of unequal mass.

the left. What is their common velocity just after impact?

Solution. After deriving Eq. (17.8) from the general principle, Eq. (17.7), and using the convention that to the right is the positive direction, we obtain

$$v_{B2} = \frac{(0.50 \text{ kgm})(0.10 \text{ m/sec}) + (0.25 \text{ kgm})(-0.15 \text{ m/sec})}{0.50 \text{ kgm} + 0.25 \text{ kgm}}$$

$$= \frac{0.050 - 0.0375}{0.75} \frac{\text{m}}{\text{sec}} = 1.7 \times 10^{-2} \frac{\text{m}}{\text{sec}}.$$

Since this value is positive, the balls move toward the right after impact.

PROBLEM 17.7. A ball of mass 1.5 kgm collides inelastically with a ball of mass 1.2 kgm and initial velocity 1.2 m/sec toward the left. What must be the initial velocity of the first ball so that the final velocity of the pair will be zero?

PROBLEM 17.8. Two balls of equal mass approach each other with equal speeds. What can be said about the speeds of the balls after collision (a) if it is not known whether the collision is elastic or inelastic? (b) If the balls stick together? (c) If they separate after collision?

17.5 Explosions and other recoil phenomena. *Illustration 1.* In Chapter 4 we described the reaction-car experiment (Fig. 17.4) and, by directly applying Newton's laws of motion, showed that it could be used to compare the inertial masses of two bodies. Let us now show how this same conclusion is reached when we directly apply the momentum principle to the experiment. If the mass of the compressed spring and the effects of friction are negligibly small, we may regard the pair of cars as constituting a closed system to which Eq. (17.6) applies. The two cars initially are at rest, or $v_{A1} = v_{B1} = 0$. So Eq. (17.6) becomes here

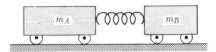

FIG. 17.4.   Representation of the reaction-car experiment.

$$0 = m_A \mathbf{v}_{A2} + m_B \mathbf{v}_{B2},$$

$$m_A \mathbf{v}_{A2} = -m_B \mathbf{v}_{B2}. \tag{17.9}$$

In terms of magnitudes only, and without regard to sign,

$$\frac{m_A}{m_B} = \frac{v_{B2}}{v_{A2}}. \tag{17.10}$$

In words, the two cars, in recoiling from rest, acquire momenta that are equal in magnitude (though opposite in direction). Note that Eq. (17.10) has the same form and meaning as Eq. (4.11).

Illustration 2. In Fig. 17.5, a gun of mass m_G, mounted on wheels so that it is free to roll backward when fired, is pictured firing a projectile of mass m_P and muzzle velocity $\mathbf{v}_P$ in a horizontal direction. Here, as with the reactions cars, the total momentum of the system, gun and projectile, is zero before firing and, being conserved, must therefore also be zero after firing; thus

$$0 = m_G\mathbf{v}_G + m_P\mathbf{v}_P,$$

where $\mathbf{v}_G$ is the recoil velocity of the gun. If any three of the quantities in this equation are known, we can solve for the fourth. For example, the recoil velocity is given by

$$\mathbf{v}_G = -\frac{m_P}{m_G}\mathbf{v}_P.$$

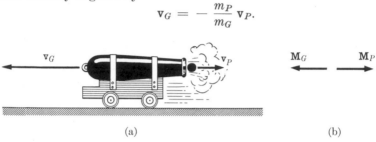

(a)   (b)

Fig. 17.5. Momentum conservation for a gun and its projectile. If the gun and projectile are at rest before firing, $\mathbf{M}_G$ and $\mathbf{M}_P$ are equally large and oppositely directed after firing.

If we take the direction of the projectile velocity v_P to be positive, then v_G will be negative, telling us, as it must, that the recoil velocity of the gun is in a direction opposite to the velocity of the projectile. Obviously, the gun in Fig. 17.5 is old-fashioned; modern guns ordinarily are anchored in some way, to the earth or to a ship. In such a case the earth or the ship becomes part of the "closed system" to which the principle of conservation of momentum applies, and participates in the recoil. For example, a battleship firing broadside recoils perceptibly through the water.

Problem 17.9. (a) Is Eq. (17.9) applicable to the reaction-car experiment no matter how strong the spring may be or how tightly it is compressed? (b) Is the mass of the spring of any importance here?

Problem 17.10. A 1000-kgm gun, mounted on wheels and initially at rest on level ground, fires a 10-kgm projectile horizontally with a muzzle velocity of 800 m/sec northward. Compute the velocity imparted to the gun.

Problem 17.11. Indicate a plan (with quantitative details) for stopping or even reversing the earth's motion around the sun.

Problem 17.12. When the fuel in a rocket is burned, the resulting gases flow out at the rear of the rocket, as shown in Fig. 3.12. (a) Analyze this means of propulsion. Why does the rocket move forward? Can this method of propulsion be employed when the rocket moves through a vacuum? Why are rockets and jets called *reaction* engines? (b) A 5000-kgm rocket reached an altitude of 30 km within 2 min after being fired from rest. Assuming constant acceleration and neglecting air friction, compute the final momentum of the rocket. (c) If the fuel burned had a total mass of 500 kgm, calculate the order of magnitude of the speed at which the exhaust gas must have left the rocket.

Illustration 3. When a projectile explodes while traveling through the air toward a target, its fragments, although dispersing in all directions, have the same total momentum immediately after the explosion as the whole projectile had immediately before. In other words, the *center of mass* of the fragments continues along the same path as if no explosion had occurred. This new concept, center of mass, is an important one. By definition, the center of mass of two particles is the point that divides the line joining them inversely as their masses. By extending this definition from the case for two particles to a system of any number of particles, we can, in principle, locate the center of mass of any configuration of particles. The principle of conservation of momentum can be rephrased to state that the center of mass of a system of bodies stays fixed if the only forces on the members of the system are the forces of mutual interaction (that is, if the system is closed and the total momentum therefore remains always unchanged).

PROBLEM 17.13. Two fragments of masses 1 and 4 gm are situated 100 cm apart. Show that the center of mass of the pair is on the line joining them and 20 cm distant from the 4-gm fragment.

PROBLEM 17.14. The earth has a mass of 5.98×10^{24} kgm and the moon a mass of 0.0123 times the mass of the earth. How far is the center of mass of the earth-moon system from the center of the earth?

PROBLEM 17.15. Using a "fixed star" as the frame of reference, we know that when an object falls toward the earth through a distance d_O, the earth *during the same time interval* moves toward the object through a distance d_E. With the help of the momentum principle, prove that the ratio of the distances moved is equal to the inverse ratio of the masses, or that $d_O/d_E = m_E/m_O$. Then show that the center of mass of the system of earth and object has stayed fixed during this change in positions.

A problem similar to Problem 17.15 provided one of the earliest statements foreshadowing the principle of conservation of momentum. In 1609 Kepler wrote in the *Astronomia nova:*

If two stones were removed to any part of the world, near each other but outside the field of force of a third related body, then the two stones, like two magnetic bodies, would come together at some intermediate place, each one approaching the other through a distance proportional to the mass of the other.

The "intermediate place," in more modern terms, is the center of mass of the pair of stones.

Illustration 4. A man stands on a log that is floating motionless in water. As he starts to walk along the log, the log moves backward, for the total momentum of the system log-and-man was initially zero and hence must remain zero at every subsequent moment. This statement neglects the momentum imparted to the water by the moving log and supposes that the water can be considered outside the system log-and-man.

Note that the forces involved in this interaction between man and log are mainly frictional forces, whereas in our earlier illustrations they were of other kinds. In problems involving the principle of conservation of momentum the nature of the force is unimportant. Indeed, one of the great merits of the principle is that it can be applied to a system of inter-acting bodies even when we have no knowledge whatever of the character or origin of the mutual forces involved.

PROBLEM 17.16. Imagine that a man of mass 75 kgm is standing on a flat platform of mass 1250 kgm, placed in interstellar space. From our position on the earth, we observe that, relative to the "fixed stars" as a frame of reference, the man and platform are initially at rest, and that the man then walks in 3 sec a distance of 5 m, with constant velocity. (a) Describe the motion of the plat-form while he begins to walk, proceeds, and stops, as seen by us. (b) If the man uses the platform for his frame of reference, how far will he think that he has walked? (c) Explain the difference between his observations and ours.

Illustration 5. Some of the most interesting applications of the momentum principle can be made to the "explosions" of atoms and to collisions among atoms and sub-atomic particles. One example is concerned with the explosive break-up, or "fission," of a uranium atom into two fragments of approximately equal mass. Figure 17.6 is a photo-graph made with the help of a *cloud chamber*, an important tool of con-temporary research that grew out of a device designed in 1895 by the British physicist C. T. R. Wilson. Before fission, the uranium atom was at rest in the thin foil of metal that stretches horizontally across the picture. When the atom was "trig-gered off" by an incident neutron, the two fission fragments recoiled

FIG. 17.6.   Cloud-chamber photo-graph showing fission of a uranium atom. [From an article by Bøggild, Brostrøm, and Lauritsen, *Phys. Rev.*, v. 59 (1941), p. 275.]

from each other along the two long white lines on opposite sides of the foil; the fragments themselves cannot be directly observed, but their paths are indicated by the thin streaks of fog they produced in moving through the vapor with which the chamber is filled. The fragments, slowed by the vapor and air through which they must plow, come to a stop after a few centimeters of travel, but from such data as the length and density of the fog tracks we can compute the initial speeds of recoil. With these speeds known, the principle of conservation of momentum (e.g., in the form of Eq. 17.9) can be applied to find the ratio of the masses of the two fission fragments. To simplify this account, we have neglected the contributions to the total momentum made by neutrons released in the fission process, which are not apparent in Fig. 17.6, and by the neutron that started the fission. The tracks of other particles, not concerned in this reaction, may also be seen in the photograph.

PROBLEM 17.17. A uranium atom "explodes," and the products are three neutrons, and two large fragments of masses 2.3×10^{-25} kgm and 1.5×10^{-25} kgm. Neglecting the momentum contributions of all the neutrons, compute the ratio of the recoil speeds of the two large fragments.

Illustration 6. Figure 17.7 is a cloud-chamber photograph of a stream of alpha particles (which are high-speed projectiles identical in structure to the nuclei of ordinary helium atoms) emitted during the radioactive disintegration of an element like polonium. One of the alpha particles has collided with an oxygen atom in the air. The motion of these two particles after collision also illustrates the principle of conservation of momentum.

This is our first example in which the interacting objects do not all move along one straight line. Consequently, in this general case the vector sum can no longer be obtained by simple algebraic summation, but involves

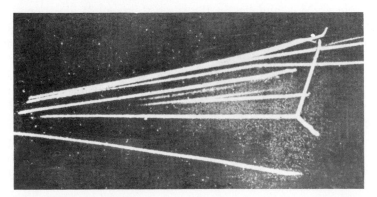

FIG. 17.7. Alpha particles cross the view field from left to right. One has hit an oxygen atom and has glanced off to the upper right corner, while the oxygen atom moves away to the lower right corner.

the methods of vectorial algebra used in Chapter 3 and summarized in Appendix G. To illustrate, consider a simplified form of Fig. 17.7 in which the incident particle of mass m_A is considered to move along the horizontal or x-coordinate with velocity $\mathbf{v}_{A1}$ toward a stationary body; after the collision the particles move away, as shown in Fig. 17.8(a), with velocity $\mathbf{v}_{A2}$ and $\mathbf{v}_{B2}$ respectively. What can the principle of conservation of momentum tell us about this situation?

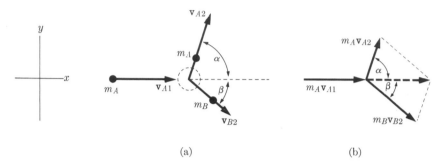

(a)   (b)

Fig. 17.8. Analysis of the nuclear collision in Fig. 17.7.

Applying its most general form, Eq. (17.3), we obtain here

$$m_A\mathbf{v}_{A1} = m_A\mathbf{v}_{A2} + m_B\mathbf{v}_{B2}$$

or

$$\mathbf{M}_{A1} = \mathbf{M}_{A2} + \mathbf{M}_{B2},$$

where the plus sign must be clearly understood to refer to vectorial addition. $\mathbf{M}_{A2}$ and $\mathbf{M}_{B2}$ must add up to a resultant momentum vector which is as large as $\mathbf{M}_{A1}$ and lies in the same (horizontal) direction. This is indicated graphically in Fig. 17.8(b), where the heavy dashed diagonal in the parallelogram represents the sum of $m_A\mathbf{v}_{A2}$ and $m_B\mathbf{v}_{B2}$ and is as long as the arrow representing $m_A\mathbf{v}_{A1}$.

This situation yields two separate equations. First, since the resultant of the two vectors $\mathbf{M}_{A2}$ and $\mathbf{M}_{B2}$ is entirely in the x-direction, the upward y-component of $\mathbf{M}_{A2}$ must cancel the downward y-component of $\mathbf{M}_{B2}$. Hence

$$m_A v_{A2} \sin \alpha = m_B v_{B2} \sin \beta. \qquad (17.11)$$

Second, the x-components of $\mathbf{M}_{A2}$ and $\mathbf{M}_{B2}$ together must account fully for the resultant momentum after collision, which, by the principle of conservation, is numerically equal to $\mathbf{M}_{A1}$, the total momentum before collision. Hence

$$m_A v_{A1} = m_A v_{A2} \cos \alpha + m_B v_{B2} \cos \beta. \qquad (17.12)$$

Equations (17.11) and (17.12) together involve seven parameters; if five of these are known, the remaining two can be calculated. For example, the mass m_B and the speed v_{B2} of the heavier, recoiling particle can be obtained if α and β are measured and m_A, v_{A1}, and v_{A2} are known from independent considerations; or v_{A2} and v_{B2} can be obtained from a knowledge of the other five parameters.

The same analysis applies if the incident particle does not glance off but is briefly absorbed before the occurrence of an explosion which blows the fragments apart.

PROBLEM 17.18. An alpha particle glances off a virtually stationary oxygen nucleus, making an angle of 76° with respect to its initial direction of motion; the oxygen nucleus simultaneously recoils at 45° to the other side. If the masses of the particles are respectively 6.64×10^{-27} kgm and 2.66×10^{-26} kgm, find the ratio of their speeds after the collision.

Illustration 7. A relatively simple method for investigating nuclear reactions is illustrated by Fig. 17.9. Here a cloud chamber is not used. Instead, the particles to be studied (such as those emitted by radioactive substances, or appearing as components of cosmic rays, or produced in big accelerators) travel into a photographic emulsion. The moving particles act on the emulsion and, when the plate is developed, their paths

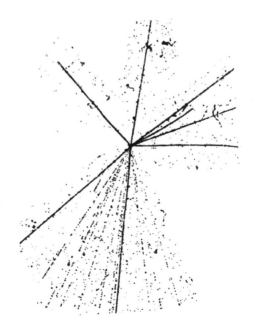

FIG. 17.9. Nuclear disintegration induced by cosmic-ray bombardment. (After C. F. Powell.)

appear as exposed streaks when observed under a microscope. If such a particle encounters a suitable atomic nucleus in the emulsion, it may trigger off the sort of nuclear explosion seen in Fig. 17.9. The tracks made by the incident particles and fragments are evaluated in the same way as those in a cloud-chamber picture. The particle masses or speeds are computed with the aid of the momentum principle, according to which the momentum of the particle incident on the stationary nucleus is equal to the vector sum of the momenta of all fragments.

17.6 Conclusion. We have seen that the principle of conservation of momentum is a very versatile tool for the analysis of the physical behavior of systems, even when the details of the motion or forces concerned are not accessible to direct study. We dealt with situations involving several types of explosion, and found solutions without having to investigate the magnitude or nature of the various forces involved. It is no wonder that in practice the physical scientist prefers to attack his problems through principles such as this one, and we shall not be surprised to meet further references to the principle of conservation of momentum in the chapters that follow.

ADDITIONAL PROBLEMS

17.19. From the point of view of the principle of conservation of momentum, analyze the method by which a propeller-driven aircraft obtains its forward speed. Do the same for a propeller-driven ship, for a swimmer, and for a man walking on the ground.

17.20. In Chapter 4 it was pointed out that Newton's laws of motion hold strictly only when the velocities and accelerations involved are measured relative not to the earth, but to the "fixed stars" as the frame of reference. Is this also true of the principle of conservation of momentum? Why or why not? In the light of your answer, discuss the validity of these statements: if you jump upward, the earth will recoil with an initial momentum that is equal in magnitude but opposite in direction to your initial momentum; during each moment you are in the air, your momentum and that of the earth will be of equal magnitude and opposite direction.

17.21. A gun of mass 1200 kgm and with a barrel of length 3 m is initially at rest. It fires a 10-kgm projectile horizontally with a muzzle speed of 1000 m/sec. (a) Compute the average force on the projectile, due to the expanding gases of combustion, from the moment of firing until the projectile leaves the barrel. (b) What average force of recoil is experienced during the same time by the gun itself?

17.22. A 5000-kgm rocket is to be fired vertically upward. The initial "thrust" supplied to the rocket by the exhaust gas may be obtained from an equation such as Eq. (17.1); it is given by the change of momentum imparted to the gas per second. If the exhaust speed is 1000 m/sec, how much gas must be ejected per second to provide enough thrust (a) just to overcome the rocket's own weight, (b) to give the rocket an initial acceleration of 20 m/sec^2?

17.23. If it were possible to construct a pendulum bob of such large size that its mass would be comparable to the mass of our planet, what would be the motion of this system (a) as the pendulum just starts to descend from one side on its arc, (b) as the pendulum just goes through its lowest point of the swing, and (c) as the pendulum momentarily reaches its highest position on the other side?

SUPPLEMENTARY READING

FURRY, W. H., E. M. PURCELL, and J. C. STREET, *Physics for science and engineering students* (Blakiston, 1952), Sections 2–10 and 2–11.

HOLTON, G., *Introduction to concepts and theories in physical science* (Addison-Wesley, 1952), pp. 303–312 on conservation of angular momentum.

MACH, E., *The science of mechanics* (Open Court Publishing Co., 1942; original edition, 1883), particularly pp. 396–418. The mathematical arguments may be largely omitted at this stage.

MAGIE, W. F., *A source book in physics* (McGraw-Hill, 1935), Chap. 2, pp. 50–51. Excerpt from Descartes.

MILLIKAN, R. A., D. ROLLER, and E. C. WATSON, *Mechanics, molecular physics, heat, and sound* (Ginn, 1937), Chap. 5.

SHORTLEY, G., and D. WILLIAMS, *Elements of physics* (Prentice-Hall, 1955), Chap. 7.

CHAPTER 18

THE PRINCIPLE OF CONSERVATION OF ENERGY IN MECHANICS

18.1 *Vis viva.* The basic quantities of mechanics are usually taken to be length, mass, and time. We have used combinations of these three quantities to set up the derived concepts of velocity, acceleration, force, and momentum, each of which has found a prominent role in some fundamental physical law or principle. Now we are about to introduce the last of the great mechanical concepts that will be needed for our purposes, the concepts of *energy* and *work*. With these we can construct the mighty principle of conservation of energy.

The full history of these concepts and of the energy principle is lengthy and involved; it took more than 150 years from their first adumbration to the point where even the basic terminology itself was fully worked out. Yet the roots lie in the very same problem that gave rise to the concept of momentum and the momentum principle, namely, the problem of what changes in motion occur when bodies collide with one another. And significantly, in examining the first major contribution to this subject, we encounter the same man who 30 years earlier had helped to formulate the principle of conservation of momentum: Christiaan Huygens (Fig. 18.1), the Dutch physicist of whom it has often been said that he was in many respects Galileo's and Newton's peer.

Fig. 18.1. Christiaan Huygens (1629–1695).

Huygens was not only an outstanding mathematician (Newton referred to him as one of the three "greatest geometers of our time"), he also made an improved telescope, resolved the rings of Saturn, and, building on Galileo's work, invented the first practical pendulum clock. Among his great accomplishments in physics are the first theorems of centripetal force, the conservation principles applied to elastic impact, the theory of oscillating systems, and a treatise that laid the foundations for the wave theory of light.

The starting point for our topic is Huygens' postulate that during the collision of two perfectly elastic spheres ". . . the sum of the product of their masses times the square of their velocities will remain the same before and after the impact . . ." (From the posthumous treatise *De motu corporum ex percussione*, 1703.)

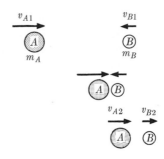

FIG. 18.2.   Collision between two moving spheres.

We shall first discuss this postulate in terms of a concrete but general example, as in Fig. 18.2. Two unequal but perfectly rigid spheres approach each other with unequal speeds, collide, and separate. To be sure, from our previous discussion we know well that the principle of conservation of momentum demands

$$m_A \mathbf{v}_{A1} + m_B \mathbf{v}_{B1} = m_A \mathbf{v}_{A2} + m_B \mathbf{v}_{B2}, \tag{18.1}$$

but this is no longer the issue. What Huygens is proposing here is that, at the same time, an additional relation is fulfilled (which, unlike Eq. [18.1], is not directly derived from Newton's laws), namely

$$m_A v_{A1}^2 + m_B v_{B1}^2 = m_A v_{A2}^2 + m_B v_{B2}^2. \tag{18.2}$$

To the quantity mv^2, the German philosopher and scientist Gottfried Wilhelm Leibniz gave the name *vis viva*, in 1695. Therefore Huygens' statement, as expressed by Eq. (18.2), may be called the *principle of conservation of* vis viva *for perfectly elastic impact*.

Let there be no mistake about it: Eq. (18.2) cannot be derived from Eq. (18.1). The two equations are *independent;* they supplement each other, each giving information not provided by the other. And notice how they differ: Eq. (18.1) is a *vector* equation. Equation (18.2), on the other hand, is a *scalar* equation, involving the squares of the velocities, not the velocities themselves, and consequently in using this equation differences in the direction of motion need not be taken into consideration.

An illustration will show the usefulness of the *vis viva* principle.

Illustration 1. Recall Illustration 1 in Section 17.4. There a rigid ball A of mass m_A was shot with velocity $\mathbf{v}_{A1}$ toward a rigid ball B of equal mass $(m_B = m_A)$ that was initially at rest on a table $(\mathbf{v}_{B1} = 0)$. The problem was to find $\mathbf{v}_{B2}$, the velocity of ball B after impact. Applying the momentum principle, we wrote

$$m_A\mathbf{v}_{A1} + m_B\mathbf{v}_{B1} = m_A\mathbf{v}_{A2} + m_B\mathbf{v}_{B2}. \tag{18.3}$$

Or, since $m_A = m_B$ and $\mathbf{v}_{B1} = 0$, and the velocities are in the same line, the speeds are related by

$$v_{A1} = v_{A2} + v_{B2}. \tag{18.4}$$

Now in Illustration 1 of Section 17.4 we were *given* an additional datum, namely, that the ball A was observed to remain at rest on the table after the impact, or that $v_{A2} = 0$. Therefore, from Eq. (18.4), $v_{B2} = v_{A1}$. Thus we found that B gained as much speed as A lost.

Suppose, however, that we did not know that ball A remains at rest after impact. Then there are two unknown quantities, v_{A2} and v_{B2}, in Eq. (18.4). But now that we have been told that balls A and B are perfectly elastic, the *vis viva* principle is applicable here, and so we have the new additional relation

$$m_A v_{A1}^2 + m_B v_{B1}^2 = m_A v_{A2}^2 + m_B v_{B2}^2,$$

or, since here $m_A = m_B$ and $v_{B1} = 0$,

$$v_{A1}^2 = v_{A2}^2 + v_{B2}^2. \tag{18.5}$$

Now we have two equations (18.4 and 18.5) containing *three* different quantities; therefore we need to know only one of these quantities, say v_{A1}, in order to be able to solve for the other two. To solve the two simultaneous equations, let us first square both members of Eq. (18.4):

$$v_{A1}^2 = v_{A2}^2 + 2v_{A2}v_{B2} + v_{B2}^2.$$

This expression for v_{A1}^2 may then be substituted into Eq. (18.5) to obtain, after simplification,

$$v_{A2}v_{B2} = 0.$$

From this result we conclude that either v_{A2} or v_{B2} is zero. But the second of these alternatives is physically meaningless, for it could be realized only if the solid ball B remained at rest while ball A passes through it with speed v_{A2}. Consequently the other alternative is the correct one; it is v_{A2} that is zero. Then, finally, from Eq. (18.4), $v_{B2} = v_{A1}$.

Thus we have arrived at the same result as in Section 17.4. However, the present method of solution is more powerful because we have been able to calculate both final speeds from data that refer only to conditions before impact; we did not need prior knowledge of the magnitude of $\mathbf{v}_{A2}$. The same applies in any problem involving direct collision of two rigid objects; with the aid of both the momentum and the *vis viva* principles, the final velocities of both objects can be found when only the initial velocities (and masses) are known.

PROBLEM 18.1. In the posthumous edition of Huygens' treatise *De motu corporum ex percussione* (1703), there appears this assertion: "If two equal bodies [bodies of equal mass] moving in opposite directions with equal speeds meet each other directly, each of them rebounds with the same speed with which it came." Show that this result follows from the momentum and *vis viva* principles, provided it is assumed that the collision is perfectly elastic. (Note that the initial conditions are $m_A = m_B$, $\mathbf{v}_{A1} = -\mathbf{v}_{B1}$.)

The usefulness of the principle of conservation of *vis viva*, as demonstrated, is considerable, but *unlike* the momentum principle *it is strictly limited to impacts between bodies* that for practical purposes may be regarded as *perfectly elastic*. In truth, the matter is even more serious, for generally it is not possible to judge before the collision actually takes place whether it will be sufficiently close to being perfectly elastic to permit the use of the *vis viva* principle, and so the decision whether the principle applies to a specific collision ought to be made only after a tentative calculation, made with the help of the principle, is found to be in accord with subsequent observations of the actual collision. This *a posteriori* procedure is rather like diagnosing whether a sick man has malaria by seeing whether a malaria cure will put him on his feet.

Evidently what is needed is to find some way to extend the principle of conservation of *vis viva* so that the extended principle will, like the momentum principle, apply to all types of interactions. This was brilliantly accomplished in the 19th century, but to bring it about required much clarification of thought and development of some important new concepts.

18.2 Further examination of the role of force. Consider a body in motion, perhaps a block sliding across a table. If you try to stop it quickly by interposing your hand in its path, you will feel the block exerting a force on you, perhaps a considerable one. Is this some new force we have not yet discussed? Does a body exert a force upon an obstacle "by virtue of being in motion," as one might say a spring exerts a force "by virtue of its inherent elasticity," or a magnet "by virtue of its inherent magnetism"?

These seem to be common-sense questions, but they mirror the phraseology of the 17th century and earlier, and lead to very little explanation and sometimes to serious semantic confusion. As Newton was aware, such phraseology encourages attempts to explain force by a "living force of motion," elasticity by elasticity, magnetism by magnetism, and so on. Therefore, instead of speaking of an innate quality or inherent force, we today seek the relationship between the force under examination and its observable effects. Looking in this way at the force exerted by a moving object on an obstacle like our hand, we see at once that this is not some new "living force," as was sometimes thought. Instead, what our hand experiences (in accord with Newton's third law) is nothing but the force of reaction to the decelerating or braking force which, by Newton's second law, the hand must apply to the moving object to change its momentum (see Section 17.2). This decelerating force, and also the reaction to it, are, of course, numerically equal to ma, the product of the mass m of the object and its deceleration a. Similar conditions hold when the hand is used to set an object into motion. No longer do we say that the hand imparts a "living force" to the object, but rather that the hand applies a forward accelerating force ma and at the same time experiences a contrary force of reaction of equal magnitude.

A problem that eventually was seen to have far-reaching significance was posed by Galileo when he asked, in essence: if a body moves through a distance s while an accelerating force is acting on it, is there any simple relationship between s and the change of velocity undergone by the body? Let us investigate this problem in a modern setting.

Suppose a car of mass m to be moving on a level road with speed v_1. A forward accelerating *net* force $\mathbf{F}_{net}$ is now applied to the car, and this force is kept constant until the car has traveled a distance s and has reached a higher speed v_2 (Fig. 18.3). What relationship exists between the given quantities F_{net}, m, v_1, v_2, and s?

FIG. 18.3. A car accelerated by a force $\mathbf{F}_{net}$.

The accelerating force on the car is given by $F_{net} = ma$. In this problem we do not know the acceleration a; but since the force and hence the acceleration are assumed to be constant, we can make use of Eq. (1.6), according to which

$$a = \frac{(v_2^2 - v_1^2)}{2s}.$$

Therefore $F_{\text{net}} = ma = m(v_2^2 - v_1^2)/2s$ and, after some rearrangement, this becomes

$$F_{\text{net}}\, s = \tfrac{1}{2}mv_2^2 - \tfrac{1}{2}mv_1^2. \tag{18.6}$$

Although derived here in connection with a specific problem, Eq. (18.6) will be found to have tremendous general significance.

EXAMPLE 18.1. A bullet of mass 0.012 kgm is fired with a muzzle speed of 500 m/sec. The gun has a smooth bore, and the length of the barrel is 0.75 m. Neglecting friction, find the average net force on the bullet during firing.

Solution. Here $s = 0.75$ m, $m = 0.012$ kgm, $v_1 = 0$, and $v_2 = 500$ m/sec. From Eq. (18.6),

$$F_{\text{net}} = \frac{\tfrac{1}{2}mv_2^2 - 0}{s} = \tfrac{1}{2} \times 0.012 \text{ kgm} \times \frac{(500 \text{ m/sec})^2}{0.75 \text{ m}}$$

$$= 2.0 \times 10^3 \text{ kgm·m/sec}^2 = 2.0 \times 10^3 \text{ new.}$$

PROBLEM 18.2. (a) Using Eq. (18.6), prove that if a given moving object strikes an obstacle that always offers the same retarding force, the distance the object moves before coming to rest is proportional to the square of the speed with which it strikes the obstacle. (b) When the brakes were strongly applied to a certain car moving with speed 30 mi/hr, the car slid 75 ft before coming to rest. Assuming that the braking force remained the same throughout, how far would the car have slid before stopping if its initial speed had been 60 mi/hr?

18.3 The concept of work. One of the new concepts which the preceding section served to introduce is that of *work* W,* whose precise definition is: when a force F acts on a body during a displacement s of the body, *the work done by that force is the product of the component of force in the direction of motion and the distance moved by the body while the force is acting*, or in equation form,

$$W = (F \cos \theta) \times s,$$

or more usually,

$$W = Fs \cos \theta, \tag{18.7}$$

where θ is the angle between the directions of the force and the displacement of the body (Fig. 18.4). In Fig. 18.3 the accelerating force F was *in the same direction* as the car's displacement s, and so $\theta = 0$, $\cos \theta = 1$, and therefore $W = Fs$. (But note well that it is incorrect to write $W = Fs$ if θ is not zero.)

---

*Recall that our symbol for *weight* was not W, but F_{grav}.

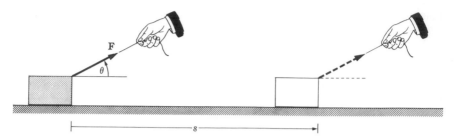

FIG. 18.4. The work done by the applied force **F** is given by $Fs \cos \theta$.

The units in terms of which work is expressed are those of force times distance. Hence, in the mks system, the unit of work is *newton* × *meter*, for which the briefer name *joule* (j) is used, in honor of the British scientist James P. Joule, whose contribution to physical science we are to examine in a later chapter.

It is important to emphasize that work is a scalar quantity; that is, a statement of the amount of work done never includes direction. We do not say "so many joules of work toward the north," even though the force F and the direction s in the defining expression $W = Fs \cos \theta$ have directional (vector) properties. The important specifications of work are what force or agency acts to do work, on what object or against what resistance the work is done, and whether the numerical value of the work is positive or negative. The following examples and problems will help to clarify this important concept in terms of everyday applications.

EXAMPLE 18.2. In Fig. 18.4, how much work is done on the block by a force F_1 of 20 new as it pulls the block for 30 cm, if the angle θ between force and displacement is 30°?

Solution. $W = F \times s \times \cos \theta = 20 \text{ new} \times 0.30 \text{ m} \times 0.87 = 5.2 \text{ new·m} = 5.2 \text{ j.}$

PROBLEM 18.3. A horse pulls a cart with a force of 2.0×10^3 new directed 25° above the horizontal. If the displacement of the cart is 3.0×10^3 m, how much work is done by the horse on the cart?

PROBLEM 18.4. A stone of mass 0.10 kgm falls freely through a distance of 1.5 m. Air friction is negligible. Show that the force acting on the stone does 1.5 joules of work.

Suppose that a car is rolling slowly along a road and a man, by pushing backward on it with a force F_1, brings the car to rest within a distance s. Here the force F_1 on the car and its displacement s are in opposite directions, $\theta_1 = 180°$ and $\cos \theta_1 = -1$; thus the work done by the man *on the car* is $F_1 s \cos \theta_1 = -F_1 s$, a *negative* quantity. At the same time, according to Newton's third law, the car has been exerting on the man a force F_2 of magnitude equal to F_1 but directed along the displacement s, so that θ_2, the angle between F_2 and s, is zero, and $\cos \theta_2 = 1$. Thus the work done *on the man* by the car is $F_2 s \cos \theta_2 = F_2 s$, a *positive* quantity. Evidently, to say that the man has done negative work on the car is equivalent to saying that the car has done positive work of an equal amount on him.

EXAMPLE 18.3. A boy pushes horizontally on one end of a wagon with a force F_A of 30 new to the right, while another boy opposes him by pushing on the other end with a force F_B of 24 new to the left. If the wagon moves 1.5 m to the right, how much work is done on it by (a) the first boy, (b) the second boy, (c) both boys together?

Solution. (a) The force exerted by the first boy is in the direction of the displacement; hence $\theta_A = 0$, $\cos \theta_A = 1$, and $W_A = 30$ new $\times$ 1.5 m $= 45$ j. (b) For the second boy, $\theta_B = 180°$, $\cos \theta_B = -1$, and $W_B = 24$ new $\times$ 1.5 m $\times (-1) = -36$ new·m $= -36$ j; or, to put this another way, the work done by the wagon on the second boy is 36 j. (c) The total work done on the wagon by both boys is $45 j + (-36 j) = 9 j$. Note that the total work done on the wagon by the boys could also have been obtained by multiplying the displacement by the difference of the forces, $(F_A - F_B)$, with the result $(30 - 24)$ new $\times$ 1.5 m $\times 1 = 9$ j.

PROBLEM 18.5. A man applies a force of 230 new to a car that is rolling slowly along a level track. Find the work that he does on the car if it moves 10 m while he pushes (a) in the direction of the displacement, (b) in a direction making an angle of 45° with the displacement, (c) in a direction opposite to that of the displacement, and (d) in a direction at right angles to that of the displacement.

If an object of weight F_{grav} is slid a distance s across a level table or floor, no work is done by or against the force of gravity, for F_{grav} and s, although each may be large, are at right angles to each other, and $\cos 90° = 0$. Similarly, when a man carries a load across level ground and so applies an upward force F, as in Fig. 18.5, he does no *net* work against gravity, although he may become fatigued. For one thing, he alternately raises and lowers the object and himself slightly while walking; thus he alternately does work against gravity and has work done on him by gravity. But even if the man merely stands and holds the load, and no net work is done against gravity, he will tire because his tensed muscles are continually contracting and relaxing in minute movements. He could also become exhausted by pulling on a heavy object that won't budge, but he will not thereby have done any *work* on it as

FIG. 18.5. A force at right angles to the displacement does not result in work being done.

defined in physical science. It is important not to let our subjective notions of activity, achievement, or fatigue become confused with this very different use of the word "work."

PROBLEM 18.6. (a) When an object is moving in a circular path, how much work is done by the centripetal force? (b) What can you say about the work done by the "central" force acting on a planet in its *elliptical* path around the sun? (Start by making a large drawing of an ellipse with large eccentricity.)

18.4 Work involving frictional forces.

By far the most frequent case of doing work would seem to be work involving the force of friction. Suppose we are pulling a block through a distance s along a level table by applying to the block a horizontal force F_{ap}. If we keep this force F_{ap} always equal in magnitude to the backward frictional force between block and table, the block will move with constant velocity. The magnitude of the frictional force is equal to μmg, where μ is the coefficient of sliding friction and mg is the weight of the block (see Section 4.12), so the work we do is $F_{ap}s \cos \theta = \mu mgs$. If we cease to apply the force F_{ap}, then the frictional force soon brings the block to rest. All the work μmgs previously done on the block seems to have disappeared, although we may notice some heating up of the block and table surface where they rubbed against each other.

If we regard the work against friction, μmgs, as "wasted" or "dissipated," it is only so by comparison with certain other situations in which, as it will turn out, some or all of the work done can be directly recovered when the applied force is removed. For example, if we compress a spring and then release it, the spring, unlike the block on the table, does not simply remain at rest, but flies back out again; except for a little heating of the spring, the work done in compressing it is directly recoverable, for it might put in motion some other object as it relaxes to its initial state.

EXAMPLE 18.4. A block on a level table, after being given a push, slides 100 cm before coming to rest. The mass of the block is 500 gm, and the coefficient of friction is 0.20. How much work is done on the block by the frictional force in bringing it to rest?

Solution. The frictional force μmg acting on the block is opposite in direction to the displacement s, and hence $\theta = 180°$. So the work done on the block by the frictional force is $W = \mu mgs \cos \theta = 0.20 \times 0.500 \text{ kgm} \times (9.8 \text{ m/sec}^2) \times 1.00 \text{ m} \times (-1) = -0.98 \text{ kgm·m}^2/\text{sec}^2 = -0.98 \text{ new·m} = -0.98 \text{ j}$. At the same time, the block does 0.98 j of work against the frictional force.

PROBLEM 18.7. An automobile of mass 1.6×10^3 kgm is pushed with constant velocity along a level road for 1.4 km by a man exerting a force of 200 new. How much work is done on the automobile by the man?

PROBLEM 18.8. A boy pulls a sled 1 km along level ground by applying to it an average horizontal force of 40 new. (a) How much work does the boy do on the sled? (b) If the sled moves with constant velocity, how much work is done on the sled by the frictional force? (c) How much work is done on the sled by the earth's gravitational force?

PROBLEM 18.9. A railway train consists of 14 loaded cars and an engine. Each car weighs about 30 tons, and the coefficient of rolling friction is 0.002. How much work does the engine do on the cars in hauling them 100 km on a straight, level track?

PROBLEM 18.10. Make a quantitative estimate of how much work you could do in a day. State your assumptions.

18.5 Work involving inertial forces; kinetic energy. Let us concentrate next on situations in which the frictional forces are so small that they may be neglected. Suppose that a block is sliding with some constant speed v_1 across a highly polished horizontal surface. Now we apply a horizontal force F_{net} while the block moves a distance s and accelerates to a speed v_2. The work done on the block is given by Eq. (18.6):

$$F_{net}\, s \; = \; mas \; = \; m\,\frac{(v_2^2 - v_1^2)}{2},$$

or

$$F_{net}\, s \; = \; \tfrac{1}{2}mv_2^2 - \tfrac{1}{2}mv_1^2. \tag{18.6}$$

The term $\tfrac{1}{2}mv^2$, which will be recognized as being one-half of the *vis viva*, appears so often in the equations of physics that about a century ago the concept was given a name of its own, *kinetic energy*. Thus we find that the *work done by the net force on a body is equal to the change in kinetic energy of the body*. Our symbol for kinetic energy is E_k, and Eq. (18.6) can be written

$$F_{net}\, s \; = \; (E_k)_2 - (E_k)_1,$$

or, more generally,

$$\text{Work done by net force} \; = \; \Delta E_k. \tag{18.8}$$

EXAMPLE 18.5. An object of mass 3 kgm is falling toward the ground. What is its kinetic energy at the moment when it has reached a speed of 20 m/sec?

Solution. By definition, $E_k = \tfrac{1}{2}mv^2 = \tfrac{1}{2} \times 3$ kgm $\times 400$ m²/sec² $= 6 \times 10^2$ kgm·m²/sec² $= 6 \times 10^2$ new·m $= 6 \times 10^2$ j. Note that kinetic energy and work are measured in the same units, as they must be in view of Eq. (18.8).

EXAMPLE 18.6. A cyclotron is to be used to accelerate a proton, which is a nuclear particle of mass 1.7×10^{-30} kgm. If the proton starts from rest, how much work must be done to give it a final speed v_2 of 3×10^7 m/sec, which is one-tenth the speed of light?

Solution. Here $v_1 = 0$. Then, from Eq. (18.8), the work done $= \tfrac{1}{2}mv_2^2 = \tfrac{1}{2} \times 1.7 \times 10^{-30}$ kgm $\times (3 \times 10^7$ m/sec)² $= 7.7 \times 10^{-16}$ j. Even though this is an exceedingly small amount of work, the difficulties of supplying it are as varied as are the effects produced with such high-speed particles. (Incidentally, the accelerating force in the cyclotron is of electrical origin.)

PROBLEM 18.11.   A 0.75-kgm block is sliding across a highly polished floor with a speed of 0.20 m/sec. Use Eq. (18.8) to show that a horizontal net force of 0.11 new must be applied to the block to change its speed to 0.70 m/sec while it moves a distance of 1.5 m.

Work done on an object that results in an increase in the object's kinetic energy is, in a sense, directly recoverable, for when the moving object strikes another object, it does work on the latter while losing a corresponding amount of kinetic energy. That a moving object has this capacity for doing work when it is slowed down is illustrated by the damage a moving car or projectile can do upon striking an obstacle, or by the use of a falling sledge hammer driving a stake into the ground, and by other everyday phenomena almost countless in number.

EXAMPLE 18.7.   From what height must one drop a 0.5-kgm metal object down on a nail so that the latter would be driven 5 cm into a wooden plank against a force of friction of 80 new?

Solution. The kinetic energy of the metal object just before hitting the nail will be $\frac{1}{2}mv^2$, and it is assumed that in stopping, the object loses its kinetic energy but supplies the nail with 80 new $\times$ 0.05 m $=$ 4 j of work to overcome the frictional force. Thus

$$\frac{1}{2}\,mv^2 = 4\text{ j}, \qquad v^2 = \frac{2 \times 4\text{ j}}{0.5\text{ kgm}}, \qquad v = \sqrt{\frac{8\text{ j}}{0.5\text{ kgm}}} = \frac{4\text{ m}}{\text{sec}}.$$

To reach such a speed in free fall, we must drop the object from a height given by Eq. (1.6):

$$s = \frac{v^2}{2g} = \frac{16\text{ m}^2/\text{sec}^2}{2 \times 9.8\text{ m/sec}^2} = 0.8\text{ m}.$$

Obviously, this was a very tortuous calculation. But now we are approaching the formulation of a general principle of conservation of energy, whose great merit is that such problems can be solved in a direct and neat way.

PROBLEM 18.12.   The frictional force on a block sliding on a rough table is found to be 1.2 new. An additional force of 3.5 new, in the direction of the motion, is applied to the block while it moves 1.25 m. Compute the increase in kinetic energy.

18.6 Work involving gravitational forces; potential energy. Consider now a situation in which work is done *on* a body; for example, an object of mass m is lifted from the floor to a height h above it. The constant upward force needed here is numerically equal to mg, enough to balance the weight, provided we can neglect air resistance and also proceed so slowly that there is no sensible increase in kinetic energy. The work done on the object is therefore mgh. But where does this work mgh go, if not to air resistance or kinetic energy? It is not lost, for the block, if released, will be accelerated downward by gravity through the distance h and, just before it strikes the floor, will have acquired kinetic energy of exactly the same number of joules as the work we had expended in lifting it. The work done against gravity in raising a body is completely recoverable in the form of kinetic energy obtained during free fall.

Now it is intellectually unsatisfactory to think of this kinetic energy as gradually increasing from zero at the start to the full value at the end of the fall while the object is "on its own." To deal with this difficulty we formulate a new concept, called *potential energy*, E_p. We say that the work done in lifting the body against the gravitational pull of the earth is "stored," as it were, as *potential energy* in the system containing the body and the earth; in fact, one may at first imagine that the potential energy is stored in the general region around the body, in the *gravitational field*. When the object is allowed to fall, this potential energy is gradually given up by the field and is converted into kinetic energy of the object. Thus on raising the level of an object of mass m through a distance h, the work mgh that we must do on the object is converted into potential energy of amount mgh. And when the body falls, the "work done by the gravitational force" represents only a withdrawal from a bank account of energy which had been accumulated on the way up; on returning to the original lower level, all of the energy has become kinetic.

In this way, work, kinetic energy, and potential energy all become related and interconvertible concepts. When we raise a hammer to let it drop on a nail, we first do work on the hammer and so energy from our muscles goes into the form of potential energy of the hammer; as it drops, potential energy is gradually converted into kinetic energy, and while the nail is being driven in, the kinetic energy of the hammer is converted into work done against the force of friction between nail and plank.

In thinking of the seat of potential energy, we should avoid trying to make the picture too material or "concrete" in character; at this stage the picture should be regarded as a heuristic device, a valuable aid to comprehension and investigation, without necessarily having any other physical meaning.

Another caution to be observed here has to do with the *level of reference* to be used in computing potential energy. If we see a book of mass m on a desk in the second-floor study and are asked what its potential energy is, we may reply that it is mgh. But from what level is h to be measured? From the floor of the room? Or from the street below? Or from the center of the earth? The fact is that potential energy is always calculated with respect to some arbitrary specified level, usually, for convenience, the lowest level which the body attains in the course of a problematical situation. And the reason this can be done, as you will notice, is that we shall always deal with *differences* or *changes* in the potential energy between two points; the difference of E_p is independent of the original level of reference. In the same way the amount of money spent during a day is the difference between what you had in the morning ($9) and in the evening ($2); the cash value of the purchase made would have been the same if you had started the day with $100 or $10. Clearly, then, if differences alone count, the "zero level" or level of reference may as well be chosen as the lowest level àt which the body finds itself in the problem. The following examples will illustrate this point.

EXAMPLE 18.8. A 1.0-kgm object rests on a table 1.0 m above the floor, and the floor is 4.0 m above the street. (a) What is the potential energy of the object *with reference to* (1) the table top, (2) the floor, and (3) the street? (b) Now the object is put on the floor. Find the change in potential energy for this decrease of 1.0 m in the height of the object when the reference level is (1) the table top, (2) the floor, and (3) the street.

Solution. (a) $E_p = mgh = 1.0$ kgm $\times$ $(9.8$ m/sec$^2) \times h = 9.8$ new $\times h$. (1) Measured from the table top, the height is zero, $h = 0$, $E_p = 0$. (2) Measured from the floor, $h = 1.0$ m, $E_p = 9.8$ new $\times 1.0$ m $= 9.8$ new·m. (3) Measured from the street, $h = 5.0$ m, $E_p = 49$ new·m.

(b) (1) If the object is moved down 1.0 m, and the potential energies are computed relative to the table top, initially $(E_p)_1 = mgh = 1.0$ kgm $\times$ $(9.8$ m/sec$^2) \times 0 = 0$; finally, $(E_p)_2 = mgh = 1.0$ kgm $\times (9.8$ m/sec$^2) \times (-1.0$ m$) = -9.8$ new·m. Note that we have a negative value for h because the object is *beneath* the reference level. Then the change in potential energy is $\Delta E_p \equiv (E_p)_2 - (E_p)_1 = -9.8$ new·m $- 0$. (2) If now we compute the initial and final potential energies relative to the floor, the initial and final heights are 1.0 m and zero, respectively. $\Delta E_p = (E_p)_2 - (E_p)_1 = 0 - 1.0$ kgm $\times$ $(9.8$ m/sec$^2) \times 1.0$ m $= -9.8$ new·m, the same as before. (3) The change in potential energy relative to the street level is $\Delta E_p = 1.0$ kgm $\times$ $(9.8$ m/sec$^2) \times 4.0$ m $- 1.0$ kgm $\times (9.8$ m/sec$^2) \times 5.0$ m $= -9.8$ new·m, again the same.

Note that we can handle problems like this more easily by writing $\Delta E_p = (E_p)_2 - (E_p)_1 = mgh_2 - mgh_1 = mg(h_2 - h_1)$. But $h_2 - h_1$ is just the change in height Δh. Therefore $\Delta E_p = mg\, \Delta h$. Thus only the *change* in height is important in computing *changes* in potential energy.

EXAMPLE 18.9. A book weighing 10 new is raised 2.0 m. Compute (a) the work done on it, and (b) the increase in potential energy.

Solution. (a) The upward force needed to raise the book must be just a little larger than 10 new when the motion is starting and just a little less than 10 new when it is stopping, but taking the operation as a whole, no kinetic energy is imparted to the book and hence, neglecting air resistance, the average force that must be applied is 10 new. Therefore $W = F_{ap}\, s \cos \theta = 10$ new $\times 2.0$ m $\times \cos 0° = 20$ j. (b) The increase in potential energy can be computed by choosing the starting point as the reference level; then $\Delta E_p = mgh - 0 = 10$ new $\times 2.0$ m $= 20$ j. Clearly, ΔE_p is numerically equal to W.

EXAMPLE 18.10. A block of mass 2.0 kgm is pushed slowly up a smooth inclined plane until it has reached a vertical height of 4.0 m, having traveled

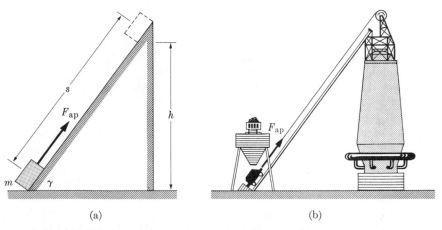

FIG. 18.6.   (a) Inclined plane.   (b) Practical application of inclined plane problem (Problem 18.14).

5.0 m along the plane [Fig. 18.6(a)]. Find (a) the gain in the potential energy of the block, (b) the work done on the block, and (c) F_{ap}, the force applied parallel to the inclined plane to do this work.

Solution. (a) $\Delta E_p = mgh - 0 = 2.0 \text{ kgm} \times (9.8 \text{ m/sec}^2) \times 4.0 \text{ m} = 78 \text{ j}$; note that the gain in potential energy depends on the change in vertical height and not at all on the length of the path traveled on the incline, which here was 5.0 m. (b) In the absence of friction or of any appreciable gain in kinetic energy, the work done is 78 j. (c) Since $W = F_{ap} s \cos \theta$, we have $F_{ap} = W/s \cos \theta = 78 \text{ j}/(5.0 \text{ m} \times \cos 0°) = 16 \text{ j/m}$. But 1 j $\equiv$ 1 new·m. So $F_{ap} = 16$ new·m/m = 16 new.

EXAMPLE 18.11. A preliminary experiment shows that the frictional force between a certain block of wood of mass 3.50 kgm and an inclined plane is 0.10 new. The block is now dragged slowly and with constant speed up the incline through a distance of 120 cm by applying to it a force of 4.0 new parallel to the incline. Compute (a) the work done on the block to overcome the frictional force, (b) the work done on the block to overcome the pull of gravity, (c) the gain by the block in potential energy, and (d) the height h of the block above the bottom of the plane.

Solution. (a) Part of the applied force, namely 0.10 new, serves to balance the frictional force; hence the work done because of friction is 0.10 new × 1.20 m × $\cos 0° = 0.12$ j. (b) Assuming that the block acquires negligible kinetic energy, the remainder of the applied force, namely $(4.0 - 0.10)$ new, serves to balance the effect of gravity; hence the work done against gravity is $(4.0 - 0.10 \text{ new}) \times 1.20 \text{ m} \times \cos 0° = 4.7 \text{ j}$. (c) The gain in potential energy, ΔE_p, is equal to the work done against gravity, namely 4.7 j.

(d) $\Delta E_p = mgh - 0$, taking as the zero level the lowest position; therefore $h = \Delta E_p/mg = 4.7 \text{ j}/(3.50 \text{ kgm} \times 9.8 \text{ m/sec}^2) = 0.14 \text{ j/new} = 0.14 \text{ m}$.

PROBLEM 18.13. A 68-kgm man pedals a 20-kgm bicycle up a slope of length 200 m and height 25 m. (a) Find the gain in potential energy of the man and bicycle together. (b) If his velocity does not change and the force of friction is negligible, how much work does the man do?

PROBLEM 18.14. In an industrial plant a loaded coal car with a mass of 3200 kgm is accelerated from rest up a smooth 45° incline 25 m in length by a constant force parallel to the incline; see Fig. 18.6(b). If the acceleration is 1.0 m/sec², (a) what is the gain in kinetic energy of the car? (b) How much work is done on the car by F_{ap}?

18.7 The principle of conservation of energy in mechanics. The following typical problem in mechanics will serve as a summary of our discussion of the three reasons for the necessity of doing work on a body, i.e., to overcome friction, or inertia, or gravitation. A block of mass m starts up a rough inclined plane with a speed v_1 and ascends it for a distance s while being acted on by an applied force F_{ap}, as shown in Fig. 18.6(a). The angle θ between F_{ap} and s is zero. We are told that the angle of inclination of the plane is γ and that the coefficient of sliding friction between block and plane is μ. The questions might be: How much does the kinetic energy of the block change, and what is the final speed v_2 at the top of the incline? The work done by the applied force may, in general, be split into three not necessarily equal parts that serve to do work against friction, change the kinetic energy, and change the potential energy. Thus we write the important and general equation,

$$\begin{Bmatrix} \text{Work done by} \\ \text{applied force} \end{Bmatrix} = \begin{Bmatrix} \text{Work done against friction} + \text{change in ki-} \\ \text{netic energy} + \text{change in potential energy} \end{Bmatrix} \quad (18.9)$$

In our present example (Fig. 18.6), the work done against the frictional force F_f is $F_f s$, or $\mu F_n s$, or $\mu(mg \cos \gamma)s$. The change in potential energy of the block on rising through a vertical distance h is mgh, or $mgs \sin \gamma$. Thus Eq. (18.9), which may be written symbolically as

$$F_{ap}s \cos \theta = F_f s + \Delta E_k + \Delta E_p, \quad (18.10)$$

reduces here to

$$F_{ap}s = \mu mg \cos \gamma \cdot s + (\tfrac{1}{2}mv_2^2 - \tfrac{1}{2}mv_1^2) + mgs \sin \gamma. \quad (18.11)$$

Evidently, with F_{ap}, s, μ, m, g, and γ known, the change in kinetic energy and also the final speed v_2 can be found.

Note that F_{ap} refers to the force applied to the block by means of a hand or rope or some other external agency but leaves out of account entirely the frictional and gravitational forces on the block, the effects of which are accounted for in the right-hand members of Eqs. (18.9) and (18.10).

The argument used in the foregoing example is probably quite plausible; but is it self-evident, or have we even proved it to be correct? Neither! The fact that there are three ways in which the work done on a body undergoes transformation does not mean that the sum of the three terms is necessarily exactly equal to the work done by the applied force. There could be drains on the available energy other than those we have thought of, or perhaps the moving body may receive energy from some source other than the applied force. We have assumed that this does not happen in the present simple mechanical example, but this is something that can be determined only by experiment.

Experiment does verify the postulate implicit in Eq. (18.9), a postulate that has come to be called the *principle of conservation of energy in mechanics* that *every joule of work supplied to a body can be accounted for by corresponding changes in kinetic and potential energies and in work done against friction.*

As a more general example of the principle of conservation of energy, imagine a closed system consisting of a box filled with blocks, elastic balls, inclined planes, and other objects. If we now add some energy to the system, perhaps by opening the box momentarily and pushing one of the objects to set it into motion, we would later find that the bodies by mutual collision have so rearranged their speeds and positions that the energy we added is exactly equal to the frictional losses and changes in kinetic and potential energies that have occurred since the moment of interference. In short, Eq. (18.9) is applicable to any closed system within which only mechanical interactions occur.

"Dissipative system" is the term applied to a system in which some of the mechanical energy is used to do work against friction. In contrast, "conservative systems" show no such conversion of energy; for them, the energy principle assumes a simpler form, since the work done by external forces serves solely to change the kinetic and potential energies of the system. If the conservative system were totally isolated, unable to receive energy from or give it up to the rest of the world, then $\Delta E_k + \Delta E_p = 0$, a specialized case of the energy principle that was first expressed with most telling power and elegance in J. L. Lagrange's *Analytical mechanics* (*Méchanique analitique*) of 1788, but was used long before in one guise or another.

PROBLEM 18.15. In the inclined plane problem of Fig. 18.6(a), what simpler form would Eq. (18.11) assume if (a) the incline were made perfectly smooth, $\mu = 0$; (b) the system were conservative; (c) the "incline" were made horizontal, $\gamma = 0$; (d) the "incline" were horizontal and the system conservative; (e) if no work were done on the system by an applied force; (f) the system were conservative and totally isolated?

PROBLEM 18.16. A boy pulls a 3-kgm sled up a 30° slope for a distance s of

10 m (Fig. 18.7). He is already moving at the bottom of the incline with a speed of 0.5 m/sec; by applying a force F_{ap} making an angle θ of 10° with the incline, he hopes to acquire a speed of 3 m/sec by the time he reaches the top. The frictional force is 3 new. (a) How much work does the boy do on the sled on the way up? (b) How much of this work goes into frictional losses, change of kinetic energy, and changes of potential energy respectively?

FIG. 18.7.   Motion of a sled on an inclined plane.

EXAMPLE 18.12. As an important sequel to Problem 18.16, suppose that the boy is now sitting on the sled at the top of the incline and, starting from rest, coasts to the bottom. What form does Eq. (18.11) assume in this case?

Solution. Here $F_{ap} = 0$, v_1 (at top) $= 0$, and m is now the combined mass of the boy and sled. In this case, Eq. (18.11) reduces to

$$0 = \mu mg \cos \gamma \cdot s + \tfrac{1}{2}mv_2^2 \text{ (at bottom)} - 0 \text{ (at top)} + (0 - mgh).$$

Note that the change in potential energy is negative, since the change is always given as the difference between final and initial values; here it is mgh at the top of the incline subtracted from zero at the bottom.

PROBLEM 18.17. In Example 18.12, suppose that the frictional force between the sled runners and snow were negligibly small. (a) Show that, in this case, all the potential energy at the top is converted into kinetic energy at the bottom. (b) Find the expression for the speed at the bottom. (c) Show that the speed is the same for free fall through the same difference of vertical level and explain why this is so.

EXAMPLE 18.13. A car of mass m is moving with speed v_1 on a wet, level road. Suddenly the driver sees an obstacle and slams on the brakes. The wheels lock and the car slides to a stop, dissipating its kinetic energy through sliding friction between tires and roadbed. (a) Through what distance s does the car slide? (b) If the initial speed is 60 mi/hr and $\mu = 0.25$, what is the value of s?

Solution. Here $F_{ap} = 0$, $\gamma = 0$, $v_2 = 0$, h ($= s \sin \gamma$) $= 0$. (a) From Eq. (18.11), $0 = \mu mgs - \tfrac{1}{2}mv_1^2$, or $s = v_1^2/2\mu g$.

Note that the mass m does not appear in this expression! Thus a truck and a bicycle of equal initial speeds will skid equal distances if v_1 and μ are equal. This result becomes more understandable when we recall that both the kinetic energy which is being dissipated and the frictional force are directly proportional to the mass of the vehicle.

(b) If $v_1 = 60$ mi/hr ($= 27$ m/sec) and $\mu = 0.25$, then $s = 146$ m or about 500 ft! (Note the danger of suddenly applying the brakes hard at high speeds.)

PROBLEM 18.18. A 2-kgm block having an initial speed of 60 m/sec slides up an incline for which $\gamma = 12°$ and $\mu = 0.2$. If no external force F_{ap} is applied to the block, how far up the incline will it be when it stops?

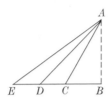

FIG. 18.8. Final speeds are equal on inclined planes of equal height.

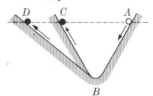

FIG. 18.9. A ball on friction-free planes ascends to its initial level.

PROBLEM 18.19. Here are two crucial postulates upon which Galileo based many of his arguments. (a) "The speeds acquired . . . moving down [frictionless] planes of different inclinations are equal when the heights of these planes are equal . . ." (Fig. 18.8). (b) ". . . a body which descends along any inclined [frictionless] plane and continues its motion along a plane inclined upward will, on account of the impetus acquired, ascend to an equal height above the horizontal; so that if the descent is along AB [Fig. 18.9] the body will be carried up the plane BC as far as the horizontal line ACD; and this is true whether the inclinations of the planes are the same or are different, as in the case of the planes AB and BD." Show that each of these postulates, which Galileo used without having a clear conception of either momentum or energy, can be derived from the principle of conservation of energy.

18.8 Pendulum motion.

Yet another application of the principle of conservation of energy relates to the varied and illuminating experiments with pendulums, favorite examples since before the time of Galileo. In Fig. 18.10 a simple pendulum is released at its topmost position a, swings to the lowest position c, and then rises again on the other side. While the bob swings down the arc from a to c, it undergoes a vertical displacement h_a. Now we apply the energy principle as expressed by Eq. (18.10) to this situation. There is a force F_{ap} applied on the bob (it is the tensile force in the string), but this acts at 90° to the path of the bob at every instant, and therefore can do no work. Hence if the frictional force

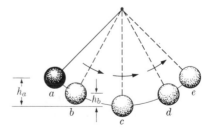

FIG. 18.10. The pendulum.

is negligibly small, Eq. (18.10) becomes, for the pendulum,

$$0 = 0 + \Delta E_k + \Delta E_p.$$

Thus for any two positions 1 and 2 of the bob along the path,

$$0 = 0 + (\tfrac{1}{2}mv_2^2 - \tfrac{1}{2}mv_1^2) + mg(h_2 - h_1),$$

where m is the mass of the bob. Specifically, if the two positions are a and c, and noting that $v_a = 0$ and $h_1 - h_2 = h_a$, we have

$$0 = 0 + (\tfrac{1}{2}mv_c^2 - 0) - mgh_a,$$

from which

$$\tfrac{1}{2}mv_c^2 = mgh_a \qquad \text{or} \qquad v_c = \sqrt{2gh_a}.$$

Thus it turns out that the speed of the pendulum bob as it passes through the lowest point c after release from a is exactly the same as it would be if the bob were simply to *drop* through the same height h_a. Furthermore, we see that the bob, in swinging on through the point c, must rise to the height h_a in order that all the kinetic energy at the bottom may be converted into potential energy at the top position e; that is, a and e are on the same horizontal level. If there were no way for its energy to escape, the pendulum, once started, would incessantly go through its symmetrical motion, continually exchanging its initial amount of energy back and forth between potential and kinetic energy.

PROBLEM 18.20. The 100-gm bob of a simple "frictionless" pendulum is released from a vertical height h_a of 5 cm. (a) Compute the speed of the bob at the bottom position c of the swing. (b) What is its kinetic energy E_k at c? (c) Compute E_p and E_k for a point on the path that is halfway, vertically, between the bottom and top of the swing.

PROBLEM 18.21. One of Galileo's famous arguments involved the arrangement shown in Fig. 18.11. First let a simple pendulum swing freely back and forth between points A and E. Now fix a nail or a peg in position F, so that the pendulum, released again from A, cannot reach E; the string is bent at F and the bob rises to G before returning. The significant thing is that G lies on the horizontal line AE even though the pendulum, on the right-hand part of its trip, now swings through the smaller arc HG rather than HE. As Galileo has Salviati say in the *Two new sciences:* "Now, gentlemen, you will observe with

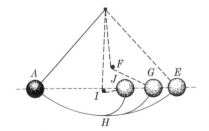

FIGURE 18.11

pleasure that the ball swings to the point G on the horizontal, and you would see the same thing happen if the obstacle were placed at some lower point, say at I, about which the ball would describe arc HJ, the rise of the ball always terminating exactly on the line AE." Explain these observations by means of the energy principle.

18.9 Collision problems. By now it is surely evident that the principle of conservation of *vis viva* (Eq. 18.2) was not only the original stimulus for the more general principle of conservation of energy (Eq. 18.9) but represents merely a special case of the latter. For example, suppose that two spheres A and B rolling on a smooth table undergo perfectly elastic collision, which is merely another way of saying that none of their kinetic energy is lost irretrievably by frictional or other processes during the collision. Then Eq. (18.10) reduces simply to

$$0 = 0 + \Delta E_k + 0,$$

or

$$0 = 0 + (\tfrac{1}{2}m_A v_{A2}^2 - \tfrac{1}{2}m_A v_{A1}^2) + (\tfrac{1}{2}m_B v_{B2}^2 - \tfrac{1}{2}m_B v_{B1}^2) + 0,$$

which, upon rearrangement and cancellation of the factor $\tfrac{1}{2}$, is precisely Eq. (18.2).

An especially interesting collision problem (an elaboration of the case shown previously in Fig. 17.2) involves a series of billiard balls of equal mass m in a line on a smooth table, each ball in contact with the next (Fig. 18.12). A ball A of the same mass is shot against one end of the series with speed v_A. What will be observed is that ball A comes to rest while E moves off to the right with speed $v_E = v_A$. In appearance, it is almost as if ball A penetrates the line of motionless balls and emerges at the other end with undiminished speed. But why does only ball E move off? Why not several or all of them, of course with speeds smaller than v_A?

FIG. 18.12.   Why does only ball E move off?

Let us see what light the energy and momentum principles throw on this problem. Assume, for the sake of argument, that both D and E do move off to the right after the collision; we can try to calculate their speeds v_D and v_E. Since billiard balls are highly elastic, the kinetic energy of the system after collision will be practically equal to that before collision. If ball A comes to rest, as observed, we have

$$\tfrac{1}{2}mv_A^2 = \tfrac{1}{2}mv_D^2 + \tfrac{1}{2}mv_E^2,$$

or

$$v_A^2 = v_D^2 + v_E^2. \tag{18.12}$$

This equation will be satisfied by an infinite number of pairs of values of v_D and v_E. So we call upon the momentum principle for additional information. It yields $mv_A = mv_D + mv_E$, or $v_D = v_A - v_E$, or $v_D^2 = v_A^2 - 2v_Av_E + v_E^2$. Substitution of this expression for v_D^2 in Eq. (18.12) yields

$$v_A^2 = (v_A^2 - 2v_Av_E + v_E^2) + v_E^2,$$

or

$$v_E = v_A.$$

When this value for v_E is substituted into either the energy or momentum equation, we find that $v_D = 0$. Thus it is, after all, not possible for two balls to move off from the series. The problem has a single solution only if we assume that A comes to rest. Try to get the general solution, also for several incident balls or a heavier ball. [See J.V. Kline, *American Journal of Physics* **28,** 102–103 (1960)].

PROBLEM 18.22. Three steel balls are suspended from strings so as to be in contact (Fig. 18.13). Use the conservation principles to calculate what can happen (a) if one ball is drawn back and allowed to fall against the others, all three having the same mass m, (b) if two balls are drawn back and released simultaneously against the third, each having the same mass m, (c) if a single ball of mass $2m$ is allowed to swing against the two other balls, each of mass m.

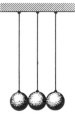

FIGURE 18.13

18.10 Applications of the energy principle to machines. A machine, as the term is used in physical science, is a device that transmits and modifies force or motion. Among the simplest machines are the lever, pulley, wheel and axle, inclined plane, and screw. By applying the energy principle to several of these machines, we can easily understand their action.

(a) *Levers.* The lever in Fig. 18.14 consists of a straight bar supported on a pivot, or *fulcrum*, that divides the length of the bar into two parts, or *lever arms*, l_1 and l_2. A load or weight F_2 on one end of the bar is kept balanced by a force F_1 applied at the other end. To lift the load, F_1 must be slightly increased, but only momentarily, to get the system into motion.

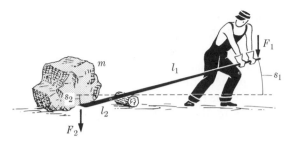

FIG. 18.14. The lever.

While F_1 depresses one end through the arc s_1, the other rises through the arc s_2. If the angle covered is very small, s_1 and s_2 are sufficiently close to being straight lines and perpendicular to the horizontal so that the work done on the system by F_1 is given by $F_1 s_1$. This work serves to change the kinetic energy and potential energy of load and lever bar, and to overcome friction in the fulcrum. However, three of these factors often can be neglected here: (1) the frictional force in the fulcrum, (2) the change in the kinetic energy, which is small if the speed of operation is kept small, and (3) the weight of the lever bar, which is often small in comparison with the forces F_1 and F_2. In such "ideal" circumstances, the only significant job done by the work $F_1 s_1$ supplied to the lever and load is to increase the potential energy of the load by the amount $F_2 s_2$ ($= mg s_2$). Thus,

$$F_1 s_1 = F_2 s_2 \qquad \text{or} \qquad \frac{F_2}{F_1} = \frac{s_1}{s_2}.$$

But for small angles, s_1 and s_2 can be considered sides of similar triangles in Fig. 18.14, and hence $s_1/s_2 = l_1/l_2$. Substitution yields

$$\frac{F_2}{F_1} = \frac{l_1}{l_2}. \tag{18.13}$$

In words, *the ratio of the load to the applied force is equal to the inverse ratio of the respective lever arms.* This is the *law of the lever*, known in classical antiquity. The law, here derived from the energy principle, can also be derived from other postulates. The most famous name associated with it is that of Archimedes of Syracuse (*c.* 287–212 B.C.).

PROBLEM 18.23. A board of length 12 ft and balanced at its midpoint on a barrel is used by a 75-kgm man and a 25-kgm boy as a see-saw. If the boy sits at one end of the board, where should the man sit?

PROBLEM 18.24. In Problem 18.23, suppose that the man and boy sit at the extreme ends of the board. If the mass of the plank can be neglected, where must the barrel be placed if there is to be balance?

(b) *Pulleys.* The combination of pulleys shown in Fig. 18.15 was considered by Aristotle and analyzed by Archimedes. In our discussion, let us use the simple approach afforded by the energy principle. As the hand pulls on the free end of the rope, moving it a distance s_1, the lower pulley and the load attached to it are raised through a distance s_2. If the frictional forces, the speed of operations, and the weights of lower pulley and rope are negligibly small, it follows that the work $F_1 s_1$ done by the applied force is equal solely to the work $F_2 s_2$ done on the load, or

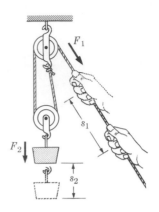

FIG. 18.15. Lifting a load with a block and tackle.

$$F_1 s_1 = F_2 s_2;$$

therefore

$$F_2 = F_1 \frac{s_1}{s_2}. \tag{18.14}$$

For this particular two-pulley system, measurement shows that s_1 is always twice s_2 (why must this be so?). If the system consists of more than two pulleys, Eq. (18.14) still holds, but the measured values of s_1/s_2 for these more elaborate systems may be much larger than 2. In every such case, however, if we determine s_1/s_2 experimentally, then Eq. (18.14) enables us to predict what force F_1 is needed, under ideal conditions, to lift a given load F_2; and we can do this no matter how little we know about the details of construction and operation of the pulley system.

(c) *Machines in general.* We may carry this last thought one step further and generalize on all simple machines or combinations of them. As in Fig. 18.16, any such machine may be regarded as equivalent to a "black box" to which we supply work at some *input* point and get useful work done on a load or other resisting force at some *output* point. We may know or understand nothing whatever about the details of the mechanism hidden in the box. Yet

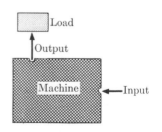

FIG. 18.16. Schematic representation of a machine.

we may be sure, from the principle of conservation of energy, that

Input of work = Output of work + work done within the machine
itself (to overcome friction, change the kinetic
or potential energy of the parts of the machine,
and so on).

Evidently, if the work done within the machine itself is large, a small output of work will be obtained for a given input. By definition, a machine's *efficiency*, η (Greek letter eta), is the ratio of output to input:

$$\eta = \frac{\text{Output of work}}{\text{Input of work}}. \tag{18.15}$$

For an *ideal* machine the output is equal to the input, and η is 1.00, or 100%. However, for many machines in actual practice, η may be as low as 0.1 (10%) or less.

PROBLEM 18.25. If the block and tackle of Fig. 18.15 were weightless and frictionless, an applied force of only 100 new would be needed to lift steadily a load of 200 new. But in using an actual block and tackle of this type, it was found that 125 new had to be applied to raise a 200-new load steadily. For this particular pulley system, if the load is lifted through 1.0 m, (a) through what distance s_1 is it necessary to apply the force F_1? (b) What is the output of work and the input of work? (c) What is the efficiency of the machine? (d) Since the input of work here exceeds the work that is needed to raise the load directly without using the machine, why use it at all?

18.11 Elastic deformation and elastic potential energy. In most of the problems examined so far, we have treated the bodies involved as if they remained unchanged in size and shape when acted upon by forces. This notion of bodies as perfectly rigid is, of course, an idealization, although a very useful one in many types of problems. For example, the lever could not be treated so simply if it bent under the load. In many collision problems we have restricted ourselves to situations where we could assume rigidity of the objects, because deformation during collision may lead to friction among the parts inside the colliding objects and to their permanent change of shape; this would make equations like (18.5) more complex by requiring addition of a term to account for the work done against friction in deformation.

However, we now must consider that all objects are in fact more or less deformable, that none are perfectly rigid. Our concern for the present will be with bodies that tend to return to their original size or shape when the forces that deformed them are removed. Such materials are called *elastic*, whether they deform easily (rubber) or very little (steel and many other metals). Bodies made of elastic materials rebound upon collision. If their total kinetic energy is not diminished as a result of the impact, the latter is said to be *perfectly elastic*. If it is diminished, the impact is called *partially elastic*. On the other hand, clay and putty are not elastic. They stick together after impact and form a single body. Such impacts are called *completely inelastic*.

Elastic deformation, even though not permanent, does require energy (which may be retrieved as the body returns to its initial state). As an initial example, consider a steel spring (Fig. 18.17). As Robert Hooke was the first to show, in the mid-seventeenth century, the force needed to compress any such spring increases with the amount of compression, and indeed is directly proportional to it (Hooke's law). Thus, as the spring is compressed through a distance x, the applied force F must be increased from zero at the start to $F = kx$ at the end, where k is a constant quantity for any particular spring. The average value of this force is

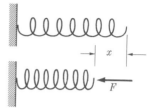

FIG. 18.17. Work is done in compressing a spring.

$$\overline{F} = \tfrac{1}{2}(0 + kx) = \tfrac{1}{2}kx.$$

Thus the work done in compressing the spring, $\overline{F}x$, is given by $\overline{F}x = \tfrac{1}{2}kx^2$. If the applied force is removed, the spring will snap back and can do work (say, on a clock or some machine) equal (except for frictional losses) to the work $\tfrac{1}{2}kx^2$ done in compressing it in the first place. The interesting question is this: Where is this energy stored while the spring is under compression?

From one point of view, the work done on the spring vanishes, and reappears only when the spring is released, just as the work done in raising an object vanishes and then, when the object is permitted to fall, reappears as kinetic energy. This analogy suggests a new concept, which we call *elastic potential energy:* the work done in compressing the spring is converted into the potential, or stored, form of energy. Then, when the spring is released, this potential energy is converted into the kinetic energy of the expanding spring, or otherwise given to a system connected to the spring. This solution is similar to that employed in Section 18.6, where, when we introduced the concept of *gravitational potential energy*, we said that the work done in raising an object against gravity does not vanish but goes into increasing the object's gravitational potential energy. For the spring, the work done in compressing it against elastic forces also does not vanish, but serves to increase the spring's elastic potential energy.

The argument applied to the compression of a spring may also be used when the spring is stretched or, more generally, when any elastic object is deformed in any manner. Thus when two elastic spheres collide, their kinetic energy is briefly converted to the potential energy of elastic deformation while they are in contact, only to appear again as kinetic energy as the spheres push each other apart after impact.

As a last example of this type, consider an elastic ball that falls and bounces from a hard floor. During the fall, the ball loses gravitational potential energy while gaining kinetic energy; the loss of the former equals the gain of the latter, so that when the floor is reached, all the energy is kinetic. During the next brief moment, the ball is compressed and brought to rest by the floor, the kinetic energy of the ball thereby being converted into elastic potential energy. Then the ball begins to expand again and to spring upward, thus acquiring kinetic energy very nearly equal to its original energy.

Evidently the justification for the two concepts of potential energy lies in the consistent and coherent picture of phenomena that they help to provide. They enable us to extend the principle of conservation of energy so that, for a still wider range of phenomena, we may say that energy does not disappear, but is merely converted from one form to another. Thus in Eq. (18.9), the term "change in potential energy" can be taken to mean change in either gravitational or elastic potential energy, or both, depending on the particular problem.

18.12 Kinetic energy of rotation. To this point we have only considered the kinetic energy of a body that is moving along as a whole, that is, with all points of the body moving in straight lines parallel to one another. But what of a wheel turning about a fixed axis? The wheel as a whole does not move in any particular direction, yet work is surely required to set it in motion. What happens to this work? Moreover, if the wheel should burst while it is spinning, the flying fragments may exhibit dangerously large amounts of kinetic energy. Where does it come from?

The difficulty vanishes if we narrow our attention to a particle of mass m moving in a circle with a speed v; its kinetic energy clearly is $\frac{1}{2}mv^2$. But a wheel is simply a collection of such particles, all moving in circles about the axle as a center, and the kinetic energy of the wheel is simply the total kinetic energy of the individual particles. The computation of this kinetic energy is usually complicated, because the farther from the center a particle is the greater is its speed v. But the case of a thin ring or hoop spinning about its center is simple, for then all the particles are at the same distance from the axis of spin and consequently are moving with the same speed v. If these particles have, respectively, masses m_1, m_2, m_3, $\ldots$, their total kinetic energy E_k is

$$\tfrac{1}{2}m_1v^2 + \tfrac{1}{2}m_2v^2 + \tfrac{1}{2}m_3v^2 + \cdots = \tfrac{1}{2}(m_1 + m_2 + m_3 + \cdots)v^2$$

$$= \tfrac{1}{2}m_Rv^2 \quad (=E_k),$$

where m_R is the total mass of the ring, i.e., the sum of the masses of all the individual particles.

EXAMPLE 18.14. A hoop of mass 0.4 kgm, having a radius r of 0.5 m, is spinning about an axis through its center and perpendicular to its plane with a frequency n of 2 rev/sec. Compute the kinetic energy of rotation.

Solution. From Section 5.2, $v = 2\pi rn$. Hence $E_k = \tfrac{1}{2}m_Rv^2 = \tfrac{1}{2}m_R(2\pi rn)^2 = 2m_R\cdot\pi^2r^2n^2 = 7.9$ j.

If an object is both spinning (*rotational motion*) and moving along as a whole (*translational motion*), it is convenient, in our thinking, to separate the kinetic energy of rotation and that due to translation. Thus if a ring is rolling steadily along a table, we may think of this relatively complex motion as consisting of a rotation of all particles in the ring with constant speed around the center of the ring, coupled with a simultaneous translation of all particles in a straight line along the table. The total kinetic energy of such a ring at any moment is composed of two parts: the rotational, $(E_k)_{rot}$, and the translational, $(E_k)_{trans}$. Thus in Eq. (18.9), which is our general statement of the energy principle for mechanics, we must recognize that the term "change in kinetic energy" properly refers to the total kinetic energy, rotational as well as translational:

Change in E_k = Change in $(E_k)_{rot}$ + change in $(E_k)_{trans}$.

EXAMPLE 18.15. Find the kinetic energy of a hoop of mass 0.5 kgm that is rolling without slipping on a table with a forward speed of 2 m/sec.

Solution. $(E_k)_{trans} = \tfrac{1}{2} \times 0.5\text{ kgm} \times (2\text{ m/sec})^2 = 1$ j. To find $(E_k)_{rot}$, we must know how fast the hoop is rotating about its center. Suppose that we watch a point on the hoop that is initially in contact with the ground. As the hoop rolls, this point will rise, move around, and eventually come back to the ground. While this point thus traverses the circumference once, the hoop "lays off" along the ground a distance just equal to the circumference, and the center of the hoop moves forward by the same amount. So the speed of rotation of any point of the hoop about its center has the same value as the forward speed of all points. Therefore, for this case of no slipping, $(E_k)_{rot} = 1$ j, and $(E_k)_{total} = (E_k)_{rot} + (E_k)_{trans} = 2$ j.

EXAMPLE 18.16. A ring of total mass 0.20 kgm rolls on level ground. The frictional force F_f between ring and ground averages 0.10 new. If the initial forward speed v_1 is 3.0 m/sec, what is the speed v_2 after the ring has rolled a distance s of 10 m?

Solution. Here there is no change in potential energy and there is no external pull on the ring to provide an applied force. Hence Eq. (18.9) becomes

$$0 = F_f s + (\tfrac{1}{2} m_R v_2^2 - \tfrac{1}{2} m_R v_1^2)_{\text{rot}} + (\tfrac{1}{2} m_R v_2^2 - \tfrac{1}{2} m_R v_1^2)_{\text{trans}} + 0,$$

or (see Example 18.15),

$$0 = F_f s + 2(\tfrac{1}{2} m_R v_2^2 - \tfrac{1}{2} m_R v_1^2) + 0.$$

Therefore

$$v_2 = \sqrt{v_1^2 - \frac{F_f s}{m_R}} = \sqrt{9.0 \frac{\text{m}_2}{\text{sec}^2} - \frac{0.10 \text{ new} \times 10 \text{ m}}{0.20 \text{ kgm}}}$$

$$= \sqrt{9.0 - 5.0} \frac{\text{m}}{\text{sec}} = \frac{2.0 \text{ m}}{\text{sec}}.$$

PROBLEM 18.26. A 1-kgm metal ring of diameter 1 m is thrown through the air with a forward motion of 3 m/sec and a simultaneous spin of 18 rev/min about an axis through its center and perpendicular to its plane. Find the total kinetic energy.

PROBLEM 18.27. A 4-kgm hoop starts from rest and rolls without slipping down a rough incline of height 5 m and length 30 m.. If the average frictional force is 0.6 new, what is the forward speed of the hoop at the bottom?

18.13 Conclusion. In this chapter we have seen the energy principle gradually extended by incorporating into Eq. (18.9) such concepts as gravitational potential energy, elastic potential energy, and kinetic energy of rotation. But there are a number of other physical processes that will have to be taken into account in further extensions of the energy equation. For instance, if some of the objects are electrically charged, then there is a change in electrical potential energy as they approach or recede from one another, and this term also has to be included in the total change of potential energy. Or if chemical energy is set free in a system, it must not be omitted. Heat, too, is to be counted as a form of energy, so that heat supplied to a system, or generated within it by the transformation of other forms of energy to heat, must be considered. Altogether, the complete story would seem to produce a very bulky equation for the energy principle, something like this:

> External work done on, or other energy supplied to, a system of bodies = Work done against friction + changes in E_k of all types + changes in E_p of all types + changes in chemical energy + $\cdots$ (18.16)

This is equivalent to the more colloquial statement that energy is not created or destroyed but is conserved, although it may be transformed from one form to another.

Although the comprehensive equation for the principle of conservation of energy seems formidable indeed, in actual practice we almost always find that only two or three of the many types of possible energy changes are of importance in a particular problem. But the all-inclusiveness of the equation is what makes it so powerful. If energy of one form appears in a system, we may be sure that an equal amount of energy of one or more other forms has disappeared. The kinetic energy imparted to a baseball can be traced to a diminution of chemical energy within the batter's muscles. When a magnet imparts kinetic energy to an iron nail by moving it, the magnetic potential energy of the system is reduced. The extension of the principle of conservation of energy will be presented further in Chapter 20, together with an account of the historical development and some applications of this remarkable principle to problems involving heat. In preparation for this, we now leave the study of mechanics and turn to the study of heat.

ADDITIONAL PROBLEMS

18.28. A car equipped with "frictionless" bearings is pulled 90 cm along a straight horizontal track in the laboratory, by applying to it a horizontal force of 0.20 new making an angle of 20° with the direction of motion. Show that the increase in the car's kinetic energy is 0.17 j.

18.29. A 3-kgm object is accelerated from a velocity of 10 cm/sec eastward to one of 40 cm/sec northward during a 2-sec interval. (a) What is the increase in kinetic energy? (b) What accelerating net force was needed to produce this increase?

18.30. In Huygens' *Horologium oscillatorium* (1673), we find this proposition: "If a simple pendulum . . . descends through the whole quadrant of a circle [Fig. 18.18], when it comes to the lowest point in the circumference, it stretches the string with three times as great a force as it would if it were simply suspended by it." Prove this proposition with the aid of the energy principle. (*Hint*: Recall that the net force experienced by the bob is equal to the centripetal force.)

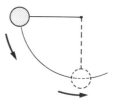

FIGURE 18.18

18.31. To measure the speed of a bullet used to be difficult. One early solution was found in the so-called "ballistic pendulum" of Benjamin Robins (1742). The projectile of known mass m_P and unknown velocity v_P is fired horizontally toward and imbeds itself in the previously motionless bob (of mass m_B) of a freely hanging simple pendulum. The maximum height h to which the pendulum rises after the inelastic collision with the bullet is then measured (Fig. 18.19). (a) Use the *energy* principle to derive expressions for the speed of the system bullet-bob, immediately after impact, in terms of m_P, m_B, and h. (b) Use the *momentum* principle to obtain an expression for the velocity of the bullet before impact.

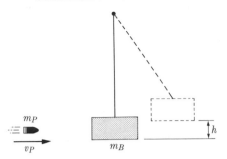

FIGURE 18.19

18.32. Solve the problem posed in Example 18.7 (Section 18.5) with the aid of the principle of conservation of energy. Consider the weight, nail, and plank, together with the earth, as a closed system. Note the relative simplicity of this method of solution.

18.33. How much chemical energy is needed to cause the explosion described in Problem 17.17 (Section 17.5)?

18.34. A particle of known mass m_A is shot at known initial speed v_{A1} against a stationary particle of unknown mass m_B. After an elastic collision, particle A is observed to glance off at an angle α and particle B recoils at an angle β, somewhat as shown in Figs. 17.7 and 17.8, except that, by measurement, $\alpha + \beta = 90°$ in this case. Show that it follows from these data that $m_B = m_A$.

18.35. A 3-kgm ball is released from a height of 2 m above the earth and falls freely. (a) Use the principle of conservation of momentum to calculate the ratio of the speeds of earth and ball in their motion toward each other, just before they collide. (b) Use the principle of conservation of energy to obtain numerical values for each of these speeds. (c) Then explain why, in most free-fall problems, the earth is regarded as fixed.

SUPPLEMENTARY READING

BACON, R. H., "The collision of two particles," *American Journal of Physics*, v. 8 (1940), pp. 154–161.

BONNER, F. T., and M. PHILLIPS, *Principles of physical science* (Addison-Wesley, 1957), Chap. 10.

FERENCE, M., H. B. LEMON, and R. L. STEPHENSON, *Analytical experimental physics* (University of Chicago Press, 2nd edition, 1956), Chap. 4.

KOLIN, A., *Physics, its laws, ideas, and methods* (McGraw-Hill, 1950), Chaps. 9 and 10.

MAGIE, W. F., *A source book in physics* (McGraw-Hill, 1935). Excerpts from the work of Descartes (pp. 50–51), Leibniz (pp. 51–55), d'Alembert (pp. 55–58), and Young (pp. 59–60).

RUSK, R. D., *Introduction to college physics* (Appleton-Century-Crofts, 1954), Chap. 11.

TAYLOR, L. W., *Physics, the pioneer science* (Houghton Mifflin, 1941), Chaps. 16–18.

CHAPTER 19

HEAT PHENOMENA AND THE CALORIC THEORY

The phenomena of heat have not yet entered into our consideration, for not until the 1840's was it generally recognized that heat, the mechanics of moving bodies, and the structure of matter are overlapping fields of study. Prior to that recognition, thermal phenomena were treated in terms of a theory of heat which, though eventually replaced, was in its own day and in its limited field of application not only successful but esthetically very satisfactory. This was the *fluid* or *caloric* theory of heat, which merits our attention in its role both as a historic step toward a better understanding of the nature of heat and matter and as a case study of theory in physical science. Along with the rise and decline of the caloric theory, we can also develop the basic concepts in the study of heat which led to the replacement of the theory itself.

19.1 Temperature. Although the main events of this story took place in the 18th century, many thermal phenomena were well known to the peoples of antiquity: the warmth of a fire, the cooking of food, the protection against cold offered by clothing. The important place given such phenomena, for thousands of years, is emphasized by the inclusion of "Fire" among Empedocles' four elements, and by the role that Fire played in the experiments of the medieval alchemist. Yet despite this early emergence of the importance of thermal phenomena, fruitful study of them began only after the advent of the Scientific Revolution, when the thermometer was invented and the concept of temperature was introduced. This sequence itself—the introduction of measuring devices and of quantitative concepts infusing new life into a whole field of study—illustrates a typical feature in the growth of science.

Toward the close of the 16th century, Galileo invented an instrument that, in the hands of his successors, developed into the thermometer. The long history of thermometry and the establishment of the concept of *temperature* is an interesting story in its own right, but here we shall simply define the temperature of a thermometer as being the number read from its scale, and the temperature of an object as *the scale reading of a suitable thermometer in contact with the object.* The two common temperature scales are the *Celsius*, formerly called "centigrade," and the *Fahrenheit.* On the Celsius scale, which is the one generally used in scientific work, the freezing and boiling points of water are arbitrarily assigned the respective values zero and one hundred, and are written as 0°C and 100°C. The scale is named in honor of Anders Celsius (1701–1744), a

Swedish astronomer and physicist who introduced the convention of subdividing the thermometer scale in this manner. On the Fahrenheit scale, devised by the German physicist Gabriel Daniel Fahrenheit (1686–1736), the freezing and boiling points of water are designated as 32°F and 212°F. The symbol usually used for temperature on either scale is t (unhappily the same as for *time*).

19.2 Thermal equilibrium. The thermometer first became a powerful research tool in the hands of Joseph Black (1728–1799), a doctor of medicine who taught medicine and chemistry at the University of Glasgow and, later, at Edinburgh. His work in both thermal physics and chemistry was published posthumously from his lecture notes under the title of *Lectures on the elements of chemistry* (1803). Therein he wrote:

> An . . . improvement in our knowledge of heat, which has been attained by the use of thermometers, is the more distinct notion we have now than formerly of the *distribution* of heat among different bodies . . . even without the help of thermometers, we can perceive a tendency of heat to diffuse itself from any hotter body to the cooler [ones] around [it], until it be distributed among them in such a manner that none of them is disposed to take any more heat from the rest. The heat is thus brought into a state of equilibrium. This equilibrium is somewhat curious. We find that, when all mutual action is ended, . . . the temperature of them all is the same . . . No previous acquaintance with the peculiar relation of each [body] to heat could have assured us of this, and we owe the discovery entirely to the thermometer. We must therefore adopt, as one of the most general laws of heat, [the principle] that *all bodies communicating freely with one another, and exposed to no inequality of external action, acquire the same temperature, as indicated by a thermometer.*

Thus, for example, if a number of objects of different temperature are placed together in a closed room, the hotter objects will cool and the colder ones will warm until all are at the same temperature.

This common observation of the tendency to reach thermal equilibrium suggests the following experiments. Suppose that we place two objects of different initial temperatures in contact with each other, and observe the final temperature reached by them; two quantities of liquid are convenient "objects" for this purpose because of the ease with which they can be brought into intimate contact by mixing in one vessel. Now we mix 1 kgm of water of temperature 15°C with an equal mass of water at 27°C. The final temperature of this mixture will be found to be 21°C, which is midway between the two initial temperatures. If, however, 2 kgm of water at 15°C is mixed with 1 kgm of water at 27°C, the final temperature will be 19°C. Here the rise in temperature of 2 kgm of initially cooler water is only half as much as the drop in temperature of 1 kgm of initially warmer water.

19.3 The fluid theory of heat. Experiments of this sort allow us to describe what changes in temperature occur in various circumstances. An *explanation* of these observations, stemming mostly from Black's work, was found by postulating the existence of an invisible "heat fluid" or "caloric," as this hypothetical substance later came to be called. According to this view, all temperature changes result from the addition or withdrawal of heat fluid, producing a rise or a drop in temperature. An object placed near a fire presumably receives heat fluid from the fire and therefore warms up; when removed from the fire, it gives up some of the heat fluid and cools. A hot piece of metal dropped into water gives up some heat fluid to the water and cools, and consequently the water becomes warmer.

In the light of Black's various experiments, the notion of a heat fluid was gradually developed into a theory containing the following two basic postulates, among others:

(1) *Heat fluid is indestructible and uncreatable.* When two objects initially at different temperatures come into temperature equilibrium with each other in a thermally isolated system, heat fluid is neither created nor lost, but is only redistributed within the system, flowing from the initially hotter parts to the others. This "principle of conservation of heat" was from the first regarded as plausible, for if heat fluid were a material substance, as was tacitly assumed, then it ought to be indestructible, by analogy with ordinary matter.

(2) The amount of heat fluid that must be supplied to or withdrawn from an object in order to change its temperature by a certain amount is *proportional to the mass of the object and to the desired change of temperature.* If we let the symbol H represent the quantity of heat fluid added to or subtracted from an object of mass m, and let Δt represent the change in temperature, then $H \propto \Delta t$, or

$$H = cm \, \Delta t, \tag{19.1}$$

where c is the constant of proportionality.

The usefulness of these physical postulates, as of all others, can be tested only by making deductions from them and comparing the latter with experiments. Consider the experiments described in Section 19.2, in which cold water and warm water were mixed together. According to postulate (1), the heat H_1 gained by the cold water was equal to the heat H_2 lost by the warm water, or $H_1 = H_2$. According to postulate (2), $H_1 = cm_1 \, (\Delta t)_1$ and $H_2 = cm_2 \, (\Delta t)_2$. Therefore,

$$cm_1 \, (\Delta t)_1 = cm_2 \, (\Delta t)_2. \tag{19.2}$$

Now in the first experiment in Section 19.2, equal masses of warm and cold water were mixed, or $m_1 = m_2$. Equation (19.2) therefore predicts that $(\Delta t)_1 = (\Delta t)_2$, and this was just what was found in the experiment, for $\Delta t_2 = 21°C - 15°C = 6°C$ and $\Delta t_1 = (27°C - 21°C) = 6°C$.

In the second experiment, the mass of the cold water was twice that of the warm water, or $m_1 = 2m_2$. In this case, Eq. (19.2) becomes

$$2m_2 (\Delta t)_1 = m_2 (\Delta t)_2, \qquad \text{or} \qquad (\Delta t)_1 = \tfrac{1}{2} (\Delta t)_2;$$

this is in accord with the result of this experiment, for $(19°C - 15°C)$ is one-half of $(27°C - 19°C)$. Thus we see that Eq. (19.2), deduced from postulates (1) and (2), correctly predicts the results obtained in these two mixing experiments. It is important to note that Eq. (19.2) applies only if the experiment is carried out in such a manner that no appreciable amount of heat is lost to or gained from the containing vessel or other surroundings during the experiment.

EXAMPLE 19.1. Water of mass 0.5 kgm and temperature 19°C is mixed with 3 kgm of water initially at 26°C. Find the final temperature t_f of the mixture.

Solution. $m_1 = 0.5$ kgm, $(\Delta t)_1 = t_f - 19°C$, $m_2 = 3$ kgm, $(\Delta t)_2 = 26°C - t_f$. By Eq. (19.2),

$$c \cdot 0.5 \text{ kgm } (t_f - 19°C) = c \cdot 3 \text{ kgm } (26°C - t_f).$$

Solving for t_f, we obtain $t_f = 25°C$.

PROBLEM 19.1. Predict the final temperature when 1.5 kgm of water at 80°C is mixed with 0.5 kgm of water at 20°C.

PROBLEM 19.2. When 0.70 kgm of water at 25°C was poured into a vessel containing water at 37°C, the final temperature acquired by the mixture was observed to be 35°C. What was the mass of the warm water before mixing?

19.4 Specific heat capacity. Equation (19.2) is valid only when the two "objects" brought into contact with each other are of the same material, for example, water and water, or mercury and mercury. If 1 kgm of mercury at 15°C is mixed with 1 kgm of mercury at 27°C, the temperature of the mixture will be 21°C, just as in the case of a water mixture. But when Black investigated the mixing of two different materials, for example water and mercury, he found the situation to be more complicated. When 1 kgm of water at 15°C is mixed with 1 kgm of mercury at 27°C, the temperature of the mixture turns out to be only slightly more than 15°C, instead of the 21°C expected when equal masses of water and water or mercury and mercury are mixed.

Black noted that this result could be explained by assuming that a given quantity of heat H produces a much smaller temperature change in 1 kgm of water than it does in 1 kgm of mercury. In other words, the factor of proportionality c in Eq. (19.1) is different for water and for mercury, and indeed for every different substance. Equation (19.1) provides a definition for c:

$$c = \frac{H}{m \, \Delta t}. \tag{19.3}$$

The factor c is known as the *specific heat capacity* or *specific thermal capacity*, for it indicates the capacity of unit mass of the material for absorbing or giving up heat fluid when its temperature is raised or lowered one degree. In the light of this discovery that different materials have different specific heat capacities, we now replace Eq. (19.2) by the more general equation

$$c_1 m_1 \, \Delta t_1 = c_2 m_2 \, \Delta t_2. \tag{19.4}$$

Note that this equation is valid only for *two* materials in a thermally isolated system.

EXAMPLE 19.2. When water at 15.0°C is mixed with an equal mass of mercury at 27.0°C, the resulting temperature is observed to be 15.4°C. How does the value of the specific heat capacity for mercury compare with that for water?

Solution. $m_1 = m_2, \Delta t_1 = (15.4 - 15.0)°C = 0.4°C, \Delta t_2 = (27.0 - 15.4)°C = 11.6°C$. From Eq. (19.4), $c_1 \cdot 0.4°C = c_2 \cdot 11.6°C$, or $c_2/c_1 = 0.4/11.6 = 0.03$. Thus the specific heat capacity of mercury is only 0.03 times that for water.

PROBLEM 19.3. What mass of water at 15°C must be mixed with 1 kgm of mercury at 27°C in order to obtain a final mixture temperature of 21°C?

PROBLEM 19.4. When 1.0 kgm of water at 25°C is poured into a 500-gm porcelain dish of temperature 90°C, the final temperature is found to be 32°C. Compute the specific heat capacity of the porcelain relative to that of water.

19.5 Thermal units. Nothing has yet been said about units for measuring quantity of heat H and specific heat capacity c. One of Black's contemporaries suggested that water be taken as a *standard* in defining these thermal units, and this is the practice still followed today. Accordingly, the unit for H in the mks system is defined as *the quantity of heat that enters or leaves* 1 *kgm of water when it undergoes a temperature change of one Celsius degree* (1 C°). This unit is called the *kilocalorie* (kcal) and is the same unit as the "Calorie" (note capital letter C) used in dietetics.* While the choice of water as a convenient reference for thermal behavior is arbitrary, it is no more so than the nomination of a certain lump of metal as the standard mass of 1 kgm or of the distance between two marks on a certain bar as the standard length of 1 m.

---

*One kilocalorie is 1000 times as large as one *calorie* (cal; note small initial letter) which is the unit of heat quantity in the cgs system; one calorie is the quantity of heat that enters or leaves 1 gm of water when its temperature change is 1 C°.

When Eq. (19.3) is applied to water, H is 1 kcal when m is 1 kgm and Δt is 1°C; hence

$$c \text{ (for water)} = \frac{H}{m \, \Delta t} = \frac{1 \text{ kcal}}{1 \text{ kgm·1°C}} = 1 \frac{\text{kcal}}{\text{kgm·°C}} \cdot$$

Thus, by definition, the specific heat capacity of water is unity. For other substances, as Black pointed out, the specific heat capacities must be found by experiment, for example, by means of mixing experiments in conjunction with Eq. (19.4). Values for various substances are given in Table 19.1.

EXAMPLE 19.3. How much heat is needed to raise the temperature of 12 kgm of iron from 20°C to 100°C?

Solution. For iron, $c = 0.11$ kcal/kgm·°C (from Table 19.1), $m = 12$ kgm, $\Delta t = (100 - 20)$°C $= 80$°C. Therefore, $H = cm \, \Delta t = (0.11 \text{ kcal/kgm·°C}) \times 12 \text{ kgm} \times 80$°C $= 1.1 \times 10^2$ kcal.

PROBLEM 19.5. If the addition of 2.6 kcal of heat to a 1.2-kgm piece of glass changes the temperature from 14°C to 26°C, what is the specific heat capacity of the glass?

PROBLEM 19.6. What temperature rise will occur in 500 gm of ice initially at -20°C if 2.0 kcal of heat is added to it?

PROBLEM 19.7. Temperature variations on small islands or on the coasts of large bodies of water are not as marked as they are a few miles inland. Can you explain this?

Table 19.1. Some specific heat capacities.

Substance	Specific heat capacity, c (kcal/kgm·°C)
Air (constant pressure)	0.24
Brass	0.08
Charcoal	0.16
Copper	0.093
Glass, thermometer	0.20
Ice	0.50
Iron	0.11
Marble	0.21
Mercury	0.033
Steam	0.48
Water	1.000

PROBLEM 19.8. A 1-kgm brass ball of unknown temperature is dropped into 1.5 kgm of mercury which is at a temperature of 23°C. If the final temperature

reached by both ball and mercury is 100°C, what was the initial temperature of the ball? (Assume that the vessel containing the mercury absorbs a negligibly small quantity of heat.)

EXAMPLE 19.4. A 2.0-kgm iron vessel contains 3.0 kgm of water, the temperature of both vessel and water being 21°C. If a 2.5-kgm piece of copper at 90°C is dropped into the water, what will be the final temperature of the mixture?

Solution. The heat gained by the vessel and water is equal to the heat lost by the copper, provided that the system is thermally insulated from the surroundings. In symbols: $c_1 m_1 \Delta t_1$ (gained by vessel) $+ c_2 m_2 \Delta t_2$ (gained by water) $= c_3 m_3 \Delta t_3$ (lost by copper). From the given data and those listed in Table 19.1,

$$\frac{0.11 \text{ kcal}}{\text{kgm} \cdot {}^\circ\text{C}} \times 2.0 \text{ kgm} \times (t_f - 21{}^\circ\text{C}) + \frac{1.0 \text{ kcal}}{\text{kgm} \cdot {}^\circ\text{C}} \times 3.0 \text{ kgm} \times (t_f - 21{}^\circ\text{C})$$

$$= \frac{0.093 \text{ kcal}}{\text{kgm} \cdot {}^\circ\text{C}} \times 2.5 \text{ kgm} \times (90{}^\circ\text{C} - t_f),$$

from which $t_f = 25.6{}^\circ\text{C}$.

PROBLEM 19.9. Outline a simple procedure for determining the specific heat capacity of a newly discovered metal. What sources of error do you foresee?

19.6 Freezing and melting. From the mid-18th century on there was growing awareness among investigators that many liquids (besides the obvious cases such as water) can be frozen into solid form and then melted back to a liquid state. Black said, "We may consider all . . . liquids as solids melted by heat." Conversely, liquids may be solidified by the removal of heat. Moreover, Black pointed out that in most cases a substance freezes or melts at a definite temperature, called its *freezing point* or *melting point.** For example, if heat is added to a piece of ice, the ice warms up until its temperature is 0°C, whereupon it melts; and if the resulting water is again cooled, it freezes at 0°C. Similarly, mercury freezes or melts at −38.9°C.

Black reported the then prevailing notion that melting was "produced by the addition of a very small quantity of heat to a solid body, once it had been warmed up to its melting point." But from his studies he concluded that "liquefaction is produced by heat in a very different manner from that which has commonly been imagined":

The opinion I formed from attentive observation of the facts and phenomena is as follows. When ice or other solid substance is melted, I am of the opinion

---

*Black noted exceptions, for example glass and waxes, which pass gradually through all stages of viscosity in melting or solidifying. Glass begins to soften at a temperature lower than that at which it becomes completely liquid, and there is no definite temperature at which it may be said to melt.

that it receives a much larger quantity of heat than what is perceptible in it immediately afterwards by the thermometer. A large quantity of heat enters into it, on this occasion, without making it apparently warmer, when tried by that instrument. This heat must be added in order to give it the form of a liquid; and I affirm that this large addition of heat is the principal and most immediate cause of the liquefaction induced.

On the other hand, when we freeze a liquid, a very large quantity of heat comes out of it, while it is assuming a solid form, the loss of which heat is not to be perceived by the common manner of using the thermometer. The apparent temperature of the body, as measured by that instrument, is not diminished, or not in proportion to the loss of heat which the body actually suffers on this occasion; and it appears, from a number of facts, that the state of solidity cannot be induced without the abstraction of this large quantity of heat. And this confirms the opinion that this quantity of heat, absorbed, and, as it were, concealed in the composition of liquids, is the most necessary and immediate cause of their liquidity.*

To illuminate these conclusions, consider the following experiment, which is similar to one carried out by Black. Put 0.5 kgm of water and a thermometer in a vessel, and set the vessel in a freezing mixture until the water is not only frozen but is cooled well below its freezing point, say to −20°C. Then remove the vessel to a warm room and, at suitable intervals of time, observe the temperatures of the ice as it warms to the melting point, and then melts. If the temperature is plotted as a function of the time of observation, a graph similar to Fig. 19.1 will be obtained. Note that, while 5 min were sufficient to raise the ice from −20° to 0°C, 40 min were needed to melt the ice, without any rise in temperature. Once all the ice was melted, the temperature began to rise again, although not as quickly as before.

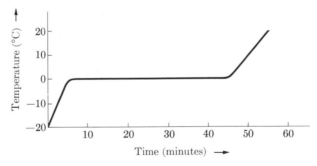

FIG. 19.1. Typical change in temperature of a quantity of water when heat is supplied constantly.

---

*Because the meanings of many words have changed since Black's day, we have modernized his terminology in these quotations.

PROBLEM 19.10. In an experiment of the type just described (Fig. 19.1), 0.5 kgm of water was warmed from 0° to 20°C in 10 min. (a) Calculate the rate of transfer of heat from room to water in kcal/min. Then show from Fig. 19.1 that (b) the specific heat capacity of ice is 0.5 kcal/kgm·°C and that (c) the quantity of heat required to melt 1 kgm of ice is 80 kcal. (*Note*: In this experiment it has been assumed that the rate of heat transfer to the ice or water is constant throughout. This assumption is reasonable only if there is a large temperature difference between the hot chamber and the ice or water.)

Black's discovery that a relatively large amount of heat is needed merely to melt a substance suggested that it would be useful to define a new physical quantity, which has come to be called the *heat of fusion*, L_f (sometimes *latent heat of fusion*). It is defined as the quantity of heat required to melt unit mass of a substance without any change of temperature taking place (Table 19.2). Black also performed the converse experi-

Table 19.2.   Some heats of fusion.

Substance	Heat of fusion, L_f (kcal/kgm)
Copper	42
Gold	16
Lead	5.9
Mercury	2.8
Sodium	32
Sulfur	13
Water	80

ment of measuring the heat released by the resulting liquid upon freezing, and found that the quantities absorbed and released are equal. This convinced him of the soundness of his postulate that the heat absorbed during melting is not destroyed, but remains "latent" and can be completely recovered from the liquid by freezing it. He was now able to extend the principle of conservation of heat (Section 19.3) to allow for "latent" heat of fusion as well as for heat that produces changes of temperature. If, for example, a solid body of mass m_1, specific heat capacity c_1, heat of fusion L_f, and initial temperature t_i is brought to the melting point t_m and is fully molten at the same temperature, the heat absorbed is given by $m_1 c_1 (t_m - t_i) + m_1 L_f$.

PROBLEM 19.11. How much heat would be needed to convert 100 gm of solid gold at 1063°C into liquid gold at the same temperature?

PROBLEM 19.12. How much heat is given up by 1 kgm of water which is initially at 90°C when it is converted into ice at −10°C?

PROBLEM 19.13. Referring to the old-fashioned type of icebox, in which the cooling is produced by ice, comment on the suggestion that money can be saved by wrapping the ice in newspaper, since it will then melt more slowly.

PROBLEM 19.14. A 1-kgm piece of ice at 0°C is put into a 2.0-kgm copper vessel initially at a temperature of 100°C. If all the heat given up by the copper is absorbed by the ice, what will be the final temperature of the mixture?

19.7 Boiling and condensation. Joseph Black also investigated the phenomenon of boiling. Speaking of liquid heated in a vessel over a fire, he said:

> The liquid gradually warms, and at last attains that temperature which it cannot pass without assuming the form of vapor. In these circumstances, we always observe that the water [or other liquid] is thrown into violent agitation, which we call *boiling* . . .
>
> Another peculiarity attends this boiling of liquids which, when first observed, was thought very surprising. However long and violently we boil a liquid, we cannot make it the least hotter than when it began to boil. The thermometer always points at the same degree, namely, the vaporific point of that liquid. Hence the vaporific point of a liquid is often called its *boiling point* . . .
>
> It used to be taken for granted that, after a liquid was heated up to its boiling point, nothing further was necessary but the addition of a little more heat to change it into vapor. It was also supposed that when this vapor was so far cooled as to be ready for condensation, this condensation, or return to the liquid state, would happen at once, in consequence of the vapor's losing only a very small quantity of heat.
>
> But I can easily show, in the same manner as in the case of liquefaction, that a very large quantity of heat is necessary for the production of vapor . . . [and that it] enters into the vapor gradually, while it is forming, without making this vapor hotter . . .

Black showed, moreover, that when vapor is condensed back into liquid, "the very same large quantity of heat comes out of it into the colder surrounding matter by which it is condensed."

From this study of vaporization emerged still another new physical concept, the *heat of vaporization* of a substance (L_v). It is defined as the quantity of heat needed to vaporize unit mass of a liquid without any change of temperature taking place. (Note the value for water in Table 19.3; as in the previous two tables, it is exceptionally large.) This new concept allows us once more to expand the equations governing heat transfer to and from substances by adding the term (mass $\times L_v$) for each change of state from liquid to vapor or vapor to liquid.

To this point, the application of the caloric theory as presented by Black has met with success. Increase in temperature is produced by the addition of heat fluid and this fluid can also cause melting of solids and vaporization of liquids. The same amount of fluid enters on melting and leaves on freezing, and similarly for vaporization and condensation. The theory has been proved adequate for the explanation of a large range of phenomena.

Table 19.3. Heats of vaporization of some substances at their boiling points.

Substance	Heat of vaporization, L_v (kcal/kgm)	Boiling point (°C)
Bromine	44	59
Helium	6	−269
Mercury	71	357
Sulfuric acid	122	338
Water	540	100

PROBLEM 19.15. How much heat is required to convert (a) 2 kgm of water at 100°C into steam at 100°C, and (b) 0.5 kgm of liquid mercury at 357°C into mercury vapor at 357°C?

EXAMPLE 19.5. How much heat is needed to convert 100 kgm of water at 20°C into steam at 100°C?
Solution. The heat H_1 needed to warm the water up to 100°C is $H_1 = cm\,\Delta t = (1\ \text{kcal/kgm·°C}) \times 100\ \text{kgm} \times (100 - 20)\text{°C} = 8000\ \text{kcal}$. The additional heat H_2 needed simply to vaporize the water is $(540\ \text{kcal/kgm}) \times 100\ \text{kgm} = 54{,}000\ \text{kcal}$. The total heat needed is therefore $H_1 + H_2 = 62{,}000\ \text{kcal}$.

PROBLEM 19.16. How much heat is required to convert 500 gm of water at 95°C into steam at 105°C? (Take the specific heat capacity of steam to be 0.48 kcal/kgm·°C.)

PROBLEM 19.17. How much heat is required to convert (a) 1.5 kgm of ice at −10°C into steam at 110°C, and (b) 100 gm of liquid mercury at 17°C into mercury vapor at 357°C?

19.8 Further successes of the caloric theory. From the 1760's on, developments in thermal science proceeded at an accelerated pace, first mainly through the work of Black and his colleagues. The usefulness of the principle of conservation of heat in Black's hands undoubtedly had helped to sway 18th-century opinion toward the view that heat is a material fluid, for it was in line with the prevailing opinion that material substances are conserved. Moreover, the fluid theory of heat gave a simple and plausible picture of what happens when substances of different temperatures are brought together: the excess of heat fluid would flow from the hotter to the colder substance until equilibrium had been reached.

It was almost inconceivable to most scientists that even such a simple observation could be accounted for by another view of the nature of heat that existed at the time, namely, that heat is a form of *motion*, "a tremulous, or other, motion of the particles of matter."

The concept of heat fluid (named the *caloric* by Lavoisier in 1787) began to take on even greater plausibility when two further properties were postulated for it: that the particles of caloric, unlike those of *ordinary* matter, (1) repel one another, but yet (2) are attracted by the particles of ordinary matter, the magnitude of this attraction being different for different substances and for different states of the matter. Therefore, if heat is applied to a body, the caloric may be pictured as diffusing rapidly throughout the body and clinging to its particles. Each ordinary particle is thus surrounded by an atmosphere or shell of caloric, and these shells repel one another.

It follows that if the ordinary particles of matter are free to move, as indeed they are in a gas, they will tend to disperse, and this tendency will increase as the particles are crowded closer together or have more heat applied to them. This picture, we see, is in accord with the observation that when a gas is compressed or heated it tends to exert a greater pressure on the walls of its container. If, however, the heated substance is in the solid or liquid state, the mutual attraction among its material particles (then considered to be a gravitational attraction) is relatively so strong that the caloric shells can provide mutual repulsion sufficient only for the slight expansion observed in a solid or liquid when heated. As for the marked rise in temperature observed in a gas when it is rapidly compressed or in a piece of metal when it is strongly hammered, these observations could be regarded as evidence of a squeezing-out of caloric from the spaces between the ordinary particles as they are forced closer together.

To account for Black's discoveries that large quantities of heat are needed to melt a solid or vaporize a liquid, it was postulated that caloric combines "chemically" with ordinary particles to form the liquid or vapor, and when thus combined is "latent" and can have no effect on the temperature of the substances. From this point of view, melting or vaporization results in the formation of a new substance, a chemical compound in liquid or vapor form; as in ordinary chemical combinations, the formation takes place only in definite proportions and in definite circumstances.

These plausible pictures and the experimental successes based on the caloric theory persuaded almost all investigators from the 1780's on of the usefulness of this conceptual scheme in providing a firm theoretical framework for experimentation and interpretation of the observed facts. Yet the theory did have one troublesome feature. If heat were a material fluid, it should have weight; but the attempts to detect this weight, made repeatedly and often ingeniously by various 18th-century experimenters, were not conclusive. Early experiments were made with solid metals, which were weighed when cold and then when hot. Black's discoveries suggested a simplification: if heat did have weight, this might be detected more easily by melting or freezing a substance, for then the heat would be added or subtracted in much larger quantities than in experiments in which solid substances were merely changed in temperature. But the results varied widely. In some experiments the addition of heat appeared to result in an increase of weight, in others in a decrease, and sometimes no change of weight was apparent. As most of the experimenters were well aware, these conflicting results were probably due to the many difficulties involved in making accurate measurements of weight while the temperature of the substance or of its surroundings was varying.

19.9 Rumford's attacks upon the caloric theory. One capable experimenter to turn to this problem was Count Rumford (Fig. 19.2). This amazing American began life as Benjamin Thompson of North Woburn, Massachusetts, and by 1798, having left his native land because of Royalist sympathies during the Revolution, had been knighted by King George III

Fig. 19.2. Benjamin Thompson, Count Rumford (1753–1814).

and was in the employ of the Elector of Bavaria as Chamberlain, Minister of War, and Minister of Police. Yet he found time apart from his many duties and projects to initiate an extensive program of experiments designed to throw light on questions concerning the nature of heat. Rumford had access to one of the best balances in Europe, and he made exhaustive experiments on the problem of "the weight of heat." For example, he compared the weight of frozen water at 0°C with that of liquid water at the same temperature, and found no increase in weight in the latter case, although "caloric fluid" was supposedly added during melting. On the basis of experiment, Rumford felt able to state with confidence in 1799:

> I think we may safely conclude that *all attempts to discover any effect of heat upon the apparent weight of bodies will be fruitless.*

Granting the validity of this conclusion, we are faced with the question of what justification there is in retaining the notion of the caloric, a fluid that supposedly has certain material properties but which is not only invisible but unweighable, and which is inaccessible to *direct* experimentation through lack of one of the most general characteristics of materiality, weight. Rumford, like some philosophers a century earlier, rejected imponderable fluids in part because he simply could not imagine a fluid that was material and yet lacking in one of the most characteristic properties of ordinary matter. But his inability to conceive of an imponderable caloric appears, at first glance, to be due simply to lack of imagination. The scientific world of the 18th century generally was certainly able to imagine and accept not only imponderable caloric but a number of other imponderables and ethers, for example, phlogiston and electricity, as then conceived.

Let us for a moment examine our own first impulses in this regard. Nowadays we are probably tempted to reject the notion of imponderable fluids outright. If urged to explain, we might perhaps confess the feeling that to believe in a physical entity we must be able to discover it directly and tangibly. But this attitude would be naive; we must discard it now before we go on to study phenomena involving subatomic entities. *We must be prepared to accept certain concepts in physical science even though they may not sound plausible or cannot be imagined by analogy.* We must be prepared to welcome any concept that may be needed for a conceptual scheme, if only it fulfills these two requirements: it should be definable, without internal contradiction and ambiguities, in terms of observable and measurable effects, whether these be direct or not; and it should prove useful in a wide variety of descriptions and laws, long known as well as newly deduced. The caloric fluid met both these criteria at the time.

But this was not the reasoning that led the calorists to accept the imponderable; indeed, they were not greatly bothered by Rumford's experimental conclusion and even saw ways to get around it. As for Rumford, he was not so naive as to reject the caloric fluid solely because it lacked measurable weight; his search for its possible weight was only one part of a 30-year experimental attack on the whole caloric theory. In time, he succeeded in discovering its real Achilles' heel: namely, there are certain phenomena for which one is forced to conclude that heat *can* be created; and if heat is creatable, it is not a material substance in any sense. His description in 1798 of this far-reaching discovery begins as follows:

> Being engaged, lately, in superintending the boring of cannon, in the workshops of the military arsenal at Munich, I was struck with the very considerable degree of Heat which a brass gun acquires, in a short time, in being bored; and with the still more intense Heat (much greater than that of boiling water, as I found by experiment) of the metallic chips separated from it by the borer.
>
> The more I meditated on these phaenomena, the more they appeared to me to be curious and interesting. A thorough investigation of them seemed even to bid fair to give a farther insight into the hidden nature of Heat; and to enable us to form some reasonable conjectures respecting the existence, or nonexistence, of an igneous [heat] fluid: a subject on which the opinions of philosophers have, in all ages, been much divided.

This was a commonplace type of observation, except for the uncommonly high temperature developed, but Rumford saw its significance and began a series of experiments on "the source of the heat which is excited by friction." His initial observation was therefore the effective beginning of the idea that heat *fluid* in enormous quantities can be generated by friction.

Supporters of the caloric theory pointed out that the metallic chips or dust produced during the boring of the cannon might be the source of the large quantity of heat released. If it could be shown that the specific heat capacity of the chips was smaller than that of the metal in bulk, this could be interpreted to mean that the attractive force was smaller between the particles and caloric in the chips than between the bulk metal and caloric, and therefore that caloric would be set free during the boring and would produce the observed rise in temperature. This led Rumford to make experiments with the chips and with the bulk metal of the cannon itself, and he found that their specific heat capacities were the *same*. The heat generated in friction was not squeezed-out caloric.

What is even more significant, subsequent experiments revealed that heat continues to be steadily generated so long as one cares to continue the friction experiment; the source of the heat generated by friction "appeared to be inexhaustible."

> It is hardly necessary to add that anything which any *insulated* body, or system of bodies, can continue to furnish *without limitation*, cannot possibly be a material substance: and it appears to me to be extremely difficult, if not quite impossible, to form any distinct idea of anything capable of being

excited or communicated, in the manner the Heat was excited and communicated in these Experiments, except it be MOTION.

And throughout his voluminous writings Rumford continues to affirm those "very old doctrines which rest on the supposition that heat is nothing but a vibratory motion taking place among the particles of the body."

These and a great variety of other experiments, executed mostly by Rumford, struck key blows against the caloric theory. But that was not enough to convert the calorists and topple their views, for the simple reason that there was no well-developed conceptual scheme to offer instead. In truth, Rumford was able to show that the picture of heat as a vibratory (or other) motion of the ordinary particles of a substance would account qualitatively for a variety of phenomena—not only for production of heat by friction and compression, but also for expansion by heating, conduction of heat, changes of state, and so on. But this picture of "heat as motion" lacked definiteness and was purely qualitative; it had not yet been expressed in terms of the precise quantitative concepts of mechanics, for thermal science and mechanics were still almost completely separate disciplines.

As a consequence, the caloric theory continued to be regarded for over a generation as the more practical and plausible conceptual scheme. Even today we often find it convenient in dealing with many problems to think of heat as a fluid. We do this whenever the particular phenomena under study can be explained without having to make any assumption concerning the nature of heat except that heat in a thermally isolated system is conserved, and indeed heat *is* conserved in any closed system provided no transformation of heat from or into any other form of energy takes place. This, of course, is the case in calorimetric experiments on mixtures of materials at different temperatures, the very experiments that led Black to the caloric theory of heat. Once more we find that old conceptual schemes continue their usefulness in a restricted range even though the larger field has undergone a profound change.

Rumford's work did not revolutionize thermal physics at once; rather, as has often happened in the history of science at the start of a conceptual revolution, he succeeded only in throwing doubt on the old system, weakening it, and preparing the way for its inevitable overthrow later by a theory that was more complete, more comprehensive, and freer from internal contradictions. What had to be done next was to show (1) that heat is simply the kinetic energy associated with random motions of the small particles of ordinary matter, and (2) that the mode-of-motion theory is superior to the caloric scheme both in the number of phenomena to which it applies and the precision with which it can predict them. This development of the theory became possible as the result of work initiated mainly by Mayer and Joule in the 1840's; we now turn to their contributions.

PROBLEM 19.18. Was the *concept* "caloric" right or wrong? Was the caloric *theory* right or wrong? Explain your answers.

PROBLEM 19.19. Show that, after Black made his several discoveries, it was no longer acceptable to define *heat* qualitatively as that which always increases the temperature of a body to which it is added.

PROBLEM 19.20. (a) Derive an equation for converting any temperature on the Celsius scale to the equivalent Fahrenheit reading. (b) Mercury freezes at approximately −40°C. Express this temperature in degrees Fahrenheit.

PROBLEM 19.21. Equal volumes of mercury and water contained in similar vessels are exposed to the same steady source of heat. Using the data in Table 19.1 and the fact that mercury is 13.6 times as dense as water, show that to produce the same temperature rise in both liquids, only 0.45 as much heat must be added to the mercury as to the water. Would this value be different if you could take into account the specific heat capacity of the material comprising the vessels?

SUPPLEMENTARY READING

ELLIS, G. E., *Memoir of Sir Benjamin Thompson, Count Rumford* (American Academy of Arts and Sciences, 1871).

MAGIE, W. F., *A source book in physics* (McGraw-Hill, 1935). Selections from Black, Rumford, and Davy, pp. 134–164.

McKIE, D., and N. H. DE V. HEATHCOTE, *The discovery of specific and latent heats* (Edward Arnold, 1935).

ROLLER, D., *Early development of the concepts of temperature and heat* (Harvard University Press, 1950); also available in Harvard case histories in experimental science (Harvard University Press, 1957), v. 1, pp. 117–214.

CHAPTER 20

EXTENSION OF THE PRINCIPLE OF
CONSERVATION OF ENERGY

The preceding two chapters have been devoted to discussions of two separate principles, conservation of mechanical energy and conservation of heat fluid. In the middle of the 19th century, the concept of a heat fluid was finally abandoned, and the energy principle was extended to incorporate the thermal phenomena previously explained with the help of the independent principle of conservation of heat fluid. This extension, one of the great events in the history of scientific thought, clarified and brought together the several separate energy concepts, and gave us the first *general principle of conservation of energy*.

It will be best to reserve for a later chapter the details of the modern theory of the nature of heat that replaced the caloric theory, and to concentrate here on those aspects that permit extension of the energy principle. Indeed, this principle is so powerful mainly because it can be formulated and applied without a detailed knowledge of the physical mechanisms that might explain the form or the presence of energy in a body.

20.1 Heat liberated by friction. It is evident that there is a definite relationship between mechanical energy and heat. For example, the kinetic energy of a bullet disappears when the bullet is stopped in a target, whereupon heat appears in an amount that may be sufficient to melt part of the bullet. Again, work done against friction may produce a great deal of heat; even prehistoric man knew how to make fire by rubbing sticks together. Nevertheless, it is too large a jump from these observations to the statement "therefore one must conclude that mechanical energy or work can be *converted* to heat." The caloric theory, we will recall, explained the appearance of heat in experiments like those just cited as the liberation of heat fluid already present in the body. Moreover, before Rumford it was not clear at all *how much* heat was liberated when mechanical energy or work was "used up against friction." Rumford carried some of his observations to a point where a simple estimate could have been made of the quantity of heat developed when a certain amount of work was done against friction. In one series of his experiments, work was done by letting a blunt tool in a horse-driven lathe turn inside a metal cylinder, originally part of a casting for a gun but "designed for the express purpose of generating heat by friction." A wooden jacket or box which contained water

341

was built around the cylinder, and in one such experiment, the water, initially at room temperature, was brought to a boil by the friction in the cylinder in $2\frac{1}{2}$ hours of continued action. A rough calculation could then be made of the quantity of heat developed, for Rumford knew the masses and specific heat capacities of the metal and surrounding water, as well as their rise in temperature. The quantity turned out to be, in modern units, 1.2×10^3 kcal. This calculation was to be considered "rough" because, as Rumford pointed out, "no estimate was made of the heat accumulated in the box [the wood itself], nor of that dispersed during the experiment."

Rumford was content with showing that the quantity of heat developed in friction experiments could be very large and, moreover, that the source of heat thus generated is apparently inexhaustible. He did say that his boring apparatus "could be driven by the force of one horse," but he did not calculate the work done by the horse. Very likely he did not know that James Watt, on the basis of experiments, had estimated that a "mill horse" could do work at the rate (in modern units) of about 750 joules per second. By definition, the unit called the "horsepower" is today defined as equivalent to 746 j/sec, and assuming this value for Rumford's horse, we find that the work done by the horse in $2\frac{1}{2}$ hr was 6.7×10^6 j. Then, disregarding the fact that some work had to be done against the frictional forces in the machinery connecting the horse to the boring tool, we equate the work done in $2\frac{1}{2}$ hr to the heat developed in the cannon metal and water during the same time: 6.7×10^6 j $= 1.2 \times 10^3$ kcal, or 1 kcal $= 5.6 \times 10^3$ j. This statement of equivalence between thermal and mechanical units came to be called the *mechanical equivalent of heat* and, later on, the *Joule equivalent*. We shall soon obtain a more accurate value for the number of joules per kilocalorie, a ratio often designated by the letter J.

PROBLEM 20.1. Show that the foregoing expression for the Joule equivalent as calculated from Rumford's data can be interpreted as follows. The quantity of heat capable of increasing the temperature of 1 kgm of water by one degree Celsius is equivalent to the work that would be done in raising an object of weight 5600 new through a vertical distance of 1 m.

PROBLEM 20.2. In the foregoing calculation of the Joule equivalent, suppose that we had known how much heat "accumulated in the box" and how much work was done against friction in the connecting machinery. Would our calculated value for the number of joules equivalent to 1 kcal then have been larger or smaller than 5600? If you are given the modern experimental value, $J \doteq 4200$ j/kcal, comment on the relative importance of the main sources of error in Rumford's experiment.

But mark well: the foregoing calculation of a relation between the kilocalorie and the joule does not by itself constitute a demonstration that heat is a form of energy. We have not yet shown that there is an exact and fixed rate of exchange between mechanical energy and heat in *enough different* situations to convince us that the relation is universal; moreover, we have yet to show that this equivalence also holds when forms of energy other than work done against friction are involved, and that it applies to the converse convertibility of heat to work.

20.2 Toward a general equivalence between heat and mechanical energy. There were other indications in Rumford's day of a relationship between various forms of energy and heat. That kinetic energy was converted to heat by the quick hammering of a nail on an anvil was common knowledge, although it was not expressed in this manner, and so was the liberation of heat in chemical reactions. About 20 years before Rumford, Lavoisier and Laplace had introduced experimental evidence from physiology to show that the animal heat developed by a living guinea pig after eating food was approximately equal to the heat produced by the same amount of food during the chemical process of burning it. In 1819, the French chemist and physicist, P. L. Dulong, showed that heat produced in a gas when the gas is quickly compressed is proportional to the work done in compressing it, and research had also begun on the heat produced by an electric current.

There were several other forward steps of importance at about this time. The energy concept was becoming more clearly defined; indeed, the term *energy*, in its modern meaning, dates from 1807. And, as was particularly illustrated in the work of the British physicist Michael Faraday on the interrelationships of electric current, magnetism, and light, there spread increasingly a belief that these several types of phenomena, along with mechanical and thermal effects, were all interconnected and would ultimately be found to be part of a single unified story. In reviewing this period prior to the 1840's we are struck by the widespread groping toward a general principle of conservation of energy from many different sides, often far beyond the context, the available evidences, or the clarity of the concepts themselves.

One very practical influence here was the steam engine, which had been developed and improved earlier by James Watt and was now coming into comparatively wide use. No other mechanism more obviously demonstrated the close relationship between heat supplied and work done. Moreover, there was need for studying the operation of these engines so that their efficiency might be improved. Especially in France, there was much early interest in the effects of heat on steam and other gases, and on the work done by them. In an investigation that later assumed particular significance, the chemist L. J. Gay-Lussac showed that if a gas were allowed to expand freely into a tank that had been evacuated, no prominent change could be detected in the over-all temperature of the gas. But if the gas were allowed to expand into some surrounding medium, such as the air, so that work was done in pushing the medium aside, then the gas exhibited a very noticeable temperature drop.

20.3 Mayer's work. The conclusions cited above and various other clues were pulled together in 1842 in a short essay that definitely suggested *a general equivalence and conservation of all forms of energy,* of which the equivalence of heat and work was only a special case. This essay was so full of imaginative, almost metaphysical, but largely unsupported generalizations that one of the great journals of physics refused to publish it; eventually it was accepted by a chemistry journal. The essay was the work of Julius Robert Mayer (Fig. 20.1), then a young physician in the German town of Heilbronn, his native city. Mayer later said that his thoughts first turned to this subject when, as a ship's doctor in the tropics, he observed venous blood to be of a brighter red color than he had expected from experience in cooler climes, and that subsequently, the voyage evidently being long and uneventful, he began to speculate upon the relation between animal heat and chemical reaction, and from there went on to consider the interchangeability of all energies in nature.

The essay, entitled *Remarks on the energies* of inorganic nature,* states:

Fig. 20.1. Julius Robert Mayer (1814–1878).

---

*In the German original, the old term *Kraft* (force) was used when energy was meant. We have substituted the word *energy* throughout.

Energies are causes: accordingly, we may in relation to them make full application of the principle—*causa aequat effectum*. If the cause *c* has the effect *e*, then $e = c$; ... In a chain of causes and effects, a term or a part of a term can never, as plainly appears from the nature of an equation, become equal to nothing. This first property of all causes we call their indestructibility ... If after the production of [effect] *e*, [cause] *c* still remained in whole or in part, there must be still further effects [*f*, *g*, ...] corresponding to the remaining cause. Accordingly, since *c* becomes *e*, and *e* becomes *f*, etc., we must regard these various magnitudes as different forms under which one and the same entity makes its appearance. This capability of assuming various forms is the second essential property of all causes. Taking both properties together, we may say, causes are quantitatively *indestructible* and qualitatively *convertible* entities ... Energies are therefore indestructible, convertible entities.

This, then, is the first published voicing of the conservation and equivalence of all energies. But this way of arguing was, of course, false. "Causes" do not have the properties derived by this private logic, nor can one equate energy with "cause" unless there is prior *experimental* proof of the indestructibility and convertibility of energy.

Further on in the essay, Mayer develops his argument as follows:

In numberless cases we see motion cease without having caused another motion or the lifting of a weight; but an energy once in existence cannot be annihilated, it can only change its form; and the question therefore arises, What other forms is energy, which we have become acquainted with as potential energy and kinetic energy [modern terminology], capable of assuming? Experience alone can lead us to a conclusion.

Later, he argues further that if heat can be generated when two rough surfaces in motion rub against each other, then heat must be a form of motion. This point of view had been advanced repeatedly before, had been employed efficiently by Rumford, and was to be firmly established within a decade—although not on such grounds as Mayer's. From his fundamental proposition, Mayer concludes further:

If potential energy and kinetic energy are equivalent to heat, heat must also naturally be equivalent to kinetic energy and potential energy ... [Consequently] we will close our disquisition, the propositions of which have resulted as necessary consequences from the principle *causa aequat effectum* and which are in accordance with all the phenomena of nature, with a practical deduction ... How great is the quantity of heat which corresponds to a given quantity of kinetic or potential energy?

This is indeed the crucial point. Mayer's presentation so far has been almost completely qualitative, and indeed rather reminiscent of Scholastic science in many ways. This is partly understandable from the fact that Mayer himself had then no facilities for experimentation and found the physicists of his time quite uncooperative. But here, at the end of his paper, deceptively like an afterthought, is finally promised a derivation of the equivalence between heat and work, and by an approach opposite to that of Rumford. Here is the chance for empirical verification.

Mayer's solution is only sketched out, but we can reconstruct the steps. In the circumstances, he had to fashion his illustrative computation from the data of an earlier experimenter, the significance of which had by and large not been noted. In doing this he showed great sagacity, for aside from Rumford's cannon-boring experiments, the type of experiment which Mayer chose to consider was the only one available at the time upon which a calculation of the mechanical equivalent of heat could have been based.

This type of experiment arose from a striking difficulty that had been encountered in the study of the thermal properties of gases, that is, that the specific heat capacity of a gas depends markedly upon the method of measurement. Suppose a sample of air is heated while in a tight enclosure, so that its volume remains constant and its pressure rises. The specific heat capacity of the air thus kept *at constant volume* turns out to be 0.170 kcal/kgm·°C. Next, suppose that the same sample of gas is enclosed in a cylinder having one free- ly moving side or piston (Fig. 20.2). Now the gas, when heated, expands and pushes the cylinder outward in such a way that the pressure exerted by the gas remains constant and equal to the outside air pressure. The specific heat capacity of the air thus kept *under constant pressure* is found to be 0.238 kcal/kgm·°C, which is about one-third more than before. For a gas, then, we must be careful to specify whether we are dealing with the specific heat capac- ity at constant volume or that at constant pressure.

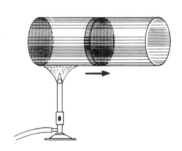

FIG. 20.2. A sample of gas being heated in a cylinder. The cylinder con- tains a piston free to move, so that the gas is always under atmospheric pres- sure.

Mayer saw why this distinction must be made. He assumed that for both modes of measurement, 0.170 kcal/kgm is required to raise the tem- perature of the air by one degree Celsius; and that, in the second of these experiments, the excess, (0.238 − 0.170) kcal/kgm, or 0.068 kcal/kgm, is needed to supply the work done by the expanding air in pushing against atmospheric pressure on the "outside" face of the piston. *Pressure P is* defined as force per unit area,

$$P = F/A;$$
(20.1)

therefore the total force F on the piston of area A under pressure P is

$$F = PA.$$

If the expanding gas pushes the piston out a distance s (Fig. 20.3), the work done by the gas on the piston is Fs, or PAs. But As, the area of the piston multiplied by the distance it moves, is simply the increase in volume of the gas as a result of the heating. Thus the work PAs done by a gas in expanding when under a constant pressure P is just the pressure multiplied by the change in volume, ΔV.

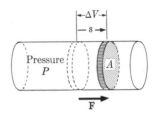

Both of these quantities are known: when the balancing atmospheric pressure is at its normal value of 1.01×10^5 new/m^2 the change in volume of the enclosed air for each degree Celsius rise in temperature is known by experiment to be 2.83×10^{-3} m^3/kgm. The work done by the enclosed gas in expanding against the pressure of the surrounding atmosphere is therefore $(1.01 \times 10^5$ new/m$^2) \times (2.83 \times 10^{-3}$ m^3/kgm$) = 286$ new·m/kgm $= 286$ j/kgm.

FIG. 20.3. If the gas in the cylinder is heated, the pressure inside remains constant as the piston moves a distance s. The work done on the piston by the gas during expansion against the balancing pressure of the atmosphere on the outside of the piston is given by the pressure P multiplied by the increase in volume, ΔV.

According to Mayer's assumption, this work of 286 j/kgm of gas came from the additional 0.068 kilocalorie of heat supplied per kilogram of air. Consequently, 286 j are the equivalent of 0.068 kcal; hence 1 kcal $= 4200$ j, or $J = 4200$ j/kcal.

In this calculation of the mechanical equivalent of heat, using the conversion of heat to work as an example, we have used modern data. The data known to Mayer yielded 1 kcal as equivalent to 3600 j, and one of Rumford's experiments on the conversion of work to heat yielded 5600 j. Considering the expected uncertainties in the earlier data, these equivalence values compare not badly with the modern value.

For about 20 years, Mayer's work received virtually no recognition from the scientific world. Scientists quite rightly are wary of such largely qualitative efforts, and in this case there was no generally recognized conceptual crisis that Mayer's new ideas would have resolved. But the lag also shows that scientists are by no means always immediately perceptive of the long-range significance of an unorthodox contribution, for Mayer did develop his principle of general indestructibility and strict convertibility of energy further in several subsequent essays, sometimes using quantitative illustrations that extended the principle with remarkable boldness and insight to chemical, astronomical, and biological processes.

During much of this time Mayer suffered from a severe mental disorder that the strain of his work and the lonely fight for its recognition seemed to aggravate. Eventually he recovered and, although no longer engaged in creative work, he witnessed growing recognition and honor in the closing years of his life.

20.4 The work of Joule. The change of Mayer's personal fortunes was by no means a sign that scientists had become sentimental about his condition; rather, it was the consequence of a general acceptance of the energy principle on the basis of concurrent series of events, above all, the remarkable and persistent experimental work of a British amateur of science, James Prescott Joule (1818–1889). The characteristic difference between the two men has been well pointed out by John Tyndall in his still very readable classic *Heat considered as a mode of motion* (1863 and later editions):

> True to the speculative instinct of his country, Mayer drew large and weighty conclusions from slender premises, while the Englishman aimed, above all things, at the firm establishment of facts. And he did establish them.

Joule was born near Manchester, the son of a well-to-do brewer to whose business he succeeded. But his dedication from the start was to science. At 17, he was a pupil of the chemist-physicist John Dalton, and at 22 he had begun a series of investigations that was to occupy the greater part of his life—the proof that when mechanical work gives rise to heat in any circumstance, the ratio of work done to heat evolved has a constant and measurable value. In part, Joule's motivation seems to have been the same as that of all other proponents of a conservation law; in his words, it was to him "manifestly absurd to suppose that the powers with which God has endowed matter can be destroyed." There was also a practical motivation, for initially he was interested in attempts to secure cheaper motive power for his breweries. But the most powerful drive in Joule during his 40 years of investigation was undoubtedly the sheer love for experimentation.

Independently of Mayer's work (with which he said he was "only imperfectly acquainted" as late as 1850), Joule announced in 1843 the first result of his labor, the comparison of the mechanical work needed to operate an electric generator and of the heat produced by the current so generated. In experimentation of this kind, it is extremely difficult to obtain reproducible data because of the unavoidable leakage of heat and the like, but by averaging the data from 13 such experiments, Joule arrived at the equivalence 1 kcal = 4510 j. Later in the same year, he measured the heat of friction for water flowing through thin pipes and also the work needed to maintain this flow, and obtained $J = 4140$ j/kcal. He concluded:

> We shall be obliged to admit that Count Rumford was right in attributing the heat evolved by boring cannon to friction ... I shall lose no time repeating and extending these experiments, being satisfied that the grand agents of nature are, by the Creator's fiat, *indestructible;* and that whenever mechanical force [energy] is expended, an exact equivalent of heat is *always* obtained.

Despite the coolness with which his work was generally received, Joule continued with almost obstinate zeal. In 1844 he measured the ratio of work needed to compress a gas to the heat so created, a method that in principle was much like the one on which Mayer had based his calculation of 1842. Joule here obtained $J = 4270$ j/kcal. A little later he initiated a long series of increasingly accurate frictional experiments in which water in a heat-insulated container was stirred by paddlewheels (Fig. 20.4). Because the temperature rise of the water is quite small, this is a delicate experiment, and his result (4780 j/kcal) was markedly different from the others. By 1847 the technical difficulties were in hand; stirring water and also sperm oil gave very closely the same result, 4200 j/kcal.

In reporting this particular experiment at a scientific meeting in 1847, a crisis arose. Joule was asked by the chairman to confine himself to a "short verbal description," partly because his previous communications, as Joule himself recalled later, "did not excite much general attention."

> This I endeavoured to do, and, discussion not being invited, the communication would have passed without comment if a young man had not risen in the Section and by his intelligent observations created a lively interest in the new theory. The young man was William Thomson.

Thomson (afterward raised to peerage as Lord Kelvin), then 23 years old and destined to become one of the foremost British scientists, had grasped the significance of Joule's paper, and by his discussion made it the high point of the meeting.

The next year brought further results from Joule's experiments involving friction in water, in mercury (where the temperature rise is larger because of the smaller specific heat capacity), and for two iron disks rubbing against each other. He compared these experiments with Rumford's, to which they were similar in principle; indeed it was Joule who made the calculation given in Section 20.1. Then he summarized all his previous work and assigned to the relation between the thermal and mechanical units of energy the value 4150 j/kcal. Today, as a result of a century of increasingly refined precision methods, the value generally accepted is

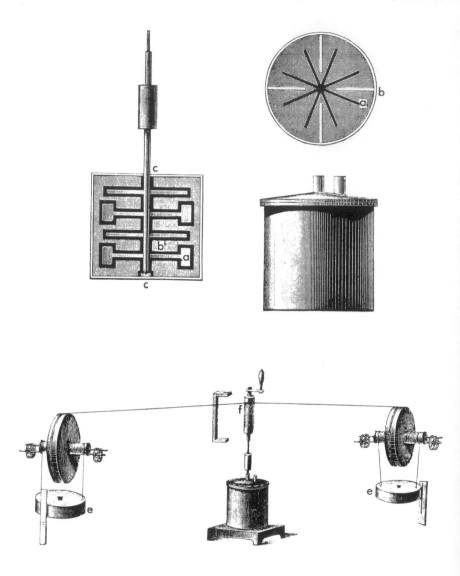

FIG. 20.4. Joule's apparatus for measuring the heat generated by stirring a liquid. The cross-sectional diagrams, upper left and right, show the axle cc and paddles a rotating inside the baffles b which are fixed to the walls of the container. The lower sketch indicates that handle f is used to raise weights e. When f is released, the weights descend; the rotating paddles agitate the liquid, and by friction convert into heat that part of the initial potential energy of the weights which does not go into kinetic energy of the moving parts of the apparatus.

$$1 \text{ kcal} = 4185 \text{ j},$$

or

$$J = 4185 \text{ j/kcal}.$$

With greatest justice this, the "mechanical equivalent of heat," is nowadays also referred to as the Joule equivalent.

PROBLEM 20.3. A 1-kgm ball of lead (specific heat capacity, 0.03 kcal/kgm·°C) falls freely from a height of 10 m and is stopped suddenly by the floor. (a) What is the largest temperature rise of the lead that could be expected? (b) Cite several reasons why the observed temperature rise will be smaller than the one computed.

20.5 Acceptance of the energy principle. By 1850 Joule saw his work being taken more seriously, the gratifying result of a well-planned experimental assault. During the next 18 years, he carried through three further sets of determinations of J. Doubtless it was the sum of all this persistent work that was the biggest factor in making acceptable the idea of accommodating in one general principle of conservation all forms of energy. Nevertheless, as usually happens, Joule's triumph depended in important ways on developments beyond his own participation. For one thing, the general thinking on the nature of matter itself was undergoing profound changes. The rise of the view that matter is composed of atoms and molecules, to which the next two chapters will be devoted, made more plausible the proposition that heat is a form of energy, namely, the kinetic energy associated with the motion of the molecules of matter. This conception removed the cause of much of the original resistance to Rumford, Mayer, and Joule.

Furthermore, the conception of a general energy principle was beginning to find able and eloquent champions, particularly at first in the young German physiologist and physicist, Hermann von Helmholtz, then 26 years old. He did what Mayer, then still in oblivion, had not quite done and Joule had never attempted, that is, he showed by mathematical demonstration the precise extent of the validity of the conservation principle in various fields (mechanics, heat, electricity, magnetism, physical chemistry, and astronomy) and, with its aid, he derived explanations for old puzzles as well as new and confirmable quantitative relationships, in terms that the professional scientist would at once recognize. Indeed, Mayer's vision had been prophetic: the principle of conservation of energy provided striking general connections among the sciences. It was perhaps the greatest step toward unity in science since Newtonian mechanics, and it was a powerful guide in the exploration of new fields. For this reason, and also because of its practical value, the principle may be regarded as one of the great achievements of the human mind.

There is one aspect of the history of the principle of conservation of energy that should be mentioned because it is representative of what often happens during the establishment of a new conceptual scheme. As Mayer's and Joule's work finally won partisans, and in ironic contrast with the earlier loneliness and rejection of both men, there developed a sometimes rather bitter fight as to which of the two had been the real originator of the general doctrine of conservation of energy in its various forms. The Joulites disparaged Mayer's contribution of 1842 that gave him priority of publication over Joule, whose first but quite independent paper was dated 1843; and Joule himself wrote in 1864:

> Neither in Séguin's writing [of 1839] nor in Mayer's paper of 1842 were there such proofs of the hypothesis advanced as were sufficient to cause it to be admitted into science without further inquiry . . . Mayer appears to have hastened to publish his views for the express purpose of securing priority. He did not wait until he had the opportunity of supporting them by facts. My course, on the contrary, was to publish only such theories as I had established by experiments calculated to commend them to the scientific public, being well convinced of the truth of Sir J. Herschel's remark that *"hasty generalization is the bane of science."*

On the other side, and often not much more fairly, those partial to Mayer's claim to priority would say with Helmholtz:

> The progress of natural science depends on this: that new [theoretical] ideas are continually induced from the available facts; and that afterwards the consequence of these ideas, insofar as they refer to new facts, are experimentally checked against actuality. There can be no doubt about the necessity of this second endeavor; and often this second part will cost a great deal of labor and ingenuity, and will be thought of as a high accomplishment on the part of him who carries it through well. But the fame of discovery still belongs to him who found the new idea; the experimental investigation is afterwards a much more mechanical type of achievement. Also, one cannot unconditionally demand that the inventor of the idea be under obligation to carry out the second part of the endeavor. With that demand one would dismiss the greatest part of the work of all mathematical physicists.

Here we see an old fight, or rather two fights: one for priority (and each great idea, after it is accepted, tends to give rise to such a dispute), and second, the fight concerning the relative merits of the experimentalist and the theoretician. Both afford yet another illustration of the human element behind the logical structure of scientific knowledge.

20.6 Various formulations of the energy principle. The principle of conservation of energy may assume any one of a variety of forms, depending on the intended application, but broadly speaking, we have met three main groups of formulations:

(a) *For an isolated or closed system,* the sum of all forms of energy remains constant (the net changes add up to zero) although the energies in the system may assume different forms as time progresses. Examples are perfectly elastic collisions between molecules and disintegrations in radioactivity.

(b) *For a system to which energy is added,* including work done on or heat supplied to it, *but which does not in turn give energy to the world outside the system,* the energy supplied to the system is equal to the total change in internal energy of all forms. An example is a gas in a cylinder which is being compressed by a piston.

(c) *For a system to which energy is supplied and which also does work on or loses energy to the outside world,* the energy supplied to the system is equal to the total change of internal energy of the system, *plus* the energy given up by the system. Examples are machines, heat engines, electric motors, and Joule's paddlewheel experiment with heat leakage.

But of course the energy principle is a *single* generalization, and the particular form it takes depends only on how large we choose the "system" under consideration to be. Thus when a man hoists a load by means of a pulley, statement (c) applies if the pulley alone is regarded as the whole system, and statement (a) if the pulley, load, man, and earth are considered to be the system. Furthermore, statements (a) and (b) are but special cases of (c), with one or more of the factors equal to zero.

In scientific writings the energy principle is phrased in many different ways. When the interchange of heat and mechanical energy is involved, the principle of conservation of energy may be referred to as *the first law of thermodynamics.* Another formulation of the energy principle consists of the statement that a perpetual motion machine is impossible or, to put it another way, that it is impossible to construct a machine or engine with an efficiency exceeding 100 percent—one for which the output of energy exceeds the input. The continued unsuccessful attempts to invent such a device were in fact partly responsible for the rise of the energy principle in mechanics; in earlier centuries this search engaged even some of the greatest intellects, for it was in itself no less plausible or challenging than the parallel, and equally fruitless, search for the Philosopher's Stone. The search for the *perpetuum mobile* also reflected a preoccupation of an increasingly more machine-minded civilization or, equally well, that most human of all traits, the wish to get something for nothing.

The empirical statement of the impossibility of making a perpetual motion machine, which now has acquired the status of a physical principle, is one example of a class of so-called *postulates of impotence* that have profoundly influenced physical science. Among other examples is the recognition of the impossibility of transmuting matter in chemical reactions, a generalization that in its day helped to shape the idea of chemical elements.

Another is the statement that it is impossible to obtain net work from a medium by cooling it below the temperature of its surroundings; this is the effective content of the *second law of thermodynamics*. Machines for obtaining energy by such a process, often called "perpetual motion machines of the second kind," were once as eagerly and as vainly sought after as were those of the first kind mentioned earlier. Still another example is the postulate of impotence basic to the theory of relativity, namely that it is impossible to transfer energy between material systems with a speed greater than that of light.

20.7 Heat engines. In this and the three sections that follow, evidence will be provided for the wide range of applicability and usefulness of the energy principle. Its most general form, item (c) of the preceding section, may be written as follows:

$$
\begin{aligned}
&\text{(A)}\\
&\left\{ \begin{array}{l} \text{Work done by } F_{\text{ap}} \text{ on system,} \\ \text{or energy supplied to system} \end{array} \right\} =
\end{aligned}
$$

$$
\begin{aligned}
&\text{(B)}\\
&= \left\{ \begin{array}{l} \text{Work done against friction, } or \\ \text{heat energy thereby generated} \end{array} \right\}
\end{aligned}
$$

$$
\begin{aligned}
&\text{(C)}\quad\text{(D)}\qquad\qquad\text{(E)}\\
&+ \Delta E_k + \Delta E_p + \left\{ \begin{array}{l} \text{Change in quantity of heat} \\ \text{other than by friction} \end{array} \right\}
\end{aligned}
$$

$$
\begin{aligned}
&\text{(F)}\\
&+ \left\{ \begin{array}{l} \text{Other changes of energy} \\ \text{in system (chemical, etc.)} \end{array} \right\}
\end{aligned}
$$

$$
\begin{aligned}
&\text{(G)}\\
&+ \left\{ \begin{array}{l} \text{Energy supplied to and/or} \\ \text{work done on outside world} \end{array} \right\} \qquad\qquad (20.2)
\end{aligned}
$$

PROBLEM 20.4. Show that Eq. (18.9) is merely a special case of Eq. (20.2), and specify the circumstances that make Eq. (18.9) simpler than Eq. (20.2).

The use of this general equation, in which the seven terms have been identified by letters (A) through (G), may be illustrated by applying it to the case of the heat engine. Figure 20.5 represents schematically the functions of a simplified steam engine. Heat energy enters through the walls of the boiler and generates steam at high pressure. In the cylinder, the steam expands and pushes the piston out, thereby causing the wheel to turn and the load to rise. As the wheel continues to turn by its inertia,

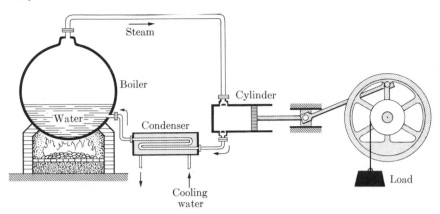

FIG. 20.5. Schematic representation of the steam engine.

it pushes the piston back; the steam leaves the cylinder and passes through the condenser, where it cools and liquefies. The water is pumped back into the boiler and so is ready to start on its next cyclical journey. For energy considerations, the *system* consists of the boiler, water, steam, cylinder, piston, and wheel, but does not include the fire under the boiler, the load, or the condensing device. Therefore term (A) in Eq. (20.2) is the heat energy supplied to the boiler during some chosen time interval, perhaps the time needed for the whole engine to go through one cycle of operation. For the sake of illustration, let us take this energy to be 5.0 kcal. To keep consistent energy units throughout, we may choose to use either kilocalories or joules for all terms. If the latter choice is made, term (A) is 5.0 kcal $\times$ 4185 j/kcal $= 2.1 \times 10^4$ j.

The engine may be assumed to have been already in full motion, and so the speed and position of all its parts are the same at the start of a cycle as at its end; consequently, terms (C) and (D), namely ΔE_k and ΔE_p of the engine, are both zero during this time interval. Term (B), in any good engine, will be kept to a minimum by good design and maintenance, but friction of the parts is rarely negligible. Let us assume here that by separate experiment we know that 3×10^3 j of work are done against internal friction. Note that we have the choice in term (B) of counting either this work or the equivalent amount of heat generated in the engine owing to frictional "losses" (namely, 3000 j $\times$ 1 kcal/4185 j) *but not both*. To cite an analogy, if we wish to calculate our income, we must not count both the money received *and* the value of the things purchased with it.

Term (E) in Eq. (20.2) will also be zero in one complete cycle of the heat engine, for while during the cycle 5.0 kcal may be thought of as being used to heat up and evaporate some of the water in the boiler, the resulting steam is cooled and so gives up an equivalent amount of heat during the cycle, partly to the cylinder during expansion, and partly to the condenser before returning to the boiler. In short, during a complete cycle a given quantity of water returns to its initial state, having neither gained nor lost heat energy. Term (F) is also zero, for no net changes of chemical or physical nature occur during one cycle in the engine which constitutes the system. This leaves term (G), "energy supplied to and/or work done on outside world," that is, the world outside the specified system.

In our case, term (G) covers two different items: (1) The cooling water of the condenser carries away some heat, measurable as the product of the mass of cooling water used during the cycle and the increase in temperature of its outflow over the inflow; a reasonable value in this operation would be 3.1 kcal or 1.3×10^4 j. (2) The other part of term (G), of course, is the work done on the load, the real reason for employing the engine. In our example this would be 2.1×10^4 j $- (3 \times 10^3$ j $+ 1.3 \times 10^4$ j$) = 5 \times 10^3$ j during this one cycle, perhaps used to raise a 500-new weight a distance of 10 m.

In summary, the energy balance in our simplified steam engine, taken term by term, stands as follows:

$$\underset{(A)}{2.1 \times 10^4 \text{ j}} = \underset{(B)}{3 \times 10^3 \text{ j}} + \underset{(C)}{0} + \underset{(D)}{0} + \underset{(E)}{0} + \underset{(F)}{0}$$

$$+ \underset{(G)}{(1.3 \times 10^4 \text{ j} + 5 \times 10^3 \text{ j})}.$$

The "input" into this system is term (A), and the useful work output from the system is the second half of term (G). Thus the efficiency η is

$$\eta = \frac{\text{output}}{\text{input}} = \frac{5 \times 10^3 \text{ j}}{2.1 \times 10^4 \text{ j}} = 0.24 = 24\%.$$

20.8 Animals as machines. Once it was thought that animals, including man, must eat only in order to grow and to rebuild used-up tissue. That food also provides heat and other energy for the functioning of the body was realized only slowly. At the danger of simplifying a complex topic, we may compare the body to a type of chemical engine: the oxygen we breathe combines with the sugars, fats, and some of the proteins from our digested food intake; these complex molecules are converted primarily into carbon dioxide, water and other waste products. This process liberates heat and, in the contraction of muscles, provides mechanical work.

The energy intake in the form of "combustible" food and the corresponding work and heat output have been measured with precision, partly in an effort to check whether life processes are describable by the same conservation principles as apply to the phenomena of inanimate nature. Since the 1890's this question has been settled in the affirmative. In a representative case the daily food intake is such that if the food were burned directly outside the body, it would yield about 3000 kcal; and the daily amount of heat given up, together with the work done and the energy in the waste products, come to the same figure within a small experimental uncertainty. But the body, considered as an engine for doing mechanical work, ordinarily has an efficiency of less than 20 percent. Therefore if one must do a large amount of physical work in a short time, the attendant heat output will be correspondingly larger, and since those bodily devices that serve to dissipate heat are not very flexible, the body may heat up drastically.

20.9 Photosynthesis. If the energy of animals had to be derived from fuels such as oil and coal, the food supply on this earth would have been exhausted long ago. Happily, the food upon which present forms of animal life are dependent come directly or indirectly from chemical syntheses occurring in green plants, which are uniquely able to absorb carbon dioxide and water from their surroundings (both are waste products of animal life) and to recombine the aggregates of carbon, hydrogen, and oxygen, along with some mineral salts, into more complex "organic" compounds, each with a large amount of "built-in" chemical potential energy. It is this energy that is released during decomposition inside the animal body. For good measure, while the plants build our food, they also release the oxygen we inhale, thus making possible the oxidation or "burning" of our food.

Except for some lower organisms that live by fermentation, all animal life depends on this cycle of processes. But is all this not a contradiction of the principle of conservation of energy? Is not the over-all activity of the plant and animal worlds an example of perpetual motion—going on indefinitely without any need of energy? The answer is "no," because the energy stored in the organic compounds manufactured in the plants comes from solar energy absorbed by the plant. These chemical reactions, which depend on the availability of sunlight (and on the presence of chlorophyll and other catalysts) is appropriately termed *photosynthesis*. In a sense, all our food is largely sunlight.

If not eaten, the energy-rich plant material in the open air soon decays into its original constituents, but if submerged or otherwise suitably kept from undergoing oxidation, it may turn into coal or some other fuel by slow chemical decompositions that favor the retention of carbon-rich materials.

20.10 Origin of the solar system. One famous puzzle to which the energy principle in its early days seemed to give an immediate answer was how the sun could continuously emit energy at the staggering rate of about 4×10^{26} j/sec, or about 9×10^{22} kcal/sec.

PROBLEM 20.5. (a) Outline a procedure that might be used to arrive at the value of the rate of emission of energy by the sun. (b) Express the value in units of horsepower (1 hp = 746 j/sec).

The ancient view that the sun is an incandescent object that is gradually cooling off cannot possibly account for the energy which we now know has been given off in its lifetime. That it is a mass of burning coal or some similar fuel is another old hypothesis that does not pass the quantitative test, for since we know the mass of the sun and the heats of combustion of various fuels, we can easily show that the sun, in producing energy at the rate it does, would have been entirely consumed soon after its creation. Mayer, Helmholtz, and others proposed two alternative hypotheses: (1) the sun is slowly shrinking and the gravitational potential energy thus lost is being converted into the energy radiated, and (2) the sun is continually capturing comets and meteors, the kinetic energies of which are converted into heat and then into the energy radiated. But the first hypothesis was disproved when it was calculated that the sun's diameter would have to shrink 1 part in 10,000 every 2000 years to provide radiation in this manner at the present level, and this is too fast to account for the long history of life on earth. Nor is there evidence of sufficient meteoric matter near the sun to account for the rate at which energy is radiated, and so the second hypothesis had to be discarded. The now accepted conception of the source of the sun's energy as a series of nuclear reactions was of course not imaginable until fairly recently. The fundamental idea in the proposals of Mayer and Helmholtz is useful in another context, however, for the general mechanism of conversion of gravitational potential energy to heat is invoked today in theories concerning the creation of the solar system.

Any tenable theory of the origin of the solar system must account for all the following facts: (1) At least half of all the stars in our galaxy are binaries (double stars) or stars of higher multiples, and most of them revolve quickly about one another. (2) Of the single stars, those of high temperature usually spin on their axes at enormous rates, whereas the "cooler" ones, like our sun, spin quite slowly. (3) In our own solar system, all the planets revolve in the same direction about the sun, and their orbits are in practically the same plane.

Present-day theories, while differing in accent on the details to be explained, all begin with the same general proposition that the solar system started by the gathering together of a thinly spread cloud of cosmic dust, like the interstellar cosmic dust clouds that are observable with our telescopes. It may be that radiation from some surrounding stars pushed the dust particles sufficiently close together to allow their mutual gravitational attractive forces to predominate. Calculations indicate that such a mass would coalesce in about 10^9 years.

As the isolated cloud shrinks, any initial spinning motion that it may have, no matter how small, will increase progressively, just as air spins faster the nearer it gets to the center of a tornado or hurricane. Also, as the gravitational forces pull the particles together, the gravitational potential energy is converted into heat. According to one line of thought, in the final stages of this process the central portion of the cloud gathers up into one bright, spinning central star (or two or more stars), leaving the outlying and still revolving parts to condense into the planets and their satellites.

Although such a conceptual scheme appears to explain many of the facts about the solar system, certain details seem to be objectionable, and so a modified scheme has been advanced, although it too has its adverse critics. The entire initial dust cloud is pictured as shrinking into a single, very rapidly spinning star. Eventually the star spins so fast that it breaks into two (or more) sections; or what may be more likely, the star becomes so hot that nuclear reactions are set off and it explodes rather in the manner of a "nuclear bomb." Such an explosion is accompanied by a sudden and large increase in brightness, and also by the production of an extensive envelope of surrounding gas. The explosion may also separate the original star into two or more stars; and as these double or multiple stars revolve about one another against the resistance of the gaseous envelope, they slow down, come closer and closer together under their mutual gravitational attraction, and ultimately combine into a single star again. During this process much of the gaseous envelope scatters into space, and what is left coalesces into planets and satellites. Incidentally, this picture of stellar evolution permits the speculation that each exploding star may give rise to a planetary system. On this basis it has been estimated that the known universe contains perhaps as many as 10^{11} planetary systems.

In closing this chapter on the powerful and intriguing role that the energy principle has played in the drama of science, we cannot forego the opportunity it offers for pointing out a typical interaction between science and philosophy. As indicated, there is much yet to be done in the development of a satisfactory quantitative theory of stellar evolution; indeed, so many new and perplexing discoveries are being made that the formulation of a single, comprehensive theory coordinating all of them seems quite distant. Nevertheless, it is almost inevitable that eventually we shall have such a theory, one that will prove that the formation and arrangement of the solar system, including the regularities pointed out by the Bode-Titus law, can be explained by straightforward physical processes. But if the past is a guide, this will be interpreted by some as another serious blow of science against religion, for it has generally been held as axiomatic that the sciences could not provide such an explanation, that a theistic assumption was consequently necessary and that, indeed, the lack of a scientific alternative was demonstrable proof of the existence of the Deity. Thus Newton himself, in discussing the planets and comets, noted in Book III of the *Principia:*

> But though these bodies may, indeed, continue in their orbits by the mere laws of gravity, yet they could by no means have first derived the regular positions of the orbits themselves from those laws. The six primary planets are revolved about the sun [roughly] in circles concentric with the sun, and with motions directed towards the same parts, and almost in the same plane. Ten moons are revolved about the earth, Jupiter, and Saturn, in circles concentric with them, with the same direction of motion, and nearly in the planes of the orbits of those planets; but it is not to be conceived that mere mechanical causes could give birth to so many regular motions, since the comets range over all parts of the heavens in very eccentric orbits ... This most beautiful system of the sun, planets, and comets, could only proceed from the counsel and dominion of an intelligent and powerful Being ...

The same dependence on a theistic assumption prevailed in connection with the problem of the descent of man prior to the development of the theory of organic evolution, it prevailed in explaining the existence and distribution of the chemical elements until nuclear physics recently began to supply us with promising explanations of their genesis, and so on with many other similar examples. Each time, the finding that the facts could be accounted for without resort to a theistic assumption came as a shock. But such events should teach us that it is not only folly but blasphemy to let one's belief in the Deity be based on premature estimates of what science can *not* do. The opposite course, namely the deification of the discoveries of science, is in truth quite as precarious, for science changes, and even the most useful knowledge of one period may prove to be far less useful in the next. The secure basis for belief, as all great religious leaders have taught, is not to be found in the judgment of man's intellectual capacities or of his limitations, and not in science's presumed powers or inadequacies; rather, it is to be found only in faith.

ADDITIONAL PROBLEMS

20.6. In 1845 Joule wrote: "Any of your readers who are so fortunate as to reside amid the romantic scenery of Wales or Scotland could, I doubt not, confirm my experiments by trying the temperature of the water at the top and bottom of a cascade. If my views be correct, a fall of 817 feet will of course generate one degree [a temperature rise of $1°F$, or $5/9°C$] ... and the temperature of the river Niagara will be raised about one-fifth of a degree [F] by its fall of 160 feet." He later checked this general prediction at a high waterfall in

Switzerland while on his honeymoon.   Compute the value of the mechanical equivalent of heat that he was using at the time.   (*Hint:* Consider what happens to 1 kgm of water; it starts essentially from rest at the top of the free fall and is stopped abruptly at the bottom.)

20.7. Use the principle of conservation of energy to explain these observations: (a) A sample of naturally radioactive material maintains its temperature above that of its surroundings. (b) While a mass of air is rising to a great height, the water vapor in it may freeze. (c) While a battery generates electric energy, chemical decomposition occurs at the plates or electrodes.

20.8. Reread the quotations from Joule and Helmholtz at the end of Section 20.5 and, in the light of evidence available to you, discuss the fairness of each.

SUPPLEMENTARY READING

BONNER, T., and M. PHILLIPS, *Principles of physical science* (Addison-Wesley, 1957), Chaps. 10 and 11.

CHALMERS, T. W., *Historic researches* (Scribner's, 1952), Chap. 2.

CHERONIS, N. D., J. B. PARSONS, and C. E. RONNEBERG, *The study of the physical world* (Houghton Mifflin, 1955).   Chapter 34 on sources of energy. Chapter 47 on theories of cosmogony.

MACH, E., *History and root of the principle of conservation of energy* (original edition 1872; Open Court Publishing Co., 1911).

MAGIE, W. F., *A source book in physics* (McGraw-Hill, 1935). Selections from Mayer, Joule, Leibniz, d'Alembert, and Young.

MILLIKAN, R. A., D. ROLLER, and E. C. WATSON, *Mechanics, molecular physics, heat, and sound* (Ginn, 1937), Chap. 14.

NASH, L. K., *Plants and the atmosphere* (Harvard University Press, 1952); also in *Harvard case histories in experimental science* (Harvard University Press, 1957), v. 2, p. 323. An account of the discovery of photosynthesis.

TYNDALL, J., *Heat, a mode of motion.* (6th edition, D. Appleton, 1893.) A classic on the principle of conservation of energy. Chapter 18 reviews Mayer's work.

WOOD, A., *Joule and the study of energy* (G. Bell, London, 1925).

Part VI
ORIGINS OF THE ATOMIC THEORY
IN PHYSICS AND CHEMISTRY

(1766–1844)

ORIGINS OF THE ATOMIC THEORY
IN PHYSICS AND CHEMISTRY

The story of the development and the gradual acceptance into science of the atomic view of matter is astonishing in many ways—in its origins, in the length and vigor of the debate, in the diversity of men and fields involved, in the often quite unexpected concurrence of separate arguments, and in the ever-growing flood of consequences that has finally swept over all fields of study.

The account in this section will carry the development to about the end of the 19th century. In retrospect it is clear that the model of the atom at that point had grown out of three kinds of questions: What is the physical structure of matter, particularly of gases? What is the nature of heat? What is the basis of chemical phenomena? Although at first glance these three topics may seem completely dissociated, the answers were obtained simultaneously, in a *joint* conceptualization of the nature of heat, of gases, and of chemical reactions, in terms of one quantitative atomic scheme. In fact, the atomic view and the conservation of energy were very closely linked concepts, and the fight for both involved the same set of protagonists. As in a fugue, the separate themes introduce themselves, approach one another in the development, superpose, grow apart, and in the end again coalesce.

The concepts and derivations we shall encounter in this story are not always simple, but there exists hardly a better example on this level to show a conceptual scheme evolving from the labors of generations—a tapestry spun out of widely scattered experimental observations, shrewd assumptions, simplifying approximations, detected errors, penetrating intuitions, and mathematical manipulations. And there are three other important reasons why the closer study of this topic may be fruitful. First, it will give us a historically important and generally useful model of the elementary structure of matter. From this model, and from the outburst of successful speculations which it generated, there arose much of the physics and chemistry of the period immediately preceding the 20th century, and its failures were the stimuli for much in the new physical science of our own time. Second, not only is the kinetic theory a connecting link between the Newtonian and the contemporary approaches to physics, but it leads from *macrocosmic* physics to the world of *submicroscopic* phenomena. And finally, this topic will introduce us, though of necessity rather sketchily, to the important type of physical law that deals with a multitude of events instead of with individual events.

CHAPTER 21

GASES AND THE STRUCTURE OF MATTER

21.1 Early views of the structure of matter. From the time of the earliest recorded philosophic speculations, thoughtful people have been intrigued by a paradoxical proposition concerning the structure of matter. On the one side we can with our own hands cut or subdivide such gross matter as a rock, a piece of cloth, or a quantity of water into smaller and smaller parts, until the crudeness of our tools or the deficiency of our sight, *but never the material itself,* calls a halt to the operation. Consequently, we might conclude that matter is infinitely subdivisible. On the other hand, our imagination does not deal easily with such a view and readily permits us to entertain the alternative hypothesis that subdivision of any piece of matter, if carried far enough, would bring us to particles that cannot be subdivided or cut.

This second hypothesis was proposed and developed into an atomistic theory by the Greek philosophers Leucippus and Democritus, and later extended by Epicurus. Matter, they assumed, is indeed divisible far beyond ordinary experience, but consists ultimately of uncuttable, indivisible particles, which might provisionally be named *corpuscles* or *atoms* (from the Greek *atomos*, indivisible). Democritus taught: "The only existing things are the atoms and empty space; all else is mere opinion."

The Roman poet Lucretius, whose *De rerum natura* was cited earlier in discussing the origins of the principle of conservation of mass, served as the most eloquent expositor of the atomistic theory of antiquity. The leading theme of his philosophic poem is that all matter is composed of these two realities: solid, everlasting particles, and the void, or empty space, in which these particles "are placed and through which they move about." It was a challenging and spectacular picture—a world consisting solely of atoms and empty space, neither directly perceptible! However, for many centuries there were few fruitful and unambiguous consequences that could be drawn from this concept. Only about 160 years ago, with the accumulation of new concepts and experimental tools and techniques, was a start made in the formulation of our modern atomic theory, and even at the end of the 19th century, when extensive confirmation of the usefulness of that theory was at hand, there were important scientists who found the evidence unconvincing and rejected the concept of the atom.

From the beginning, speculation concerning the structure of matter attracted the attention of important thinkers. Plato, Aristotle, and many of their followers rejected atomism, at least partly because the everyday sort of observations available to them favored such rejection. By the 17th century such men as Francis Bacon, Descartes, Gassendi, Newton, and others were finding the atomistic picture useful in explaining various phenomena, despite its speculative character. Newton occasionally used the atomistic picture, and he seemed to have no doubt that the view of matter as composed of separate particles or atoms would prove to be correct. For example, we find in his *Opticks* this visionary, yet still un-formalized opinion on atomism:

> All these things being consider'd, it seems probable to me that God in the beginning form'd matter in solid, massy, hard, impenetrable, movable particles, of such sizes and figures, and with such other properties, and in such proportion to space, as most conduced to the end for which he form'd them; and that these primitive particles being solids, are incomparably harder than any porous bodies compounded of them; even so very hard, as never to wear or break in pieces; no ordinary power being able to divide what God himself made one in the first creation. . . And therefore, that nature may be lasting, the changes of corporeal things are to be placed only in the various separations and new associations and motions of these permanent particles; compound bodies being apt to break, not in the midst of solid particles, but where those particles are laid together, . . .
>
> Now by the help of these principles, all material things seem to have been composed of the hard and solid particles above-mention'd, variously associated in the first creation by the counsel of an intelligent agent. For it became him who created them to set them in order. And if he did so, it's unphilosophical to seek for any other origin of the world, or to pretend that it might arise out of a chaos by the mere laws of nature; though being once form'd, it may continue by those laws for many ages.

Part of Newton's preoccupation here is theological, and for a most important historical reason that must not be passed over if we wish to understand fully the development of the atomistic view. Since its inception, atomism has often been regarded as atheistic; as the excerpt from Lucretius (Section 16.1) indicates, the early atomists openly professed to give an explanation of matter and events *not* in terms of impenetrable designs of an ever-present Creator and Ruler, but in terms of the mechanical interplay of the atoms of material bodies. Newton's solution to the problem of accepting atomism while rejecting atheism was essentially the one adopted in the mechanistic philosophy of the 18th century: the Deity designed and created the World Machine, but from then on He permitted it to run without continual intervention; consequently, all observable events are due to the configurations, sizes, and shapes of the eternal particles under the rule of the mathematical laws of force and motion.

21.2 Some properties of gases. Boyle's law. The atomistic view of matter gained ground in the meantime through investigations in an entirely different field, namely through quantitative research on gases. In 1643 Evangelista Torricelli (1608–1647) suggested that we are living at the bottom of a deep "sea of air" and that the weight of this air exerts a pressure on us and everything around us. To measure this pressure he invented a device known as a *barometer* (from the Greek, *baros*, pressure, and *metron*, to measure). More significant for the progress of science than the hypothesis of the "sea of air" was the realization that the space above the mercury in a barometer column is a vacuum (Fig. 21.1). Others had tried to produce a vacuum, but after Torricelli's invention, this objective became more practical. By 1650 the air pump had been invented by Otto von Guericke (1602–1686) in Germany; and when this news reached England, about 1657, Robert Boyle (Fig. 21.2) and his colleagues began notable work on improving such air pumps and carrying on experiments in small evacuated containers.

By comparison with modern pumps, those of Guericke and Boyle were crude indeed, but they did provide a tool for studying gases which had previously appeared elusive, mysterious, and even non-material. By connecting a pump to a glass vessel, one could prepare an *experimental space* in the vessel in which to discern how light, sound, and electric or magnetic forces were affected when in an atmosphere rarefied in varying degrees. By weighing a hollow vessel before and after evacuating it, the weight of the gas it had contained could be determined, and conversely, by using a compression pump a gas could be forced into a vessel and experiments made with pressures higher than normal.

That air and other gases could be compressed had been realized for some time, but it was Boyle's celebrated experiment, described in his *New experiments physico-mechanical, touching the spring of the air* (second edition, 1662), that showed just how such changes in the volume of a gas

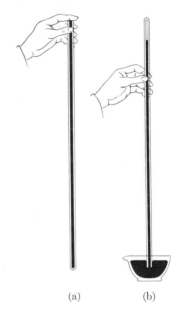

(a)   (b)

FIG. 21.1. Production of a Torricellian vacuum. (a) A glass tube, more than 30 in. long, is filled with mercury and closed with the finger. (b) The tube is inverted, the open end placed in a bowl of mercury, and the finger removed. The mercury level in the tube drops until it is about 30 in. above the level of the mercury in the bowl. The top part of the tube is then empty (a vacuum).

FIG. 21.2. Robert Boyle (1627–1691). At the right is shown one of his air pumps attached to a glass globe.

were related to the gas pressure. This relation is now known as *Boyle's law:* if a given mass of gas is trapped in a vessel of variable volume, and if the temperature of the gas is kept constant, then any decrease of volume increases the gas pressure proportionally, and vice versa. In other words,

$$P \cdot V = \text{constant (for any fixed mass of gas}$$
$$\text{kept at constant temperature)},   \tag{21.1}$$

where P is the pressure exerted by the gas on the walls of the containing vessel (expressed, for example, in newtons per square meter) and V is the corresponding volume of the gas (in cubic meters, for example).

EXAMPLE 21.1. A balloon is filled with air at ordinary atmospheric pressure (1 atm or 1.013×10^5 new/m^2). Its volume is 0.14 m^3. When the balloon is squeezed down to one-half this volume, what is the new pressure?

Solution. Using the subscripts 1 and 2 to indicate the initial and the final conditions, we have $P_1 = 1$ atm, $V_1 = 0.14$ m^3, $V_2 = 0.07$ m^3, $P_2 = ?$ From Eq. (21.1),

$$P_2 V_2 = P_1 V_1, \text{ or } P_2 = P_1 V_1 / V_2 = 1 \text{ atm} \times 0.14 \text{ m}^3 / 0.07 \text{ m}^3 = 2 \text{ atm}.$$

PROBLEM 21.1. A certain mass of hydrogen is confined in a cylinder equipped with a movable piston. When the volume occupied by the hydrogen is 0.60 m^3, the pressure exerted by the gas is found to be 2.0×10^5 new/m^2. The piston is now pulled out until the volume of the gas is 1.5 m^3. Assuming that time is allowed for the gas to regain its original temperature, show that, according to Boyle's law, the pressure exerted by the gas is now 8.0×10^4 new/m^2.

21.3 The law of Charles and Gay-Lussac. Boyle's law applies only when the temperature of the gas is constant. Now suppose that we wish to warm or cool the gas while keeping the *pressure* constant. How would the volume be affected? The answer was not forthcoming until more than a century after Boyle's law became known. Then Jacques Charles (1746–1823) and, independently, Joseph Louis Gay-Lussac (1778–1850) discovered the relation now known as the law of Charles and Gay-Lussac: if, on heating a given sample of confined gas, it is desired that a constant pressure be maintained, one must let the volume of the gas increase by an amount ΔV that is proportional to the rise Δt in the temperature; in brief,

$$\frac{\Delta V}{\Delta t} = \text{constant (for a fixed mass of gas under constant pressure).} \qquad (21.2)$$

Figure 21.3 shows a way to test this law. The sample of gas is confined in a bulb by means of an indicating drop of mercury that moves with little friction forward or backward in the stem as the temperature of the gas is increased or decreased. The end of the stem is open, and therefore

Fig. 21.3.   Apparatus for experimenting with a gas sample at constant pressure.

the pressure exerted on the right-hand side of the drop of mercury is atmospheric. If this exceeds the pressure on the left-hand side of the drop (the pressure within the bulb) the drop moves inward, compressing the gas until its pressure increases to atmospheric pressure. Similarly, excessive pressure inside will cause the drop of mercury to move outward until the inside pressure is reduced to atmospheric. In short, in experiments with this apparatus the pressure can be assumed constant. Warming the gas from temperature t_1 to temperature t_2 (so that $\Delta t = t_2 - t_1$) will result in an increase in volume from V_1 to V_2 (thus $\Delta V = V_2 - V_1$), and Eq. (21.2) assures us that this change in volume is proportional to the change in temperature.

Experiments such as this revealed a surprising similarity in behavior among almost all gases. Gases ordinarily differ very little in the fractional or percentage increase in volume per degree temperature rise, even though their chemical constitutions are different. Indeed, *when heated from 0°C to 1°C, almost all gases expand about 1/273 (0.37%)* in volume; similarly, they contract by 0.37% in volume when cooled from 0°C to −1°C. The importance of this similarity among gases can perhaps be best appreciated by pointing out the lack of similarity among solid and liquid substances. If solids or liquids are heated while being held under constant pressure, most will, like a gas, undergo a volume expansion that usually is proportional to the temperature change but, unlike gases, different solids or liquids will vary greatly in the *amount* of increase in volume per degree rise in temperature. For example, the increase per degree Celsius temperature rise is about 0.01% for ice, 0.0035% for quartz, 0.02% for mercury and for water, and 0.15% for acetone.

The thermal expansion of gases was also found to be fairly linear over ordinary ranges of temperature; therefore one might conjecture that if any gas were cooled to −273°C (that is, to 273 Celsius degrees below the ice point), its volume would disappear or become insignificant (Fig. 21.4). Actually, however, all gases that have been tested are found to liquefy before the temperature −273°C is reached, and then the gas

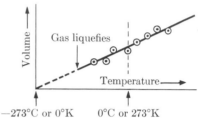

Fig. 21.4. The change in volume of a gas at constant pressure is proportional to the change in temperature.

laws are no longer applicable. This seemingly lowest attainable temperature has, however, proved to be important in another way. For if −273°C (or, more accurately, −273.15°C) is made the *absolute zero point* of a new temperature system, to be called the *absolute system*, it follows from the aforementioned linear relation that the volume of a gas is directly proportional to the absolute temperature. Denoting temperatures expressed in the absolute system by the symbol T, we have

$$V \propto T, \quad \text{or} \quad V/T = \text{a constant (for a fixed mass of}$$
$$\text{gas under constant pressure),} \quad (21.3)$$

which is a more general and useful form of the law of Charles and Gay-Lussac than is Eq. (21.2).

The absolute scale of temperature may be thought of as the Celsius scale with −273°C redesignated as 0° abs; the two scales are shown side by side in Fig. 21.5. It is clear that an interval of 1° on the Celsius scale corresponds to an interval of 1° on the absolute scale. In honor of Lord Kelvin, 19th-century contributor to the theory of heat, the symbol °K is used for temperatures on the absolute scale. Therefore a given temperature of t°C is equal to $(t + 273)$°K. For example, 0°C is 273°K, 21°C (a common room temperature) is 294°K, the boiling point of water is 373°K, and a temperature *difference* of one degree in the Kelvin system is just as large as a one-degree interval in the Celsius system. Note that the absolute system does away with the need for using negative numbers to indicate temperatures in discussing heat phenomena.

EXAMPLE 21.2. In Fig. 21.3, suppose that the volume of the confined gas is 500 cm³ when the temperature is 21.0°C. What will the volume become if the temperature is raised to 42.0°C and there is no change in the atmospheric pressure?

Solution. Here $V_1 = 500$ cm³, $T_1 = 294°K$, $V_2 = ?$, $T_2 = 315°K$. According to the law of Charles and Gay-Lussac (Eq. 21.3), $V/T = a$ constant, therefore $V_2/T_2 = V_1/T_1$, or $V_2 = V_1T_2/T_1 = 500$ cm³ $\times$ $315°K/294°K = 536$ cm³.

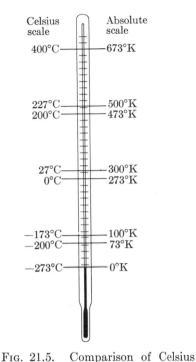

Celsius scale — Absolute scale

400°C — 673°K

227°C — 500°K
200°C — 473°K

27°C — 300°K
0°C — 273°K

−173°C — 100°K
−200°C — 73°K

−273°C — 0°K

FIG. 21.5.   Comparison of Celsius and absolute systems. The temperature in the absolute system is simply 273° more than it is in the Celsius system.

PROBLEM 21.2. In Fig. 21.4 are plotted the observed volumes and corresponding temperatures for a sample of air kept at constant pressure. Within the limits of experimental error, does the graph indicate that (a) $\Delta V/\Delta t =$ constant? (b) $\Delta V/\Delta T =$ constant? (c) $V/t =$ constant? (d) $V/T =$ constant? The symbols t and T denote temperature expressed in the ordinary Celsius and absolute systems, respectively.

21.4 The general gas law. Two laws for gases are now available, Eqs. (21.1) and (21.3), and a mathematical step serves to combine these laws in a single, more general statement. Since we have $V \propto 1/P$ (for constant T), which is one way of writing Boyle's law, and $V \propto T$ (for constant P), which is the law of Charles and Gay-Lussac, it follows that V is *jointly* proportional to $1/P$ and T, or $V \propto T/P$. Any statement of proportionality can be converted to equation form by introducing a constant of proportionality. In the present instance, let this constant be represented by the symbol r. Then we have $V = r \cdot T/P$, or

$$PV/T = r, \qquad\qquad (21.4)$$

which is a more general law than Boyle's or Gay-Lussac's, and incorporates both. Indeed, Eq. (21.4) is one form of the so-called "general gas law" or "equation of state of a gas." The value of the constant r depends on the mass of the sample and the kind of gas under test. Evidently r can be computed for any particular gas if any one set of simultaneously occurring values of P, V, and T for the sample are known. Once r is determined, the whole history, past or future, for this sample is uncovered through Eq. (21.4); for example, for any condition of pressure and volume, the temperature is at once known.

PROBLEM 21.3. It is known that 2.0 gm of hydrogen gas occupies 22.4 liters ($= 2.24 \times 10^{-2}$ m^3) when under so-called *standard conditions* of temperature and pressure (STP), that is, under a pressure of 1 atm ($= 1.013 \times 10^5$ new/m^2) and at a temperature of 0°C ($= 273.16$°K). (a) Show that the value of r for this 2.0-gm sample is 8.3 j/°K. (b) What volume will the 2.0-gm sample of hydrogen occupy when under a pressure of 9.0 atm and at room temperature (21°C)? (c) Compute r for 1.0 gm of hydrogen gas.

PROBLEM 21.4. At a time when the temperature is 15°C, an automobile tire is pumped up until the tire gauge registers 29.4 lb/in^2 (2.0 atm). If, in driving, the temperature of the tire rises to 65°C, what pressure will the gauge now indicate? Assume that the volume of the confined air does not change appreciably and that the outside atmospheric pressure remains at 1.0 atm. (*Note:* A tire gauge indicates *gauge pressure*, which is the pressure exerted by the gas in *excess* of atmospheric pressure. It should be carefully noted that in Eqs. (21.1) and (21.4) the pressure P is the total pressure.

PROBLEM 21.5. The tops of tanks for the storage of natural gas can move up and down to change the inside volume. In such a tank the pressure exerted by the gas is observed to be 2.0 atm above atmospheric pressure, when the volume is 1000 m^3 and the temperature is -10°C. What will be the total pressure if the volume is increased to 2000 m^3 and the temperature is raised to 27°C?

21.5 Two gas models. We are immediately tempted to interpret the quantitative observations on gases and the general gas law which summarizes them in terms of some model or structure. Even the qualitative observation that all gases are highly compressible and expandable (the "spring of the air") demanded some special explanation. Boyle himself, in 1660, described two opposing explanations, both in the form of models and both atomistic, for he and his contemporaries had begun to accept atomism as part of the rising materialistic world view. The opposing explanations he presented may be called (a) the *static* and (b) the *kinetic* models:

(a) If a gas consists of contiguous particles at rest, the large compressibility of gases demands that the corpuscles must themselves be compressible, rather like little springs or, as Torricelli preferred, like pieces of wool. (b) If, on the other hand, the corpuscles of the gas do not touch at all times, they need be neither variable in size themselves nor capable of existing as a static assembly, but then they must be in violent agitation, whirling through all available space, and perhaps embedded in an all-pervading and turbulent though "subtle" fluid. We recall that the notion of a subtle fluid, proposed by Descartes to account for the motion of planets, had soon captured the imagination throughout Europe, and it did seem to explain qualitatively the behavior of gases well enough. Indeed, Boyle tried to find experimental evidence for the existence of this subtle fluid, separated from the particles on which it supposedly acted, thus marking the start of a 250-year futile search for direct evidence that ethereal fluids existed.

In the static model the springlike elasticity assumed for the particles could not easily account for one very conspicuous property of gases, namely their ability to expand indefinitely in all directions, without the additional assumption that each atom itself was capable of growing in size without limit during the expansion. But this seemed fantastic; a pile of ordinary springs resists compression but does not disperse continuously when the compressing force is removed. Therefore some followers of the static view felt it necessary to advance the new assumption that the gas corpuscles did not greatly change in size, but instead were capable of repelling one another at a distance. Evidently this meant that some special new agency of repulsion, some new force among gas atoms, would have to be invented. It could not be a gravitational force, for that was always found to be attractive, at least for large bodies; moreover, the assumption of an attractive gravitational force between the particles comprising *solids* and *liquids* was being used to explain why matter in both of these states holds together instead of expanding without limit as does a gas.

Newton, in the *Principia*, lent some aid to the static picture; he did not suggest a physical agency that would cause repulsion, but he demonstrated mathematically that *if* a sample of gas consists of mutually repulsive particles, and *if* the force of repulsion between any two particles is *inversely proportional* to the distance between their centers, then it follows that the gas pressure in this sample must be inversely proportional to the volume. Thus the two assumptions lead to a prediction that is in accordance with Boyle's empirical law.

Newton did not intend this as proof that gases actually conform to his model; he wrote, "But whether elastic fluids do really consist of particles so repelling each other, is a physical question" (one that must be settled by appeal to experience). As a matter of fact, it can be shown that if the force between pairs of gas particles were repulsive and inversely proportional to the distance between them, then the pressure in the gas could be changed simply by changing the shape of the containing vessel and nothing else; but this is not borne out by observation. Moreover, if there were forces between gas particles, then a gas, when allowed to expand into a vacuum, should change its temperature by virtue of the interchangeability between the potential energy and the thermal energy of the particles; this, too, is not in accord with experience. Nevertheless, although it was more of a mathematical exercise than a physical argument, Newton's was the first *quantitative* deduction pertaining to the behavior of gases on the basis of any atomistic hypothesis, and it appears to have made a strong impression.

If it had not been for the apparently inescapable hold that the notion of an all-pervading ether had on the thinking of the time, the *second* or kinetic view of the structure of gases might have been formulated without recourse to a subtle, turbulent fluid to account for the motion of the particles. For it had been the opinion of the Greek atomists that the particles comprising matter, especially those of air, are "ever passing about in the great void," just as minute specks of dust can be seen dancing irregularly in a sunbeam that pierces a darkened room. If it had been objected that such incessant motion of corpuscles on their own is impossible, then it could have been pointed out that the eternal turbulence of the ether, as in Descartes' vortices, is open to the same objection.

21.6 Bernoulli's model. In 1738, the great Swiss physicist Daniel Bernoulli (1700–1782) published a description of a model for gases that was not only quantitative in character but did not invoke the notion of any ethereal fluid. He thought the "corpuscles" of a gas to be so minute that they were "practically infinite in number" under ordinary conditions, even in a small container. In their rapid motion hither and thither these corpuscles collide with one another and also with the walls of the vessel. Bernoulli assumed these collisions to be perfectly elastic; therefore, as we would put it today, the total kinetic energy of the particles is conserved, and their motion can continue undiminished and indefinitely. The pressure that a gas exerts on all the walls of the container is thus considered to be the result of the incessant impacts of billions of high-speed particles; hence the name *impact theory* of gas pressure for this type of explanation.

Suppose now that a gas is enclosed in a cylinder equipped with a piston (Fig. 21.6) and that the piston is slowly pushed down. The corpuscles will crowd together more and more as the volume occupied by the gas progressively decreases and the number of collisions per second with the walls correspondingly increases. In consequence the pressure should become greater, as actually is observed. Bernoulli even calculated the magnitude of this expected increase and found that it corresponded with the predictions from Boyle's experimental law. Then he continued:

The elasticity of air [the pressure it exerts on the container walls] is not only increased by . . . [decrease of volume] but by heat supplied to it, and since it is admitted that heat may be considered as an increasing internal motion of the particles, it follows that if the elasticity of air of which the volume does not change is increased [by warming the air], this indicates a more intense motion in the particles of air; which fits in well with our hypothesis . . .

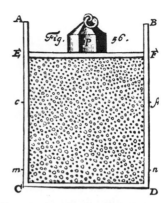

FIG. 21.6. Gas model, from Daniel Bernoulli's *Hydrodynamica* of 1738. The piston *EF* carries the weight of *P*, and moves down until the downward force is balanced by the impact of the high-speed gas particles on the underside of the piston.

Bernoulli's kinetic model and this line of reasoning anticipated work that more than a century later clarified and brought together some basic problems concerning gases, heat, and chemical phenomena. Why this model received little attention for such a long time is not entirely clear. Although Bernoulli's theory was incomplete for want of certain concepts and data that were not available until after his day, he nevertheless made two enormous advances in scientific thought that figuratively put him more than three generations ahead of his time. First, he recognized the equivalence between heat and mechanical energy, as in his hypothesis that an increase in heat corresponds to an increase in the speed of the particles; and second, he conceived the possibility that a well-defined numerical relationship, such as Boyle's law, could be deduced from the chaotic picture of randomly moving particles. We may perhaps compare Bernoulli's insight to some quick, isolated, premature stab from a general front far through enemy lines, with no valuable strategic consequences until the whole main force has moved ahead to link up with this almost forgotten outpost.

We shall return to this model of gases as assemblies of moving particles, because eventually it was victorious. But first it will be helpful to turn to some chemical concepts and basic chemical properties of matter, for it is from the direction of the atomic theory of chemistry that the atomic theory of physical matter was most strongly advanced in its historical development.

ADDITIONAL PROBLEMS

21.6. Show that Eqs. (21.1), (21.2), and (21.3) are all derivable from, and special cases of, Eq. (21.4).

21.7. Sketch graphs representing the relations expressed by Eqs. (21.1), (21.2), (21.3), and (21.4).

21.8. In connection with Eq. (21.4) it was mentioned that the constant r for each sample depends on the mass of the sample and the kind of gas. Show that r is directly proportional to the mass of the gas. (*Hint:* Consider the change in pressure as gas at constant temperature is pumped into a rigid container.)

21.9. A small bubble is caught in a bend of the fuel line of an aircraft engine. At take-off, "standard" conditions of temperature and pressure prevail (see Problem 21.3), and the volume of the bubble is 3.0 mm^3. What will be the volume at an altitude where the pressure is 4.5×10^4 new/m^2 and the temperature in the line is 50°C?

21.10. In a mountain region where the atmospheric pressure is 0.7 atm, what is the actual pressure in an automobile tire if the tire gauge reads (a) zero, (b) 27 lb/in^2? (See the Note in Problem 21.4.)

21.11. Boyle's law is often written in the alternative form $P \cdot V = m \cdot$ constant, where m is the mass of the confined gas and the constant has a value that depends on the kind of gas and its temperature. In view of this equation and the definition of density (namely, mass per unit volume), show that Boyle's law can also be stated in the form: *under isothermal conditions the pressure in a gas is proportional to the density and is independent of the mass of the gas.*

SUPPLEMENTARY READING

CONANT, J. B., *Robert Boyle's experiments in pneumatics* (Harvard University Press, 1950); also in *Harvard case histories in experimental science* (Harvard University Press, 1957).

GREGORY, J. C., *A short history of atomism* (A. and C. Black, London, 1931), Chaps. 1–6.

MAGIE, W. F., *A source book in physics* (McGraw-Hill, 1935). Selections from Torricelli, Boyle, Mariotte, Gay-Lussac, Bernoulli, and Kelvin.

NEWMAN, J. R., *The world of mathematics* (Simon and Schuster, 1956), pp. 771–777, Bernoulli's kinematic theory of gases.

CHAPTER 22

DALTON'S ATOMIC THEORY OF CHEMISTRY

22.1 The chemical elements and atoms. From antiquity to the beginning of the 19th century the words "atom," "corpuscle," "particle," and the like were used more or less interchangeably to refer to invisibly small and indivisible constituent parts of objects. However, no conceptual scheme of either the structure of matter or the nature of heat that was even reasonably unambiguous and precise had emerged. While the assumption of the existence of atoms was attractive, the choice of details was wide.

Yet, between the publication of Robert Boyle's *Sceptical chymist* in 1661 and Lavoisier's death in 1794, there had developed a basic concept that was destined to play a vital role in rendering the atomic hypothesis more precise. This was the concept of *chemical element*. Boyle had proposed that chemistry must be built on an identification and knowledge of those chemical substances *that cannot be separated into different components by any means*. No other substances, Boyle maintained, were worthy of the suggestive and ancient name "element":

> And to prevent mistakes I must advertize you, that I now mean by elements, as these chymists that speak plainest do by their principles, certain primitive and simple, or perfectly unmingled bodies; which not being made of any other bodies, or of one another, are the ingredients of which all those call'd perfectly mixed bodies are immediately compounded, and into which they are ultimately resolved: . . . (*Sceptical chymist*)

By the end of the 18th century this idea had indeed finally proved to be the sound basis for explaining such chemical reactions as combustion. Lavoisier himself, in the preface to the *Elements of chemistry* (1789), had written this revealing and, in part, quite modern analysis of the concept "element" and of its relation to the atomistic hypothesis of his predecessors:

> . . . if, by the term *elements*, we mean to refer to those simple and indivisible atoms of which matter is composed, it is extremely probable we know nothing at all about them; but, if we apply the term *elements* . . . to express our idea of the last point that [chemical] analysis is capable of reaching, we must admit, as elements, all substances into which, by any means, we can decompose bodies. Nothing entitles us to affirm that these substances we consider as simple may not be compounded of two, or even a larger number of principles; but, since these principles cannot be separated [from one another], or rather since we have not hitherto discovered the means of separating them, they act with regard to us as simple substances, and we ought never to suppose them compounded until experiment and observation have proved them to be so.

Some substances known since antiquity (for example, the more common metals and sulfur) were now being regarded as elements, and new ones were being similarly identified, bringing the total to about one-third of the elements known today. Of course, the list of "elements" included also many recalcitrant compounds that remained there until electrolysis and other powerful means of decomposition became available to separate their components. At that time "caloric" (heat substance) was also generally considered to be one of the chemical elements.

With the concept of element well established, a natural question was whether an atomistic hypothesis is useful in explaining the existence of the elements and their various properties. It is to this and related problems that we find the Englishman, John Dalton (1766–1844), devoting much of his energy from about 1800 onward. Dalton was largely self-taught. He was a retiring person, son of a humble hand-loom weaver, and he supported himself poorly as a teacher (as early as his twelfth year) and general tutor in Manchester. Dalton possessed a strong drive and a rich imagination, particularly along the line of mechanical models and clear mental pictures, but his great gift was an astonishing physical intuition which allowed him to arrive at useful conclusions despite being only "a coarse experimenter," as his contemporary Humphry Davy called him.*

22.2 Dalton's model of gases. Dalton's main work grew out of an interest in the *physical* properties and structure of gases. He said that through his interest in meteorology he had been led to wonder how the earth's atmosphere, which is a mixture of gases of greatly different densities (mainly nitrogen, oxygen, and water vapor), nevertheless could be so homogeneous. He found that air samples taken at different altitudes all had the same proportion of these components, whereas one might expect that nitrogen, being less dense than oxygen, would "float" on top of the latter, somewhat like oil on water.

Rumford would have had an answer to the puzzle, for in discussing an analogous example, that of mixed liquids, he pointed out how the individual particles, by their "peculiar and continual motion" (thermal agitation) may diffuse among one another and thus mix thoroughly. Dalton could not give such an answer, for he had adopted the static rather than the kinetic model of gases, being (wrongly) convinced that the great Newton had *proved* the validity of the static view in the brief passage from the *Principia* which we have discussed in Section 21.5.

---

*In preparing the remainder of this chapter we have relied heavily upon Leonard K. Nash's *The atomic-molecular theory* (*Harvard case histories in experimental science, No. 4*, Harvard University Press, 1950, reprinted in *Harvard case histories in experimental science*, 1957, v. 1, pp. 215–321) and his article "The origins of Dalton's chemical atomic theory," *Isis*, v. 47 (1956), pp. 101–116.

Dalton's rejection of the kinetic model of gas structure meant rejection also of the kinetic view of heat; Dalton held to the caloric theory, which in his day was still the generally accepted conceptual scheme for thermal phenomena. As for the problem of homogeneity of gas mixtures, this too he had to approach in terms of the static model of gases; he did so by adopting the following set of assumptions and lines of reasoning:

(a) *Each particle of a gas is surrounded by an atmosphere of caloric.* As Dalton put it in his main work, "A vessel full of any pure elastic fluid presents to the imagination a picture like one full of small shot. The globules are all of the same size; but the particles of the fluid differ from those of the shot, in that they are constituted of an exceedingly small central atom of solid matter, which is surrounded by an atmosphere of heat, of greater density next the atom, but gradually growing rarer according to some power of the distance." (*A new system of chemical philosophy*)

(b) *The caloric shells of adjacent atoms are in contact with one another* (see Fig. 22.1, top). To Dalton the only way in which one object could exert a force on another was by direct contact; the notion of attraction at a distance was as uncomfortable to him as it had been to most of Newton's contemporaries. Moreover, this picture of a "pile-of-shot" stacking of atoms which are essentially at rest assures that all space is filled.

(c) *All gas particles of any particular chemical substance have the same over-all diameter,* counting in the caloric atmosphere or shell, but *the particles of different gases have different over-all diameters.* This interest in the relative sizes of the atoms, while originally prominent in Dalton's thought, was later diverted to their relative *weights;* we shall see that relative weights were a far more fruitful subject of inquiry than were the sizes.

(d) Turning back to the initial problem, Dalton concluded that the nitrogen of the atmosphere does not

FIG. 22.1. Photograph of a page from Dalton's notebook, showing his representation of two adjacent atoms (top) and of a molecule or "compound atom" (bottom).

"float" on top of the oxygen because the neighboring particles of different sizes tend to push one another away through the mutual repulsion of their caloric shells until the mixture becomes homogeneous.

Every one of the assumptions (a) through (d) soon had to be abandoned, and some of them were found to be not even mutually consistent. Newton's discusssion of a static model of a gas was not a proof that it applied to actual gases. The caloric theory of heat, invoked by Dalton, was doomed to be overthrown. Dalton's own experiments were often inadequate to support his arguments, and his final conclusion did not even follow from the assumptions. Nevertheless, it was this study of the atmosphere that drew Dalton's attention *to the atom and its characteristics*, with the tremendously fruitful results to which we shall now turn.

22.3 Dalton's atoms and molecules. Dalton's treatise, *A new system of chemical philosophy*, was published in two parts, in 1808 and 1810. From that work and from other of his writings we can abstract the main postulates of what came to be known as Dalton's atomic theory of chemistry, a theory that was destined to become the foundation of modern chemical science:

(a) *Matter consists of indivisible atoms.* "Matter, though divisible in an *extreme degree*, is nevertheless not *infinitely* divisible. That is, there must be some point beyond which we cannot go in the division of matter. The existence of these ultimate particles of matter can scarcely be doubted, though they are probably much too small ever to be exhibited by microscopic improvements. I have chosen the word *atom* to signify these ultimate particles . . ."

(b) *Each element consists of a characteristic kind of identical atoms. there are consequently as many different kinds of atoms as there are elements;* The atoms of an element "are perfectly alike in weight and figure, etc." Here Dalton was simplifying beyond earlier atomists, who usually had felt it necessary to allow different-sized atoms for the same element, just as pebbles made of the same material might have different sizes and shapes.

(c) *Atoms are unchangeable.* The atoms of different elements "never can be metamorphosed, one into another, by any power we can control," as the failure of centuries of alchemy had made clear. This was a postulate of impotence (see Section 20.6); no one had been able to effect a transmutation of elements, for example a change of iron into gold.

(d) *When different elements combine to form a compound, the smallest portion of the compound consists of a grouping of a definite number of atoms of each element.* Dalton called these smallest portions of a compound the "compound atoms," but today they are called *molecules*. Speaking of carbonic acid as an example, Dalton said that each of its compound atoms "may be divided, yet it [then] ceases to be carbonic acid, being resolved by such division into charcoal [carbon] and oxygen." He thought of a "compound atom" (molecule) as "globular" in shape, with the two or more atoms comprising it "retained in physical contact by a strong affinity and supposed to be surrounded by a common atmosphere of heat." (See Fig. 22.1, lower diagram.)

(e) *In chemical reactions, atoms are neither created nor destroyed, but only rearranged:*

Chemical analysis and synthesis go no farther than to the separation of particles from one another and to their reunion . . . We might as well attempt to introduce a new planet into the solar system, or to annihilate one already in existence, as to create or destroy a particle of hydrogen.

From postulates (c) and (e) taken together, we may deduce that whenever two or more elements combine chemically, the sum of the masses of the elements is equal to the mass of the resulting compound. Thus the principle of conservation of mass, which Lavoisier previously had postulated and tested experimentally (Section 16.5), attained a simple physical interpretation and found a place as an integral part of Dalton's hypothesis.

22.4 Dalton's ideographs and modern symbols. To think and write about chemical processes, Dalton invented simple but ingenious ideographs, shown in Fig. 22.2. The alchemists had represented different substances by different symbols, but Dalton's ideographs represented *individual atoms* and combinations of individual atoms. Thus 1 through 20 in Fig. 22.2 represent the atoms of different elements: the first six symbols represent atoms of hydrogen, nitrogen, carbon, oxygen, phosphorus, and sulfur, respectively. Comparison with the modern list would show that some of Dalton's "elements" are now known to be compounds, but Dalton had to classify them as elements because, to his knowledge, no one had been able to separate them into component substances.

The symbols from 21 on stand for molecules of compounds whose component elements had been determined. For example, 21 represents a molecule of water, which he considered to be a *binary* compound whose molecules ("compound atoms") are made up of one atom of hydrogen and one of oxygen. Number 22 is a molecule of ammonia, its component atoms being "one of azote [the then current name for nitrogen] and one of hydrogen." Among the *ternary* compounds (having three atoms to the molecule) is 26, nitrous oxide, still called thus, although the name "laughing gas" may be more familiar. Number 28 is "carbonic acid," now called carbon dioxide. In the same fashion, Dalton pictured other molecules believed to consist of four, five, or some larger number of atoms.

In 1819 the Swedish chemist Berzelius proposed a system of chemical symbols that soon replaced Dalton's and is essentially the one in use today. Letters represent the atoms: H, for hydrogen; O, for oxygen; N, nitrogen;

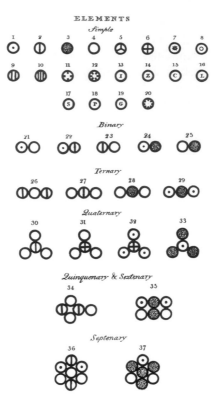

FIG. 22.2. Dalton's ideographs as shown in his *New system of chemical philosophy*. Each numbered sign is identified in a list (not shown), the upper three rows representing atoms, the remaining rows representing "compound atoms" or molecules.

Cl, chlorine; Fe (from the Latin *ferrum*), iron; etc. The full list appears in Appendix C. As for molecules, these are represented simply by joining the symbols for the particular atoms involved: HCl for hydrogen chloride (hydrochloric acid); NaCl for sodium chloride (table salt); CO_2 for carbon dioxide (one atom of carbon and two of oxygen in each molecule); NaOH for sodium hydroxide (one atom of sodium, one of oxygen, and one of hydrogen).

Chemical *reactions* may also be represented by means of these symbols. For example, the burning of carbon to form carbon dioxide may be symbolized by $C + O + O \rightarrow COO$ or, more compactly, CO_2. Of course, Dalton's symbols could have been similarly used: ⊛ + ○ + ○ → ○⊛○.

22.5 The law of definite proportions. During several decades preceding the publication of Dalton's treatise more and more accurate chemical data were gradually being collected. One result was the sharpening of various notions, for example the distinction between compounds and mixtures. Another was the formulation in 1797, by the French chemist J. L. Proust, of an extremely important and fruitful generalization now known as the *law of definite proportions,* meaning "definite proportions with respect to weight." The law of definite proportions holds that *the proportions by weight in which the elements enter into any given compound are invariable,* no matter in what locality the compound is found, or whether it is prepared artificially or taken from nature. For example, in the formation of water, hydrogen and oxygen will unite without leaving any free hydrogen or free oxygen only when the weight of hydrogen bears to the weight of oxygen one definite proportion, namely 1 to 8, to quote the approximate value accepted today.

This rule, whose usefulness was established in a wide range of experiments, was immediately found to be explainable in terms of Dalton's atomic-molecular theory and, through this achievement, the theory itself was further strengthened. From Dalton's postulates it follows that all the atoms of any given element have the same weight, and that the molecules of any particular compound are always of the same atomic composition. For example, if elements A and B combine to form a compound, each molecule is symbolized by $A_a B_b$, where a is the constant number of A-atoms and b is the constant number of B-atoms in a molecule of the compound. Evidently, the relative weights of the two elements needed to complete the synthesis of compound $A_a B_b$ is given by

$$\frac{\text{wt. of element A in a sample}}{\text{wt. of element B in same sample}} = \frac{a \times \text{wt. of one atom of A}}{b \times \text{wt. of one atom of B}}. \qquad (22.1)$$

The weights in the term on the left may be readily determined by weighing the quantity of each element separately, either before the reaction (thus obtaining the "combining weights") or afterwards by decomposing the sample into its constituent elements. But in Dalton's time *none of the factors on the right-hand side were directly determinable.*

If we *assume,* as Dalton did, that a water molecule consists of one atom of hydrogen and one of oxygen, then $a = 1$, $b = 1$, and the molecular formula is HO. It follows from the experimentally determined ratio of $\frac{1}{8}$ for the combining weights of these elements in water and from Eq. (22.1) that

$$\frac{1}{8} = \frac{1 \times \text{wt. of hydrogen atom}}{1 \times \text{wt. of oxygen atom}};$$

that is, an oxygen atom weighs 8 times as much as a hydrogen atom. On the other hand, if the molecular constitution of a water molecule is assumed to be not HO but H_2O (that is, $a = 2$, $b = 1$, and $H + H + O \rightarrow H_2O$), then

$$\frac{1}{8} = \frac{2 \times \text{wt. of H-atom}}{1 \times \text{wt. of O-atom}}$$

or

$$\frac{1}{16} = \frac{\text{wt. of H-atom}}{\text{wt. of O-atom}}.$$

In that case, the oxygen atom weighs 16 times as much as the hydrogen atom. Other assumptions concerning the values of a and b yield correspondingly different ratios of atomic weights or *relative atomic* weight, if we arbitrarily decide to measure all atomic weights on a scale on which 1 is assigned, say, to the hydrogen atom.

The experimentally determined combining weights by themselves afford no clue as to whether the molecular constitution is given by HO, H_2O, HO_2, or, for that matter, $H_{22}O_7$. How are we to make a choice? If we are to obtain relative atomic weights, we must have a criterion for deciding on the molecular formula. And this criterion, one which by necessity could not be based on direct experimental evidence, was contained in Dalton's next proposal (Section 22.6).

EXAMPLE 22.1. Upon decomposing a 5.0-gm sample of ammonia gas into its component elements, nitrogen and hydrogen, 4.2 gm of nitrogen were obtained. *Assuming* that the molecular formula for ammonia is NH_2, find the weight of a nitrogen atom relative to that of a hydrogen atom.
Solution. Here,

$$\frac{\text{wt. of nitrogen in sample}}{\text{wt. of hydrogen in sample}} = \frac{4.2 \text{ gm}}{(5.0 - 4.2) \text{ gm}} = \frac{4.2}{0.8} = 5.25; \quad a = 1, \quad b = 2.$$

Substituting in Eq. (22.1), we have

$$5.25 = \frac{1}{2} \times \frac{\text{wt. of N-atom}}{\text{wt. of H-atom}},$$

or the weight of the nitrogen atom is 10.5 times that of a hydrogen atom. (Note that this calculation is based on the assumption that the molecule of ammonia is NH_2. This will turn out to be an incorrect assumption; the correct formula is NH_3.)

PROBLEM 22.1. (a) Suppose that in Example 22.1 the molecular formula of the ammonia atom is assumed to be, not NH_2, but NH, or NH_3, or N_3H. What does the ratio of atomic weights turn out to be in each of these cases? (b) How much nitrogen and how much hydrogen is needed to make 1.2 kgm of ammonia gas?
PROBLEM 22.2. A 1.00-gm sample of nitric oxide gas, after separation into its components, is found to have contained 0.47 gm of nitrogen. As is ordinarily done

in modern practice, assign to the atomic weight of oxygen the number 16. Then find the corresponding number that expresses the atomic weight of nitrogen relative to oxygen on the assumption that the molecular formula of nitric oxide is (a) NO, (b) NO_2, (c) N_2O.

22.6 Dalton's rule of simplicity. Clearly the knowledge of molecular constitutions was the missing link for both the determination of relative weights of atoms and the understanding of chemical reactions. To find a way out of this difficulty, Dalton added to his conceptual scheme a new *postulate* which stands as typical of the advantages and dangers of any hypothesis. It may be called *the rule of greatest simplicity:*

> When only one combination of two bodies [elements] can be obtained, it must be assumed to be a binary one, unless some other cause appears to the contrary ... When two combinations are observed, they must be presumed to be a binary and a ternary ...

Similarly, the simplest formulas were presumed to apply when more than two "combinations" (compounds) of the same elements are obtained.

Specifically, *water* was believed to be the only existing combination of hydrogen and oxygen (hydrogen peroxide, another compound of these two elements, had not been identified); thus, in accord with the rule of simplicity Dalton regarded water as a binary compound and therefore representable by the formula HO. For carbon and oxygen, *two* combinations were known; to the less dense of these two gases (the highly poisonous gas now called *carbon monoxide*) the molecular formula CO was assigned, and to the other one (now called *carbon dioxide*) the formula CO_2. The formula NH was assigned to ammonia, the most common compound of nitrogen and hydrogen. Ethylene and methane were given the formulas CH and CH_2 (present-day assignments are C_2H_4 and CH_4).

One brief glance at a modern list of molecular formulas suffices to convince us that Dalton's rule of simplicity did not stand the test of time. For example, the only known compound of iron and iodine, iron iodide, according to present theory is not binary but has the formula FeI_2. The simplest compound of iron and chlorine is not represented by FeCl but by $FeCl_2$. The formulas for the common oxides of iron are not FeO, FeO_2, and Fe_2O, as Dalton might have expected, but are FeO, Fe_2O_3, and Fe_3O_4.

However, in some important cases, such as for the carbon oxides and nitrogen oxides, Dalton's rule led to the modern formulas. And in most other cases, the analytic data available to Dalton were too inaccurate and ambiguous to show that the rule could lead to contradictions of the type to be shown in Problem 22.3. Indeed, this circumstance may have been fortunate, for Dalton's devotion to the ancient notion of the inherent simplicity of natural phenomena did make possible a start, and a fruitful one, toward the establishment of molecular formulas. When some early guess about a molecular formula led to contradictions in later work, the guess could then be improved upon, exemplifying again the dictum that through devoted work, truth can come out of error more easily than out of chaos.

PROBLEM 22.3. The three iron phosphides to which one would have to give the formulas FeP_2, FeP, and Fe_2P according to Dalton's rule of simplicity have the following experimental combining weights of iron and phosphorus: 55.9 gm with 31.0 gm, 111.8 gm with 31.0 gm, and 167.7 gm with 31.0 gm. (a) Compare the relative atomic weights of iron and phosphorus as obtained from Dalton's assumptions and data in each case. (b) Obtain the relative atomic weights on the modern assumption that the molecular formulas of these three compounds are FeP, Fe_2P, and Fe_3P.

22.7 The law of multiple proportions. Dalton's theory helped to guide him to the formulation of a new and extraordinarily striking insight which was immediately borne out by experiment: *Whenever two elements combine to form more than one compound, that is, combine in more than one proportion by weight, these different proportions always bear simple ratios to one another.* This is the *law of multiple proportions.* That it follows by necessity from the postulates of Dalton's theory is easily shown. For example, let a molecule of each of the two gases known today as carbon monoxide (CO) and carbon dioxide (CO_2) be pictured in Dalton's manner (see Nos. 25 and 28, Fig. 22.2), namely by ○◉ (carbon monoxide) and ○◉○ (carbon dioxide). If a sample of each gas were decomposed into the two constituent elements, we would clearly expect to find that a given weight of carbon is associated with twice as much oxygen by weight in the second case as compared with the first. In other words, Dalton's atomic theory suggests that for a given weight of carbon, the weight of oxygen in the second gas is to the weight of oxygen in the first gas as 2 is to 1.

The supporting data for the experimental test of this prediction actually were available before Dalton's time, although their meaning had not been suspected. They appeared in about the form suggested by the following example.

EXAMPLE 22.2. For carbon monoxide, the weights of the oxygen and carbon were found to be, respectively, 57% and 43% of the total weight of the sample; that is, the weight of oxygen relative to that of carbon was 57/43, or close to 4/3, in one of the substances formed by the two elements. In the other substance, carbon dioxide, the amounts by weight of oxygen and carbon were 73% and 27%, thus giving a relative weight of 73/27, or close to 8/3. Therefore the *ratio* of these proportions, which gives the relative amount by weight of oxygen in the two compounds, was (8/3)/(4/3) or 2:1—a simple ratio of whole numbers, as expected on the basis of the law of multiple proportions.

According to the law of multiple proportions, the ratio so obtained was expected to be formed by small integers in all other cases also. Some confirmation was obtained in new experiments by Dalton himself, in addition to the confirmations that now became evident in previously published work. One could say that the facts had been readily available, but that the simplicity of the relation among them had remained unnoticed until there was good reason to look for it. As previously noted, we cannot see much without having hypotheses as a guide in forming perceptions; in this sense the saying "seeing is believing" might well be replaced by "believing is seeing."

The discovery of the law of multiple proportions stimulated a great deal of new research. Given any one proportion of combining weights for two elements, an investigator could now predict the composition of other possible compounds of the same elements. However, it should be noted that this rule of "simple" ratios is known today to have limited applicability. In particular, the molecules of organic compounds, most of which were inaccessible to study in Dalton's day, may each consist of several dozens of atoms of a few elements. For example, the ratio of carbon-to-hydrogen proportions for the two organic compounds $C_{23}H_{22}O_6$ and $C_{22}H_{42}O_3$ obviously is not a simple one.

PROBLEM 22.4. Nitrous oxide, one compound of nitrogen and oxygen, is found upon decomposition to yield 64% of nitrogen by weight; another, nitric oxide, is 47% nitrogen by weight. For each compound, compute the weight of nitrogen relative to that of oxygen. Do the results bear out the law of multiple proportions?

PROBLEM 22.5. If it is established that the combining weights of hydrogen gas and oxygen gas is 1:8 for water, how many grams of each gas would you use in searching for the possible synthesis of another compound of these elements? Give several possibilities, but note that only one of these exists in actual fact as a stable compound, reminding us that the law of multiple proportions does not point out which of the possibilities do or do not exist in nature. (Nor does the law indicate whether a compound can be made by a *direct* combination; in this case, it is not possible.)

PROBLEM 22.6. In the following table are listed Dalton's data of 1810 for five different gases that are compounds of nitrogen and oxygen (the names in the table are Dalton's and those in quotation marks do not agree with modern usage). To the least dense of these, "nitrous gas," Dalton assigned the molecular

Compound	Relative density	Percentages by weight	
		Nitrogen	Oxygen
"Nitrous gas" (NO)	12.1	42.1	57.9
Nitrous oxide	17.2	59.3	40.7
"Nitric acid"	19.1	26.7	73.3
"Oxynitric acid"	26.1	19.5	80.5
"Nitrous acid"	31.2	32.7	67.3

formula NO (or rather $\oplus \bigcirc$). (a) On the basis of Dalton's data and hypotheses, decide on the molecular formula for each of the remaining four gases. (b) Do these data for the five gases provide confirmation of the law of multiple proportions?

22.8 Atomic weights.   Another achievement of Dalton's theory, one without which modern chemistry would be unimaginable, was the start toward the determination of atomic weights. In Dalton's words, "Now it is one great object of this work, to shew the importance and advantage of ascertaining the relative weights of the ultimate particles, . . ." How the relative weights of the atoms of the various elements were to be computed is already clear to us from the discussion of Eq. (22.1) and the rule of greatest simplicity that helped Dalton to assign molecular formulas that tell us the number of atoms of each element in a molecule of a specific compound. When the proportions by weight in which each element enters into the compound is measured, everything in Eq. (22.1) is known except the ratio of the weights of the two atoms, and this can be computed. For example, using the data given in Problem 22.6 and assuming that the first compound has a formula NO, we can make five different computations of the ratio of the weight of an atom of nitrogen to the weight of an atom of oxygen, and all five turn out to be approximately 6/8.2 (modern data yield the value $\frac{7}{8}$). As one more example, Dalton synthesized water and found the combining proportions by weight of the elements hydrogen and oxygen to be 1:6 (later, improved data yielded 1:7; today the accepted value is about 1:8). As the molecular formula for water Dalton had adopted the simplest possible one, HO; therefore the relative weights of the two atoms was believed to be 1:6.

By making compromises among various results of this sort, Dalton assembled a table of the most probable values for the relative atomic weights of most of the elements known to him.   To make the table less complicated and easier to interpret, he assigned the arbitrary value of unity to the weight of the lightest atom, that of hydrogen, and then referred all other values to this. Thus one of his early tables (1808) listed the following relative atomic weights: hydrogen, 1; nitrogen, 5; carbon, 5; oxygen, 7; phosphorus, 9; sulfur, 13.

PROBLEM 22.7.   Early data yielded 6/8.2 for the weight ratio of nitrogen and oxygen atoms, and 1/7 for the weight ratio of hydrogen and oxygen atoms. Show that these results lead to a value of 5 for the relative atomic weight of nitrogen, provided that the value 1 is assigned to hydrogen.

As can be seen from a modern list of elements (Appendix D), our present reference element is not hydrogen but oxygen. By a rather arbitrary convention, the element oxygen is assigned an atomic weight of 16.0000; in other words, atomic weights are now expressed in terms of a unit that is equivalent to $\frac{1}{16}$ the weight of the chemical atom of oxygen. In terms of this unit the atomic weight of hydrogen is 1.0080. (Note that relative atomic weights are numbers without units, and that the word "relative" is usually dropped.)

Dalton also tried to determine *molecular* weights, the weights of the molecules of compounds, by a simple extension of his previous argument: the molecular weight of any compound is equal to the sum of the atomic weights of all the atoms in a molecule of the compound.

PROBLEM 22.8. (a) The molecular formula for carbon dioxide is CO_2, and the atomic weights of carbon and oxygen, in terms of modern units, are 12.01 and 16.0000, respectively; show that the molecular weight of carbon dioxide is 44.00. (b) Using the atomic weights from Appendix D, compute the modern value for the molecular weight of methane, for which the formula is CH_4. (c) Similarly, compute the molecular weight of soda (sodium hydroxide, NaOH).

But Dalton soon found inconsistencies in atomic weight determinations and began to suspect that the rule of greatest simplicity was responsible. He even confessed doubt that water is a binary compound, and instead thought that it might be ternary (HO_2 or H_2O). By trying out various molecular formulas for each particular compound and gradually eliminating contradictions, Dalton might eventually have arrived at a set of atomic weights devoid of contradiction. But before this could occur, two discoveries were made, one in France and the other in Italy, that at once greatly simplified this task. They made possible the abandonment of Dalton's postulate of greatest simplicity which, while it had been essential in initiating the search for relative atomic weights, was gradually becoming more difficult to defend.

ADDITIONAL PROBLEMS

22.9. For each of the following statements, cite evidence that serves to support or deny it. (a) Dalton's chemical atom is the concept that provides a physical basis for the principle of conservation of mass and that connects the latter with the law of definite proportions. (b) Dalton did for the law of definite proportions what Newton had done for Kepler's laws of planetary motion.

22.10. Evaluate Dalton's theory of atoms and molecules from the point of view of our criteria for theories given in Chapter 8.

SUPPLEMENTARY READING

KNEDLER, J. W., *Masterworks of science* (Doubleday, 1947), pp. 247–272. Excerpts from Dalton.

LEICESTER, H. M., and H. S. KLICKSTEIN, *A source book in chemistry, 1400–1900* (McGraw-Hill, 1952), pp. 208–220. Selections from Dalton.

NASH, L. K., *The atomic-molecular theory* (Harvard University Press, 1950); also in *Harvard case histories of experimental science* (Harvard University Press, 1957), v. 1, pp. 215–321.

PAULING, L., *General chemistry* (Freeman, 2nd edition, 1956), pp. 145–155.

ROSCOE, SIR HENRY E., and A. HARDEN, *A new view of the origin of Dalton's atomic theory* (Macmillan, 1896).

CHAPTER 23

THE RISE OF MODERN CHEMISTRY

23.1 Gay-Lussac's law of combining volumes. In 1808 the French chemist and physicist, Joseph Louis Gay-Lussac (Fig. 23.1), took note of an earlier-published experiment in which water vapor had been produced by exploding a mixture of hydrogen and oxygen with an electric spark. When he saw that the data could be interpreted in terms of a beautifully simple *volumetric* relation, Gay-Lussac, a master experimenter, repeated the experiment. He found that 2 volumes of hydrogen combined with 1 volume of oxygen to form 2 volumes of water vapor, and because his experiment had been so carefully carried out, he could say that the ratio of the combining volumes of hydrogen and oxygen differed from 2 to 1 by no more than 0.1%. No such simplicity had been noted in the volumes of reacting liquids or solids.

Fig. 23.1. Joseph Louis Gay-Lussac (1778–1850).

391

Gay-Lussac knew that the physical properties of gases as a group have a characteristic simplicity and uniformity (recall the laws of Boyle and of Charles and Gay-Lussac, Chapter 21), and so he speculated whether other gases, and not just hydrogen and oxygen, also show simple proportions by volume in chemical reactions. This conjecture was borne out by his own careful experiments, as well as by analyses he made of data published by earlier experimenters: "It appears to me," he wrote, "that gases always combine in the simplest proportions [by volume] when they act on one another . . ."; furthermore, he noted, if the compound resulting from the chemical reaction remains a gas or vapor at the temperature of the experiment, the volume of the compound is also simply related to the volumes of the participating elements. We may write results of this kind as follows:

2 vol hydrogen gas + 1 vol oxygen gas → 2 vol water vapor,
1 vol nitrogen gas + 3 vol hydrogen gas → 2 vol ammonia gas,
1 vol nitrogen gas + 1 vol oxygen gas → 2 vol nitric oxide,
1 vol hydrogen gas + 1 vol chlorine gas → 2 vol hydrochloric acid gas,
2 vol carbon monoxide gas + 1 vol oxygen gas → 2 vol carbon dioxide gas.

To summarize, *reactive gases, under conditions of equal pressure and temperature, combine in simple volumetric proportions.*

When Gay-Lussac put forward this strikingly simple generalization, Dalton utterly rejected it, and held to this view to the very end, for several reasons. We recall that Dalton's model of gases for explaining the observed homogeneity of the atmosphere involved the assumption that the atoms of different elements are of different diameters, and that the atoms in a sample of gas are in contact with one another (along their caloric shells), completely filling the volume and with no empty space between them (Section 22.2). But to accept the validity of the law of combining volumes seemed to Dalton tantamount to accepting the notion that equal volumes of different kinds of gases (when at the same temperature and pressure) contain equal numbers of atoms or, in any event, multiples thereof; this in turn pointed to the possibility that the atoms of different elements do not differ in size. To have admitted this would have meant giving up his static model. Dalton took refuge in the results of his own volumetric experiments (actually, they were poorly done), which contradicted those of Gay-Lussac. Moreover, Gay-Lussac had admitted that owing to the unavoidable experimental uncertainties and errors in the raw data, his results in some cases fell short of simple whole-number volumetric relations by up to a few percent. To Dalton (who unwittingly had far larger margins of experimental error) this meant that the whole-number relations were of no significance. Actually, the discrepancies in Gay-Lussac's data were explainable and relatively small—a testimony to his skill, for it was not easy to measure gas volumes under conditions of constant pressure and temperature.

In this dispute about the validity of the law of combining volumes, we again see some typical features of the life of science: the search for simplicity and the difference of opinion as to what constitutes simplicity, the fascination integers hold for many scientists, the fact that every measurement involves some degree of uncertainty, and the extent to which a theory influences interpretation of experimental results.

23.2 Avogadro's model for gases. Despite its many successes, Dalton's theory of atoms and molecules could not at the time provide an interpretation of Gay-Lussac's empirical law of combining volumes. Moreover, it was found that this inadequacy could not be remedied merely by abandoning Dalton's postulate of different sizes for different atoms. Some additional amendment of the theory was needed. Such an amendment was offered in 1811 in an obscurely phrased essay by the Italian physicist, Amedeo Avogadro (Fig. 23.2). As a result, the atomic theory ultimately emerged stronger than ever and in approximately the form that it has today.

Fig. 23.2. Amedeo Avogadro (1776–1856).

Avogadro's main achievement was a revised model for gases. Our discussion of its features may, for convenience, be divided into four parts:

(a) *Particles are not in contact.* As had been persistently suggested by Gay-Lussac and others, Dalton's picture, in which the gas particles are in contact, was now replaced by one in which the particles are quite small compared with the distances between them; indeed, so small that they occupy only a negligible fraction of the total volume of any gas sample. It is a return, we might say, to the ancient "atom and void" picture of the gas.   In adopting this model, we must forego the expectation that any information on the relative diameters of the particles can be obtained from data on combining volumes; the volumes concerned are mostly empty space according to our model, and we can have no precise idea of what fraction is taken up by the atoms. But the problem of atomic sizes, so important to Dalton, plays no significant role in this new formulation.

(b) *Avogadro's "law."* A most important part of Avogadro's proposal is a postulate now generally referred to as Avogadro's hypothesis or law: *Under conditions of equal temperature and pressure, equal volumes of all gases—whether elements or compounds or even mixtures—contain equal numbers of particles.* This hypothesis or "law" has turned out to have a high degree of validity, although at the time it was little more than a thoughtful guess on Avogadro's part. But it had some puzzling and important implications. As a specific example, one that exhibits some typical features of scientific thinking, let us represent Gay-Lussac's experiment with water vapor by means of the diagram of Fig. 23.3. Each square represents a unit volume at some one temperature and pressure.

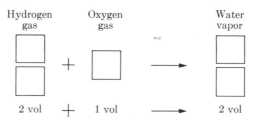

FIG. 23.3. Volume relation in Gay-Lussac's experiment on the formation of water vapor.

According to Avogadro's law, these equal volumes contain equal numbers of particles. For simplicity, imagine the volumes to be so small that each contains only one particle. Using Dalton's ideographs, we may try to represent this situation as in Fig. 23.4. But in following Dalton's conception of the structure of a molecule of water, namely that it is ⊙ O (or HO), we immediately obtain a self-contradictory result: we have pictured the reaction as beginning with *one* atom of oxygen and have ended with *two.*

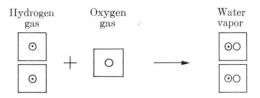

FIG. 23.4. Representation of the self-contradictory hypothesis.

This would appear to be a violation of the principle of conservation of mass, or at any rate of the axiom that an atom is not divisible. To find a way out of the difficulty, Avogadro was led to propose an additional postulate that was as bold as it was new.

(c) *Molecules of elements.* Dalton, and everyone else, had assumed that the gases of the elements were always composed of single atoms. Now Avogadro proposed as a second postulate that *at least for some elements the smallest particles were not single atoms but groups of atoms.* Heretofore we have reserved the term *molecule* to refer to the smallest unit into which a compound can be divided without changing its chemical properties. But now, following Avogadro, we investigate the possibility that many of the elements may also consist of molecules made of two (or more) atoms each. However, for a particular element the molecule consists of atoms of that element only, "united by attraction to form a single whole," whereas for a compound the molecule consists of atoms of at least two different elements.

Applying this postulate to the formation of water vapor, suppose we assume that each particle (molecule) of the gaseous element oxygen is diatomic, that is, consists of two oxygen atoms (OO or O_2). Then we have a particle that can be split without having to split the atom. The pictorial representation becomes that of Fig. 23.5; in modern symbols, this is written

$$2H + O_2 \rightarrow 2HO.$$

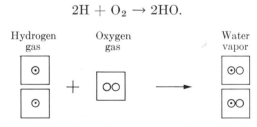

FIG. 23.5. Scheme for a consistent hypothesis.

It should be noted that this conception of the reaction is not self-contradictory, and is in accord with Gay-Lussac's experimental observation concerning the volumes obtained, with Dalton's choice that water is HO, and with Avogadro's law. Evidently the concept of the indivisible atom can be saved by the use of Avogadro's hypothesis that elements may have molecules made of more than one atom.

But at the same time, this hypothesis opens the way to a flood of new possibilities. For example, we must now consider whether perhaps the hydrogen molecule also is diatomic, and whether some elements have more than two atoms to one molecule. For example, it is in complete accord with Gay-Lussac's data, and with Avogadro's postulates given as in (b) and (c) above, to say that the formation of water vapor proceeds either according to the scheme or *reaction equation*

$$2H_3 + O_2 \rightarrow 2H_3O,$$

or to

$$2H + O_4 \rightarrow 2HO_2,$$

or to some other equation. (Here we have abandoned Dalton's choice that water molecules have two atoms, as we were prepared to do if necessary.) The fact is that Avogadro's postulates, applied to a particular reaction, do not suffice to determine uniquely which of many possible molecular formulas and reaction equations is actually involved.

PROBLEM 23.1. (a) Sketch a diagram similar to Fig. 23.5 that pictures the hypothetical reaction $2H_3 + O_2 \rightarrow 2H_3O$. Show that this possibility also does not necessitate splitting individual atoms. (b) Develop two reaction equations, in addition to the four given so far, which qualify to be considered for representing the formation of water in accord with Gay-Lussac's results and with Avogadro's postulates.

PROBLEM 23.2. What are the reasons for rejecting Dalton's reaction equation $H + O \rightarrow HO$ on the basis of Avogadro's law and Gay-Lussac's results? What were the reasons for rejecting the reaction equation $2H + O \rightarrow H_2O$?

PROBLEM 23.3. If it is assumed that hydrogen as well as oxygen has diatomic molecules, what then will be the simplest possible reaction equation and the molecular formula for water vapor?

PROBLEM 23.4. Using the information available to you so far, show that the oxygen molecule must contain an even number of atoms.

At this point it may appear that the acceptance of Avogadro's postulates would result in the sacrifice of the simplicity of Dalton's theory without gaining equivalent advantages, a step that seemed unreasonable to most of Avogadro's contemporaries. For example, in questioning Dalton's simple reaction equation, we have discovered several possible choices, any of which may be equally correct. Nevertheless, the situation is not hopeless. Certain of the alternatives can at once be excluded by considering how any particular gas enters into several different reactions. Let us again consider hydrogen which, according to another of Gay-Lussac's experiments, combines with nitrogen in the following volume relation:

3 vol hydrogen gas + 1 vol nitrogen gas → 2 vol ammonia gas.

An attempt to treat this graphically (as before) will show that the reaction cannot be pictured satisfactorily without assuming both nitrogen and hydrogen to be at least diatomic, so that the three hydrogen atoms may be split evenly among the two ammonia molecules (Fig. 23.6). The simplest possible reaction equation is therefore

$$3H_2 + N_2 \rightarrow 2NH_3.$$

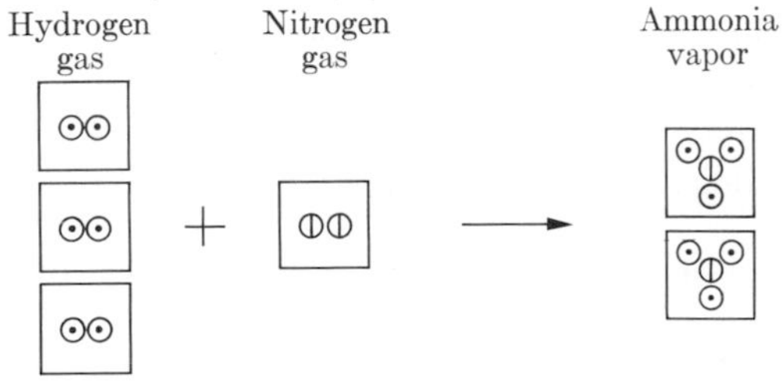

FIG. 23.6. Formation of ammonia vapor; the simplest of the possible representations.

The same type of argument rules out the possibility that hydrogen has 3, 5, 7, . . . atoms per molecule, but fails to show that it could not have 4, 6, 8, . . . atoms per molecule.

Returning to the problem of the formation of water vapor and adding the simplest assumption that is in accord with Gay-Lussac's experiments on ammonia vapor and Avogadro's postulates, namely that hydrogen molecules are diatomic, we obtain the possibility shown in Fig. 23.7, for which the reaction equation is

$$2H_2 + O_2 \rightarrow 2H_2O.$$

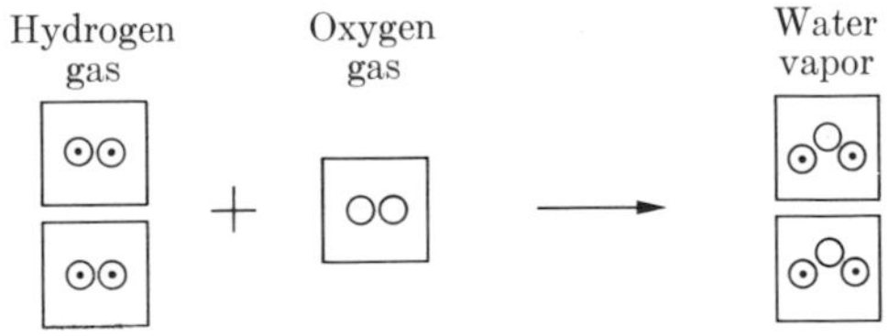

FIG. 23.7. The correct representation for the formation of water.

Of the possibilities thus far considered, the last is as yet the only one that fits both Avogadro's postulates and the observed way in which hydrogen gas enters into two separate chemical reactions.

(d) *Avogadro's rule of simplicity.* A number of other reaction equations would also meet the sort of requirements just mentioned, for example,

$2H_4 + O_6 \rightarrow 2H_4O_3$. But upon examining these we find that none is as *simple* as the process $2H_2 + O_2 \rightarrow 2H_2O$; that is, none involves such small integers. At this point Avogadro proposed a third postulate: if more than one assumed process is in harmony with both the experimental results and the other postulates of the theory, *choose as correct the one that is simplest.* On this basis we finally select as correct the process symbolized in Fig. 23.7.

Perhaps this step is a bit disappointing, because we may have hoped that Avogadro could do without an arbitrary rule of simplicity. However, there is this difference: Dalton's rule of simplicity (Section 22.6), by assigning molecular formulas on the basis of fairly incomplete data, soon led to conflicts, whereas Avogadro's rule of simplicity may be used as a final criterion of choice *after* all the known conflicts have been considered.

PROBLEM 23.5. List the experimental and theoretical steps (a) that led Dalton to choose HO as the molecular formula for water, and (b) that led us to choose H_2O as the formula. (c) In each case, was there any alternative formula that could be justified, and if so, why was it not chosen?

PROBLEM 23.6. Show that Avogadro's postulates, together with the experimentally determined relation

1 vol hydrogen gas + 1 vol chlorine gas → 2 vol hydrochloric acid gas,

lead to the conclusion that the molecules of hydrogen and chlorine cannot be monatomic, as was thought earlier, but must be at least diatomic.

PROBLEM 23.7. (a) Show that the expression $N_2 + O_2 \rightarrow 2NO$ is consistent with both Avogadro's postulates and Gay-Lussac's volumetric experiment on the formation of NO, nitric oxide (Section 23.1). (b) Why can we be sure that this reaction is not correctly described by the expression $N + O \rightarrow NO$? (c) Given that the production of nitrous oxide (N_2O) is described by the expression $2N_2 + O_2 \rightarrow 2N_2O$, what volumetric relation do you predict for this reaction?

23.3 Objections raised to Avogadro's views. Avogadro's work, unlike Dalton's, lay almost neglected for nearly half a century. This was partly due to the obscure manner of presentation and to a large admixture of dubious conclusions. But even the most valuable features of Avogadro's scheme were criticized or neglected, and often for reasons that seemed thoroughly plausible at the time:

(a) Avogadro gave no physical reason for the so-called Avogadro's law, other than that it helped to explain gaseous reactions. Dalton, on the other hand, could cite the features of his simple static model as providing plausible physical arguments for rejecting Avogadro's idea.

(b) In postulating that gaseous elements may have molecules of more than one atom, Avogadro could offer no mechanism to explain why chemically identical atoms in a gas would cling together only in, say, twos or threes. If like atoms had forces of attraction between them, why, it was asked, did not the whole bulk of the gas condense into a single cluster? On such grounds Dalton himself, in 1809, had rejected as absurd the notion that gaseous elements consisted of two or more atoms as their smallest "particles." Nor did others take more kindly to the notion.

After 1811, chemists began to think more and more of the stability of molecules such as those of water vapor as the result of positive or negative electric charges attached to the atoms of different elements. But from electrical studies it was known that electric charges of the same sign (+ and +, or − and −) repel one another. Therefore it was asked how two hydrogen atoms, which presumably would have charges of the same sign and so would repel each other, could be firmly bound together to form a hydrogen molecule. An answer to this question has become possible only within the last few decades.

(c) Avogadro's model of gases worked well at the outset for the only four elements known to exist in the gaseous form (nitrogen, oxygen, hydrogen, and chlorine) and for chemical reactions involving them, provided diatomic molecules for each were assumed. Later it became possible to experiment at the higher temperatures at which the elements mercury, phosphorus, arsenic, and sulfur also exist as gases, but for these Avogadro's scheme worked well only if the assumption were made that their molecules were *not* all diatomic—that, instead, the molecular formulas were Hg, P_4, As_4, and, depending on the temperature, S, S_2, S_6, and S_8. Why this diversity? Had Avogadro, while striving for simplicity, merely produced confusion? It took time to become accustomed to and to accept this profusion of possibilities.

(d) Although Avogadro, in his law, asserted that equal volumes of gases at the same temperature and pressure contain the same number of molecules, he did not provide a way for determining how many molecules were present. He merely suggested that the number was very large, even for ordinary volumes. Experiments in many separate branches of physical science since that time have indirectly yielded values that are in fairly close agreement. Thus, for a gas at 0°C and under a pressure of 1 atm, the presently accepted value is 2.69×10^{25} molecules per cubic meter. The methods for obtaining this numerical value—this incredibly large number of unimaginably small objects—will be given in Chapter 28.

23.4 Chemistry after Avogadro. Determination of molecular weights.

Some of the points mentioned in the previous section help to explain why Avogadro's work of 1811 lay neglected for many years, during which time chemistry, initially spurred on by Dalton's contributions, progressed vigorously. But this very activity had an inevitable result; more and more experimental data were collected that testified to the insufficiency of

Dalton's conceptual scheme. Possible amendments to Dalton's scheme other than Avogadro's were strongly debated. However, all of them contained certain unsatisfactory ideas (for example, the assumption that the particles of a gas are contiguous). The unavoidable contradictions were so discouraging that from the early 1840's on a gradual loss of faith in the whole atomic theory of chemistry became evident.

The solution to these difficulties began in 1858 when the Italian chemist Stanislao Cannizzaro called for a revival of Avogadro's theory and showed that it indeed provided a reasonable basis for chemistry. This was the final stage of the chemical revolution of the 18th and 19th centuries; the result was the development and sharpening of many of the fundamental concepts upon which modern chemistry is built. But if Cannizzaro was successful, his persuasiveness had a powerful ally. By that time chemists were better prepared to accept the kinetic model of a gas because of the revolution underway in thermal physics, the abandonment of the caloric theory and the growing acceptance of the kinetic theory of gases. Thus the atomic theories in chemistry and in physics aided each other.

Let us now survey some of the developments in chemistry that came with the revival of the Dalton-Avogadro theory. As was shown in Section 23.2, when Dalton's rule of simplicity is replaced by Avogadro's postulates, a new basis is provided for the determination of molecular formulas. And at once the way is open for a simple though only approximate method of determining the relative weights of molecules and atoms.

For gases the procedure is very simple. (a) Equal volumes of the various gases are weighed when all are at the same temperature and pressure. (b) Since, by Avogadro's law, these equal volumes contain equal numbers of molecules, the ratio of the weights of the gas samples (or, for that matter, the ratio of their masses) is equal to the ratio of the weights of the individual molecules. (c) To express the relative molecular weights as numbers, some arbitrary value is assigned to one of them; in practice, the value 32.0000 is given to the molecular weight of the diatomic oxygen molecule O_2, the value 16.0000 having already been assigned to the oxygen atom (Section 22.8).

By definition, the *relative molecular weight M* of a gas, whether it is an element or a compound, is 32.0000 times the ratio of the weight of a sample of the gas to the weight of an equal volume of oxygen gas at the same temperature and pressure. Avogadro's law assures us that this is the weight of a molecule of the gas relative to the weight of a molecule of oxygen, taking the latter to be 32.0000.

EXAMPLE 23.1. 500 cm^3 of nitrogen gas and 500 cm^3 of oxygen gas are at the same pressure and temperature. Their measured masses are respectively 1.251 gm and 1.429 gm. Compute the relative molecular weight of nitrogen.

Solution. The weight of each sample is the actual weight w of each molecule times the number of molecules, N, in the sample. Thus

$$\frac{\text{Wt. of nitrogen sample}}{\text{Wt. of oxygen sample}} = \frac{N_{\text{nitrogen}} \times w_{\text{nitrogen}}}{N_{\text{oxygen}} \times w_{\text{oxygen}}}.$$

But by Avogadro's law, N_{nitrogen} and N_{oxygen} are equal in this case; moreover, the ratio of the weights of the two samples is numerically equal to the ratio of their masses (since g has the same value for all substances in a given locality). Therefore we may write

$$\frac{\text{Wt. of nitrogen sample}}{\text{Wt. of oxygen sample}} = \frac{1.251 \text{ gm}}{1.429 \text{ gm}} = \frac{w_{\text{nitrogen}}}{w_{\text{oxygen}}}.$$

The ratio of actual weights of individual molecules, by definition, is also the ratio of their relative molecular weights M. Consequently

$$\frac{w_{\text{nitrogen}}}{w_{\text{oxygen}}} = \frac{1.251}{1.429} = \frac{M_{\text{nitrogen}}}{M_{\text{oxygen}}}.$$

Therefore

$$M_{\text{nitrogen}} = \frac{1.251}{1.429} M_{\text{oxygen}}.$$

But, by convention, we assign $M_{\text{oxygen}} = 32.0000$. So finally, on the basis of our experimental data, the relative molecular weight of nitrogen is found to be

$$M_{\text{nitrogen}} = \frac{1.251}{1.429} \times 32.0000 = 28.01.$$

As Table 23.1 shows, the present accepted value (on the basis of more refined procedures than implied above) is 28.016. Parenthetically, we note that the word "relative" is usually dropped from the phrase "relative molecular weight."

PROBLEM 23.8. At 0°C, 1000 cm³ of fluorine gas has a mass of 1.69 gm and 1000 cm³ of oxygen gas has a mass of 1.43 gm. What is the relative molecular weight of fluorine?

In a less strict sense, the concept of molecular weight is used even for a gaseous mixture such as air (see Table 23.1), and also in reference to solids and liquids.

23.5 Determination of atomic weights. To obtain the *relative atomic weight* of an element, we simply divide the molecular weight of the element by the number of atoms per molecule. Thus for nitrogen the molecular weight is 28.016 and the number of atoms per molecule is 2; hence the relative atomic weight (abbreviated at. wt.) is 28.016/2 or 14.008. By definition, the relative atomic weight of an element is the weight of one of its atoms relative to the weight of an oxygen atom taken as 16.0000. Modern atomic weights are given in Appendix D.

Table 23.1. Molecular weights of some elements and compounds.

Substance	Molecular formula	Molecular weight M
Elements:		
Hydrogen	H_2	2.016
Helium	He	4.003
Nitrogen	N_2	28.016
Oxygen	O_2	32.0000 (Definition)
Fluorine	F_2	38.000
Argon	A	39.944
Chlorine	Cl_2	70.914
Phosphorus	P_4	123.900
Mercury	Hg	200.61
Compounds:		
Water vapor	H_2O	18.02
Carbon monoxide	CO	28.01
Carbon dioxide	CO_2	44.01
Uranium hexafluoride	UF_6	352.07
Mixture:		
Air	N_2 (78%), O_2 (21%), CO_2 (0.03–0.04%), also water vapor, rare gases, etc.	29 (approximate average)

To compute an atomic weight by the foregoing method, we must, of course, know the molecular formula, which may be obtained through experiments (such as those described in Section 23.2) with the element in the gaseous state. However, the postulates of the atomic theory make it plausible that an atomic weight established from gaseous reactions is equally valid for the same element when it is in the liquid or solid state.

PROBLEM 23.9. Compute the atomic weight of fluorine, argon, and phosphorus (use data from Table 23.1).

PROBLEM 23.10. By using the values for atomic weights listed in Appendix D, compute the molecular weights of methyl (wood) alcohol, CH_3OH; ethyl alcohol, C_2H_5OH; diethyl ether, $(C_2H_5)_2O$.

PROBLEM 23.11.   (a) Does the chemical evidence that we have studied preclude the possibility that the molecular formula for hydrogen gas is H_4? (b) What type of experiments would be needed to prove or disprove the hypothesis that it is H_4? (c) If it did turn out to be H_4, what would the experiments cited in this chapter tell us about the molecular formulas for the other gases in Table 23.1? (d) How would the molecular weight of methyl alcohol be modified?

23.6 Determination of combining weights and reaction equations.
Suppose that two elements A and B, whose relative atomic weights are
written at. wt. of A and at. wt. of B respectively, are found to combine
to form a compound. We may assume that the compound has a molecular
formula of the type A_aB_b. The weight ratio of the samples used to form
the compound may be written (wt. of A)/(wt. of B). A typical task in
chemistry is to find a relation between the combining weights, the subscripts in the molecular formula, and the relative atomic weights.

This is not difficult. Each molecule of the compound A_aB_b contains a
atoms of A, so that the share of element A in the relative molecular
weight of the compound is ($a \times$ at. wt. of A). Similarly, the share of substance B in the relative molecular weight of the compound is ($b \times$ at. wt.
of B). All the molecules of a sample of the compound are presumably alike;
if there are N molecules in a sample, the relative share of material A in
the sample is $N \times$ ($a \times$ at. wt. of A), and the share of material B in the
sample is $N \times$ ($b \times$ at. wt. of B). The ratio of these weights, ($N \cdot a \cdot$ at. wt.
of A)/($N \cdot b \cdot$ at. wt. of B), or ($a \cdot$ at. wt. of A)/($b \cdot$ at. wt. of B), is the
same thing as the ratio of the combining weights (wt. of A)/(wt. of
B). Therefore

$$\frac{\text{Wt. of A}}{\text{Wt. of B}} = \frac{a}{b} \cdot \frac{\text{at. wt. of A}}{\text{at. wt. of B}}. \tag{23.1}$$

The range of application of this argument is illustrated in the following
examples.

EXAMPLE 23.2. Find the atomic weight of hydrogen, given that the molecular
formula for water is H_2O and that hydrogen gas and oxygen gas combine in the
weight ratio 1.01/8.00.
Solution. Here (wt. of hydrogen)/(wt. of oxygen) = 1.01/8.00, $a = 2, b = 1$,
and at. wt. of oxygen = 16.0000 (by definition). Substituting in Eq. (23.1), we
have at. wt. of hydrogen/16.0000 = $\frac{1}{2}$(1.01/8.00), or at. wt. of hydrogen = 1.01.

EXAMPLE 23.3. One way to obtain iron is to heat carbon with the iron ore
named *hematite* (Fe_2O_3). Given the reaction equation

$$Fe_2O_3 \quad + \quad 3C \quad \rightarrow \quad 2Fe \quad + \quad 3CO$$
$$\text{(hematite)} \qquad \text{(carbon)} \qquad \text{(iron)} \qquad \text{(carbon}$$
$$\text{monoxide)}$$

and the relative atomic weights for iron (55.85) and carbon (12.01), compute the
ratio by weights of hematite (a) to the carbon consumed, and (b) to the iron
produced.
Solution. (a) From considerations analogous to those used in deriving Eq.
(23.1), we obtain

$$\frac{\text{Wt. of hematite}}{\text{Wt. of carbon}} = \frac{2 \times \text{at. wt. of iron} + 3 \times \text{at. wt. of oxygen}}{3 \times \text{at. wt. of carbon}}$$

$$= \frac{2 \times 55.85 + 3 \times 16.00}{3 \times 12.01} = 4.432.$$

(b) Similarly, (wt. of hematite)/(wt. of iron) $= 159.70/111.70 \doteq 1.43$. Thus to obtain 50.0 kgm (110 lb) of iron we must provide 1.43×50.0 kgm $= 71.5$ kgm of hematite and 71.5 kgm/4.432 $= 16.1$ kgm of carbon (pure coal or its equivalent).

PROBLEM 23.12. (a) In Example 23.3, how much carbon would be needed to obtain 80 tons (73,000 kgm) of iron? (b) How much carbon monoxide will have to be disposed of in this case?

PROBLEM 23.13. Depending on the temperature of the furnace, the reaction in smelting hematite either may be that given in Example 23.3 or it may be $Fe_2O_3 + 3CO \rightarrow 2Fe + 3CO_2$. Find the ratio of the combining weights of hematite and iron for this reaction.

EXAMPLE 23.4. When a mixture consisting of 304 gm of a certain oxide of chromium and 108 gm of aluminum (at. wt. of Al $\doteq$ 27) is ignited, there are produced 208 gm of the pure metal chromium (at. wt. of Cr $\doteq$ 52) and some aluminum oxide. From these data, (a) predict how much aluminum oxide is produced, and (b) find the equation for this reaction.

Solution. (a) The principle of conservation of mass enables us to predict that $(304 + 108 - 208)$ gm, or 204 gm, of aluminum oxide is produced. (b) Although not given any of the formulas involved, we can tentatively write the equation for the reaction in the form

$$Cr_xO_y + z\,Al \rightarrow x\,Cr + Al_zO_y,$$

where x, y, and z represent the numbers of the various atoms involved. That there must be as many atoms of each element on one side of the equation as on the other follows from the postulates that atoms are indivisible and unchangeable; that is, the equation must balance. Our task is to find the values of x, y, and z.

By the same argument as in Example 23.3, we may write

$$\frac{\text{Wt. of chromium oxide}}{\text{Wt. of chromium}} = \frac{x \cdot \text{at. wt. of Cr} + y \cdot \text{at. wt. of O}}{x \cdot \text{at. wt. of Cr}},$$

$$\frac{304 \text{ gm}}{208 \text{ gm}} = \frac{x \times 52 + y \times 16}{x \times 52},$$

which, after simplification, yields $x/y = \frac{2}{3}$. This is the ratio of the subscripts in the formula Cr_xO_y. In the absence of other information, *we choose the smallest integral values of x and y that will satisfy this relation*, namely, $x = 2$, $y = 3$; hence we tentatively adopt Cr_2O_3 as the empirical formula and thus are able to rewrite our equation for the reaction as

$$Cr_2O_3 + z\,Al \rightarrow 2Cr + Al_zO_3.$$

To evaluate z, we use the same argument to write

$$\frac{\text{Wt. of aluminum}}{\text{Wt. of chromium}} = \frac{z \cdot \text{at. wt. of Al}}{2 \cdot \text{at. wt. of Cr}},$$

$$z = \frac{2 \times 52}{27} \times \frac{108}{208} = 2.$$

We conclude that the complete equation for the reaction is

$$Cr_2O_3 + 2Al \rightarrow 2Cr + Al_2O_3.$$

PROBLEM 23.14. Experiment shows that 66.8 gm of aluminum chloride combines completely with 34.5 gm of the metal sodium to produce 13.5 gm of aluminum and some sodium chloride. Without being given in advance any of the specific molecular formulas, find the simplest equation that will describe this reaction. The atomic weights for aluminum, chlorine, and sodium are given in Appendix D.

23.7 Avogadro's number. A concept that serves to simplify many calculations is the *gram-molecular weight,* or *mole,* of a substance. It is a measure of quantity of matter, or mass; to say that we have 1 gram-molecular weight or 1 mole of a substance means that we have M grams of it, where M is numerically equal to the molecular weight. Thus for oxygen (O_2), 1 mole is 32.0000 gm; for hydrogen (H_2), 1 mole is 2.016 gm; for water (H_2O), 1 mole is 18.016 gm. By n moles of a substance is meant $n \times M$ grams; thus for oxygen, 2.0 moles is equal to 64 gm, and 0.20 mole = 6.4 gm. Conversely, the number of moles n in a sample is given by the mass of the sample (in grams) divided by its molecular weight. Thus 45.0 gm of chlorine corresponds to $n = 45.0/M_{Cl} = 45.0/70.914 = 0.635$ mole. In the case of helium, which has monatomic (single-atom) molecules and therefore has the same values for the atomic and molecular weights, namely 4.003, a sample of 6.2 gm corresponds to $n = 6.2/4.00 = 1.55$ moles. (When we speak of monatomic substances, the term gram-*atomic* weight is usually substituted for gram-molecular weight.)

The concept of mole assumes special usefulness when we realize that *all pure elements and compounds, whether gases, liquids, or solids, must have the same number of molecules in one mole.* To demonstrate this, let w be the weight of a single molecule and N_0 the number of molecules *in 1 mole.* Then the weight of one mole of the substance is the weight of one molecule times the number of molecules in one mole, or $w \times N_0$. For any two substance A and B,

$$\frac{\text{Wt. of one mole of } A}{\text{Wt. of one mole of } B} \equiv \frac{w_A \cdot (N_0)_A}{w_B \cdot (N_0)_B}. \tag{23.2}$$

Since the molecular weight of each substance is proportional to the weight of one molecule of the substance, w_A/w_B is equal to the ratio of the molecular weights of A and B, namely M_A/M_B. But by the definition of mole, the ratio (wt. of one mole of A)/(wt. of one mole of B) must also be the ratio of the molecular weights of A and B. Therefore Eq. (23.2) can be written

$$\frac{M_A}{M_B} = \frac{M_A(N_0)_A}{M_B(N_0)_B},$$

and consequently

$$\frac{(N_0)_A}{(N_0)_B} = 1, \qquad (N_0)_A = (N_0)_B.$$

Note that this proof that a mole of A contains the same number of molecules as a mole of B involves no assumptions regarding the condition or state of the substance.

The number of molecules per mole, N_0, is called *Avogadro's number*. It can be determined in a variety of ways by experiments, as will be shown later; the currently accepted value is 6.023×10^{23} molecules/mole. This, then, is the number of molecules in 2.016 gm of hydrogen, in 32.0000 gm of oxygen, in 18.016 gm of water, and so on. Empirically it is found that the volume occupied by one mole of any gas is 22.4 liters* at 0°C and 1 atm pressure. This brings us to a common alternative way of stating Avogadro's law: *one mole of any gas contains 6.023×10^{23} molecules and occupies a volume of 22.41 liters at standard temperature and pressure.*

The following argument reveals another way in which the concept *mole* is highly useful. If, for some particular chemical reaction, we know that every molecule of substance X joins with y molecules of substance Y, then it follows that we must provide for each mole of X exactly y moles of Y to assure a complete reaction without any of X or Y being left over. Similar conditions apply to fractions or multiples of moles. Thus we see that the equation for a reaction also specifies the number of moles that combine. For example, the reaction equation in Example 23.3 tells us that 1 mole of hematite combines with 3 moles of carbon to produce 2 moles of iron and 3 moles of carbon monoxide. If we were to begin with 0.2 mole of hematite, we must provide 0.6 mole of carbon, etc. Other applications are illustrated in the following examples and problems.

_____

*The *liter* is a useful unit in terms of which to measure the volume of a vessel of irregular shape, for it is defined as the volume occupied by 1 kgm of pure water at the temperature of maximum density (4°C) and under a pressure of 1 atm. Experiment shows that for all practical purposes, 1 liter is equivalent to 0.001 m^3 (1000 cm^3); more precisely, it is larger than this by $2.8 \times 10^{-8} \text{ m}^3$ or 0.028 cm^3.

PROBLEM 23.15.   (a) How many moles of ammonia (NH_3) are equivalent to 1 gm of that vapor?   (b) How many molecules?   (c) How many atoms? (d) What volume would the 1 gm of vapor occupy at 100°C and 5 atm pressure? (e) How many moles of hydrogen are there in 1 gm of ammonia?   (f) Show that from the knowledge of Avogadro's number and the empirical value of 2.69×10^{25} molecules of gas per cubic meter at 0°C and 1 atm (called the Loschmidt number), it follows that one mole of gas under these standard conditions fills 22.4 liters.

PROBLEM 23.16.   The reaction that represents the rusting of iron may be written as

$$3Fe + 4H_2O \rightarrow Fe_3O_4 + 4H_2.$$

(a) Summarize all the information implied in this set of symbols.   (b) How many moles of hydrogen are liberated for each gram of iron completely rusted?

PROBLEM 23.17.   The following table shows the experimentally determined compositions of five compounds, each containing only two elements.   The last column gives the modern values of the ratio of the numbers of atoms in the molecules of these compounds.

	Carbon	Hydrogen	Sulfur	Oxygen	Atomic ratio
Carbon monoxide	3 gm			4 gm	C/O = 1/1
Water		1 gm		8 gm	H/O = 2/1
Methane	3 gm	1 gm			
Sulfur dioxide			1 gm	1 gm	S/O = 1/2
Carbon disulfide	3 gm		16 gm		

(a) Starting from the given atomic ratios for water and carbon monoxide, show from the data in the table that a methane molecule contains 4 atoms of hydrogen for one of carbon.

(b) Starting from the given atomic ratios for carbon monoxide and sulfur dioxide, show that a carbon disulfide molecule contains two atoms of sulfur and one of carbon.

PROBLEM 23.18.   In the preparation of phosphorus, sand (silica, SiO_2) is added to react with calcium phosphate [$Ca_3(PO_4)_2$] to form calcium silicate ($CaSiO_3$) and phosphorus pentoxide (P_2O_5).   (a) Write the balanced equation for this process.   (b) Suggest a process and write its equation for reducing phosphorus pentoxide with carbon.

EXAMPLE 23.5.   Compute the actual or "absolute" mass in grams and the weight in dynes of an *atom* of hydrogen, helium, or oxygen.

Solution.   A mole of hydrogen is 2.016 gm and, since hydrogen is diatomic, the number of its *atoms* in a mole is $2N_0$. Therefore $m_{hydrogen} = 2.016 \text{ gm}/(2 \times 6.02 \times 10^{23}) = 1.66 \times 10^{-24}$ gm. The weight of one atom of hydrogen in dynes is $w_{hydrogen} = m_{hydrogen} \cdot g = 1.66 \times 10^{-24} \text{ gm} \times 980 \text{ cm/sec}^2 = 1.63 \times 10^{-21}$ gm·cm/sec^2 = 1.63×10^{-21} dyne, or 1.63×10^{-26} new. The method of calculation is the same for the two other cases, except that helium, being monatomic, has N_0 atoms per mole.

The calculation of the approximate *size* of an atom is a rather spectacular application of the concept of mole and of Avogadro's postulates. In a crystal, the atoms may be thought to be closely packed together in a regular lattice array. In rock salt (NaCl), for example, the atoms of Na and Cl are arranged in a cubic lattice, as is shown not merely by the external appearance of the crystal but also by the symmetry of its physical properties or by the patterns of x-rays scattered by such a crystal. One mole of NaCl would be $(23.0 + 35.5)$ gm, or 58.5 gm, and should contain $2 \times 6.02 \times 10^{23}$ atoms, or 12.04×10^{23} atoms. By ordinary measurement, we can ascertain that 58.5 gm of salt has a volume of 27.0 cm^3. This allows, on the average, a volume of $27.0/12.04 \times 10^{23}$ cm^3 for each atom, or 2.24×10^{-23} cm^3. Into this space would fit a sphere of radius $r = [(3/4\pi) \times 2.24 \times 10^{-23}]^{1/3} = 1.75 \times 10^{-8}$ cm. This figure should give at least the order of magnitude of the size of atoms such as sodium and chlorine.

23.8 Valence. The Dalton-Avogadro theory offers a very simple interpretation of the empirical law of definite proportions. Each molecule of carbon monoxide, for example, always consists of one atom of carbon and one of oxygen; each molecule of ammonia invariably consists of one nitrogen atom combined with three hydrogen atoms, and similarly for each molecule of any other compound. However, contemplation of this gratifying regularity soon raises perplexing questions. Why do atoms combine in such fixed ways? For what reasons do the atoms H and Cl always form the molecule HCl and not HCl_3, H_5Cl_2, or some other combination? Why do hydrogen and oxygen atoms form either H_2O or H_2O_2 (hydrogen peroxide), but not HO_2, or H_3O_2? Or, given C and O, why can we find CO or CO_2 but not, say, C_2O?

As a crude but helpful first approach to these questions, picture all the atoms as having something like "hooks" that serve to couple or bind them together. To explain the existence of the molecules HCl and H_2O, we assign one hook to the hydrogen atom, one to the chlorine atom, and

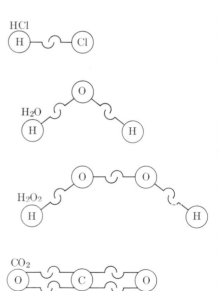

FIG. 23.8. The formation of molecules pictured in terms of coupling "hooks."

two to the oxygen atom (Fig. 23.8). With this scheme we can also obtain a "picture" for H_2O_2, the hydrogen peroxide molecule, but we are led to predict that there is no such substance as H_3O_2. Moreover, we are tempted to regard the unavailability of a substance such as HO_2 as a sign that the atoms H and O, at any rate, will not form a stable molecule unless all of their "hooks" are engaged.

The formula CO_2 implies that each carbon atom has four "hooks," so as to engage the two of each oxygen atom (Fig. 23.8). But in CO it would seem that two of the four hooks of the carbon atom are left unengaged after all, and thus are ready to couple with those of another oxygen atom— a simple picture that accounts for the fact that carbon monoxide readily burns to form carbon dioxide.

Although this primitive scheme eventually turned out to be grossly inadequate, it pointed the way to a really powerful explanation, leading, in the 1850's, to the concept of *valence*, today indispensable for the description and understanding of chemical processes. Using pictorial language in this first introduction of the concept, we may say that the valence of an element is the number of "hooks" or couplers that each of its atoms can put out to provide chemical bonds with other atoms or groups of atoms. Examples of such groups are SO_4 and OH; each behaves as a unit that remains unchanged in many reactions. These groups are called *radicals*.

Hydrogen is regarded *a priori* as having a valence of 1; we say that it is *monovalent*. The simplest way to find the valence of an element is to look up the molecular formula of some substance (if it exists) that involves only this element and hydrogen. For example, the formulas H_2O, NH_3, and CH_4 indicate that the valence of oxygen is 2 (*divalent*), of nitrogen 3 (*trivalent*), and of carbon 4 (*tetravalent*). The formula H_2SO_4 shows that the sulfate radical SO_4 is divalent. A valence may also be found by noting the number of hydrogen atoms that an atom of the element can *displace* in a molecule during a reaction. Thus in the reaction $Ca + H_2O \rightarrow H_2 + CaO$, Ca replaces the H_2 of H_2O; hence calcium is divalent. The molecular formulas HF or H_2F_2 for hydrofluoric acid and OsF_8 for osmium octafluoride show that osmium can have a valence of 8, which is the highest of all the valence numbers.

PROBLEM 23.19.   Given the molecular formulas HCl, NaCl, $CaCl_2$, $AlCl_3$, $SnCl_4$, and PCl_5, find possible valence numbers of sodium, calcium, aluminum, tin, and phosphorus.

When we extend our examination to include still other molecular formulas, a complexity arises. For example, the formulas CH_4 and CO_2 indicate that carbon is tetravalent. But what about the formula CO, which indicates that carbon is divalent, assuming that oxygen is always divalent?

One way out of this difficulty was to say that the valence of carbon is 4 in CH_4 and CO_2, but 2 in CO. In the long run this mode of expression was found preferable, even though it led to the disappointing realization that carbon and many other elements can assume different valences, depending upon what compound they help to form. Thus the valence of iron is 2 for FeO, $FeCl_2$, and $Fe(NO_3)_2$, but is 3 for Fe_2O_3, $FeCl_3$, and $Fe(NO_3)_3$. Uranium can have five different valences, chlorine six, and rhenium seven.

Historically, the possibility of multiple valences was the subject of considerable debate throughout the last half of the 19th century. Other difficulties also arose. For example, some molecular formulas lead to anomalous valence numbers. Thus the formula Fe_3O_4 suggests a valence of 8/3 for the iron. However, the anomaly disappeared when it was recognized that this compound probably is a mixture of two different kinds of molecules, FeO and Fe_2O_3.

PROBLEM 23.20. Assuming the valence of oxygen to be 2 throughout, find the valence to be assigned to nitrogen for each of the following oxides: N_2O, NO, N_2O_3, NO_2, N_2O_5.

Of the many valuable consequences of the valence concept, one is particularly noteworthy at this point. The notion of valence bonds, essentially the same as the "hooks" of Fig. 23.7, supplemented Dalton's pictorial representation of the atoms themselves (Section 22.4) and invited speculation about how the atoms of a molecule are arranged. They were useful in pictorial presentations of complex compounds (Fig. 23.9), if only to serve as a mental crutch.

These "structural formulas" were all the more necessary when the existence of *isomers* (Greek *isos* + *meros*, composed of equal parts) was discovered. These compounds have precisely the same chemical molecular formula but have different chemical and physical properties, and the only hope for explaining these differences lay in the hypothesis that while the kind and number of atoms in the molecules of any set of isomers were the same, the arrangement of the atoms within the molecules was different. Figure 23.9 shows the isomers $C_6H_{12}O_6$, one of which is glucose (also called dextrose and grape sugar) and the other fructose (or levulose, fruit sugar). Figure 23.10 shows two representations of the isomers of butane, C_4H_{10}, a constituent of petroleum. In each case, the schematic two-dimensional structural formula is accompanied by a scale model of the molecule.

PROBLEM 23.21. Find the number of possible isomers of pentane (C_5H_{12}) and give the structural formula for each case.

In the 1860's, when structural formulas first came into wide use among chemists, there was reluctance to regard them as anything more than

$$H-\overset{\overset{\displaystyle H}{|}}{\underset{\underset{\displaystyle H}{|}}{C}}-\overset{\overset{\displaystyle H}{|}}{\underset{\underset{\displaystyle H}{|}}{C}}-H$$

Ethane
(C_2H_6)

$$H-\overset{\overset{\displaystyle H}{|}}{\underset{\underset{\displaystyle H}{|}}{C}}-\overset{\overset{\displaystyle H}{|}}{\underset{\underset{\displaystyle H}{|}}{C}}-O-H$$

Ethyl alcohol
(C_2H_5OH)

Benzene
(C_6H_6)

Glucose
($C_6H_{12}O_6$)

Fructose
($C_6H_{12}O_6$)

FIG. 23.9. Some structural formulas. Note the two isomers of $C_6H_{12}O_6$.

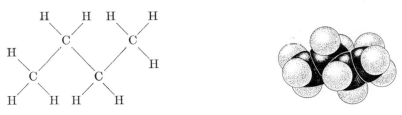

(a) Normal butane (*n*-butane)

(b) Isobutane

FIG. 23.10. Representations of two isomers of butane, C_4H_{10}, by structural formula (left) and scale model (right). In the scale models the black forms represent carbon atoms and the grey forms hydrogen atoms.

mental aids, without necessary relation to the actual three-dimensional and then essentially inaccessible structure of molecules. Although the graphical formula has proved to be indispensable as a rough sketch of a molecule, the correct disposition of atoms and groups of atoms in a molecule of a compound is generally difficult to determine even with our present powerful tools of research.

To answer the initial question of why atoms have specific valences, more was necessary than an accurate knowledge of molecular structure. The key was found in the nature of the *forces* that bind atoms together to form molecules, and so these questions of chemistry had to wait for the development of atomic physics. The discussion in Part VIII will bring us back to the problem of valence. But even before the necessary steps were taken to clarify the physical basis of valence, the concept itself became a keystone in the construction of another inspired scheme, *the periodic classification of the elements*, that was to contribute to the advance of chemistry as much as had the atomic-molecular theory of Dalton and Avogadro.

Supplementary Reading

Bonner, F. T., and M. Phillips, *Principles of physical science* (Addison-Wesley, 1957), Chaps. 5–8.

Chalmers, T. W., *Historic researches* (Scribner's, 1952), Chap. VI.

Gregory, J. C., *A short history of atomism* (A. and C. Black, London, 1931).

Holmyard, E. J., *Makers of chemistry* (Oxford University Press, 1931).

Leicester, H. M., and H. S. Klickstein, *A source book in chemistry, 1400–1900* (McGraw-Hill, 1952). Selections from Avogadro and Gay-Lussac.

Nash, L. K., *The atomic-molecular theory* (Harvard University Press, 1950); also in *Harvard case histories of experimental science*, 1957, v. 1, pp. 215–321.

Pauling, L., *General chemistry* (Freeman, 1947, 1953), Chaps. 4 and 7.

Rochow, E. G., and M. K. Wilson, *General chemistry* (Wiley, 1954), Chap. 1.

CHAPTER 24

THE PERIODIC SYSTEM OF THE ELEMENTS

As the number of known elements became larger and larger, and as their chemical and physical properties became increasingly better established in the 19th century, there arose rather naturally the urge to find a relationship among the elements that would bring them into some sort of systematic sequence—a quest analogous to that of Kepler's for rules that would relate the planets of the solar system. On first thought the task looks quite hopeless, for the most compelling observation would seem to be that each element has properties that distinguish it from all the others. The variety is striking. Although most of the elements are solids at ordinary temperatures, several are gases and two are liquids. They differ widely in their relative abundance on the earth and also in such physical properties as density, elasticity, boiling point, and the like.

Nevertheless, some clues exist in the search for order and regularity among the elements. As early as 1815 the English physician William Prout suggested that the atoms of all elements were but combinations or "condensations" of different numbers of hydrogen atoms, the latter being the only truly fundamental particles. On this basis the atomic weights could be expected to be integral multiples of the atomic weight of hydrogen; and indeed this consequence of Prout's hypothesis was supported by the early values of the atomic weights determined by Dalton (Section 22.8). However, more accurate determinations were soon forthcoming, for example those of Jöns Jacob Berzelius (1779–1848), and all showed marked deviations from an integral-multiple rule. Actually, only a few of the atomic weights are even close to being exact multiples of the atomic weight of hydrogen, as a glance at the modern list in Appendix D will show. Thus Prout's hypothesis, despite its appeal of simplicity, had to be abandoned.

24.1 Families of elements. Granting that atomic weights were not as simply related as Prout had proposed, there was nevertheless some correlation between the atomic weights and the properties of certain chemical elements. It had long been known that dispersed throughout the list of elements are "families" of elements of similar chemical behavior. An example is the *halogen family*, which includes the elements fluorine (F), chlorine (Cl), bromine (Br), and iodine (I). Although these four elements exhibit some marked dissimilarities (for example, ordinarily the first two are gases, the third a liquid, the last a volatile solid) they have also much

413

in common. They all combine violently with many metals to form white, crystalline salts (*halogen* means "salt-former") having similar formulas, such as NaF, NaCl, NaBr, and NaI, or AlF$_3$, AlCl$_3$, AlBr$_3$, and AlI$_3$; that is to say, all four members of the family have the same valence with respect to any other particular element. With hydrogen, all four elements form simple compounds (such as HCl and H$_2$F$_2$) that dissolve in water and form acids. All four, when vaporized under ordinary conditions, have diatomic molecules.

While these properties are the *same* for all four halogens, other properties *vary progressively* with the atomic weights, as shown in Table 24.1. Note

Table 24.1. Properties of the halogens.

Element	Atomic weight	Melting point (°C)	Boiling point (°C)
Fluorine (F)	19.00	−223°	−187°
Chlorine (Cl)	35.457	−101.6°	−34.6°
Bromine (Br)	79.916	−7.2°	58.8°
Iodine (I)	126.91	113.5°	184°

that the melting and boiling points increase with the atomic weights. The solubility of the halogens in water decreases with the atomic weights and so does the chemical activity, as manifested by the speed of reaction and amount of energy released. Here, then, is strong evidence of a correlation between atomic weight and chemical and physical behavior.

Another family of chemical elements, called the *alkali metals*, includes lithium (Li), sodium (Na), potassium (K), rubidium (Rb), and cesium (Cs), with approximate atomic weights 6.94, 23.0, 39.1, 85.5, and 133. Here, too, there is a long list of chemical and physical properties that are either common to all the members of the family or that change progressively with their atomic weights.

24.2 Other early searches for regularity. In 1829 the German chemist Johann Wolfgang Döbereiner noted that within each of several chemical families, the atomic weight of any element is equal, or nearly so, to the average of the atomic weights of its two immediate neighbors. Thus for the alkali metals, 23.0 for Na is halfway between 6.94 for Li and 39.1 for K; and for the halogens, 79.9 for Br is roughly the average of 35.5 for Cl and 127 for I. In brief, it looked as if the atomic weights within any particular family might be in arithmetic progression. No physical meaning could be given at the time to such numerical regularities, and the situation was thus reminiscent of Kepler's laws prior to Newton's work, or of Bode's law. And as in the case of Bode's law, the physical explanation of the regularities among the elements turned out to be extremely complex and has even yet not been fully given. But the search for numerical regularities of this kind has always been popular even when no physical cause could be assigned, and here it was carried on with vigor. Although much of this research proceeded along lines that eventually reached dead ends, it nevertheless gradually made more plausible the notion that some systematic relation did exist among elements.

From 1860 on, about the time when Cannizzaro's agitation on behalf of Avogadro's modified atomic-molecular theory began to succeed, it became possible in principle to fix with very good accuracy the atomic weights of almost all the known elements. The English chemist J. H. Gladstone pointed out that the elements could usefully be listed simply in the order of increasing atomic weight. For when this was done, a curious fact became evident: not only were the atomic weights of the elements within any one family regularly spaced, as Döbereiner had suggested, but there was also in the whole list a periodic recurrence of elements with similar properties. In the words of the English chemist J. A. R. Newlands, one of several to seek such a regularity of spacing, "the eighth element, starting from a given one, is a kind of repetition of the first, like the eighth note in an octave of music."

Newlands' hopeful suggestion was, however, of limited use. Although it proved to be correct that chemically similar elements repeat periodically, and although it was possible to perceive several "octaves" in Newlands' arrangement, he did not realize that the periodicity changed if one proceeded far enough through the list of elements, and he did not foresee the need for leaving vacant spaces in the series in which to place still undiscovered elements. One might object that prior to the discovery of the new elements there is no possible way to know just where to leave the gap for each of them. Yet this was exactly the achievement of the great Russian chemist Dmitri Ivanovich Mendeléeff (Fig. 24.1). His method of classifying and arranging all elements, whether known or as yet undiscovered, into one coherent system, gave us the so-called *periodic system of the elements*, one of the most fundamental conceptual tools in modern chemistry.

24.3 The early periodic system of the elements. In the publications of Mendeléeff and, starting a little later, of the German Julius Lothar Meyer (1830–1895), we find the culmination of six decades of quantitative investigations and speculative inquiry that began with the announcement of Dalton's atomic theory. We shall now examine some of the most

Fig. 24.1. Dmitri Ivanovich Mendeléeff (1834–1907).

striking aspects of Mendeléeff's contributions, in a few extracts from his
very voluminous writings. In a paper of 1869 he discussed the background
material for his work:

> During the course of the development of our science, the systematic arrange-
> ment of elements has undergone manifold and repeated changes. The most
> frequent classification of elements into metals and nonmetals is based upon
> physical differences as they are observed for many simple bodies, as well as
> upon differences in character of the oxides and of the compounds corresponding
> to them. However, what at first acquaintance with the subject-matter ap-
> peared to be completely clear, lost its importance entirely when more detailed
> knowledge was obtained. Ever since it became known that an element such
> as phosphorus could appear in nonmetallic as well as in metallic form, it
> became impossible to found a classification on physical differences . . . In
> recent times the majority of chemists is inclined to achieve a correct ordering
> of the elements on the basis of their valency. There are many uncertainties
> involved in such an attempt . . .
> Thus, there does not exist yet a single universal principle which can with-
> stand criticism, that could serve as guide to judge the relative properties of
> elements and that would permit their arrangement in a more or less strict
> system. Only with respect to some groups of elements there are no doubts

that they form a whole and represent a natural series of similar manifestations of matter.   Such groups are: the halogens, the alkaline earth metals, the nitrogen group, partially also the sulfur group, the companions of platinum, the companions of cerium, and a few others . . .   The discovery of rubidium, cesium and thallium gave rise to the reflection that our knowledge of the elements is very limited; and the attempt to construct a system appears to be premature as long as there exists no hypothetical basis which could serve as the foundation of a strict system.

The investigations regarding the simple relations of atomic weights have caused many . . . to point out the numerical relations between the atomic weights of those elements that form a group [family]; but, so far as I know, they have not led to a systematic arrangement of all known elements . . . When I undertook to write a handbook of chemistry entitled *Foundations of chemistry* [published 1869–1871], I had to make a decision in favor of some system of elements in order not to be guided in their classification by accidental, or instinctive, reasons but by some exact, definite principle.   In what has been said above we have seen the nearly complete absence of numerical relations in the construction of systems of elements; every system, however, that is based upon exactly observed numbers is to be preferred of course to other systems not based upon numbers because then only little margin is left to arbitrariness.   The numerical data available regarding elements are limited at this time.   Even if the physical properties of some of them have been determined accurately, this is true only of a very small number of elements. Properties such as the optical, and even the electrical or magnetic ones, cannot serve as a basis for the system naturally, since one and the same body, according to the state in which it happens to be at the moment, may show enormous differences in this regard.   With respect to this fact, it is sufficient to remember graphite and diamond, ordinary and red phosphorus . . .

However, everybody does understand that in all changes of properties of elements, *something* remains unchanged, and that when elements go into compounds, this material something represents the [common] characteristics of compounds the given element can form.   In this regard only a numerical value is known, and this is the atomic weight appropriate to the element.   The magnitude of the atomic weight, according to the actual, essential nature of the concept, is a quantity that does not refer to the momentary state of an element but belongs to a material part of it, a part that it has in common with the free element and with all its compounds . . .   For this reason I have endeavored to found the system upon the quantity of the atomic weight.

The first attempt I undertook in this direction was the following: I selected the bodies with the smallest atomic weight and ordered them according to the magnitude of their atomic weights.   Thereby it appeared that there exists a periodicity of properties and that even according to valence, one element follows the other in the order of an arithmetic sequence:

Li $= 7$	Be $= 9.4$	B $= 11$	C $= 12$	N $= 14$	O $= 16$	F $= 19$
Na $= 23$	Mg $= 24$	Al $= 27.4$	Si $= 28$	P $= 31$	S $= 32$	Cl $= 35.3$
K $= 39$	Ca $= 40$	. . . . .	Ti $= 50$	V $= 51$	*et cetera*	

Note that in Mendeléeff's arrangement, hydrogen (the first element in the series and the least dense) is omitted, for it has rather unique properties. Also note that helium and the other elements of the family of *inert gases* had not yet been discovered. Mendeléeff has set down the first seven elements, from lithium to fluorine, in sequence of increasing atomic weights, and then has written the next seven, from sodium to chlorine, in the second row. The periodicity of chemical behavior is already obvious before going on to write the third row. In the first vertical column are the first two alkali metals; in the seventh column are the first two halogens; and indeed within *each* of the columns the elements are chemically similar (for example, having the same main valence).

When Mendeléeff now added a third row of elements, potassium (K) came below elements Li and Na, which are members of the same family and have the same valence, namely, 1. Next in the row is Ca, divalent like Mg and Be above it. In the next space to the right, the element of next higher atomic weight should appear. Of the elements known at the time, the next heavier one was titanium (Ti), and it was placed in this space under Al and B by various workers who had tried to develop such schemes. (In Newlands' table, which had coincided fairly well with Mendeléeff's up to this point, there appears in this space an element whose atomic weight actually was much too high.) It is here that we gain insight into Mendeléeff's dominant thoughts. He recognized that Ti has chemical properties similar to those of C and Si and therefore should be put in the *fourth* vertical column. Then if the classification is to be complete and meaningful, there ought to be a hitherto unsuspected element of atomic weight between that of Ca (40) and Ti (50, present value 47.9), and with a valence of 3. Here was a definite prediction, and Mendeléeff found other cases of this sort among the remaining elements.

The whole scheme up to this point may be illustrated in terms of a crude analogy. Suppose a librarian were to weigh each of his books individually and then place them on a set of shelves according to increasing weight, and found that on each shelf the first book happened to be on art, the second on biology, the third on classics, the fourth on the drama, and so on. He might not understand in the least the underlying explanation for this astonishing regularity, but if he were now to discover on, say, the third shelf a sequence of books in the order art-classics-drama, he would perhaps be tempted to leave a gap between the books on art and classics, and to suspect that there does exist a biology book of the appropriate weight to fill the gap, even though it had not come to his notice before.

Mendeléeff had no illusions that he understood why the elements could be arranged in this orderly sequence, but he firmly believed that his work would eventually lead to a physical explanation, and that, in the meantime, "new interest will be awakened for the determination of atomic weights, for the discovery of new elements, and for finding new analogies among the elements." Later he added, "Just as without knowing the cause of gravitation it is possible to make use of the law of gravitation, so for the aims of chemistry it is possible to take advantage of the laws discovered by chemistry without being able to explain their causes."

Table 24.2 is Mendeléeff's periodic system or "periodic table" of the elements in the 1872 version. We note that he distributed the 63 elements then known (with 5 in doubt) in 12 horizontal rows or *series*, starting with hydrogen at the top left, and ending with uranium at the bottom right. All are written in order of increasing atomic weight (Mendeléeff's values given in parentheses), but are so placed that elements with similar chemical properties are in the same vertical column or *group*. Thus in group VII are all the halogens; in group VIII, only ductile metals; in groups I and II, metals of small densities and low melting points; and in group I the family of alkali metals. Mendeléeff's more detailed arguments for each particular placement, as his extensive discussions show, were very delicate, guided by his profound and often almost intuitive knowledge of chemical nature.

Table 24.2 does, however, show many gaps, as indicated by the horizontal dashes:

> Vacant places occur for elements which, perhaps, shall be discovered in the course of time . . . The higher atomic weights belong to elements that are rarely encountered in nature, that do not form large deposits, and that therefore have been studied relatively little . . . With respect to the position of some elements that are rarely encountered in nature, there exists, quite understandably, complete uncertainty.

But the main part of the table is fairly complete, and another feature of this scheme reveals itself: "For a true comprehension of the matter it is very important to see that all aspects of the distribution of the elements according to their atomic weights essentially express one and the same fundamental dependence—*periodic properties.*" By this is meant that in addition to the gradual change in physical and chemical properties within each vertical group, there is also a periodic change of such properties in the horizontal sequence, beginning with hydrogen and ending with uranium.

> The properties of the elements as well as the forms and properties of their compounds are in periodic dependence on, or (to express ourselves algebraically) form a periodic function of, the atomic weights of the elements.

This *periodic law* is the heart of the matter; it is a generalization of Newlands' attempt, although Mendeléeff initially was not acquainted with that work. We can best illustrate the periodic law as Lothar Meyer did, by drawing a curve showing the values of some physical quantity as

Table 24.2. Periodic classification of the elements; Mendeléeff, 1872.

SERIES	GROUP→	I	II	III	IV	V	VI	VII	VIII
	Higher oxides and hydrides	R_2O —	RO —	R_2O_3 —	RO_2 H_4R	R_2O_5 H_3R	RO_3 H_2R	R_2O_7 HR	RO_4 —
1		H(1)							
2		Li(7)	Be(9.4)	B(11)	C(12)	N(14)	O(16)	F(19)	
3		Na(23)	Mg(24)	Al(27.3)	Si(28)	P(31)	S(32)	Cl(35.5)	
4		K(39)	Ca(40)	—(44)	Ti(48)	V(51)	Cr(52)	Mn(55)	Fe(56), Co(59), Ni(59), Cu(63)
5		[Cu(63)]	Zn(65)	—(68)	—(72)	As(75)	Se(78)	Br(80)	
6		Rb(85)	Sr(87)	?Yt(88)	Zr(90)	Nb(94)	Mo(96)	—(100)	Ru(104), Rh(104), Pd(106), Ag(108)
7		[Ag(108)]	Cd(112)	In(113)	Sn(118)	Sb(122)	Te(125)	I(127)	
8		Cs(133)	Ba(137)	?Di(138)	?Ce(140)	—	—	—	
9		—	—	—	—	—	—	—	
10		—	—	?Er(178)	?La(180)	Ta(182)	W(184)	—	Os(195), Ir(197), Pt(198), Au(199)
11		[Au(199)]	Hg(200)	Tl(204)	Pb(207)	Bi(208)	—	—	
12		—	—	—	Th(231)	—	U(240)	—	

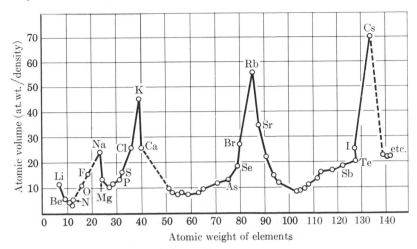

FIG. 24.2. An example of periodicity in the sequence of elements. The atomic volumes vary periodically with the atomic weights. (*After* Lothar Meyer, but using modern values.)

a function of atomic weight. Figure 24.2 is a plot of the so-called *atomic volumes* of the elements, defined as the atomic weight of the substance divided by its density in the liquid or solid phase. Each encircled point on this graph represents an element; a few of the points have been labeled with the identifying chemical symbols. Viewed as a whole, the graph demonstrates a striking periodicity: as the weight increases the atomic volume first increases to a sharp maximum, drops off, then increases to another sharp maximum, and so on. And at the successive peaks we find Li, Na, K, Rb, Cs, in short, the family of alkali metals. On the left-hand side of each peak, there is one of the halogens.

PROBLEM 24.1.   (a) State the periodic law concisely in your own words. (b) Using the data given in the *Handbook of chemistry and physics* or a similar source, plot the melting points of the elements as a function of the atomic weights for the elements from hydrogen to barium (Ba) inclusive. Then discuss the periodicities that appear on the graph as shown, for example, by the positions of the alkali metals and the halogens.

24.4 Consequences of the periodic scheme of Mendeléeff. More detailed examination of Mendeléeff's periodic scheme yields additional information of great interest.

(1) If an element (general symbol R) combines chemically with oxygen, the composition of one of R's oxygen compounds (oxides) generally is determined by the *group* to which R belongs; specifically, the valence of R will be 1, 2, 3, ... or 8, depending on whether R is in group I, II, III, ... or VIII (see the first row of Table 24.2). On the other hand, in

combining with hydrogen to form a hydride, R has a valence of 4, 3, 2, 1, depending on whether it is in group IV, V, VI, or VII.

PROBLEM 24.2. Using Table 24.2 or Appendix D, write the expected molecular formula for: (a) one oxide of magnesium (Mg), of aluminum (Al), or of carbon (C);   (b) one hydride of nitrogen (N), of oxygen (O), of fluorine (F), or of arsenic (As). (c) If you were now to analyze an oxide of magnesium or a hydride of nitrogen as found in nature, would you expect to find experimentally that your predictions in (a) and (b) will be fulfilled? Explain.

(2) As Table 24.2 shows, a distinction is made between odd-numbered and even-numbered series by a slight shift in the printing of the symbols to the right or left. Although all the elements in any particular group have similar chemical or physical properties, the similarities are sometimes closer among the elements of the group that belong to the odd series only or to the even series only. Thus in group VI, S, Se, and Te are nonmetals, whereas Cr, Mo, and W are heavy metals.

(3) Each element belongs both to a group (vertical column) and to a periodic series (horizontal row). Thus the properties of any one element are related to those of neighboring elements in Table 24.2 in somewhat the same way as a letter in a crossword puzzle is related to surrounding words, and so its properties can be predicted from what is known about neighboring regions.   Here is one example, taken from Mendeléeff's textbook:

> If in a certain group there occur elements R′, R″, and R‴, and if in that series which contains one of these elements, for instance R″, an element Q″ precedes it and an element S″ succeeds it [Fig. 24.3], then the properties of R″ are determined by the mean of the properties of R′, R‴, Q″, and S″. Thus, for example, the atomic weight of R″ = $\frac{1}{4}$(R′ + R‴ + Q″ + S″). For instance, selenium occurs in the same group as sulfur (at. wt. 32) and tellurium (127) and, in the 5th series, arsenic (75) stands before it and bromine (80) after it. Hence the atomic weight of selenium should be $\frac{1}{4}$(32 + 127 + 75 + 80) = 78.5, which is near to the generally accepted value Se = 79 (there is a possible error in the first decimal, so that 78.5 may be nearer the actual value).

Q′	R′	S′
Q″	R″	S″
Q‴	R‴	S‴

FIG. 24.3. Each element such as R″ has properties that are the average of those elements surrounding its position in the periodic table.

We see at once to what this leads:

The periodic dependence of the properties on the atomic weights of the elements gives a *new means for determining . . . the atomic weight* or atomicity of known but imperfectly investigated elements, for which no other means could as yet be applied for determining the true atomic weight. At the time [1869] when the periodic law was first proposed there were several such elements. It thus became possible to learn their true atomic weights, and these were verified by later researches. Among the elements thus concerned were indium, uranium, cerium, yttrium, and others . . . Thus a true law of nature anticipates facts, foretells magnitudes, gives a hold on nature, and leads to improvements in the methods of research, etc. . .

[Other] properties of selenium may also be determined in this manner; for example, arsenic forms H_3As, bromine gives HBr, and it is evident that selenium, which stands between them, should form H_2Se, with properties intermediate between those of H_3As and HBr. Even the physical properties of selenium and its compounds, not to speak of their composition, being determined by the group in which it occurs, may be foreseen with a close approach to reality from the properties of sulfur, tellurium, arsenic, and bromine.

(4) But there is another, still more important consequence:

In this manner it is possible to foretell the properties of an element still unknown, especially when it is surrounded by well-known elements. For instance, in the position IV, 5 [that is, in the IVth group and 5th series] an element is still wanting. These unknown elements may be named after the preceding known element of the same group by adding to the first syllable the prefix *eka-*, which means *one* in Sanskrit. The element IV, 5 follows [on the same side of the column] after IV, 3, and this latter position being occupied by silicon, I named this formerly unknown element ekasilicon and its symbol Es. The following are the properties which this element should have on the basis of the known properties of silicon, tin, zinc, and arsenic. Its atomic weight is nearly 72, it forms a higher oxide EsO_2, a lower oxide EsO, compounds of the general form EsX_4, and chemically unstable lower compounds of the form EsX_2. Es gives volatile organo-metallic compounds; for instance, $Es(CH_3)_4$, $Es(CH_3)_3Cl$, and $Es(C_2H_5)_4$, which boil at about 160°, etc.; also a volatile and liquid chloride, $EsCl_4$, boiling at about 90° and of density about 1.9. EsO_2 will be the anhydride of a feeble colloidal acid, metallic Es will be rather easily obtainable from the oxides and from K_2EsF_6 by reduction, EsS_2 will resemble SnS_2 and SiS_2, and will probably be soluble in ammonium sulphide; the density of Es will be about 5.5, and EsO_2 will have a density of about 4.7, etc. . .

This summary of his own predictions in 1871 shows fully the genius and daring of the man, the sweep and power of his scheme. And in 1887, C. Winckler of Freiberg did discover a metal, now called not ekasilicon but germanium (Ge), with the following properties: (a) atomic weight about $72\frac{1}{2}$ and density 5.5 gm/cm^3; (b) forms an oxide GeO_2 of density 4.7 gm/cm^3; (c) forms an organo-metallic compound $Ge(C_2H_5)_4$ that boils at 160°C; (d) forms a liquid chloride $GeCl_4$ with a boiling point of 83°C and density 1.9 gm/cm^3—all in accord with Mendeléeff's predictions! In a similar fashion Mendeléeff described the properties to be expected for the then unknown elements III, 4 and III, 5, now called gallium and scandium, and again his predictions turned out to be correct.

Even though not every aspect of Mendeléeff's work offered such marvelous agreement, these are indeed sensational results, reminiscent of the discovery of the asteriods in the general orbits predicted for them by Bode's law. Successful numerical predictions of this sort are among the most desired results in physical science, and the chemical profession soon cast off its initial reluctance to embrace the main conception of a periodic classification of elements.

24.5 The modern periodic table. It remains to tell briefly of some important rearrangements and additions that subsequently had to be made in the periodic table. Shown in Table 24.3 and also in Appendix D is one of its several modern forms; comparison of it with Mendeléeff's representation (Table 24.2) reveals these differences:

(1) Hydrogen is placed so as not to be uniquely associated with any single group; actually it is related chemically to both the alkali metals and the halogens.

(2) In each rectangle the symbol is placed so that elements in any vertical line belong to the same chemical family.

(3) The horizontal rows fall into 7 *periods*. Periods 1, 2, and 3 are short; 4, 5, and 6 are long, with two series each; and 7 has only three entries.

(4) In 1894 the surprising discovery was made that about 1% of our atmosphere consists of a gas, given the name *argon* (A), that had escaped previous detection because it does not enter into chemical combination with any elements. Afterward other such inert gaseous elements were discovered: helium (He), neon (Ne), krypton (Kr), xenon (Xe), radon (Rn); the six form the family of *inert gases*. The whole family could be incorporated in the periodic table simply by adding one vertical column, either interlaced with group VIII or, better, as a separate group with group number zero, to indicate that each inert gas has zero valence. This harmonious fit of a whole group of unexpected additions was a considerable triumph for the periodic scheme.

(5) Many new elements have been discovered, and there are now no more additions expected *within* the table. In the 57th place belongs not one element, but a whole set of 15 chemically almost indistinguishable elements, known as the *rare earths* or *lanthanide series*. Most of these elements were unknown in Mendeléeff's time, and indeed they somewhat disturb the symmetry of the table. Similarly, a set of over a dozen elements, forming what is called the *actinide rare earths* or *actinide series*, may best be placed in the 89th place.

(6) As we have seen, Mendeléeff arranged the elements in order of

TABLE 24.3.

PERIODIC TABLE OF THE ELEMENTS.

Atomic weights are based on the most recent values adopted by the International Union of Chemistry. (For artificially produced elements, the approximate atomic weight of the most stable isotope is given in brackets.) The full names of the elements are given in Appendix C.

Period	Series	I	II	III	IV	V	VI	VII	VIII	O
1	1	1 H 1.0080								2 He 4.003
2	2	3 Li 6.940	4 Be 9.013	5 B 10.82	6 C 12.011	7 N 14.008	8 O 16.0000	9 F 19.00		10 Ne 20.183
3	3	11 Na 22.991	12 Mg 24.32	13 Al 26.98	14 Si 28.09	15 P 30.975	16 S 32.066	17 Cl 35.457		18 A 39.944
4	4	19 K 39.100	20 Ca 40.08	21 Sc 44.96	22 Ti 47.90	23 V 50.95	24 Cr 52.01	25 Mn 54.94	26 Fe 55.85　27 Co 58.94　28 Ni 58.71	
	5	29 Cu 63.54	30 Zn 65.38	31 Ga 69.72	32 Ge 72.60	33 As 74.91	34 Se 78.96	35 Br 79.916		36 Kr 83.80
5	6	37 Rb 85.48	38 Sr 87.63	39 Y 88.92	40 Zr 91.22	41 Nb 92.91	42 Mo 95.95	43 Tc [99]	44 Ru 101.1　45 Rh 102.91　46 Pd 106.4	
	7	47 Ag 107.880	48 Cd 112.41	49 In 114.82	50 Sn 118.70	51 Sb 121.76	52 Te 127.61	53 I 126.91		54 Xe 131.30
6	8	55 Cs 132.91	56 Ba 137.36	57–71 Lanthanide series*	72 Hf 178.50	73 Ta 180.95	74 W 183.86	75 Re 186.22	76 Os 190.2　77 Ir 192.2　78 Pt 195.09	
	9	79 Au 197.0	80 Hg 200.61	81 Tl 204.39	82 Pb 207.21	83 Bi 209.00	84 Po 210	85 At [210]		86 Rn 222
7	10	87 Fr [223]	88 Ra 226.05	89– Actinide series**						

*Lanthanide series:

57 La 138.92	58 Ce 140.13	59 Pr 140.92	60 Nd 144.27	61 Pm [147]	62 Sm 150.35	63 Eu 152.0	64 Gd 157.26	65 Tb 158.93	66 Dy 162.51	67 Ho 164.94	68 Er 167.27	69 Tm 168.94	70 Yb 173.04	71 Lu 174.99

**Actinide series:

89 Ac 227	90 Th 232.05	91 Pa 231	92 U 238.07	93 Np [237]	94 Pu [242]	95 Am [243]	96 Cm [245]	97 Bk [249]	98 Cf [249]	99 E [253]	100 Fm [255]	101 Md [256]	102 No	103

increasing atomic weights. In the late 19th century, however, it was pointed out that this basic scheme breaks down in several places. For example, the chemical properties of argon (A) and potassium (K) demand that they should be placed in the 18th and 19th positions, whereas on a basis of their atomic weights alone (39.944 for argon, 39.100 for potassium), their positions should be interchanged. Other inversions of this kind have been found to be needed, for example, for the 52nd element, tellurium (at. wt. = 127.61) and the 53rd, iodine (at. wt. = 126.91). The consecutive integers that indicate the number of the best place or position for the element are called the *atomic numbers*, Z; thus for hydrogen, $Z = 1$; for tellurium, $Z = 52$; for uranium, $Z = 92$. The atomic numbers of all the elements are given both in Table 24.3 and Appendix D. To summarize, we may say that today both the chemical and physical properties of an element are recognized to be more dependent on its atomic number Z than on its atomic weight, for although usually atomic weight increases with increasing Z, there are a few inversions of the progress of atomic weights.

The need for inversions in the periodic table of the elements would have been to Mendeléeff not merely an esthetic blemish but a real catastrophe. He confidently expected, for example, that the atomic weight of tellurium (modern value = 127.61, 52nd place), when more accurately determined, would turn out to be lower than that of iodine (modern value = 126.91, 53rd place). In connection with just such a point, he said:

> The laws of nature admit of no exception . . . It was necessary to do one or the other—either to consider the periodic law as completely true, and as forming a new instrument in chemical research, or to refute it. Acknowledging the method of experiment to be the only true one, I myself verified what I could, and gave everyone the possibility of proving or confirming the law, and did not think, like L. Meyer, when writing about the periodic law that "it would be rash to change the accepted atomic weights on the basis of so uncertain a starting point."

Clearly, he overestimated the *necessity* of the periodic law in every detail, particularly as it had not yet received a physical explanation; and although the anomalous inversions in the sequence of elements have proved to be real (i.e., tellurium, in 52nd place, does have a higher atomic weight than iodine in 53rd place in the periodic table), their existence did not invalidate the scheme. As so often, the complexity of nature is here greater than any one generalization can accommodate. Yet one must understand that it was just this utter, enthusiastic belief in the existence of a simple scheme that carried Mendeléeff to his undaunted and far-reaching proposals.

The usefulness of the periodic law was not confined to the redetermination of some atomic weights and the prediction of properties of new elements. It provided an inner order in the list of elements that revealed several previously unsuspected analogies among elements. The whole study of chemistry was thereby revitalized. And perhaps most important of all, just as the Keplerian discovery of simple laws of planetary motion in elliptical orbits posed the tantalizing problem of how to account for it by a fundamental physical law, so was science now challenged to provide an explanation for the observed regularities of the periodic table in terms of a physical model of the atom.

This task, and its solution in our century, so reminiscent of Newton's solution in the analogous case, is to be developed in Part VII. The atom of the last century, however, by and large remained incapable of supplying a deeper insight into the fundamental processes of chemistry. On the other hand, it did achieve startling successes in the hands of 19th-century physicists. And we now turn to pick up that part of the story in the development of the atomic theory in chemistry and physics.

ADDITIONAL PROBLEMS

24.3. (a) Examine the modern periodic table of elements and cite all inversions. (b) Restate the periodic law in your own words, not forgetting about the inversions.

24.4. In the *Handbook of chemistry and physics* there is printed, below one of the periodic tables, a plot of valence numbers for the elements *vs.* atomic number. Neglect the *negative* valence numbers and plot (to element 65) a graph of *maximum* valences observed *vs.* atomic *weight*. What periodicity is found? Is there any physical or chemical significance to this periodicity? Does there have to be any?

24.5. In 1871, Mendeléeff reported that the value of the atomic weight for the then-unknown metal germanium is expected to be "nearly 72." Show what calculation he made to obtain this prediction, using atomic weights available to him at the time (Table 24.2). Would this method of calculation have worked reasonably well if *modern* data had been available and used?

24.6. Prepare a table comparing Mendeléeff's prediction of 1871 for the properties of ekasilicon and the corresponding measured values for the element germanium, discovered in 1887.

24.7. In the 1897 English edition of his book *Principles of chemistry*, we find Mendéeleff's own summary of his original work on the periodic table. Discuss each of the eight points, choosing further illustrations from the material in this chapter:

The substance of this paper is embraced in the following conclusions: (1) The elements, if arranged according to their atomic weights, exhibit an evident *periodicity* of properties. (2) Elements which are similar as regards their chemical properties have atomic weights which are either of nearly the same value (platinum, iridium, osmium) or which increase regularly (e.g., potassium, rubidium, cesium). (3) The arrangement of the elements or of groups of elements in the order of their atomic weights corresponds with their so-called *valencies*. (4) The elements which are the most widely distributed in nature have *small* atomic weights, and all the elements of small atomic weight are characterized by sharply defined properties. They are therefore typical elements. (5) The *magnitude* of the atomic weight determines the character of an element. (6) The discovery of many yet unknown elements may be expected. For instance, elements analogous to aluminum and silicon, whose atomic weights would be between 65 and 75. (7) The atomic weight of an element may sometimes be corrected by aid of a knowledge of those of the adjacent elements. Thus the combining weight of tellurium must lie between 123 and 126, and cannot be 128. (8) Certain characteristic properties of the elements can be foretold from their atomic weights. The entire periodic law is included in these lines.

Supplementary Reading

Bonner, F., and M. Phillips, *Principles of physical science* (Addison-Welsey, 1957), Chap. 9.

Chalmers, T. W., *Historic researches* (Scribner's, 1952), Chap. VII.

Holmyard, E. J., *Makers of chemistry* (Oxford University Press, 1931), pp. 263–273.

Leicester, H. M., *The historical background of chemistry* (Wiley, 1956), Chaps. 16 and 20.

Leicester, H. M., and H. S. Klickstein, *A source book in chemistry 1400–1900* (McGraw-Hill, 1952). Selections from Mendeléeff.

Newman, J. R., *The world of mathematics* (Simon and Schuster, 1956), pp. 910–931, Mendeléeff.

Pauling, L., *General chemistry* (Freeman, 1947, 1953), Chaps. 5 and 6.

Posin, D. Q., *Mendeleyev* (Whittlesey House, 1948).

CHAPTER 25

THE KINETIC THEORY OF MATTER AND HEAT

Having watched the establishment of the chemical atomic-molecular theory through the labors chiefly of Dalton, Avogadro, and Cannizzaro, we finally come back, full circle, to problems that had their start with Democritus and Leucippus: the physical structure of matter and the nature of heat. In this chapter we shall re-examine our model of gases and our theory of heat, and bring them together into *one* conceptual scheme that serves also to explain important laws and numerous phenomena that we have previously discussed. As the scheme unfolds, we are taken through a whole spectrum of sophistication, starting with plausible and qualitative notions, and reaching at the end some rather subtle and quantitatively precise arguments.

The key investigator here, J. P. Joule, was exactly the person best fitted to accomplish the final synthesis, by virtue of having Rumford's conviction that heat is "a mode of motion," Bernoulli's disposition to treat the problem quantitatively, Mayer's faith in a principle of conservation of energy, and of course his own impressive experiments on the equivalence of heat and work. With this rich background, Joule, in lectures and published papers from 1847 to 1857, resurrected and extended the century-old gas model of Bernoulli (Section 21.6), sharpening the concepts it involved and fortifying it with convincing arguments and calculations.

25.1 Joule on matter and heat. Joule's 1847 paper, "On matter, living force, and heat," is largely an argument fashioned after the manner of Rumford; that is, he tried to make plausible the proposition that a kinetic theory of heat, joined to the picture of matter as composed of particles, can account *qualitatively* quite well for a wide variety of physical phenomena. This is shown in the following extract from the paper. In reading it, we must translate the term "living force" to *kinetic energy*, and "attraction through space" to *potential energy*.

A few words may be said . . . with respect to the real nature of heat. The most prevalent opinion, until of late, has been that it is a *substance* [caloric] possessing, like all other matter, impenetrability and extension. We have, however, shown that heat can be converted into living force and into attraction through space. It is perfectly clear, therefore, that unless matter can be converted into attraction through space, which is too absurd an idea to be entertained for a moment, the hypothesis of heat being a substance must fall

429

to the ground. Heat must therefore consist either of living force or of attraction through space. In the former case we can conceive the constituent particles of heated bodies to be, either in whole or in part, in a state of motion. In the latter we suppose the particles to be moved apart by the process of heating, so as to exert attraction through greater space. I am inclined to believe that both of these hypotheses will be found to hold good—that in some instances, particularly in the case of *sensible heat* [which is responsible for temperature changes] . . . as indicated by a thermometer, heat will be found to consist in the living force of the particles of the bodies in which it is induced; whilst in others, particularly in the case of *latent heat*, the phenomena are produced by the separation of particle from particle, so as to cause them to attract one another through a greater space. We may conceive, then, that the communication of heat to a body consists, in fact, in the communication of . . . living force to its particles.

It will perhaps appear to some of you somewhat strange that a body apparently quiescent should in reality be the seat of motions of great rapidity; but you will observe that the bodies themselves, considered as wholes, are not supposed to be in motion. The constituent particles, or atoms of the bodies, are supposed to be in motion, without producing a gross motion of the whole mass. These particles, or atoms, being far too small to be seen even by the help of the most powerful microscopes, it is no wonder that we cannot observe their motion. There is therefore reason to suppose that the particles of all bodies, their constituent atoms, are in a state of motion almost too rapid for us to conceive, for the phenomena cannot otherwise be explained. The velocity of the atoms of water, for instance, is at least equal to a mile per second of time. If, as there is reason to think, some particles are at rest while others are in motion, the velocity of the latter will be proportionally greater.

An increase of the velocity . . . of the particles will constitute an increase of temperature, which may be distributed among the neighboring bodies by what is called *conduction*, that is, on the present hypothesis, by the communication of the increased motion from the particles of one body to those of another. The velocity of the particles being further increased, they will tend to fly from each other . . . overcoming the attraction subsisting between them. This removal of the particles from each other will constitute a new condition of the body—it will enter into the state of fusion or become melted. But, from what we have already stated, you will perceive that, in order to remove the particles violently attracting one another asunder, the expenditure of a certain amount of living force or heat will be required. Hence it is that heat is always absorbed when the state of a body is changed from solid to liquid, or from liquid to gas . . . When, again, by the application of cold we condense the steam into water, and by a further abstraction of heat we bring the water to the solid condition of ice, we witness the repetition of similar phenomena in the reverse order . . .

Taken by itself, this qualitative conception of heat would hardly seem convincing. But Joule gave quantitative details in later papers, where he calculated the speed of gas particles, and where he showed that his model for gases predicted Boyle's law, gave physical meaning to the concept of absolute temperature, and provided an interpretation of the observed specific heat capacities of various gases. What is more, other contributors (A. Krönig, 1856, and R. Clausius, 1857) soon showed that from Joule's scheme one could deduce, and so "explain," a variety of other previously known results, including the laws of Charles and Gay-Lussac and of Avogadro. Yet these are hardly more than hints at the richness of conclusions and general usefulness of the kinetic theory which, through the further work of such men as Helmholtz, Maxwell, Boltzmann, and Gibbs, eventually became a major triumph of 19th-century physics.

25.2 Some qualitative features of the kinetic theory. For our purposes it will be well now to leave the strictly historical road and to summarize in modern language some of the qualitative features of the kinetic theory before we turn to its quantitative aspects.

(a) *Heating by friction.* When two objects rub against each other, forces of friction act on the respective surfaces. The "work done against friction" is in good part the work done in accelerating the particles in the surfaces, and these particles, through collisions, in turn impart greater speeds to particles in the interior of the object. Thus the work done against friction is converted at least in part into increased kinetic energy of the particles. In a solid, there is an increase in the vibrational energy of the crowded atoms; in the simplest gases, there is an increase in the kinetic energy of the molecules moving in a random fashion throughout the container; and in a liquid, both types of motion play their parts. In all three cases there is a rise in temperature corresponding to this increased kinetic energy; by this mechanism, work done against frictional forces can result in the heating of the bodies involved.

(b) *Heat conduction; thermal expansion.* Conduction of heat from a hot to a cold body consists of a transfer of kinetic energy at the surfaces of contact between the bodies, due to the bombardment of the particles of one body by those of the second body. Expansion of an object on heating is the consequence of the increased agitation of individual particles within the object and of their resulting greater separation through more violent mutual collisions. Suppose that a mercury-in-glass thermometer is inserted in a gas, and that work is then done on the gas, say, to compress it. The thermometer will soon indicate a rise in temperature because (1) the work done to compress the gas serves to increase the kinetic energy of the gas molecules, (2) these molecules in turn strike the glass of the thermometer more violently and frequently, (3) the glass particles eventually transfer some of their vibrational energy by collision to the mercury particles, and then (4) the mercury column expands as its particles separate owing to their increased agitation.

(c) *The Brownian movement.* Because atoms and molecules are roughly a thousand times smaller in diameter than either the wavelengths of light or the diameter of the sense receptors of our skin, we cannot possibly see or feel *directly* the particles or their individual motions. But a small speck of dust or of other solid matter floating in still air or suspended in a liquid can be seen to dance perpetually, as if alive, when watched through a microscope (Fig. 25.1). In fact, when first observed with tiny grains of plant pollen in 1827 by the English botanist Robert Brown, this phenomenon (now called *Brownian movement*) was compared to the motions of living matter. Actually, it was later shown that this "dance" of the visible particles was their response to bombardment from all sides by the swarm of invisible, high-speed particles of the surrounding gas or liquid.

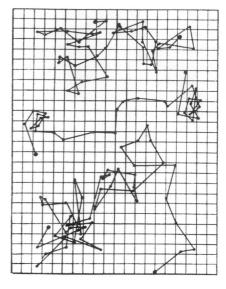

FIG. 25.1. Brownian movement. The positions of three grains, suspended in water, observed at 30-sec intervals. (*After* J. Perrin.)

(d) *Other phenomena.* As the extracts from Joule's paper have indicated, kinetic theory makes plausible the differences between the solid, liquid, and gaseous states of matter, and the reason for the existence of heats of fusion and of vaporization. It also serves to explain the following phenomena: (1) diffusion of one gas through another, due to thermally agitated molecules of one kind working their way through a space containing molecules of another kind; (2) the immediate expansion of a gas to fill any vessel no matter how large, because the attractive forces between gas molecules are almost negligibly small and the velocities of random motion are very high; (3) the pressure exerted by a gas on the walls of its container, due to billions of collisions per second of the agitated gas molecules with the walls (just as Bernoulli had postulated in 1738).

25.3 Model of a gas. In earlier chapters we encountered various simple quantitative laws that apply well to all gases, which suggests that all gases have basically the same simple structure. Thus we may hope that, at least for gases, a satisfactory quantitative theory can be obtained. Our task, quite typical of current work in any of the physical sciences, is *to construct a plausible model* of a gas in the light of all the available clues, *and then to investigate whether previously known as well as new, verifiable quantitative relations can be derived from the model.* Some of the assumptions which must enter into the construction of the model may be well-tested ones, while others may be merely plausible or even boldly new, and so will be justifiable only *a posteriori*, if they yield verifiable results. Let us summarize the assumptions upon which our initial model is to be built.

(a) *Gases consist of molecules.* The first assumption, of course, is that a gas consists of molecules, each made up of one atom or a group of atoms, depending on the particular gas with which we are dealing. If the gas is a pure element or a compound, all of its molecules are assumed to be identical. The most convincing evidence for these assumptions, the success of the Dalton-Avogadro atomic-molecular theory, originally was chemical.

(b) *The size of molecules is negligible.* The actual volume occupied by the molecules is assumed to be negligible compared with the space between them. The experimental evidence here is varied and convincing. For example, if a gas is cooled until it condenses, the resulting liquid may have a volume thousands of times smaller than that of the gas. A gas may also be compressed to a minute fraction of its original volume. Indeed, various experiments show that the diameters of molecules are of the order of 10^{-8} cm (10^{-10} m). Even molecules so large and complicated as those of some of the oils (for example, glyceryl oleate, $C_{57}H_{104}O_6$) have diameters of not more than 10^{-7} cm, for this is the approximate measured thickness of oil films spread on water.

(c) *The number of molecules is very large.* We may assume, in our model, that the number of molecules in any sample of gas is almost inconceivably large. Avogadro's number implies that for a gas under standard conditions of temperature and pressure, the number of molecules in one cubic meter is 2.7×10^{25}. And even in the best vacuum obtainable in the laboratory (down to 10^{-11} atmosphere of pressure) there are at ordinary temperatures still many million molecules in each cubic centimeter.

(d) *Molecules are in random motion.* Fundamental in the kinetic theory is the assumption that the molecules are in perpetual motion and traveling in so random a fashion that the number moving in any one direction is, on the average, the same as that moving in any other direction. Thus each molecule forever moves in a zigzag path, for it collides many million times per second with other molecules of the gas or with the particles making up the walls of the container; but these collisions are so brief that in our analysis we shall entirely ignore their duration. Moreover, the distance a molecule moves between collisions can lie between zero and thousands of times the molecular diameter, but the very short or very long distances are unusual. The *average* distance moved between collisions is called the *mean free path.* In oxygen under ordinary conditions, the mean free path is about 10^{-5} cm (10^{-7} m).

The evidence supporting these assumptions about thermal agitation and molecular paths comes from a great variety of experiments on diffusion, on the motions of electrified particles shot through a gas, on the Brownian movement, and so on.

(e) *The forces between molecules are negligible.* The molecules do not exert appreciable forces on one another except during collisions. This is an assumption we might be tempted to question, for the average distance between molecules, although large in terms of molecular dimensions, is exceedingly small compared with the distances between the ordinary bodies whose force laws we have previously examined. What, for example, would be the *gravitational* force F_{grav} between two oxygen molecules? The mutual gravitational force will be greatest when the molecules are close enough to collide, that is, when the distance d between their centers is equal to the diameter of an oxygen molecule, 3×10^{-10} m. To make this calculation, we must assume that Newton's law of gravitation, $F_{\text{grav}} = G(m_1 m_2 / r^2)$ (Eq. 11.7) holds for the submicroscopic domain. Recalling that a mole of oxygen has a mass of 32 gm and consists of about 6.02×10^{23} molecules (Avogadro's number), we see that each oxygen molecule has a mass m_0 of about $32/(6.02 \times 10^{23})$ gm, or about 5×10^{-26} kgm. Two such molecules 3×10^{-10} m apart would exert on each other the gravitational force

$$F_{\text{grav}} = G \frac{m_1 m_2}{r^2} = 6.7 \times 10^{-11} \frac{\text{new·m}^2}{\text{kgm}^2} \times \frac{(5 \times 10^{-26})^2 \text{ kgm}^2}{(3 \times 10^{-10})^2 \text{ m}^2}$$

$$= 2 \times 10^{-42} \text{ new.}$$

This maximum possible value of the gravitational attraction between molecules is evidently very small indeed, but that it is indeed negligible remains to be shown now.

PROBLEM 25.1.   Show that the weight of an oxygen molecule is about 5×10^{-25} new. This is taken to be negligibly small for most considerations; what would be the effect of the weight of molecules on their motion?

It was also suspected quite early that there may be, say, electrical as well as gravitational forces among molecules. The necessary background to discuss exactly what or how strong these other forces may be is to be given in a later chapter, but we can now examine an experiment that will show at least whether the force or forces between molecules are of significant magnitude. A gas that initially is under pressure is allowed to expand into a big evacuated vessel, so that the molecules move out to greater distances from one another. If the intermolecular forces are *attractive*, the molecules will, on the average, be slowed down while separating from one another, as the kinetic energy is being partly converted into potential energy. As we shall see later, a reduction in average kinetic energy means that the gas as a whole cools upon expanding into the vacuum. If, on the other hand, the forces are *repulsive*, the molecules will, on the average, speed up while separating and thus the gas will heat up. But both Gay-Lussac (Section 20.2) and, in 1845, Joule found experimentally that a gas does not change in temperature upon expanding into a vacuum. This indicated that there are no intermolecular forces (except, of course, the momentary ones occurring during actual collisions) or, as Joule more cautiously put it, if intermolecular forces existed, they were too weak to be detected by his experiments. A few years later, in 1852, Lord Kelvin devised a more sensitive experiment, which he and Joule carried out together. They were able to detect small temperature changes upon expansion which could be explained by assuming that there is a very slight attraction between gas molecules.

Here we may digress for a moment. Even though the forces between widely separated molecules are so small that we ignore them completely in building our model of a gas, we must still expect that when these particles of matter come closer together, as in liquids and solids, the forces between them become important. Indeed, it is the strong mutual attraction between particles crowded close together that accounts for the slowness with which a liquid evaporates. It is these forces that account for *cohesion* (binding together of like particles), as within a solid or liquid sample of a pure compound, and for *adhesion* (the attraction between different materials), as when particles of glue adhere to those of wood.

But if the particles of matter are crowded still closer together, we must assume that mutual *repulsion* begins to predominate over the attraction and that it increases rapidly with decreasing particle distance. For how else could we account for the resistance offered by liquids and solids to the slightest compression, and for the increasing resistance as the compression is increased? Even the rebounding of two gas molecules when they collide is explainable by the predominance of this mutual repulsive force when the distance between the two molecules is very small. As James Clerk Maxwell pointed out in 1860:

> Instead of saying that the particles are hard, spherical, and elastic, we may if we please say that the particles are centres of force, of which the action is insensible except at a certain small distance, when it suddenly appears as a repulsive force of very great intensity. It is evident that either assumption will lead to the same results.

Our whole discussion of the net force between the particles of matter may be conveniently assembled in a single graph of net force of attraction or repulsion, plotted as a function of intermolecular distance, as in Fig. 25.2.

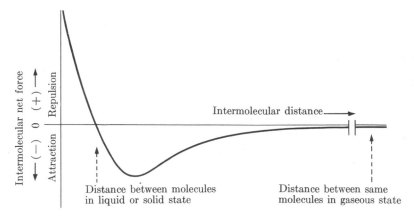

FIG. 25.2. Qualitative graph of the net force between two molecules *vs.* the intermolecular distance.

PROBLEM 25.2.   In Fig. 25.2, justify the indicated position for the average distance between the particles within liquids and solids. For example, why can this arrow not point to the minimum in the curve?

(f) *Collisions are perfectly elastic.*   Returning now to our gas model, we assume that the collisions between molecules and with the walls of the container are perfectly elastic whatever the nature of the forces during collision may be; in other words, we assume that the kinetic energy of a molecule just after an impact is the same as immediately before the impact. Only *during* the brief collision will the kinetic energy temporarily pass into potential energy of elastic distortion.

The justification for this assumption is evident. If the impacts were not perfectly elastic, the kinetic energies of the molecules would gradually become smaller, and thus a gas would eventually condense to a liquid, even if enclosed in a heat-insulated container and left completely to itself. But nothing like this has ever been observed. Nevertheless, it is safer to say that the collisions must be perfectly elastic *on the average.* Diatomic molecules or others that consist of several atoms may, upon colliding, be set into rotation and their atoms set into vibration with respect to one another, and in these cases some of the kinetic energy of forward motion is converted into energy of rotation and vibration. Although some of the forward (translational) kinetic energy thus may seem to disappear, actually it is recovered in other collisions in which the reverse effects occur.

In assuming perfectly elastic collisions and perpetual motion for the submicroscopic molecules, we must remember that no large-scale body, not even a sphere of the best steel, shows perfectly elastic impacts. There is always some loss of mechanical energy during collisions because of internal friction and a consequent rise in temperature of the sphere because of increased internal molecular agitation.   But for molecules themselves, what could be the meaning of frictional heat losses when they collide? Here is a good example of conceptions gained from large-scale experience breaking down when applied to the new realm of the submicroscopic.

In this light, one may well ask whether it is not dangerous to assume that the laws of Newtonian mechanics, which were formulated on the basis of experience with relatively large objects, hold also in the submicroscopic realm.   This is a valid reservation, but at least at the start of our work in microphysics we have no laws available other than the Newtonian ones.   Therefore we must keep our eyes open to retract this extrapolation if the facts revealed by experiment demand it.

PROBLEM 25.3.   (a) List briefly the several assumptions upon which our initial model of a gas is based. (b) Give the experimental or theoretical justification for each assumption.

25.4 Derivation of the pressure formula.   Using the foregoing assumptions, Joule, in 1848, succeeded in deducing a relationship between the pressure of a gas and the number, speeds, and mass of the molecules. This achievement, which we shall now examine, was of crucial significance. It was the first quantitative relationship or formula obtained from the general atomistic hypothesis and the kinetic theory of heat.   Therefore, when predictions based on this formula were shown to be correct, the assumptions used in the derivations became thereby "verified," and the kinetic theory was established in its earliest form.

In following these steps, we shall illustrate the usual procedure by which any theory in physical science gains plausibility: (a) assumptions are made on the basis of existing experimental or theoretical knowledge, (b) from these assumptions a deduction, preferably quantitative, is made, (c) the deduction is either directly checked or shown to be in accord with other consequences which can be checked directly, and (d) thus we are led to accept the original assumptions.   But as our discussion will also show, there are dangers in this sequence.

To deduce the formula relating the pressure of a gas and the characteristics of its molecules, as Joule did, let us picture in our minds a pure gas kept under constant pressure and temperature in a rigid cubical box with sides of length l. If this simplifying assumption seems too restrictive, remember that any real gas tank, regardless of its shape, may be thought of as consisting of many tiny cubical subspaces.

All the molecules in this pure gas have the same mass, m_0, and all are flying about in random motion in every direction, frequently colliding with one another and with the six walls of the cubical box.   Hence the average effect on the walls is the same as if $\frac{1}{3}$ of the molecules are moving back and forth in the x-direction, $\frac{1}{3}$ in the y-direction, and $\frac{1}{3}$ in the z-

direction.   Let us consider first the effect of a single molecule that we imagine to be moving back and forth in the x-direction, as in Fig. 25.3. If the speed of the molecule while moving, say, toward the fixed wall A is v, its momentum is m_0v; and, since it bounces back from wall A with the same speed with which it hits after the elastic collision, its momentum after the rebound is $-m_0v$. Therefore its change of momentum as a result of each impact with the wall is $m_0v - (-m_0v)$, or $2m_0v$. After every impact the molecule must move to the opposite wall and then back again, a total distance of $2l$; and since it moves at speed v, the time needed per round-trip distance $2l$ is $t = 2l/v$. Conversely, the number of round trips per unit time is $1/t = v/2l$; the molecule makes at a given wall $v/2l$ impacts per unit time.   Thus its change in momentum per unit time owing to collisions with wall A is $2m_0v \times v/2l$, or m_0v^2/l.

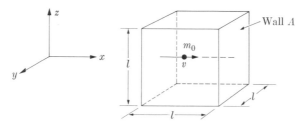

FIG. 25.3. A single molecule moving directly toward wall A in the cubical box.

Suppose now that there are N molecules in the box instead of only one. Then the average effect on wall A is the same as if $\frac{1}{3}N$ molecules are moving back and forth in the x-direction, and the total change in their momentum per unit time owing to impacts with either wall is $\frac{1}{3}N \cdot m_0\overline{v^2}/l$. Here $\overline{v^2}$ denotes the *average of the squares of the molecular speeds,* for it must be assumed that the molecules are moving with *different speeds* because of their chance collisions with one another.

If Newton's laws of motion are applicable in the submicroscopic realm, then by his second law, Eq. (17.1), the average force $\overline{F}$ exerted normally on the molecules by wall A is equal to the total change in momentum per unit time at that wall, or

$$\overline{F} = \frac{1}{3} \frac{N m_0 \overline{v^2}}{l}. \tag{25.1}$$

The hail of molecules against a wall is incomparably thicker than, say, the rain of machine-gun bullets on a target, and hence the force which the wall experiences is far steadier. Moreover, in view of Newton's third law (Section 4.14), the force which the wall exerts on the molecules is equal in magnitude, although opposite in direction, to the force with which the molecules push on the wall. Therefore we shall omit the bar over the symbol F and consider Eq. (25.1) to yield the instantaneous value of the force on the wall of the box.

Our interest is in deducing a formula for the pressure exerted by a gas, and we will recall that pressure P is defined as F/A, the perpendicular force per unit area. Therefore, by dividing both members of Eq. (25.1) by l^2, which is the area A of any one wall of the cubical box, we obtain

$$\frac{F}{l^2} \equiv P = \frac{1}{3} \frac{N m_0 \overline{v^2}}{l^3} .$$

But l^3 is the volume V of the box. Hence

$$P = \frac{1}{3} \frac{N m_0 \overline{v^2}}{V} . \tag{25.2}$$

Equation (25.2) may be called the "pressure formula," derived from our kinetic-theory model; it relates the pressure in the vessel to the volume, the number of molecules, their mass and their speeds. (Note that we have not yet produced evidence whether Eq. (25.2) is in accord with observable fact.) But since N is the number of molecules present and m_0 is the mass of each molecule, the product $N m_0$ is simply the total mass of the sample of gas, which can be determined by weighing. The pressure P and the volume V may also be directly measured. Hence, as Joule himself pointed out, Eq. (25.2) can be used to compute the expected value of $\overline{v^2}$, the average of the squares of the molecular speeds, called for the sake of brevity the *mean-square speed*.

EXAMPLE 25.1. Handbooks of physical data show that 1.00 m^3 of nitrogen under a pressure of 1 atm ($= 1.01 \times 10^5$ new/m^2) and at temperature 0°C has a mass $N m_0$ of 1.25 kgm. Compute the mean-square speed of nitrogen molecules at 0°C.

Solution. Solving Eq. (25.2) for $\overline{v^2}$ and inserting the given values for P, V, and $N m_0$, we have $\overline{v^2} = 3(PV/N m_0) = 3 \times (1.01 \times 10^5 \text{ new/m}^2) \times 1.00$ m^3/1.25 kgm $= 24.2 \times 10^4$ m^2/sec^2. This is a prediction, based on our model of gases.

25.5 Rms and average speeds. By taking the square root of $\overline{v^2}$, we obtain a quantity $\sqrt{\overline{v^2}}$ that is appropriately called the *root-mean-square* (rms) *speed*. Thus, using the value for the mean-square speed found in Example 25.1, we see that the rms speed for nitrogen molecules at 0°C is expected to be $\sqrt{24.2 \times 10^4 \text{ m}^2/\text{sec}^2}$, or 492 m/sec. This would be about $\frac{1}{3}$ mi/sec—comparable to the speed of a rifle bullet!

The rms speed is not the same thing as the ordinary average speed (arithmetic mean speed). For example, suppose we had only 3 molecules with speeds of 500, 1000, and 1500 m/sec respectively. Then the rms speed for the molecules of this "gas" is

$$\sqrt{\overline{v^2}} = \sqrt{\frac{(500)^2 + (1000)^2 + (1500)^2}{3} \frac{m^2}{sec^2}} = 1080 \frac{m}{sec},$$

whereas the average speed is

$$\bar{v} = \frac{500 + 1000 + 1500}{3} \frac{m}{sec} = 1000 \frac{m}{sec},$$

or 8% less. In general, the average speed is somewhat less than the rms speed, but in what follows, it will usually be permissible to neglect the difference. Figure 25.4 shows the difference between $\bar{v}$ and the rms speed when the distribution of speeds of the molecules is the same as in a real gas.

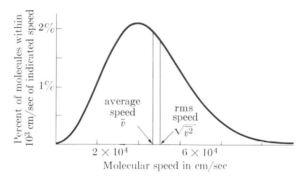

FIG. 25.4. Distribution of speeds for nitrogen molecules at 0°C.

25.6 Plausibility of the theory. For all gases, the kinetic theory predicts average molecular speeds that are enormous compared with the speeds of everyday objects. We have just seen the prediction of about $\frac{1}{3}$ mi/sec for nitrogen molecules. At first this was puzzling, but then it was noted that these molecular speeds are of the same orders of magnitude as the speeds of *sound* in the gases. Thus, for air under standard conditions of temperature and pressure, the molecular rms speed is 485 m/sec, while the speed of sound in the air is 332 m/sec. Similarly, the calculated molecular rms speed and the sound speed at STP for hydrogen are 1838 and 1284 m/sec, for ammonia vapor, 633 and 415 m/sec, and for carbon dioxide, 393 and 259 m/sec. These correspondences strongly suggest that molecular speeds are a determining factor in sound transmission.

This is what we should expect even from mere qualitative considerations of our gas model, for the obvious way to think of the propagation of sound waves is to visualize it as a directional motion of the molecules superimposed on their random chaotic motion, so that the energy of the sound wave is carried as kinetic energy from one gas molecule to the neighboring ones with which it collides. Because of the many millions of collisions per second, a molecule traverses a zigzag path such that, despite its high speed, minutes or hours may be needed for it to move even a few meters along one given direction in a quiescent gas. But the *energy* of the sound wave *is* communicated with molecular speed from molecule to molecule. As to the numerical values cited earlier, we really should not expect the speed of sound to be quite as large as the rms speed of the molecules (why not?); in fact, the numerical difference is predictable with great accuracy from the complete theory of sound propagation.

The foregoing picture of molecules restrained by mutual collisions from moving rapidly in any given direction, despite their large individual speeds, also explains why the scent of, say, perfume (a swarm of vapor molecules evaporating from the liquid perfume) travels so slowly across a room free from air currents. This explanation disposed of one of the early objections to the kinetic theory.

PROBLEM 25.4. Show that Eq. (25.2) can be written in the alternative form $P = \frac{1}{3}d\overline{v^2}$, where d is the density, or mass per unit volume, of the sample of gas.

PROBLEM 25.5. At 0°C and under 1 atm pressure, the density of air is 1.29 kgm/m^3. (a) Show that the kinetic theory predicts an rms speed of 485 m/sec for air molecules under these conditions. (b) Express this speed in miles per second. (c) What additional assumption have you tacitly introduced in the model in solving this problem?

25.7 Other phenomena explained. The general similarity between the rms speeds of molecules and sound velocities in gases does not by itself constitute a sufficiently convincing proof in favor of our model and the kinetic theory. But we have barely begun to tap the rich flow of consequences that follow from our assumptions. Of the many phenomena and regularities which can be understood in the light of the kinetic theory, two previously known empirical laws stand out.

(a) *Law of partial pressures.* In 1802, Dalton had postulated that a mixture of gases having no chemical action on one another exerts a pressure that is simply the sum of the pressures which each gas would exert if it alone occupied the same volume at the same temperature. This empirical law is explained immediately in terms of the gas-model assumption that individual molecules act independently because they are so small that they do not appreciably obstruct one another. Thus in a tank containing air, the oxygen molecules in their collisions with the walls of the tank behave as if the nitrogen and other molecules constituting air were not present, and the *partial* contribution which the oxygen molecules make to the total pressure is the pressure they would produce if they occupied the tank alone.   The total pressure is simply the sum of the partial pressures.

(b) *Boyle's law.* Let us rewrite Eq. (25.2) in the form

$$PV = \tfrac{1}{3}Nm_0\overline{v^2}. \tag{25.3}$$

If we make the plausible assumption that $\overline{v^2}$ remains constant so long as the temperature is kept constant, then Eq. (25.3) asserts that PV is constant for any fixed mass Nm_0 of gas kept at constant temperature. *But this is the empirical Boyle's law*, Eq. (21.1).   Moreover, Eq. (25.3) predicts that if the mass Nm_0 of a gas is, say, doubled without changing the volume and temperature, the pressure will be doubled; and this too is in accord with experiment.

The success of being able to interpret two well-established laws on the basis of the kinetic theory gives us additional confidence in the model, and we are now ready to expand its field of application. *We shall now assume that the "pressure formula" (Eq. 25.2 or 25.3) is correct, and see whether this assumption leads to new and verifiable results.*

25.8 Kinetic-theory interpretation of temperature.   Thus far our concern has been with gases when they are not undergoing changes of temperature.   To introduce the temperature into the kinetic theory, we may utilize the empirical gas law (Eq. 21.4), which may be written $PV/T = r$, or $PV = rT$.   Combining this expression with Eq. (25.3), we obtain

$$\tfrac{1}{3}Nm_0\overline{v^2} = rT. \tag{25.4}$$

This equation may be put into a still more illuminating form if we note that the average translational kinetic energy $\overline{E}_k$ of a molecule is $\tfrac{1}{2}m_0\overline{v^2}$. Thus, if Eq. (25.4) is first rewritten in the form

$$\tfrac{2}{3}N \cdot \tfrac{1}{2}m_0\overline{v^2} = \tfrac{2}{3}N\overline{E}_k = rT,$$

and then is solved for $\overline{E}_k$, we have

$$\overline{E}_k = \frac{3}{2} \cdot \frac{r}{N} \cdot T. \tag{25.5}$$

As noted in Section 21.4, the value of the gas constant r depends on the kind and mass of the sample of gas under consideration; N is the number of molecules in the sample.   Thus it would seem that Eq. (25.5) assigns to each molecule an average kinetic energy which goes up with temperature but which is, at a given temperature, different for each sample. But this interpretation is incorrect.   As we shall now see, the ratio r/N is a universal constant, and therefore Eq. (25.5), based on the kinetic-theory model of the gas, means that *the average kinetic energy of each molecule in every sample depends only on the temperature, and is in fact directly proportional to the absolute temperature T.* For example, if a gas is heated from 273°K (0°C) to twice this temperature, namely 546°K (273°C), the average kinetic energy of each molecule will be doubled. Indeed, Eq. (25.5) defines the *meaning* of temperature in the kinetic theory, namely that temperature is the measure of the average molecular kinetic energy. Whether Eq. (25.5) is useful is of course still to be proved; it depends upon whether it will yield predictions that are in accord with experiments.

But first to the proof that r/N in Eq. (25.5) is a universal constant. The gas law of Section 21.4 could be written

$$\frac{PV}{T} = r, \tag{25.6}$$

where the constant r was found to have a different value for each different sample. Specifically, experiments with samples of the same gas but with different total masses m would reveal that

$$\frac{PV}{T} \propto m.$$

Furthermore, choosing gas samples of equal mass but with different molecular weights M would yield the empirical relation

$$\frac{PV}{T} \propto \frac{1}{M}.$$

No other factors are found to affect the value of the ratio PV/T, and thus

$$\frac{PV}{T} \propto \frac{m}{M}.$$

But of course m/M, by definition, is the number of moles n of the sample. Therefore

$$\frac{PV}{T} \propto n.$$

To convert this proportionality into an equation, we introduce a constant R (which, unlike r, is a *universal* gas constant, having the value of 8.31 j/mole·°K for all samples of all gases; see Problem 25.7):

$$\frac{PV}{T} = Rn,$$

or, as it is more usually written,

$$PV = nRT. \tag{25.7}$$

This important equation, it must be emphasized, is an *empirical* equation; it is based on experiments with gases that are far from their liquefaction pressure and temperature. It is usually referred to as the *equation of state* of a gas, for the variables P, V, n, and T determine the physical state of a given sample of gas at any given time, and the relationship between these variables given by the equation helps us to determine the state of the sample at any other time. We note that the equation of state summarizes and contains all the other gas laws, each of which held only under some special condition (e.g., at constant temperature).

Comparison of Eqs. (25.6) and (25.7) shows that $r = Rn$. But in that case, the ratio r/N in Eq. (25.5) is

$$\frac{r}{N} = \frac{Rn}{N}.$$

The ratio n/N is merely the reciprocal of N/n (the number of molecules per mole) which, by Avogadro's law, we have already found to be a universal constant (N_0, Avogadro's number); therefore

$$\frac{r}{N} = \frac{R}{N_0}.$$

The right member is the ratio of two universal constants. *Thus r/N is itself a universal constant*, with the value of $(8.31/6.02 \times 10^{23})$ j/°K, or 1.38×10^{-23} j/°K. The symbol k is used to represent R/N_0:

$$k \equiv \frac{R}{N_0}.$$

The constant k, which is of significance in many branches of physical science, is called *Boltzmann's constant*, in honor of the Austrian physicist Ludwig Boltzmann (1844–1906), whose work paved the way for many advances in this field. Now we can rewrite Eq. (25.5) in the important form

$$\bar{E}_k \left(\equiv \frac{\overline{mv^2}}{2} \right) = \frac{3}{2} kT. \tag{25.8}$$

PROBLEM 25.6. (a) Show that the average kinetic energy of one molecule of any gas at ordinary room temperature (20°C, 293°K) is 6.07×10^{-21} j. Does this value depend on the pressure or density of the gas? (b) Compute the total kinetic energy of all the molecules comprising 1 mole of any gas at 20°C. (c) Compute $\overline{E}_k$ at −79°C, the temperature of "dry ice." (d) State the physical meaning of Eq. (25.8) in words.

PROBLEM 25.7.   Show that the universal gas constant R has the value 8.31 j/mole·°K. (*Hint:* Write Eq. (25.7) in the form $PV/Tn = R$, and insert the known value for V/n under standard conditions of P and T.)

PROBLEM 25.8.   Prove the statement that Eq. (25.7) summarizes and contains all other gas laws, for example Boyle's law.

25.9 Some new consequences of the theory.   (a) *Interpretation of absolute zero.*   If the temperature is 0°K (−273°C), $\overline{E}_k$ is zero, according to Eq. (25.8). Thus, from the point of view of kinetic theory, the absolute zero is the temperature at which gas molecules have no kinetic energy and therefore no random thermal motion. However, all gases have been found to liquefy, and even to solidify, before the absolute temperature is reached, and Eq. (25.8) is then no longer applicable.

(b) *Temperature changes during volume changes.*   From Eq. (25.8) we may predict that any increase in the average kinetic energy of the molecules is accompanied by a proportional rise in the temperature of the gas. Hence, if a mass of gas is so suddenly compressed that all the work done on it goes into increasing the kinetic energy of the molecules, there must be a proportional rise in temperature. This prediction from kinetic theory is confirmed by many experiments. Indeed, as we saw in Chapter 20, such experiments played a prominent role in the establishment of the principle of conservation of energy.

The same argument in reverse explains why a gas decreases in temperature when it is allowed to expand and do work on a receding piston, or on the inside walls of a balloon, or against another gas that is at a lower pressure. A familiar example is presented by a warm mass of humid air rising to a higher region and, on expanding against the more rarefied atmosphere, cooling to a temperature such that the moisture brought along in the air condenses to form a rain cloud.

(c) *Homogeneity of the atmosphere.*   We saw in Section 22.2 that Dalton got started on the study of the atomic theory of chemistry while trying to understand why the gases of the atmosphere were always found to be so thoroughly mixed. Adopting a static rather than a kinetic picture of gas structure, he explained the mixing as due to a brief initial period of disequilibrium among unequally large, mutually repelling atoms.   More specifically, he believed that the nitrogen of the atmosphere does not "float" on top of the more dense oxygen for the reason that the neighboring particles of the two gases tend to move away from one another, owing to the mutual repulsions of their "caloric shells," until the mixture becomes homogeneous.   But, as we saw, this explanation and the assumptions leading to it finally had to be abandoned.

In accord with kinetic theory we would expect that the atmospheric gases intermix by virtue of the thermal movements of their molecules. But we do not expect complete homogeneity. The oxygen molecules are more massive and therefore slower than the molecules of nitrogen at the same temperature; therefore the kinetic theory would lead one to expect to find a somewhat larger relative abundance of oxygen in the mixture at lower levels than higher up. Yet Dalton was not in error when he observed that the relative proportion of the gases is the same at all ordinarily accessible altitudes. It would therefore seem that Dalton's conception, and not the kinetic theory, is right after all.

The paradox is simply resolved. The prediction of kinetic theory assumes that we are dealing with a gas free from large-scale convections or turbulences, and the prediction *is* sustained when the observations are made on a gas of considerable depth that is free from disturbance. Our own atmosphere, however, is so disturbed by wind currents that its several gases exist in practically the same relative proportions throughout the region easily accessible to measurements. So, after all, a form of disequilibrium explains the observed homogeneity of the atmosphere, but it is a *continuous* disequilibrium, quite different from that envisaged by Dalton in his explanation.

(d) *Escape of the atmosphere.* The kinetic theory leads to a startling prediction concerning the escape of the atmospheres from planets and their satellites. Our moon and the smaller planets, with their smaller gravitational pulls, have long ago lost their atmospheres if they ever had any, and our earth doubtless is losing its atmosphere, although so very slowly that it may be sweeping up sufficient interplanetary gas to balance the loss. The process of escape is evident. The atmosphere, because of its weight, is "packed" more densely near the earth. But the density decreases rapidly with altitude, and the mean free path (average distance) traveled by molecules between mutual collisions correspondingly increases with altitude. Thus, while the mean free path at sea level is only 10^{-7} m, at an altitude of 1000 km it may be many kilometers. There the molecules often traverse straight paths for great distances, and those that happen to be moving away from the earth with sufficiently high initial speeds (exceeding about 10 km/sec at that altitude) may shoot too far out to be pulled back by the diminished gravitational field. Although very few molecules will have such tremendously high speeds, there will always be some, and their numbers will increase near the upper limits of the atmosphere because of the extremely high temperatures, perhaps over 1000°C. Finally, since the average kinetic energy of all molecules at a given temperature is the same (Eq. 25.8), the proportion of high-speed molecules present at any given temperature will be larger the smaller the molecular weight. Yet even for the lightest molecules, the rate of escape from our earth is exceedingly small. Indeed, calculations indicate that a hydrogen molecule, the lightest of them all, will escape on the average not sooner than 1000 years after it is liberated into the atmosphere in some chemical decomposition.

25.10 Diffusion of gases. (a) *Graham's law of diffusion.* In 1846 Thomas Graham described his experiments on the relative rates with which different gases escape from a vessel stoppered by a thin porous plug made of, say, unglazed baked clay. For our purposes we may state his conclusion as follows: for gases at the same pressures and temperatures the rate (number of molecules per unit time) at which gas escapes through a thin porous plug is inversely proportional to the square roots of the molecular weights of the gases. We shall now see that the kinetic theory not only explains this empirical law, but both deepens and broadens our understanding of diffusion processes.

Suppose that two gases of different molecular weights M_1 and M_2 are confined in separate spherical balloons having the same volume. They are placed in a large evacuated chamber, and one wall of each balloon is now pierced with a tiny pinhole, each pinhole of the same size. The number A of molecules hitting the pinhole and escaping into the evacuated chamber in any given time depends on the density of the imprisoned gas and the speed of the molecules; more precisely, A is directly proportional both to the number of molecules N in the balloon and to the average speed $\bar{v}$ of these molecules. Thus, comparing the two gases,

$$\frac{A_1}{A_2} = \frac{N_1}{N_2} \cdot \frac{\bar{v}_1}{\bar{v}_2}. \tag{25.9}$$

But, as will now be shown, one of the results of the kinetic theory is that for gases at the same temperature the average speeds of the molecules are inversely proportional to the square roots of the molecular weights; that is, $\bar{v}_1/\bar{v}_2 = \sqrt{M_2/M_1}$.

The proof is straightforward: For any two gases at the same temperature, Eq. (25.8) shows that $\overline{E}_k$, the average kinetic energy per molecule, is the same for both gases. Hence

$$\tfrac{1}{2} m_{01} \overline{v_1^2} = \tfrac{1}{2} m_{02} \overline{v_2^2}. \tag{25.10}$$

Therefore $\overline{v_1^2}/\overline{v_2^2} = m_{02}/m_{01}$, or

$$\sqrt{\frac{\overline{v_1^2}}{\overline{v_2^2}}} = \sqrt{\frac{m_{02}}{m_{01}}}. \tag{25.11}$$

The left side of Eq. (25.11) is the ratio of the rms speeds; and although the rms speed is somewhat larger than the average speed for a given molecule (by a factor of 1.09 for real gases), the *ratio* of rms speeds is the same as the *ratio* of the average speeds for the same molecules at the same temperature: $\sqrt{\overline{v_1^2}}/\sqrt{\overline{v_2^2}} = \bar{v}_1/\bar{v}_2$. Moreover, on the right side of Eq. (25.11) the ratio of the masses of the individual molecules is the same as the ratio of the relative molecular weights: $\sqrt{m_{02}}/\sqrt{m_{01}} = \sqrt{M_2}/\sqrt{M_1}$. Therefore Eq. (25.11) becomes

$$\frac{\bar{v}_1}{\bar{v}_2} = \sqrt{\frac{M_2}{M_1}}. \qquad (25.12)$$

In view of this result, Eq. (25.9) can be rewritten:

$$\frac{A_1}{A_2} = \frac{N_1}{N_2} \cdot \frac{\sqrt{M_2}}{\sqrt{M_1}}. \qquad (25.13)$$

Note that this expression for the relative numbers of molecules diffusing per unit time involves the assumption that the gases are at the *same temperature*.

If, in addition, the gases are under the *same pressure*, they will, by Avogadro's law, have the same number of molecules in the given volume; that is, $N_1 = N_2$. Then Eq. (25.13) reduces to

$$\frac{A_1}{A_2} = \frac{\sqrt{M_2}}{\sqrt{M_1}}. \qquad (25.14)$$

But this is precisely Graham's empirical law of diffusion; *here we have been able to derive it from the kinetic theory.* This is a powerful additional argument in favor of the theory.

PROBLEM 25.9. Show that, for the same conditions of pressure and temperature, the numbers of molecules that will diffuse per unit time through a thin porous barrier are in the ratio (a) 4 to 1 for hydrogen and oxygen, and (b) 1.1 to 1.0 for nitrogen and oxygen.

PROBLEM 25.10. (a) Given that the rms speed of oxygen molecules at 1090°K is 922 m/sec, show that the kinetic theory [in particular, Eq. (25.8)] predicts an rms speed of about 3680 m/sec for hydrogen molecules at the same temperature (1090°K). (b) In Brownian movement, the larger pieces of dust or pollen are seen to move more slowly than the smaller ones. Can you explain this?

(b) *Diffusion of a mixture of gases.* Our theory also enables us to compare the rates with which molecules of two gases will diffuse through a porous plug into a vacuum when the gases are initially mixed in the same vessel. Since both gases will have the same temperature, Eq. (25.9) is again applicable. Also, since they occupy the same vessel their volumes are equal. But as for pressures, each gas exerts its own partial pressure, and these pressures are not, in general, equal; hence the numbers N_1 and N_2 of the two kinds of molecules are not in general equal. Therefore, for a mixture, Eq. (25.13) applies.

PROBLEM 25.11. Inside an evacuated chamber is placed a smaller closed vessel with porous walls that contains a gaseous mixture consisting initially of 82% nitrogen molecules and 18% oxygen molecules. (a) Show that the numbers of nitrogen and oxygen molecules escaping per second are initially in the ratio of about 5 to 1. (b) Why must we say "initially"? (c) How would the rates of escape have compared if the vessel had initially contained one mole each of nitrogen and oxygen?

Building on these ideas about diffusion, Lord Rayleigh showed in 1896 that two gases forming a mixture can be partly separated by allowing some of the mixture to diffuse through a porous barrier into an evacuated space. As Eq. (25.13) shows, the lighter molecules will diffuse faster, thereby enriching the diffused portion with lighter molecules and leaving the yet undiffused remainder with a large proportion of the more massive molecules.

More recently this process became the basis of one type of large-scale separation of the "light" and "heavy" isotopes of uranium. Specifically, uranium (U), as found in nature, consists primarily of an intimate mixture of two *isotopes*, i.e., two chemically equivalent but not equally massive kinds of atoms. One of these isotopes, U^{238}, is of approximate atomic weight 238 and makes up 99.3% of natural, pure uranium metal. The other, lighter isotope, U^{235}, has an approximate atomic weight of 235 and a relative abundance of about 0.7%. There is also a minute trace of a third kind of uranium atom, U^{234}, but its presence may be disregarded in this discussion.

As will be discussed in detail in Chapter 38, during World War II a way was seen to liberate large quantities of energy from the isotope U^{235}, but only if it could be separated in very pure form from the much more abundant U^{238}. One possible separation method is gaseous diffusion. But uranium itself is not a gas (its boiling point is unpublished; it melts at 1133°C), so some compound of uranium that is a gas at ordinary temperatures had to be used. The one chosen was uranium hexafluoride, UF_6. Since there is only one kind of fluorine atom, F^{19} (of atomic weight 19), uranium hexafluoride is primarily a mixture of the two compounds $U^{235}F_6{}^{19}$ and $U^{238}F_6{}^{19}$, of approximate molecular weights $M_1 = 349$ and $M_2 = 352$ respectively. Suppose that a small part of a sample of uranium hexafluoride is allowed to diffuse through a porous barrier into an evacuated chamber. Then in Eq. (25.13), $N_1/N_2 = 0.7/99.3 = 1/142$, and $\sqrt{M_2}/\sqrt{M_1} = 1.0043$. Hence,

$$\frac{R_1}{R_2} = \frac{1}{142} \times 1.0043 = \frac{1}{141}.$$

Thus the *relative abundance* N_1/N_2 of the lighter gas $U^{235}F_6{}^{19}$ is $1/142$ in the original mixture and $1/141$ in the diffused portion. The latter value, although larger, represents an increase in relative abundance of only 0.43%. And if more than a small fraction of the original quantity of gas is allowed to pass through the porous barrier, the change in relative abundance will be less than 0.43%, and will approach zero as more and more gas diffuses.

The problem was how to obtain very large quantities of the gas $U^{235}F_6{}^{19}$ in very pure form, despite the fact that the molecular weights of the two kinds of uranium hexafluoride are so nearly equal that the enrichment resulting from the passage through the porous barrier is discouragingly small. An evident possibility here was to make some of the diffused mixture pass through a *set* of porous barriers, to obtain additional enrichment. In the words of the Smyth report on wartime atomic energy research:

> To separate the uranium isotopes, many successive diffusion stages (i.e., a cascade) must be used . . . Studies made by K. Cohen and others have shown that the best flow arrangement for the successive stages is that in which half the gas pumped into each stage diffuses through the barrier, the other (impoverished) half being returned to the feed of the next lower stage . . . If one desires to produce 99 percent pure $U^{235}F_6{}^{19}$ [with a relative abundance of about 14,000/142 as compared with the original 1/142], and if one uses a cascade in which each stage has a reasonable over-all enrichment factor, then it turns out that roughly 4000 stages are required.

The construction by 1945 of many acres of such diffusion chambers at Oak Ridge, Tennessee (Fig. 25.5), is very excitingly described in this report. The operation of this large-scale project can in a sense be regarded as additional confirmation of the kinetic theory that provided the basis for the design of the diffusion plant.

25.11 Have we now established the kinetic theory? Let us pause briefly to survey what has been gained so far in our development of the kinetic theory. The general qualitative picture of matter as composed of atoms whose motion corresponds to the heat content of the substance (Sections 25.1 and 25.2) was first elaborated in a model of a gas based on six assumptions that were plausible on the basis of prior theory or experimental observation (Section 25.3). Using this model, we were able to derive the "pressure formula," Eq. (25.2), which relates the pressure in a given volume of gas to the properties of the molecules, including the mean-square speeds $\overline{v^2}$. To verify the theory leading to Eq. (25.2), we

FIG. 25.5. Diffusion plant of the Clinton Works (now Atomic Energy Commission) at Oak Ridge, Tenn., for the separation of uranium isotopes.

might have wanted to check each of the terms in the equation separately to see whether prediction corresponds with fact, but since (until recently) the speed of gas molecules could not be found directly, the theory had to be tested indirectly by seeing whether Eq. (25.2) led to verifiable conclusions. The speed of sound in gases (Section 25.6) gave us such a check, but it was too qualitative to be convincing. The fact that the pressure formula could explain Dalton's empirical law of partial pressures and Boyle's empirical law of gases (Section 25.7) was a much better check. Emboldened by this success, we assumed that Eq. (25.2) was to be considered correct. In the form $PV = \frac{1}{3}Nm_0\overline{v^2}$, we juxtaposed it in Section 25.8 with the empirical gas law $PV = rT$, and concluded that $\frac{1}{3}Nm_0\overline{v^2} = rT$ (Eq. 25.4). This opened to us a new interpretation of the meaning of temperature as the measure of the mean translational (that is, forward) kinetic energy of each molecule (Eq. 25.8). At once, several consequences could be deduced which were indeed in accord with experience (Sections 25.9 and 25.10). Moreover, measurement of the speeds of gas molecules by means of very ingenious methods (Otto Stern, 1920, and others) gave another confirmation of Eq. (25.8). Now we surely may feel convinced of the validity of the kinetic theory. But the following sections will show that, as with most theories, there is, after all, a region of phenomena to which the theory cannot be applied without modification.

25.12 Explanation of specific heat capacities of gases. We come now to one of the most intriguing applications of our kinetic theory, namely, the values it predicts for the specific heat capacities of gases. In Section 19.4 specific heat capacity was defined as the quantity of heat absorbed or given up per unit mass of a material when its temperature is raised or lowered one degree. Our particular interest here is in the specific heat capacity *at constant volume,* for we are not concerned with the additional heat that would have to be supplied if the gas were allowed to expand and do work against the surrounding atmosphere (Section 20.3). To measure the specific heat capacity at constant volume, c_V, we confine a mass m of the gas in a container of fixed volume, feed to the gas a measured quantity of heat H, and observe the resulting rise in temperature ΔT. Then c_V can be computed by means of the defining equation $c_V = H/m\,\Delta T$. As the second column of Table 25.1 shows, the values of c_V turn out to be widely different for different gases. Note that the quantities of heat H entering into these

Table 25.1.   Experimentally obtained values of the specific heat capacity, c_V, and of the heat capacity per mole, $M{\cdot}c_V$, each for constant volume.

Gas	Specific heat capacity, c_V (j/gm·°K)	Grams per mole, M	Heat capacity per mole, $M{\cdot}c_V$ (j/mole·°K)
Helium (He)	3.13	4.00	12.5
Argon (A)	0.312	39.9	12.5
Mercury vapor (Hg)	0.0626	200.6	12.6
Hydrogen (H$_2$)	10.1	2.02	20.4
Nitrogen (N$_2$)	0.735	28.0	20.7
Oxygen (O$_2$)	0.654	32.0	20.9
Carbon monoxide (CO)	0.743	28.0	20.8
Hydrogen chloride (HCl)	0.572	36.5	20.9

values have been expressed in terms of joules rather than of kilocalories, and the unit mass chosen is 1 gm rather than 1 kgm. Therefore the values of c_V are not in kcal/kgm·°C as in Sections 19.5 and 20.3, but in j/gm·°K. This is a perfectly valid alternate system of units for c_V; the relation between the systems is simply

$$c_V \text{ (in j/gm·°K)} = c_V \text{ (in kcal/kgm·°C)} \times \frac{4185 \text{ j/kcal}}{1000 \text{ gm/kgm}}.$$

The usefulness of the system of units used in Table 25.1 will soon be apparent.

Now let us see what values for the heat capacities are *predicted by the kinetic theory.* The results are surprising. According to Eq. (25.8), for any gas at temperature T the average kinetic energy *per molecule* is $\frac{3}{2}kT$. If sufficient heat is added to increase the temperature of the gas by an amount ΔT, the result is an increase by $\frac{3}{2}k \Delta T$ in the average kinetic energy per molecule. Thus for a temperature rise of one degree ($\Delta T = 1°K$), the average increase in kinetic energy of each molecule is $\frac{3}{2}k$, or 2.07×10^{-23} j. This, according to the kinetic theory, is the value of the heat capacity *per molecule of any gas.*

Upon multiplying the foregoing value by the number of molecules in one gram of a particular gas, we evidently shall obtain the predicted value for the heat capacity per gram (c_V). As the number of molecules per gram is different for different gases, the predicted value of c_V will depend on the gas. This is in accord with experiment, as the different values of c_V listed in the second column of Table 25.1 show.

We can go a step further and make a precise quantitative prediction. If the differences in heat capacities are due to differences in the number of molecules per gram for the various gases, then these differences should disappear if we compare, not equal masses of the gases, but equal numbers of molecules. All gases have the same number N_0 of molecules per mole (Avogadro's number, 6.02×10^{23} molecules/mole, Section 23.6). Multiplying this number by the predicted value of $\frac{3}{2}k$ for the heat capacity per molecule of any gas, we obtain

$$N_0 \cdot \frac{3}{2} k = 6.02 \times 10^{23} \frac{\text{molecules}}{\text{mole}} \times 2.07 \times 10^{-23} \frac{\text{j}}{\text{molecule} \cdot °K}$$

$$= 12.5 \text{ j/mole} \cdot °K, \tag{25.15}$$

which is the *heat capacity per mole* and, according to our kinetic theory, should be the same for all gases.

Do gases actually exhibit this surprising regularity? In the last column of Table 25.1 are listed values of the heat capacity per mole, obtained for each gas by multiplying the experimental value for the heat capacity per gram (second column) by the number of grams constituting a mole (third column). For helium, argon, and mercury we see that these experimental values are almost the same and in excellent agreement with the theoretical value of 12.5 j/mole·°K.

But this is true only for *monatomic* gases! For diatomic gases such as hydrogen, nitrogen, carbon monoxide, and so on, the experimental values are found to lie around 20.8 j/mole·°K. This is about 8.3 j/mole·°K more than expected. *Diatomic molecules are able to take up more energy per degree temperature rise than monatomic molecules.* On the basis of our gas model we can say that all the heat supplied to a monatomic gas kept at constant volume does produce a rise in temperature, as expected from the kinetic theory. But when a diatomic gas kept at constant volume is heated, only 12.5/20.8, or about $\frac{3}{5}$, of the heat supplied is converted into translational kinetic energy of the molecules to cause the observed temperature rise. The remaining $\frac{2}{5}$ somehow seems to be stored in the molecules without affecting their translational kinetic energy and therefore the temperature.

Here we have a breakdown in the model, a flaw in the theory as developed so far. Joule, who brought the theory up to this point, was stumped by the discrepancy in the heat capacities of polyatomic gases, the more so because in his day no monatomic gases had yet been generally identified. In fact, his first thought was that the experimental values of c_V then available might be in error, but when new determinations only widened the gap between the predicted and experimental values, he seems to have been so discouraged that any further work on the kinetic theory appeared to him to be futile. His model had not made provision for a molecule to store energy in any other form than the kinetic energy of translational motion, and at that time no reason was apparent for revising this simple idea.

25.13 The modified theory for diatomic gases. If the kinetic theory were to survive, the gas model had to be modified so as to yield values of about 20.8 rather than 12.5 j/mole·°K for $M \cdot c_V$ in the case of diatomic gases. The modification was first provided in 1857 by Rudolf Clausius, in Germany. A monatomic molecule might indeed be a spherical atom having kinetic energy that is purely translational. But a diatomic molecule might well be thought of as a dumbbell-like object consisting of two spherical atoms a short distance apart. Such a molecule, when given energy, might be capable of being put into rotation, and associated with this rotation there would be rotational kinetic energy of perhaps significant amount.

Figure 25.6 is a crude model of a diatomic molecule. Evidently such a molecule can rotate about each of three mutually perpendicular axes,

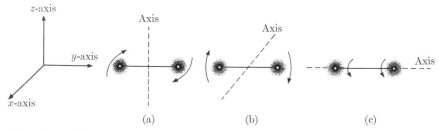

FIG. 25.6. Three independent ways in which a diatomic molecule can rotate.

one chosen along the line connecting the two atoms, the other two at right angles to this line. Any rotation can be thought of as the result of three possible independent components of rotary motion *about* the x-, y-, or z-axis, analogous to our method of differentiating between the three possible independent components of translational motion *along* these three axes.

It is useful to introduce the term *degree of freedom* to denote each of the independent ways in which a particular molecule can absorb energy. For example, a monatomic molecule has tacitly been assumed not to rotate, or at least not to use any of the energy supplied during heating to increase its rotational motion. Thus it can have changes of kinetic energy only by virtue of changes of its translational motion along the x-, y-, or z-axis. The three components of velocity which it thus may have are independent, in the sense that any one of them may increase or decrease without the other two being affected. In other words, a monatomic molecule was assumed to have three degrees of freedom, and this assumption led us to successful results.

Consider next a diatomic molecule. It can move forward as a whole and therefore has three translational degrees of freedom. But it is also capable of rotating and therefore we can conceive of three additional degrees of freedom, one for each of the three mutually perpendicular axes shown in Fig. 25.6. Thus the motion of a diatomic molecule may give it as many as six degrees of freedom altogether—six independent ways in which it may acquire kinetic energy.

However, we must be prepared to face the possibility that a molecule for some reason may not be able to take on energy corresponding to each one of the conceivable degrees of freedom that could be assigned to it purely on the basis of its geometry. For example, a monatomic molecule, despite its smallness, is not truly a *point* mass, and hence conceivably could have three rotational degrees of freedom. Yet we must deny a monatomic molecule these extra degrees of freedom, for it behaves as if it has motion of translation only. Only on this basis can we explain why the molar heat capacities of monatomic gases are all close to 12.5 j/mole·°K.

But if rotation need not be considered for a single atom, the same may be true for rotation about the line connecting the two atoms in a diatomic molecule [(c), Fig. 25.6], for the molecule does not have the distribution of mass around this axis which is characteristic of dumbbell-shaped objects. This would mean that such molecules as H_2, N_2, and CO have only five allowed degrees of freedom (three for translation, and two for rotation) or two degrees more than monatomic molecules. And, indeed, this postulate provides an explanation for the experimental results recorded in Table 25.1. All the heat supplied to a monatomic gas kept at constant volume is converted into translational kinetic energy, and therefore, by

Eq. (25.8), results in a proportional rise in temperature. But for a diatomic gas heated under the same conditions, only $\frac{3}{5}$ of the supplied energy is converted into translational kinetic energy. The remaining $\frac{2}{5}$ of the energy goes into the two active rotational degrees of freedom and, since changes of rotational motion do not reflect in a further increase of temperature, does not affect the thermometer.

In short, for a monatomic gas Eq. (25.15) continues to hold: the heat capacity per mole, for constant volume, is $N_0 \cdot \frac{3}{2}k$, or 12.5 j/mole·°K. But for a diatomic gas, whose molecules have five active degrees of freedom, the correct expression is $N_0 \cdot \frac{5}{2}k$, or 20.8 j/mole·°K. We are therefore led, by the success of these considerations, to propose a general statement, the *equipartition theorem*, which finds wide use in the physical sciences: *the available energy distributes itself in equal shares to each of the active degrees of freedom.* In one *mole* of gas, $(N_0\frac{1}{2}k)$ j/mole·°K go to each of the three degrees for monatomic gases, and to each of the five degrees for diatomic gases. In general, for δ degrees of freedom, the molar heat capacity is given by

$$M \cdot c_V = \delta \cdot \frac{N_0 k}{2},$$ (25.16)

or

$$M \cdot c_V = \delta \cdot \frac{R}{2},$$ (25.17)

since by definition $k = R/N_0$.

Applying the equipartition theorem to single molecules, we see that each active degree of freedom of each molecule, on the average, takes up $\frac{1}{2}k$ joule per degree rise in temperature; at temperature T, it can be thought to have $\frac{1}{2}kT$ joules of energy locked in each degree of freedom. To emphasize that temperature is a measure not of the total molecular energy but only of the total *translational* kinetic energy, we might now add a subscript to $\overline{E}_k$ in Eq. (25.8):

$$(\overline{E}_k)_{\text{trans}} = \tfrac{3}{2}kT.$$ (25.18)

That polyatomic molecules undergo rotations affecting neither the temperature nor the pressure has been confirmed independently by direct experiments on the Brownian movement and on the light emitted by polyatomic gases.

PROBLEM 25.12. For oxygen, the experimental value of c_V is 0.654 j/gm·°K (Table 25.1). Compute the heat capacity per mole for oxygen kept at constant volume.

PROBLEM 25.13. Show that $N_0 \cdot \frac{5}{2}k$ equals 20.8 j/mole·°K.

PROBLEM 25.14. (a) Explain why it is plausible to assume that a triatomic gas, such as carbon dioxide (CO_2), has three active rotational degrees of freedom. (b) Show that, on this assumption, the kinetic theory predicts for $M \cdot c_V$ the value of 25 j/mole·°K. (c) The experimental value is, in fact, 25 j/mole·°K. What does this prove?

PROBLEM 25.15. Review the discussion leading to Eq. (25.18) and cite the main physical principles and laws openly or tacitly employed in arriving at the equation.

PROBLEM 25.16. Suppose that a new gas were discovered that exhibits no increase in either temperature or pressure when enclosed in a rigid container and supplied with heat. What assumptions would we be forced to make concerning the motions of the molecules of this gas?

PROBLEM 25.17. Precisely why are we justified in assuming that the rotational motion of molecules does not affect the *pressure* of the gas?

25.14 Ideal versus real gases.

Even with quite simple apparatus we can show that the behavior of many gases is described fairly well *but not with full accuracy* by Boyle's law and the other gas laws (Sections 21.2 through 21.4). For such gases as hydrogen, helium, and air, the departures from Boyle's laws are quite small up to pressures of 10 atm, but for water vapor, carbon dioxide, and many other gases, particularly those not far from their liquefaction temperature and pressure, the law is not pertinent.

In fact, Boyle himself had noticed that his law did not hold accurately for air that was considerably compressed, but this was not disturbing because the simple law was generally useful over so wide a range of cases. Gases that are accurately described by the gas laws, for example by the equation of state, Eq. (25.7), are referred to as *ideal gases*—ideal in that they have simple properties and that one set of gas laws describes the behavior of all of them to a good degree of approximation. Indeed, experiments show that as the density decreases the behavior of all gases approaches that of an ideal gas.

In Section 25.7 we saw that the gas laws could be derived as theoretical consequences from the postulates that constitute our kinetic-theory model of a gas; this means that we have been constructing a model for ideal gases. An ideal gas may be defined alternatively as a gas that conforms in structure to this simple model or, more specifically, as a gas whose molecules may be assumed to have negligible size and to exert no forces on one another except during collisions. In all our work so far we have assumed that we are dealing with gases which are sufficiently close to this ideal. However, this condition is not closely met when the average distance between the molecules is small, as is true when a gas is under high pressure. For example, if the number of molecules in a given volume is large, the space they occupy is an appreciable part of the whole volume, thus reducing the space through which they can move, a fact that we ignored in deriving the pressure formula of Section 25.4.

To broaden the kinetic theory so that it will apply to gases under a wider range of pressures and temperatures, postulates (b) and (e) of Section 25.3 evidently must be modified. One way to do this was proposed in 1873 by the Dutch physicist J. D. van der Waals. His revision led beyond the ideal gas relation $PV = rT$ to a more general gas law:

$$\left(P + \frac{a}{V^2}\right)(V - b) = rT, \tag{25.19}$$

where a and b are constants that are characteristic of each gas, a/V^2 is a correction term that takes into account the attraction between molecules, and b allows for the fact that the molecules have finite volumes. This new law was found to apply fairly well not only to any gas over a wide range of pressures and temperatures, but also to the liquid formed when the gas condenses. The simpler ideal-gas equations are, however, accurate enough for a great variety of practical purposes.

25.15 Conclusion. Our simple kinetic-theory model has, in truth, shown itself to meet all the criteria for a fruitful conceptual scheme: it is based on a small number of postulates which are plausible; it has served to correlate a wealth of known facts about gases; it has yielded laws that are useful in practice; it has predicted entirely new relations; and lastly, it proved to be flexible enough to have permitted modifications that extend its range to include nonideal gas behavior. With such successes to its credit, any further revisions of the theory seemingly should prove to be minor, such as taking better account of molecular sizes and forces—factors that were already known to exist, but that often could be disregarded because of their small effects.

But this hope founders on a compelling question. In order to explain the heat capacities of gases, we were forced to make the *ad hoc* assumption that not all of the conceivable degrees of a molecule are necessarily active. Exactly what determines whether a particular degree of freedom should be active or inactive? We have not answered this question by our qualitative arguments for suppressing those degrees of freedom that we could not accommodate in our model. In fact, this question could initially not be answered; according to the principles of 19th-century physics, every geometrically possible degree of freedom should be active and thus receive a share of the energy supplied to the molecule.

The situation became even more perplexing with the astonishing discovery, in 1912, that hydrogen, H_2, has markedly different heat capacities at very low and very high temperatures (Fig. 25.7). At ordinary temperatures, the heat capacity corresponds closely to the expected value of $N_0 \cdot \frac{5}{2}k$, or 20.8 j/mole·°K, computed on the assumption that three trans-

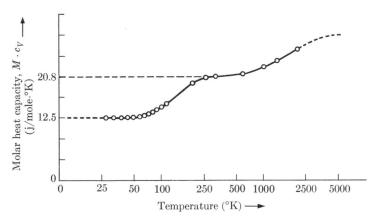

FIG. 25.7. Variation of molar heat capacity, $M \cdot c_V$, of molecular hydrogen gas. (To condense the graph, the temperature of the gas is plotted along the abscissa on a logarithmic scale.)

lational and two rotational degrees of freedom are active. But at temperatures below about 60°K, the heat capacity has dropped to a value of about $N_0 \cdot \frac{3}{2}k$, or 12.5 j/mole·°K. Here hydrogen is behaving like a monatomic gas! Apparently all three rotational degrees of freedom have become inactive. One cannot explain this phenomenon by assuming that at the lower temperatures the two hydrogen atoms have come so close together that the molecule is more nearly spherical than dumbbell-like in shape, since evidence from other sources shows that molecular dimension changes very little during cooling. What is worse, when hydrogen gas (and other diatomic gases) is heated to extremely high temperatures, the experimental heat capacity approaches the value $N_0 \cdot \frac{7}{2}k$, or 29.1 j/mole·°K, as though *seven* degrees of freedom have begun to play a part, and this is more than the total possible number of translational and rotational degrees. Nothing in our theory up to this point could account for such changes in activity.

The fact is that we have here come into an entirely new and unexpected territory, and we are encountering problems that could not be solved until a fundamental revolution in physical thought had occurred. This will be the link between our picture of atoms and molecules as given by the kinetic theory and the more recent conceptions of them in quantum theory, to be developed in later chapters.

ADDITIONAL PROBLEMS

25.18. If diatomic hydrogen gas above 2000°C has, on the average, 3 active degrees of freedom of translation plus 2 of rotation and 2 of vibration of the two atoms in each molecule with respect to each other, what is the value of $(\overline{E}_k)_{trans}$ of each molecule, and what is the expected value of c_V?

25.19. In the light of the previous problem, what could be the physical explanation of the observed value $M \cdot c_V = 41$ j/mole·°K for gaseous sulfur dioxide (SO_2) at ordinary temperatures?

25.20. Evaluate in detail this account of the kinetic theory in the light of our criteria for a good theory (Chapter 8).

25.21. Why do we believe that atoms exist? Use arguments from (a) the atomic-molecular theory of chemistry, and (b) the kinetic-molecular theory of gases and heat.

SUPPLEMENTARY READING

BLACKWOOD, O. H., T. H. OSGOOD, and A. E. RUARK, *An outline of atomic physics* (Wiley, 1955), Chap. 1.

BORN, M., *The restless universe* (Harper, 1936; Dover, 1951), Chap. 1.

CHALMERS, T. W., *Historic researches* (Scribner's, 1952), Chap. VIII.

COWLING, T. G., *Molecules in motion* (Hutchinson, London, 1950).

FURRY, W. H., E. M. PURCELL, and J. C. STREET, *Physics for science and engineering students* (Blackiston, 1952), Chaps. 14 and 15.

HOLTON, G., *Introduction to concepts and theories in physical science* (Addison-Wesley, 1952), pp. 454–459 for an account of the measurement and distribution of molecular speeds in gases.

KOLIN, A., *Physics, its laws, ideas, and methods* (McGraw-Hill, 1950), Chap. 20.

LOEB, L. B., and A. S. ADAMS, *The development of physical thought* (Wiley, 1933), Part III.

MAGIE, W. F., *A source book in physics* (McGraw-Hill, 1935), pp. 172–173, 247–261. Selections from Joule, Bernoulli, Brown, and Maxwell.

MILLIKAN, R. A., D. ROLLER, and E. C. WATSON, *Mechanics, molecular physics, heat, and sound* (Ginn, 1937), Chap. 10.

OLDENBERG, O., *Introduction to atomic physics* (McGraw-Hill, 2nd edition, 1954), Chaps. 3–5.

SMYTH, H. D., *A general account of the development of methods of using atomic energy* . . . (Superintendent of Documents, U. S. Government Printing Office, Washington, D. C. 1945), pp. 115–116.

Part VII
THEORIES OF FIELDS IN ELECTRICITY AND MAGNETISM

(1831–1879)

(Courtesy of the Cavendish Laboratory, Cambridge University)

THEORIES OF FIELDS IN ELECTRICITY AND MAGNETISM

The ruling image in the early mechanically inclined physical sciences was that of two or more material objects—whether large bodies or particles too small to be seen—interacting by virtue of direct contact, as during collisions. But when the interaction is ascribed to gravitational attraction or to electric and magnetic forces, the conception of action-by-contact is ultimately unsatisfactory; it leads necessarily to the hypothesis that the observed effects are produced by an unobservable medium having properties invented specifically for the purposes that the medium is to serve. Analogous to Newton's decision, we must refuse to frame such a hypothesis.

But how else can one understand even an effect as simple as the mutual attraction of two magnets? What mediates between them if not a material medium? The question which we have already begun to raise in connection with gravitational attraction is now answered in terms of the field concept.

The field and the particle are among the most powerful conceptual devices of science. They play complementary, not separate, roles in our effort to describe and understand what we observe. In the following chapters, we shall examine the rise and usefulness of the field concept in the study of electricity and magnetism.

CHAPTER 26

THE QUANTIFICATION OF ELECTRICAL SCIENCE

Our discussion of the chemical-physical atom of the 19th century centered around such concepts as atomic weight, mechanical force, elastic collisions, momentum, and kinetic energy. But as the century drew to a close, studies were under way not only of the atomic-molecular structure of matter as a whole but of the structure of the very atoms themselves. These studies have led in the 20th century to a model of the atom that stresses *electrical* concepts at least as much as the earlier atomic-molecular theory had stressed *mechanical* concepts.

Whereas in the last several chapters we have emphasized the importance of quantitative, measurable concepts in physical science, we shall in this chapter take advantage of the unusual opportunity afforded by the early history of electricity to see how certain physical concepts first came into being as qualitative notions; then we shall examine the circumstances in which they evolved into semiquantitative form and finally into quantitative concepts of the modern form. This chapter, then, will serve as one example of the historical development of physical concepts generally. Moreover, it allows us to prepare ourselves unhurriedly for the important and relatively subtle concepts of electricity; for whereas the study of mechanics can build on the "common sense of the muscles," we unhappily have no good *a priori* intuitions for such conceptions as charge, field, and potential. Our body uses levers, but not meters.

26.1 Summary of some modern basic knowledge. As an aid in following the historical development, we shall first summarize some main portions of the modern conceptual scheme of electricity that are relatively simple to follow and yet cover a wide range of phenomena, from the electrification of an object to the principles of operation of one type of particle accelerator or "atom smasher."

(a) An object can be electrified or "charged" by rubbing it with, say, a piece of cloth or by properly connecting it to an electric battery or dynamo generator. The object is then said to possess *electric charge*.

(b) There exist two kinds of electric charge, referred to as *positive* $(+)$ and *negative* $(-)$.

(c) Charged objects exert on one another forces that are conveniently referred to as "electric forces." If two objects have charges of the same sign (both positive or both negative), they repel each other; if their charges are unlike (one positive, the other negative), they attract each

463

other. The magnitude of this electric force of repulsion or attraction is directly proportional to the amount of electric charge on each of the two objects, and inversely proportional to the square of the distance between the "centers" of the two charges. In brief, the electrical force law is analogous in form to that for gravitation.

(d) As with gravitation, there is no visible mechanism by which one charged object exerts force on another across space that may or may not be devoid of matter. However, it has been found exceedingly helpful to think that as soon as it is given a charge an object sets up an *electric field* all around itself which so modifies the surrounding space that a second charged object placed anywhere in this space will tend to move either away from or toward the first one, depending on the signs of the two charges.

(e) When a charge is placed on certain objects (chiefly those composed of metals) it spreads at once over the whole surface; such objects are said to be good *conductors* of electricity. But for nonmetallic substances such as glass or rubber, the charge tends to remain on the part of the object to which it is applied; such poor conductors of electricity are commonly referred to as *nonconductors* or *insulators*.

(f) Any uncharged object is pictured as containing equal amounts of positive and negative charges which are so completely intermingled that the net effect is the same as if no charges were present at all. If such an "uncharged" (neutral) object A is brought into the field of a charged object B, without touching it, the side of A nearest to B will acquire an excess of charge of opposite sign to that on B, while at the farther side there will appear a charge of similar sign to that on B. Thus A is now *polarized*, although it will generally remain so only so long as it is in the field of B. This process is called *temporary charging by influence;* it explains why a charged object (B) tends to attract an uncharged object (A) in its neighborhood.

Practically all of the conceptual scheme just outlined came into existence within the last 250 years, despite two millenia of previous awareness and study of some of the electric phenomena involved. In our inquiry into the origins of electrical concepts and the reasons why some of them developed so slowly, we now should try to strip our minds of the modern scheme and start at the beginning.

26.2 The amber effect and "effluvia." For thousands of years man has known four phenomena which today we call "electrical": lightning, the ability of the torpedo fish to stun its prey, the pale glow sometimes seen on the tips of pointed objects at night (St. Elmo's fire), and the ability of amber to attract small objects when it is rubbed. The ancients, however, knew of no connection between these four diverse phenomena, and the science of electricity that ultimately brought them together grew from observation and speculation centering around a single one of these, the last, which we may call the *amber effect*. Understandably, the attraction displayed by amber was long confused with the attraction that lodestones (natural magnets) show for iron, a phenomenon that was known at least as early as the 6th century B.C. Yet even in antiquity one striking difference was remarked upon: several different substances were known to move toward rubbed amber, whereas only iron seemed to move toward lodestone.

Significantly, the earliest recorded reports of these phenomena of attraction are invariably accompanied by explanations of them. We will recall that some of the critics of Newton's 17th-century theory of gravitation were dissatisfied with his conception of one body attracting another at a distance. Similarly, the early Greek philosophers found it uncongenial to think of the motion of chaff, twigs, or bits of thread toward a rubbed piece of amber, or of iron objects toward a lodestone, without some intervening mechanism to explain it. Their explanations took various forms: some were teleological and animistic, the attracted object being thought to serve as food or to fill other needs of the amber or lodestone; others assumed a "sympathy" to exist between attracting and attracted objects; and still others, offered principally by the atomists, were mechanistic in character.

The mechanistic explanations are of especial interest to us because in the long run they were the most influential in the science of electricity. In the attempt to establish a physical contact between the attracting and attracted objects when no visible connection could be observed, an invisible connection was postulated, specifically some emission originating from the rubbed amber or the lodestone. Thus there arose the persistent notion that the attracting object was surrounded by an aura or emanation that later was made more specific and was called an *effluvium*. The views held by the Greek atomists about the material medium supposedly surrounding the lodestone is strikingly presented by the Roman poet Lucretius in his work *On the nature of things:*

> First, from this stone there must stream a shoal of seeds in a current
> Driving away with its blows all the air 'twixt itself and the iron.
> Soon as this space is made void and a vacuum fashioned between them,
> Instantly into that void the atoms of iron tumble headlong
> All in a lump; thus the ring itself moves bodily forward.

This hypothesis was presented in a slightly different form by Plutarch (1st century A.D.) so as to include the amber effect:

> In amber there is a flammeous and spirituous nature, and this by rubbing on the surface is emitted by hidden passages, and does the same that the lodestone does.

GVILIELMI GIL-
BERTI COLCESTREN-
SIS, MEDICI LONDI-
NENSIS,

DE MAGNETE, MAGNETI-
CISQVE CORPORIBVS, ET DE MAG-
no magnete tellure; Phyſiologia noua,
plurimis & argumentis, & expe-
rimentis demonſtrata.

LONDINI
EXCVDEBAT Petrvs Short ANNO
MDC.

FIG. 26.1. The title page of William Gilbert's book *De magnete* (*Concerning the lodestone;* 1600). (From the De Golyer copy in the University of Oklahoma Library.)

In the Middle Ages, when Lucretius' poem was unknown and the atomists themselves were unknown to European scholars, the ancient view that attractions were due to a sympathy between the objects involved was predominantly held. However, in the long run this explanation proved to be sterile, and with the general reawakening of interest in the atomistic views in the 15th and 16th centuries science returned to mechanistic concepts to explain both magnetic attraction and the amber effect.

26.3 Gilbert founds electrical science. In 16th-century Elizabethan England, William Gilbert (1544–1603) launched a detailed study of magnetism, and in 1600 published his extensive work in a celebrated treatise entitled *De magnete* (Fig. 26.1). Doubtless he was influenced by the rapidly expanding interest in navigation by means of the mariner's compass (while he wrote, the English were preparing for the defeat of the Spanish Armada). Although Gilbert's most important contribution to science was his conception that the earth is a huge magnet, our interest here focuses not on his work on magnetism, but on the single chapter of his treatise devoted to the amber effect.

Gilbert's aim was to draw a sharp and clear line between the amber effect and magnetism, and as an aid he invented the first electrical instrument, which he called a *versorium* (from the Latin *verso*, to turn around). It could be simply a balanced pointer of wood, pivoted to turn freely (Fig. 26.2). When a piece of rubbed amber was held close to the end of the pointer, the latter would turn toward the amber. A well-balanced versorium is a far more sensitive device for detecting the amber effect than the older method of attempting to pick up chaff or other light objects.

FIG. 26.2. Gilbert's drawing of his versorium.

During the two thousand years previous to Gilbert's work, only a very few substances had been found to exhibit the amber effect; the mineral *jet* was one example. But Gilbert, with his new instrument, discovered that the list of materials and the things they could attract when rubbed could be greatly extended. Heaping scorn upon those of his predecessors who wrote about natural phenomena while shutting their eyes to the very phenomena they discussed, Gilbert said:

> For it is not only amber and jet (as they suppose) which entice small bodies; but Diamond, Sapphire, Carbuncle, Iris gem, Opal, Amethyst, Vincentina, and Bristolla (an English gem or spar), Beryl, and Crystal do the same. Similar powers of attraction are seen also to be possessed by glass (especially when clear and lucid), as also by false gems made of glass or Crystal, by glass of

antimony, and by many kinds of spars from the mines, and by Belemnites . . . These substances draw everything, not straws and chaff only, but all metals, woods, leaves, stones, earths, even water and oil, and everything which is subject to our senses, or is solid; although some write that amber does not attract anything but chaff and certain twigs; . . .

A new world was opened up to experimenters by the discovery that so many substances were capable of attracting objects when rubbed, and that so many things were attracted. Furthermore, Gilbert developed the concept that those substances which attract when rubbed (i.e., exhibit the amber effect) form a *class*. This class he called "electrics" (from the Greek *ēlektron* for amber), and he proposed that all solid substances that do not attract when rubbed be called "nonelectrics." Moreover, he provided an operational test to distinguish between the two: hold an object in your hand, rub it with, say, a piece of cloth, and present it to the versorium; if the versorium turns, the object is an electric.

Struck by the physical similarity among most of the various electrics, Gilbert decided that they were all originally fluid and had since solidified. Gilbert vehemently opposed the notion that there was a "sympathy" between the rubbed electric and the attracted object, and instead upheld the view that an effluvium was emitted from the electric when it is rubbed. But he denied the opinion of Lucretius and Plutarch that the effluvia moved the surrounding air; a candle flame held near a rubbed electric does not waver, he said, as one would expect it to do if the effluvium set the air into motion. So he proposed an important modification of the conceptual scheme: the effluvia were to be thought of as a steady material cloud about the rubbed electric that established direct contact with the object attracted. In his own words:

> The effluvia spread in all directions: they are specific and peculiar, and *sui generis*, different from the common air; generated from humor; called forth by calorific motion and rubbing, and attenuation; they are as it were material rods—hold and take up straws, chaff, twigs, till their force is spent or vanishes; and then these small bodies, being set free again, are attracted by the earth itself and fall to the ground.

Although, as we shall see, Gilbert's effluvium theory of electrical attraction was soon to need other modifications, it afforded at the time a basis for further investigations, which is one of the important functions of a theory. However, a theory also tends to restrict thought to definite directions, and Gilbert's was no exception. For example, he utterly failed to take note of a phenomenon that must have occurred many times before his very eyes: when a small object is attracted to and makes contact with an excited electric, it may rebound violently through a distance of as much as several inches. There was no place in Gilbert's theory for such electrical *repulsion*, and he missed it entirely. Even a careful observer may have difficulty in seeing the totally unexpected, or if he sees it may dismiss it as accidental, particularly if the observation runs counter to his established preconceptions.

Electrical repulsion was discovered a few years after Gilbert's death by Nicolo Cabeo, an Italian Jesuit and a militant anti-Copernican. Significantly, Cabeo, while acknowledging the accuracy of much of Gilbert's work, felt certain that it must contain errors and omissions, for Galileo and Kepler were then using some of Gilbert's ideas on magnetism to support the Copernican planetary system that Cabeo held to be false. Thus armed with his own preconceptions, Cabeo indeed found in the course of relatively few experiments that a rubbed electric, after attracting, may sometimes repel.

PROBLEM 26.1. Suggest how Gilbert's theory of effluvia might have been modified so as to explain repulsion as well as attraction.

26.4 Gray and the discovery of electrical conduction.

By the beginning of the 18th century, a new word had come into use, *electricity*. A physics textbook of the day contained this definition:

> Electricity is that property of bodies, by which . . . [when rubbed] they attract and repel lighter bodies at a sensible distance.

Note that electricity was here defined not as a material substance, such as Gilbert's effluvium, but as a property, like hardness or transparency. Another name for it was "the electric virtue"; a rubbed electric was therefore said to possess an electricity, or the electric virtue, that is, to have the property of attracting and repelling light objects. By this time a large number of substances were known to be electrics. Among them, glass in the form of tubes and spheres was found to be especially convenient as an electric for experimental work.

In 1731, Stephen Gray (d. 1736) communicated to the Royal Society, through one of its members, a striking discovery that he had made while experimenting with a glass tube. He had found, as others had before him, that if the glass is rubbed in the dark, tiny sparks are seen to pass between the glass tube and a finger held close to it. But, he reasoned, if the rubbed glass tube communicates sparks to a nearby object, perhaps it is at the same time communicating the "electric virtue" to the object. To test this conjecture, he procured a glass tube about 3 ft long and over an inch in diameter, and he put a cork in each end of it "to keep the dust out." But being a careful experimenter, he decided to check whether the corks would interfere with the operation of the tube. Upon rubbing the tube he found that it would attract a nearby feather just as well when stopped at both ends as when left open. Holding the feather near one end of the tube, he saw it approach and touch the cork and then be repelled, just as it had at the rubbed glass surface.

Here was a new phenomenon; the cork had not been rubbed, but nevertheless it attracted the feather and hence was electrified. Seemingly, concluded Gray, the "attractive virtue" had been *communicated* to the cork, presumably because it was in contact with the excited tube. Doubtless his earlier conjecture that the "electric virtue" might be communicated along with sparks to a nearby object had prepared him to note and explain the present phenomenon. He no longer pursued that conjecture, but turned all his energies to exploit his discovery.

> Having by me an ivory ball of about 1 inch $\frac{3}{10}$ in diameter, with a hole through it, this I fixed upon [one end of] a fir stick about 4 inches long. Thrusting the other end [of the stick] into the cork, and rubbing the tube, I found that the ball attracted and repelled the feather with more vigor than the cork had done, repeating its attractions and repulsions for many times together.
>
> I then fixed the ball on longer sticks, first one of 8 inches, and afterwards on one of 24 inches, and found the effect the same.

Continuing such experiments, Gray replaced the stick of fir with metal rods of greater length. Then, to get still more length, he used string to suspend the ball from the rubbed tube. To be able to use longer strings, he stood on balconies and even planned to climb to the top of St. Paul's Cathedral!

Having succeeded in transmitting the "electric virtue" a distance of 34 ft by a vertical line, Gray decided to use a horizontal string tied at one end to the tube and suspended near the other end by a piece of vertical cord looped over a nail in a ceiling beam. But this experiment failed completely. Gray comments:

> ... I concluded, that when the electric virtue came to the loop that was suspended on the beam, it went up the same to the beam; so that none, or very little of it at least, came down to the ball.

A friend of Gray's

> ... proposed a silk cord to support the [main transmission] line along which the electric virtue was to pass. I told him that this support might do better on account of its smallness [thinness], for then there would be less virtue carried away from the line of communication ...

This plan worked, and before long the experimenters had moved outdoors and successfully transmitted the "electric virtue" along a 293-ft line.

When a still greater length was sought, the silk supporting cords broke under the weight of the line. Gray then chose brass wires to support the line, and at once the experiments failed completely. He saw that he had been in error; it was not the thinness of the supports but the material of which they were made that was the more relevant factor. So the experimenters turned back to silk supports, but now using many of them fastened to a series of poles driven into the ground. In this way they successfully used transmission lines of 650 ft and even longer. In modern terms, they had reached the recognition that substances may be divided into two categories, electrical *conductors* (such as brass) and *nonconductors* (such as silk).

The generalization that explained Gray's observations simply was proposed by Charles François de Cisternay Dufay (1698–1739), a French scientist and corresponding member of the Royal Society of London, whose interest in electricity stemmed from reading Gray's papers. Dufay pointed out that the successful transmission line should be supported by means of one of Gilbert's "electrics" and the line itself should preferably be a "nonelectric." He showed also that *any* substance whatsoever could be electrified by conduction from a rubbed "electric" provided that the substance is not held in the hand but is supported by an "electric," for example, placed on a glass stool or hung by a silk thread. In brief, Gilbert's "electrics" are what we now call nonconductors or insulators; his "nonelectrics" are what we call conductors. Both Gray and Dufay went on to electrify a vast number of things—water, chickens, coal buckets, and persons. This is a characteristic aftermath of an important discovery— nearly random experimentation directed toward its exploitation.

26.5 Dufay and the two kinds of electrification. Gray had shown that the property of attraction could be transferred from one object to another. Dufay, in addition, pursued the subject of electric repulsion. Like others before him, Dufay had noticed that an object attracted to and touching an electrified object itself becomes electrified and then is repelled. Therefore, he at first thought, two electrified objects could be said always to repel each other. But the force between two objects when *both* are electrified was a new subject for investigation, and further experimentation showed Dufay that his first hypothesis was quite untenable. For he found that, depending on the circumstances, two electrified objects may sometimes repel and sometimes *attract* each other. For example, if two pieces of glass are each rubbed with silk cloth, they repel each other. Similarly, two pieces of amber that have been rubbed with fur show this same mutual repulsion. But if glass that has been rubbed with silk is put near amber that has been rubbed with fur, they attract each other. Dufay proposed a new and important hypothesis to account for these phenomena:

> This principle is that there are two distinct electricities, very different from each other: one of these I call *vitreous electricity;* the other, *resinous electricity.* The first is that of [rubbed] glass, rock crystal, precious stones, hair of animals,

wool, and many other bodies. The second is that of [rubbed] amber, copal, gum lac, silk, thread, paper, and a vast number of other substances.

The characteristic of these two electricities is that a body of, say, the *vitreous electricity* repels all such as are of the same electricity; and on the contrary, attracts all those of the *resinous electricity*.

Dufay went on to explain electrical attraction and repulsion by assuming that a vortex of effluvium surrounded each electrified object, and that as the vortices interacted with one another, the objects associated with them were forced to move. This view was an extension of Gilbert's theory and also of Descartes' vortex theory in mechanics (which still lingered on in France, although it was soon to give way to the "action at a distance" of Newtonian mechanics). Indeed, the effluvium picture was beginning to die out as the attention of investigators was directed more and more toward the state of the electrified objects themselves rather than on the region around them. Thus Dufay's vortex theory had little effect on his successors. On the other hand, his hypothesis of two kinds of electrification was to acquire the greatest importance.

26.6 The two-fluid theory. When Dufay wrote of "two distinct electricities" he meant two states of electrification; neither he nor Gray ever spoke of electricity as being anything except a *property* of matter. But in the middle of the 18th century the term rapidly drifted toward a new meaning; "electricity" began to mean a substance or fluid that was assumed to exist within an object when it is electrified. The experiments and language of both Gray and Dufay tended to encourage this development. For example, if a glass tube with a 700-ft line attached to it is rubbed and the far end of the line becomes electrified, it is difficult to avoid the view that some fluid has moved along the line. Furthermore, fluid theories were at this time important and successful in other branches of contemporary science, for example the theories of caloric and of phlogiston.

In the hands of the Abbé Nollet (1700–1770) and others, Dufay's hypothesis was extended to what became known as the *two-fluid theory* of electricity, which postulated the existence of two electrical fluids called, in Dufay's terminology, "resinous fluid" and "vitreous fluid." When amber and fur were rubbed together, the amber was said to acquire resinous fluid and the fur vitreous fluid. Moreover, it was assumed that each object, before it was rubbed, possessed equal amounts of both fluids, and that the process of rubbing caused transfers of the fluids such as to leave the amber with an excess of vitreous fluid and the fur with an excess of resinous fluid. Then one did not have to think of the two fluids as being created; they were there all the time and were merely redistributed by the rubbing. Finally, by adding the assumption that the unlike fluids attract each other whereas the like fluids repel each other, all the diverse phenom-

ena with which investigators of the day were familiar could be accounted
for. For example, the reason that an unelectrified body does not exert
electric forces is that its equal amounts of the two fluids are so thoroughly
mixed that their effects cancel out, and when an object is attracted to and
touches rubbed amber, it acquires some of the amber's excess of resinous
fluid by conduction, whereupon the object and amber repel each other.

26.7 Electrical science becomes popular.   While these ideas were
emerging, near the middle of the 18th century, electricity was becoming
the popular rage, and lecturers were busily engaged in devising spectacular
experiments that were more nearly scientific recreations than researches.
Much stronger electrical charges were now available through the use of a
machine or "generator" consisting of a rapidly spinning glass globe fitted
with an attachment for effectively rubbing it, and by using a transmission
line to conduct the charge from the glass globe to other objects, many
spectacular and often amusing effects could be achieved.   Students at
some of the universities complained that the general public was crowding
them out of their seats at demonstration lectures.   "Courses of experimental lectures" were quickly oversubscribed. In one such "show," a girl
suspended on silk and insulators was electrified by connecting her to a
concealed generator, and then some willing member of the audience was
invited to grasp her hand or kiss her with results that, of course, were
shocking. One scientist complained to the Physical Society of Danzig in
1757 that electrical discoveries were being reported in the popular press
before being presented to the Society. In Germany, especially, artisans
were building spinning-globe generators and finding a good market for
them among well-to-do people who amused themselves by repeating experiments in their homes.

This popular interest not only stimulated and helped to finance electrical investigations, but in some instances led directly to important
advancements. It also serves to illustrate that there are many different
motives and incentives for scientific activity, and many patterns by which
a science develops.

26.8 Franklin's one-fluid theory.   Popular experiments performed in
Boston by an itinerant lecturer first brought electrical phenomena to the
attention of Benjamin Franklin (1706–1790). Upon acquiring a glass tube
from a friend in England, Franklin initiated the extensive investigations
that soon were to establish him as one of the foremost scientists of his day.
One important outgrowth was his development of an explanation of electrical phenomena in terms of a single electrical fluid. This was at about
the time when Nollet, in France, was working on the two-fluid theory.

Franklin's proposal was that every unelectrified object contains a definite, "normal" amount of a single electrical fluid. This "fluid" he pictured as consisting of electrical particles that repelled one another, but attracted the particles of ordinary matter. Electrification consisted either in the object gaining extra fluid and thus becoming *positively* electrified or in losing some of its "normal" amount, leaving it *negatively* electrified. For example, Franklin assumed that glass, when rubbed with silk, drew fluid from the silk and thus became positively charged, while the silk was left negatively charged. For the process of conduction (when two electrical conductors are touching or are close enough for a spark to pass through the air between them) he assumed that an unelectrified conductor will receive additional fluid from a positively electrified conductor and will give up fluid to a negatively electrified body. In brief, the fluid was pictured as flowing from positive to either normal (neutral) or negative, or from normal (neutral) to negative. This convention for determining the direction of a flow of electric charge (i.e., of an electric current) is still in use today.

Note that Franklin had to provide his own terminology to express his ideas, for he was unaware at the time of Dufay's introduction of the terms "vitreous" and "resinous." Evidently, any object containing more than the normal quantity of Franklin's simple fluid is in the state of electrification called positive by Franklin and "vitreous" by Dufay. Similarly, any object deficient in this simple fluid is in the negative or "resinous" state of electrification.

26.9 The principle of the conservation of charge. Franklin's assumption that the quantity of electrical fluid in any *insulated* body remains unchanged and that electrification involves merely a transfer of the fluid was perhaps the first clear statement of the important postulate that *electric charge can be neither created nor destroyed.* Although Nollet's two-fluid theory contained suggestions leading to the same postulate, it pictured the two fluids as indistinguishably mixed, so that even if both were conserved, they could not be examined separately. From the one-fluid point of view, on the other hand, if some way could be found to measure the amount of fluid acquired by an object when it is, say, rubbed against a second object, then the latter could be assumed to have lost this same amount of fluid. Hence techniques may be applied to the study of electrical phenomena that are analogous to those that were at this same time being applied to the study of heat fluid (Chapter 19).

Since the dispute about whether there are two electrical fluids or a single one could not be decided at the time, each investigator tended to adopt the point of view that appealed to him as being more useful for his own purposes. Here is a situation that is common in the history of science; we met it, for example, in the disputes over the Ptolemaic and Copernican theories of planetary motion, and over the caloric and "mode of motion" views of heat. But one conception over which there was no dispute was the principle of conservation of charge that grew out of the electrical fluid theories; it came to stay unaltered and today remains one of the most fundamental postulates of all electrical theory. It is this principle that makes the concept of electric charge so important. Moreover, until some such conservation principle had been found in electrical science, no extensive quantitative studies of electrical phenomena could be made. But ironically, today we recognize that one-fluid and two-fluid theories can serve equally well to describe the simple observations in electricity. If a body is charged positively, the situation can be represented by considering either that it has an excess of Franklin's electric fluid, *or* that it has a deficiency of some negative or "resinous" electric fluid, just as an *increase* of $1.00 in a person's wealth is equivalent to a $1.00 *decrease* of his debt.

26.10 The need for quantification. At this same time, in the middle of the 18th century, electrical studies were beginning to be compared unfavorably with the science of mechanics; spectacular tricks and popular interest could not entirely hide the simple fact that electricity as a science was progressing quite slowly. The Abbé Nollet and another contemporary experimenter, Daniel Gralath (1739–1809), were among those who expressed the growing opinion that rapid advances could not be expected until the science was put on a quantitative basis, where it might deal with mathematical relations between measurable quantities. To gain this end, Gralath plunged into measurements of electrical forces in various circumstances, declaring:

> If someone wishes to interject the question of whether or not it is too early to measure the force of electricity and to desire a mathematical cognition thereof, since . . . [electrical theory] has not yet progressed far therein and the true origin of electricity is not yet counted as certain truth, this objection is easily removed. For if one reflects that common experience and historical knowledge lie at the base of mathematical knowledge, one can very often do without . . . [theory]. Indeed one not rarely first achieves the latter when he has already the former in his power. Every operation of nature has its determined degree of force: this I can inquire into, if I consider it exactly, without knowing what brings about the operation. When Galileo wished to give a mathematical theory of the movement of heavy bodies, he did not trouble himself over the origin of weight . . .

But Gralath was wrong in his belief that "this objection" (lack of theory) "is easily removed." He had been observing the effects that electric shocks produced on animals and wanted a way to measure the strength of a shock. Observations of spark lengths had been used for this purpose, but Gralath felt that the force of attraction of the electrified object for some other object would provide a more precise measure. However, to design a fruitful experiment, he needed a suitable hypothesis to guide him, and this he lacked. Thus his measurements, although carefully made, yielded no useful further results. Simply to *measure* is not enough. There must be some basis for selecting the quantities to be measured and for fully interpreting the results.

But what basis could there be when at the time there was not a single purely electrical concept that had been defined quantitatively? In such circumstances one course that could be followed was to look for guidance in some more developed part of science that not only possessed precisely defined concepts but involved phenomena having general characteristics very similar to those found in electrical science. Gravitational science seemed to be a good possibility. So speculation arose as to whether gravitation and electricity, even though they might involve basically different phenomena, have sufficient characteristics in common for the precise quantitative relations of Newtonian mechanics to be used as guides in finding *analogous* relations in electricity. Gralath had not used such a guide; he derived the working hypothesis for his experiments from necessarily crude observations of spark strengths producing shocks.

26.11 The electrical force-distance law. A comparison with the gravitational law of attraction (Section 11.8) naturally suggested that the force of electrical attraction or repulsion between two objects might also vary inversely as the square of the distance between the objects. About 1760, Daniel Bernoulli found this to be the case when he placed an electrified metal disk parallel to and at various distances from an unelectrified metal disk, and measured the force of attraction between them. This experiment apparently excited little interest at the time, but in retrospect we note that, together with the principle of conservation of charge, it probably marked the beginning of genuine quantification in electrical science.

About a decade later, the English clergyman and schoolteacher Joseph Priestley (1733–1804) reached a similar conclusion by a different path. Through personal contact with Benjamin Franklin while the latter was in England, Priestley had been stimulated to undertake certain electrical experiments, among them one considered especially important by Franklin, i.e., to find whether any electrical force was excited on an object when it was inside an electrified metal cup. Upon electrifying "a tin quart vessel, standing upon a stool of baked wood" (a good insulator), Priestley found that a small object hanging from a silk thread and brought near to the *outside* of the electrified vessel would be attracted to it in the usual manner, but if this same object were suspended *anywhere inside* the electrified vessel, there was no indication of a force on it. He asked:

> May we not infer from this experiment that the attraction of electricity is subject to the same laws with that of gravitation, and is therefore according

to the [inverse] squares of the distance; since it is easily demonstrated that, were the earth in the form of a shell, a body in the inside of it would not be attracted to one side more than another.

Priestley was here referring to a theorem in Newton's *Principia*, that as a consequence of the inverse-square law of gravitation a uniformly thick spherical shell of matter is not expected to exert any gravitational force on an object anywhere within the shell. Of course, this did not constitute a *proof* that an inverse-square law holds for electric charges, for while there are important similarities between gravitational and electrical phenomena, there are also differences that had not been clarified at the time. In particular, the gravitational force on an object enclosed in a hollow vessel is zero only if the body is spherical in shape and has walls of uniform density, whereas for the electrical case, as we know today, the hollow vessel may be of any shape, and the only restriction on the walls is that they be conducting. But even if gravitational and electrical phenomena, in this and other respects, are not completely analogous, a partial similarity is apparent, and reasoning by plausible analogy has been exceedingly fruitful in many parts of science.

At about this time another Englishman of great creative ability, Henry Cavendish (1731–1810), expressed his conviction that the relation between electrical force and distance was, as in the gravitational case, an *inverse-square law*. About 1770 Cavendish strengthened this conviction by an experiment similar to Priestley's, but improved by the use of a conducting vessel that was spherical in shape and completely closed, thus providing a precise electrical analogy to the gravitational case. Cavendish, who was an abnormally shy man, withheld his manuscripts on this experiment and many others that probably would have hastened the advance of electrical knowledge by many years. They remained unknown until a century later, when nearly everything in them had been rediscovered by others.

26.12 Coulomb's experiments. The experiments of Priestley and Cavendish had provided indirect evidence of the probable validity of an inverse-square law for electricity, but the need now was for *direct* experiments, similar to Bernoulli's but made with electrified particles or spheres instead of disks. We recall that the distance r between two attracting objects enters into Newton's law of gravitation. If the objects are particles, there is clearly no difficulty in interpreting what r means. If they are homogeneous spheres, then, as Newton proved (Section 11.8), r is to be regarded as the distance between their centers.

Experiments showed that two electrified spheres also act on each other as if the important distance controlling the magnitude of the forces is the distance between the centers of the spheres. Thus, in retrospect at least, we can see how a direct test of the electrical force-distance law might be made by placing two electrified spherical objects at various known distances apart and, for each distance, measuring the force exerted by either object on the other. Such direct tests were carried out in France in 1785 by Charles Augustin Coulomb (1736–1806), who had made a torsion balance that was highly suitable for measuring the forces and distances. He had originally designed the torsion balance for his study of elastic twisting forces in metal wires, almost certainly without knowing that John Michell, some two decades earlier in England, had devised a similar instrument for measuring the constant of gravitation G (Section 12.1). Coulomb's balance was so sensitive that he could measure forces as small as "a ten-thousandth of a grain," which is approximately a 10^{-8} part of a pound of force, or 6×10^{-8} new.

As indicated schematically in Fig. 26.3, a light horizontal rod of poorly conducting material, carrying a small pith ball a at one end, is suspended by a delicate fiber of metal or silk, and a second pith ball t is rigidly mounted in a position close to the movable one. When both balls are given electric charges of the same sign, either $+$ and $+$, or $-$ and $-$, the balls repel each other, causing the horizontal rod to rotate until the elastic restoring

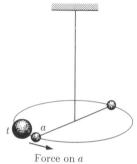

Force on a

FIG. 26.3. The torsion balance; t and a have net charges of the same sign.

force set up in the twisted suspension fiber is sufficiently large to counterbalance the effect of the electrical repulsion. Since Coulomb knew from his earlier elastic studies that the angle through which the suspension fiber is twisted is directly proportional to the twisting force applied to the ball on the end of the horizontal rod, he now had a way of computing the force from the observed angle of rotation.

Figure 26.4 is Coulomb's own drawing of the apparatus. The two pith balls, a and t, initially in contact with each other, were given charges of the same sign by means of an electrified metal pin mounted on an insulating handle (shown below the instrument in Fig. 26.4). The pin was introduced through the hole m in the top of the case until it touched the pith ball t, and was then withdrawn. The ball a immediately moved away until brought to rest by the restoring force supplied by the now twisted wire. Then by twisting the graduated knob p to which the top of the suspension fiber was attached, the centers of the two balls could be brought to any desired distance r apart, and this distance r and the force F of repulsion at that distance could then be computed from a knowledge of the angular distance between balls a and t, as shown by the scale on the case, and of

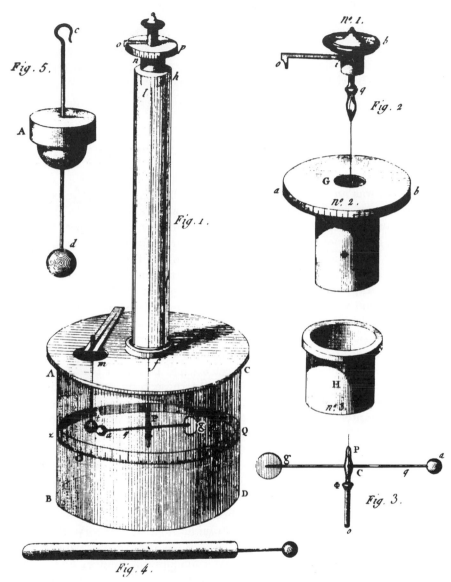

FIG. 26.4. Coulomb's torsion balance, from the drawing in his paper on electrical forces (*Histoire et Mémoires de l'Académie Royale des Sciences*, 1785).

the angle through which the top knob p had been twisted, as shown by its scale.

By many such trials, both when the two pith balls were positively (vitreously) charged, and also when they were negatively (resinously) charged, Coulomb showed that the force F of mutual electrical repulsion varies inversely with the square of the distance of separation r, or

$$F \propto \frac{1}{r^2}. \qquad (26.1)$$

Furthermore, he showed that the same inverse-square relation holds for the force of mutual attraction between two objects having charges of unlike signs.

Coulomb was an expert on measurements; his analyses of the possible sources of error in his experiments, which he always included in his published accounts, would satisfy the most meticulous modern experimenter. Moreover, he was not content with a single method for testing the inverse-square law, so he devised a different instrument for the purpose, a *torsion pendulum*. We shall not describe here this instrument and method, which provided an experimental proof of the inverse-square law completely different from that with the torsion balance. Still not satisfied, Coulomb performed a third independent demonstration of the validity of the relation, an indirect experiment similar to the unpublished one of Cavendish. The inverse-square relation for spherical, uniformly charged objects, $F \propto 1/r^2$, has since been confirmed by an indirect method to within 1 part in 1000 million. It is of course implied here that these tests refer to charged objects of relatively large size, not, for example, to nuclear particles, for which, as Chapter 39 will show, these "classical" laws of interaction between charged objects have to be modified.

26.13 The complete electrostatic force law. Once it was settled how the electrical force F varies with the distance of separation r, a next question was how F changes if two bodies are kept a fixed distance apart and the quantities of charge on either one or both are altered by definite amounts. Let us restate the problem in terms of Franklin's one-fluid theory. Suppose that Coulomb's two insulated pith balls (Fig. 26.3) have positive charges q_1 and q_2; that is, they have been given amounts of fluid q_1 and q_2 in excess of their normal, neutral amounts. Or suppose that both pith balls have negative charges $-q_1$ and $-q_2$ because these amounts of their normal fluids have been subtracted from them. Or perhaps their charges are q_1 and $-q_2$, or $-q_1$ and q_2. In any of these cases, how will the force F between the balls be affected if additional fluid is added to or allowed to escape from one or both balls, the separation r being kept at the original value by turning the knob p on the torsion balance?

Coulomb's answer was that the electrical force varies directly "as the product of the electrical masses of the two balls." In view of this wording, we can guess that, like others before him, he reached this conclusion at first by analogy with Newton's law of gravitation, $F_{grav} = G(m_1m_2/r^2)$. Since gravitational force varies directly as the product m_1m_2 of the gravitational masses (gravitational "quantities of matter") of two attracting bodies, perhaps electrical force varies directly as the product q_1q_2 of the "electrical masses" (quantities of charge) on the bodies. This notion becomes still more plausible in view of the principle that electric charge, like ordinary mass, cannot be created or destroyed (Sections 16.5 and 26.9). To summarize, Coulomb (and others) had shown experimentally that

$$F \propto \frac{1}{r^2} \text{ (if } q_1 \text{ and } q_2 \text{ are kept constant),}$$

and he now surmised that

$$F \propto q_1q_2 \text{ (if } r \text{ is kept constant).}$$

It follows that F should be jointly proportional to these factors, or $F \propto q_1q_2/r^2$, and hence

$$F = C\frac{q_1q_2}{r^2}, \tag{26.2}$$

where C is a constant of proportionality yet to be determined. The law expressed by Eq. (26.2) has come to be called *Coulomb's law of electrostatic force*, and justly so, for we shall see that Coulomb was not content to advance it simply as an analogy of the law of gravitation, but tested all of it experimentally. The adjective *electrostatic* is included here because Eq. (26.2) gives the force between electric charges that are at rest with respect to each other. As was discovered after Coulomb's time, charges in relative motion exert both electrostatic and magnetic forces on one another.

Of the various tests of Eq. (26.2) made by Coulomb, we shall mention only one. Using his torsion balance (Fig. 26.4), he electrified the two pith balls a and t in the usual manner and measured the force F between them when they were a given distance r apart. Selecting an uncharged pith ball of the *same diameter* as the fixed ball t, he lowered it on a silk thread through the hole m until it touched the ball t. Charge flowed by conduction from t to the new ball until the charge had been shared equally and on t was one-half its former amount. Then, removing the new ball, Coulomb brought balls a and t to the same distance r apart as before and measured the force; it was one-half its former value, as Eq. (26.2) predicts it should be.

PROBLEM 26.2. (a) How does the force between two charged particles change if the charge of each is halved and their distance apart is doubled? (b) What if the charge of each is doubled and the distance apart is doubled? (c) Why did we assume in the last argument above that the uncharged pith ball takes half the charge of t upon contact? How could one check experimentally on that statement?

26.14 Units of charge.

To be able to measure and express the quantity of charge, we might start by selecting some particle that is believed to have a permanent charge of fixed amount, and assign to this amount the value unity. Then, if suitable electrical measurements can be devised, the magnitude of any other charge might be expressed as a multiple of this standard unit charge. This procedure would be similar to that of finding and expressing a mass in terms of the standard kilogram, or a length in terms of the standard meter. However, such a procedure was not possible in the electrical case, not the least difficulty being the virtual impossibility of preventing the charge on an object from changing by conduction. Therefore the procedure followed was to use Coulomb's law, Eq. (26.2), to *define a unit of charge in terms of already established force and length units*, just as in Section 4.4 Newton's second law of motion was used to define the unit of force (the newton) in terms of known units of mass and acceleration.

Thus, in the cgs system of units, the unit electric charge is defined as that charge which, if placed 1 cm distant from a charge of the same magnitude and sign, will repel the latter with an electrostatic force of 1 dyne. This is called the "cgs electrostatic unit of charge" or the *statcoulomb* (statcoul). Note that the definition is designed to give the constant C in Eq. (26.2) the simplest possible magnitude, unity. For if q_1 and q_2 are equal in magnitude and are taken to be each 1 statcoul when $r = 1$ cm and $F = 1$ dyne, substitution in Eq. (26.2) gives 1 dyne $= C \cdot (1$ statcoul$)^2/1$ cm^2 or $C = 1$ dyne·cm^2/statcoul^2.

Thus we may rewrite Coulomb's equation:

$$F = \left(1 \, \frac{\text{dyne·cm}^2}{\text{statcoul}^2}\right) \frac{q_1 q_2}{r^2} \text{ (in the cgs system of units).} \qquad (26.3)$$

Since the statcoulomb represents a very small charge, another unit nearly 3000 million times larger, called the *coulomb* (coul) is commonly used for practical purposes. The more precise relation between the two units is: 1 coul $= 2.998 \times 10^9$ statcoul. The coulomb is not only more practical in size but it is also the unit of charge used in the mks system. As a result, the constant C in Eq. (26.2) is 8.988×10^9 new·m^2/coul^2, or about 9.0×10^9 new·m^2/coul^2 *if force, distance, and charges are expressed in the mks system.*

PROBLEM 26.3. Using the relation 1.0 coul = 3.0×10^9 statcoul, show that Eq. (26.3) can be written in the alternative form

$$F = \left(9.0 \times 10^9 \frac{\text{new·m}^2}{\text{coul}^2}\right) \frac{q_1 q_2}{r^2} \text{ (in the mks system of units).} \quad (26.4)$$

PROBLEM 26.4. (a) Two small spheres with their centers 20 cm apart have charges of $+50$ and -40 statcoul, respectively. Show that the electrostatic force exerted by each sphere on the other one is -5 dynes. (Note that the negative sign for the force here denotes an attraction.) (b) Find the electrostatic force between two small spheres 50 cm apart, the charge on each sphere being 3.0×10^{-7} coul.

PROBLEM 26.5. Two small spheres are supposed to be given a charge of $+1$ coul each; their centers are 1 m apart. Compute the electrostatic force on either sphere. Is this a feasible experiment?

PROBLEM 26.6. Reread carefully the definition of the unit of charge in the cgs system in Section 26.14, and note the apparent vicious circle. How can we know that the charges are of the *same magnitude* before the unit of charge has been defined? Suggest an experimental procedure to solve the difficulty.

PROBLEM 26.7. An electron has a negative charge of about -2×10^{-19} coul and a mass of about 10^{-30} kgm. Given that two electrons are at any fixed distance r apart, compute the ratio of the electrostatic force with which each electron repels the other to the gravitational force with which each attracts the other.

26.15 Charging by influence. It remains for us to mention two other methods of electrifying an object, discovered during the 18th century. Suppose that a negatively charged rod is held close to, but not touching, an insulated and initially uncharged conductor, as in Fig. 26.5(c). Tests will then show that the insulated object has become polarized; that is, the equal quantities of positive and negative charges on it are no longer thoroughly mixed, but have redistributed themselves so that there is an excess of positive charge on the side nearest the rod and an equally large excess of negative charge on the opposite side. Here we see the explanation for the earliest known of all electrical phenomena, that a rubbed object attracts one that has not been rubbed. The distance between the negative charge on the rod and the positive charge on the object is smaller than that between the negative charges on the rod and object; hence, by Coulomb's law, the force of attraction between rod and object exceeds the force of repulsion. If the insulated object is not an electrical conductor, some local polarization will occur, and so even in this case the net force between rod and object will be one of attraction.

If the negatively charged rod is now completely removed, the insulated object will return to its normal, unelectrified state; that is, the electrification of its two sides has been only *temporary*. Suppose, however, that we do not remove the charged rod, but instead perform the operation shown

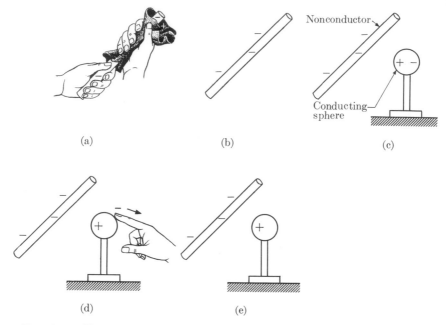

FIG. 26.5. Charging an insulated spherical conductor by electrostatic induction or "influence."

in Fig. 26.5(d); that is, we connect the polarized, insulated object to some other object, say by touching it with the hand or connecting it to the earth. The charges on the object will now further redistribute themselves over the system (object + hand) or (object + earth). There has been no net loss of charge, but since the object is the part of the system that is closest to the rod, it will now have an excess of positive charge. If, finally, the connection to the hand or earth is removed, the whole insulated object will be found to be positively charged, and permanently so [Fig. 26.5(e)]. This process is referred to as *permanent charging by influence* or by "electrostatic induction."

Note that the sign of the charge produced on the object by influence is opposite to that on the rod. Moreover, the quantity of charge on the inducing rod does not change; the rod can be used to charge innumerable other objects by influence without itself losing any charge in the process. Thus we see that charging by influence (induction) must be sharply contrasted with *charging by conduction*, when the charged rod is allowed to touch the insulated object and hence loses some of its charge to it. After this contact, the object remains charged after the rod is removed, and the sign of the charge is the same as that of the rod.

Neither charging by influence nor charging by conduction is to be confused with *charging by rubbing* or, as it is sometimes called, "by friction." In the latter case charges of opposite sign but of equal magnitude are acquired by two dissimilar substances such as glass and silk. Today we know that this separation of charges results primarily from the close contact and subsequent separation of the two substances, each of which has a different affinity for charges. The rubbing serves merely to bring large areas of the two unlike substances into very close contact.

With our discussion of 18th-century electrical developments now completed, we see that the conceptual scheme for the explanation of electrostatic phenomena has already reached the stage outlined at the beginning of this chapter. In the first part of the 19th century the scheme was further exploited and also broadened to include the new discoveries and concepts to be described in the chapter that follows.

ADDITIONAL PROBLEMS

26.8. When charging an object by influence, why is it essential to break the connection between the object and the hand or the earth before removing the electrified rod?

26.9. Explain charging by influence in terms of (a) the two-fluid theory, and (b) the one-fluid theory.

26.10. Suppose that an insulated object is charged by influence by bringing it close to a *positively* charged rod. Draw diagrams similar to those in Fig. 26.5 to illustrate the steps in this process.

26.11. Two metal spheres mounted on insulating stands are initially in contact (Fig. 26.6). While an amber rod that has been rubbed with fur is held close to, but not touching, the spheres, the one farthest from the rod is removed without touching it; then the rod is removed. Draw sketches to represent the steps and the charge distributions during this process.

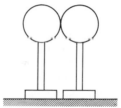

FIGURE 26.6

26.12. How is your analysis to be changed in Problem 26.11 if a spark jumps from the rod to the nearer sphere at the beginning of the experiment?

26.13. Explain each of the following observations: (a) walking across a carpet is sometimes followed by a shock when the hand touches a metal object; (b) violent motion of air or raindrops is often followed by lightning; (c) gasoline trucks usually have chains that drag on the roadway, and cars are brushed by metal strips upon approaching a toll gate.

26.14. Although every electric charge investigated has turned out to be either positive or negative, the existence of charges of other types is logically conceivable. How might an investigator go about detecting the presence of some third type of charge if it did exist; that is, what would be its properties?

26.15. A small ball of mass 2.0×10^{-3} kgm and bearing a charge of 2.4×10^{-8} coul is at a distance r from a small fixed object having a charge of $-2.0 \times$

10^{-7} coul. Assuming that the resulting electrostatic force is the only appreciable force acting on the ball, compute the acceleration of the ball at the moment when (a) $r = 0.08$ m, and (b) $r = 0.04$ m. (c) Sketch a graph for the acceleration as a function of the distance of separation r.

26.16. When two pith balls bearing charges of $+q_1$ and $+q_2$, respectively, are placed 1 cm apart, the mutual electrostatic repelling force between them is found to be F_1. (a) How does the force compare with F_1 when the balls are at each of the following distances r apart: 2, 3, 4, 5, 10, and 100 cm, and infinity? (b) On graph paper, plot these forces as a function of distance apart, and draw a smooth curve through the plotted points.

26.17. Two very large insulated metal spheres similar to those shown in Fig. 26.6 but not touching each other are given charges of magnitude q_1 and q_2, respectively. On the plausible assumption that the charge on each sphere has distributed itself uniformly over the whole surface of the sphere, and that it remains so distributed, we would suppose that the electrostatic force between the spheres can be computed by $F = Cq_1q_2/r^2$, where r is the distance between the centers of the *spheres*. However, in an experiment, the *observed* value of the force is larger than the computed one when q_1 and q_2 are of opposite sign, and is smaller than the computed one when they are of the same sign. Explain.

26.18. (a) List the similarities and outstanding differences between Newton's law of gravitation and Coulomb's electrostatic force law. (b) Can you suggest reasons for the repeated appearance of an inverse-square law of force in such different branches of physics as mechanics, electricity, and magnetism (where the force between two magnetic poles also is found to vary inversely with the square of their distance apart)?

26.19. In Fig. 26.7, suppose that the mass of each ball is 0.4 gm, that the length of each thread is 30 cm, and that the angle between the threads is 18° when the balls bear identical charges q. (a) Compute the electrostatic force (in dynes) acting on each ball; note that the weight of each ball is 0.4×980 dynes. (b) Find the magnitude of the charge q on either ball. (c) Describe a procedure which will ensure that the two balls are given charges of the same magnitude and sign.

FIGURE 26.7

26.20. Franklin, in a letter to a friend, wrote: "I erected an iron rod to draw the lightning down into my house, in order to make some experiments on it, with two bells [a so-called "electric chime"] to give notice when the rod should be electrify'd . . . I had given orders in the family that if the bells rang when I was away from home, they should catch some of the lightning for me in electric phials [condensers] . . ." The electric chime mentioned by Franklin may be constructed by mounting two small bells side by side, with one bell connected to a source of charge, the other to the earth; and between the two suspending a small metal ball on a silk thread, so that the ball can swing as a pendulum. Explain why the ball keeps swinging to and fro, alternately striking each bell.

26.21. On the supposition that electricity was a form of matter and therefore should have weight, experiments were made in the 18th century to see whether an object increases in weight upon being electrified; the results varied widely and were mostly inconclusive, but the general opinion was that there was no increase in weight. (a) What are some of the difficulties and sources of error that are likely to be encountered in performing such experiments? (b) Suppose that the sources of error and of spurious results could have been eliminated, and that it were then found that an object did not increase in weight upon being electrified. Would this have served to prove beyond question that electricity is *not* a form of matter?

26.22. Franklin found that some thunderclouds are positively charged and others are negatively charged. Using Franklin's conceptual scheme, explain the action of a lightning rod when the cloud's charge is (a) positive, (b) negative.

SUPPLEMENTARY READING

BROWN, W. H., *Lucretius on the nature of things* (Rutgers University Press, 1950), Book VI, verse 40. This translation, which is the source of the excerpt appearing in Section 26.2, presents the subject matter of the poem in a framework (hexameter verse) similar to that "wherein Lucretius himself chose to convey the content of his mind to his own countrymen."

COHEN, I. B., ed., *Benjamin Franklin's experiments* (Harvard University Press, 1941), with an introduction.

MAGIE, W. F., *A source book in physics* (McGraw-Hill, 1935), pp. 400–403, 408–420. Selections from Franklin and Coulomb.

ROLLER, D., and D. H. D. ROLLER, *Development of the concept of electric charge* (Harvard University Press, 1954). Reprinted in *Harvard case studies in experimental science* (Harvard University Press, 1957), v. 2, p. 541. A more complete and detailed account of electricity from antiquity to Coulomb than given in the present chapter, but somewhat more elementary. For a still more detailed and extensively documented treatment of the period from antiquity to Gilbert, see the same authors' paper, "The prenatal history of electrical science," *American Journal of Physics*, v. 21 (1953), pp. 343–356.

TAYLOR, L. W., *Physics: the pioneer science* (Houghton Mifflin, 1941), Chap. 40. A historical treatment of electrostatics.

CHAPTER 27

FURTHER DEVELOPMENTS IN ELECTROSTATICS

27.1 Additional applications of Coulomb's law. When more than two charged particles are in the same locality, experiment shows that the electrostatic force exerted by any particle on any of the others is still given by Eq. (26.4) and has the same value as if the other particles were not present. Suppose that the particles have charges q_1, q_2, q_3, ... and are located at known fixed positions. The net electrostatic force experienced by any one of them, say by q_1, may therefore be found by using Eq. (26.4) to compute separately the magnitudes of the forces exerted on q_1 by q_2, q_3, ..., and then, the directions of these forces being also known, they can be added vectorially to obtain the net, or total, force. Although this procedure can in general be both complicated and laborious, it is quite simple in special cases, for example where all the forces acting on the particle are directed either (1) along the same straight line, or (2) at right angles to one another. In the first case, the net force is simply the algebraic sum of the separate forces acting on the particle. In the second case, the separate forces are added in the same manner as were the displacement or velocity components discussed in Chapter 3.

EXAMPLE 27.1. Three small spheres situated on the same straight line and spaced 0.1 m apart (Fig. 27.1) bear charges $q_1 = -10^{-7}$ coul, $q_2 = 10^{-8}$ coul, and $q_3 = 2 \times 10^{-7}$ coul. Compute the net electrostatic force on q_2.

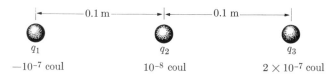

| ←————0.1 m————→| ←————0.1 m————→ |

q_1 q_2 q_3

-10^{-7} coul 10^{-8} coul 2×10^{-7} coul

FIG. 27.1. Charged spheres situated on the same straight line.

Solution. By Eq. (26.4), the force exerted by q_1 on q_2 is

$$F_{12} = (9 \times 10^9 \text{ new·m}^2/\text{coul}^2) \times (-10^{-7} \text{ coul}) \times (10^{-8} \text{ coul})/(0.1 \text{ m})^2$$
$$= -9 \times 10^{-4} \text{ new.}$$

This is an attractive force, as is indicated by the negative sign, and so is directed toward the left in Fig. 27.1. The force exerted by q_3 on q_2 is

$$F_{32} = (9 \times 10^9 \text{ new·m}^2/\text{coul}^2) \times (2 \times 10^{-7} \text{ coul}) \times (10^{-8} \text{ coul})/(0.1 \text{ m})^2$$
$$= 2 \times 10^{-3} \text{ new.}$$

This is a repulsion, as the positive value of the force indicates, and so is directed away from q_3, toward the left. Since here both forces on q_2 are in the same direction, the net force is simply $(9 \times 10^{-4} + 2 \times 10^{-3})$ new $= 3 \times 10^{-3}$ new toward the left.

EXAMPLE 27.2.   Three fixed pith balls bearing charges $q_1 = 10^{-7}$ coul, $q_2 = 10^{-8}$ coul, and $q_3 = -3 \times 10^{-9}$ coul form the vertexes of a right triangle, as shown in Fig. 27.2(a). Find the net electrostatic force F on q_1.

(a)   (b)

FIG. 27.2. Charged particles at the vertexes of a right triangle.

Solution. The force on q_1 due to q_2 is

$$F_{21} = (9 \times 10^9 \text{ new·m}^2/\text{coul}^2) \times 10^{-8} \text{ coul} \times 10^{-7} \text{ coul}/(0.05 \text{ m})^2$$
$$= 4 \times 10^{-3} \text{ new,}$$

a repulsive force on q_1 and hence directed toward the left [see Fig. 27.2(b)]. The force of q_3 on q_1 is

$$F_{31} = (9 \times 10^9 \text{ new·m}^2/\text{coul}^2) \times (-3 \times 10^{-9} \text{ coul}) \times 10^{-7} \text{ coul}/(0.03 \text{ m})^2$$
$$= 3 \times 10^{-3} \text{ new,}$$

an attractive force on q_1 and hence directed upward. The magnitude F of the net force on q_1 is, by the Pythagorean theorem,

$$F = \sqrt{F_{21}^2 + F_{31}^2} = \sqrt{(4 \times 10^{-3} \text{ new})^2 + (-3 \times 10^{-3} \text{ new})^2}$$
$$= 5 \times 10^{-3} \text{ new.}$$

The direction of the net force, i.e., the angle β that it makes with the component force F_{21} (and therefore with the horizontal), can be computed from the relation $\tan \beta = F_{31}/F_{21} = 3 \times 10^{-3}$ new$/(4 \times 10^{-3}$ new$) = 0.75$, or $\beta = 37°$.

PROBLEM 27.1.   Two small spheres, each with a charge of 2.5×10^{-9} coul, are 40 cm apart. Between them, on the line connecting these spheres and 10 cm from one of them, is placed a third small sphere bearing a charge of -2.0×10^{-9} coul. Compute the magnitude and direction of the net electrostatic force (a) on the third sphere, and (b) on the sphere that is 10 cm from the third sphere.

PROBLEM 27.2.   Three pith balls are arranged as in Fig. 27.2 except that now their charges are $q_1 = 10^{-8}$ coul, $q_2 = -6 \times 10^{-8}$ coul, $q_3 = -3 \times 10^{-8}$ coul. Find the magnitude and direction of the net electrostatic force on q_1.

27.2 Preview of the modern "fluid theory." In Chapter 26 we traced the advent of the rival one-fluid and two-fluid theories of electricity, and it was evident that 18th-century electrical knowledge and experimental facilities were not adequate for resolving the question of whether there is one electric fluid or whether there are two. Also unconceived at the time were the further possibilities that it may be neither or both—that in one sense of the word there is a single fluid, and in another sense two fluids. History reveals many such instances in which two rival views contradict each other in certain respects and yet have other features that make both of them useful. This often means that both views will later turn out to be partly valid and partly invalid, and that we may therefore expect the eventual development of a new conceptual scheme that will be a synthesis of the earlier, rival views—a synthesis that serves not only to reconcile the contradictory features, but to deal with a wider range of phenomena than did either of the earlier views alone.

This is what happened with the rival fluid theories, but not until the way had been opened by a startling new discovery made in 1800 by Alessandro Volta (1745–1827) in Italy. Volta placed strips of two dissimilar metals, such as copper and zinc, in a glass cup containing water in which acid, salt, or lye had been dissolved. When the upper ends of the strips were connected by a wire, electric charge started to flow along the wire, and this flow of charge did not cease so long as chemical action continued between the liquid and the two dissimilar metals. This electrochemical (*voltaic*) cell made it possible to support a constant flow of charge, i.e., an electric current.* The cell not only was a much more reliable source of electric charge than the generators working by friction (Section 26.7), but it also allowed a larger flow of charge, particularly when many cells were combined to make large batteries. By this means, many important developments became possible within the next few years, for example, the decomposition of water into hydrogen and oxygen by an electric current, the heating of a current-carrying wire, and the invention of the electric arc lamp. It also enabled Faraday to experiment on the flow of electricity through liquids (Chapter 28). This work began to clear up the controversy over the one-fluid and two-fluid theories, although it was not settled in Faraday's day; more experiments were needed, especially on conduction in gases, and some of these extended into the present century. We shall here summarize some essential features of the present-day picture, without describing the developments that have made it possible.

The accepted view today is that in every substance there are two different kinds of particles with primary roles in all common electrical phenomena: the *proton*, with a positive charge of about 1.6×10^{-19} coul and

---

*What "flows" is charge, not current; current *is* the time-rate of flow of charge.

essentially the same mass as a hydrogen atom (about 1.7×10^{-27} kgm), and the *electron*, with a negative charge of about -1.6×10^{-19} coul and a mass about 1/1800 that of the proton. These protons and electrons are present in equal numbers in any unelectrified substance.

When a substance is in the *solid* state, the protons are not free to move around within it, although they undergo thermal vibrations about their positions of equilibrium; but some of the electrons *are* free to move. For example, when wool and amber are brought very close together, as by rubbing, electrons pass from the wool to the amber, leaving the wool positively charged and the amber negatively charged. In *solid metals*, which were the conductors mainly studied by Franklin and his contemporaries, many of the electrons are free to move about. These "free" electrons are in continual thermal motion, much like the molecules of a gas. But their displacements ordinarily cancel on the average, that is, there is no net current in any direction. Suppose, however, that two oppositely charged metal objects are connected by a wire. Then some of the electrons, while continuing in their random motions, drift along the wire from the negatively to the positively charged object. In brief, in solid substances there are two "fluids" and yet only one "fluid": both protons and electrons are present, but only the electrons are involved in any transfer or flow of electricity.

In a *liquid* or a *gas*, electrical conduction is due chiefly to *ions*, which are charged atoms or molecules. An uncharged atom or molecule, which contains an equal number of protons and electrons, becomes a positively charged ion if it loses one or more of its normal number of electrons and a negatively charged ion if it acquires one or more extra electrons. In a conducting liquid or gas, both positive and negative ions are present, and these move simultaneously in opposite directions. Here there are not only two kinds of "fluid," but both kinds are mobile, as was visualized in the old two-fluid theory of conduction.

PROBLEM 27.3.   With the help of diagrams show how the electron-proton conceptual scheme serves to explain each of the following phenomena observed with solid objects: (a) the attraction between positively and negatively charged objects; (b) the attraction between a positively charged and an uncharged object; (c) the attraction between a negatively charged and an uncharged object; (d) the repulsion between two positively charged objects; (e) the repulsion between two negatively charged objects; (f) the attraction that may occur between two extended objects with net charges of the same sign but with a relatively weak charge on one of the objects; and (g) the operation of a versorium when used to detect the charge on a rubbed piece of glass.

PROBLEM 27.4.   Suppose that a proton p and an electron e are fixed at a distance of 10^{-8} cm apart. Compute the net electrostatic force which they exert on a second electron that is situated at a distance of 10^{-8} cm *beyond* e on the line connecting p and e.

27.3 Electroscopes. We have already encountered such detectors of electric charge as Gilbert's versorium (Fig. 26.2) and Gray's ball-and-feather combination (Section 26.4). The *leaf electroscope*, the modern form of which is shown in Fig. 27.3, was another 18th-century invention. Charge applied to the conducting plate or knob distributes itself over the knob, rod B, and leaf A, and since the leaf thus acquires charge of the same sign as its support, it is repelled. Often there is not one leaf but two side by side, as in Fig. 27.4. The larger the charges on the leaves, the more they diverge, and this divergence provides a rough measure of the charge originally given to the knob.

An electroscope that is initially uncharged cannot be used to determine the *sign* of a charge imparted to it, for the leaves will diverge whether the imparted charge is positive or negative. But suppose that the electroscope already has been given, say, a negative charge, i.e., an excess of electrons. If another negatively charged object is now brought near the knob, electrons from the knob will be driven away and into the leaves and these electrons will cause the leaves to further diverge, since the like charge on them is increased. On the other hand, if a positively charged rod is brought near the knob, electrons will be at-tracted away from the leaves to the knob, and the leaves will tend to converge or collapse. Thus when an electroscope has a charge of known sign, it can be used to find the sign of an approaching unknown charge.

A good electroscope, once charged, will hold its charge quite well for a period of some hours, as shown by the steady divergence of the leaves, if the insulation at C in Fig. 27.3, where the rod passes into the pro-tecting case D, is carefully chosen, and if there are no conducting films of moisture or grease. If, however, the air around the knob or leaves is ionized by heating or in some other way, these ions may discharge the electroscope by neutralizing its charge. Electroscopes in many dif-ferent forms are often used today to study radiation from x-ray tubes or from radioactive sources; such high-energy beams ionize the air through

Fig. 27.3.   The leaf electroscope. (Courtesy of Ealing Corporation.)

which they pass, and the rate of collapse of the leaves is a measure of the intensity of the beam.

Modern electroscopes may differ widely in details of construction. For example, one rugged type is housed in a case similar to that of a fountain pen, so that it may be carried in the pocket of any research worker who must expose himself to high-energy radiation. This electroscope is charged at the beginning of the work period, and the rate at which it discharges is observed periodically to make sure that the carrier is not receiving a dosage of radiation higher than that known to be safe.

The *cosmic rays* that are coming toward the earth from all directions in space always ionize the air around us to some extent, and contribute to the discharge of electroscopes even in the absence of any other radiation. In fact, one of the first clues to the existence of cosmic rays was the observation that the very best of electroscopes slowly but steadily lost its charge even when completely surrounded by thick layers of brick or metal.

PROBLEM 27.5. An electroscope initially has a positive charge, that is, a deficiency of electrons. Explain in words and diagrams what will happen if an object brought near the knob, without touching it, has (a) a positive charge, (b) a negative charge.

PROBLEM 27.6. When a positively charged rod is brought slowly toward a negatively charged electroscope, the leaves gradually converge and may even collapse entirely. If this occurs, what will happen if the rod is brought still closer to the electroscope knob, but without touching it? Explain.

27.4 The "ice-pail" experiment. Although the experiment represented schematically in Fig. 27.4 was carried out by Michael Faraday in 1843, note that it is very similar to Priestley's experiments with a charged metal cup made some four decades earlier. However, although a number of things that Faraday's experiment illustrates had been investigated earlier

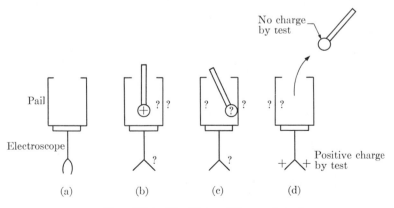

FIG. 27.4. The "ice-pail" experiment.

by Franklin and others, the leaf electroscope was available to Faraday, and so he could carry out the tests in a more quantitative fashion. The stages in the experiment, shown in Fig. 27.4, are (a) a metal can (it happened to be an ice pail) is placed on a nonconducting stand and thereby insulated, except that its outer surface is connected to an uncharged electroscope. (b) A metal ball mounted on an insulating handle is charged, say positively, and then lowered into the pail; immediately the electroscope leaves diverge and stay at a fixed angle apart, no matter where in the pail the charged sphere is held. (c) Even when the charged ball is allowed to touch the inside of the pail, no further effect on the leaves is observed; the angle between them remains the same. (d) When the ball, having touched the pail, is withdrawn, it is found to be uncharged, but the leaves still remain at the same angle apart, and a test will show that they are positively charged.

As Faraday saw, this experiment provides a precise demonstration of the principle of conservation of charge (Section 26.9) and of the quantitative aspects of the process called charging by influence, or electrostatic induction (Section 26.15). Thus in stage (b), both the leaves and the outside of the pail must be positively charged, for the leaves do not converge at any time; and since at that stage the charged ball had not yet touched the pail, it may be concluded that the charged ball has polarized the pail, producing a negative charge on the inside and a positive charge on the outside. The fact that the ball loses all of its charge as a result of having touched the pail was interpreted by Faraday to mean that the charge initially on the ball induced an equally large charge of opposite sign on the inside of the pail, and when the ball touched the pail, this induced charge and the one from the ball canceled each other. Finally, the induced charges of opposite sign on the inside and outside walls of the pail must be of equal magnitude, for the divergence of the leaves remains unchanged between steps (b) and (d), and hence the charge driven to the outer wall of the pail in (b) must have been equal to the original charge on the ball. In brief, the experiment provides a convincing demonstration of two important principles: (1) the production of a charge of one sign is always accompanied by the production of an equal charge of opposite sign, and (2) all the excess charge of a hollow conductor normally resides on the outside surface, the net charge in the interior of the conductor being zero. As an earlier and more spectacular demonstration of the latter generalization, Faraday had built a large cubical box covered on the outside with tinfoil and mounted on insulators:

> I went into the cube and lived in it, and using lighted candles, electrometers, and all other tests of electrical states, I could not find the least influence upon them . . . though all the time the outside of the cube was powerfully charged, and large sparks and brushes were darting off from every part of its outer surface. ("On induction," *Philosophical transactions*, 1837)

This is the principle of *electric screening*, i.e., the shielding of sensitive electrical devices from disturbing influences by placing them in conducting cages.

PROBLEM 27.7. (a) Redraw Fig. 27.4, replacing the question marks with the appropriate signs (+ or −) of the excess charges. Explain your choices. (b) Make a similar diagram to show the successive stages when the inducing charge on the sphere is negative rather than positive. (c) How does this sequence establish that the outside of the pail in Fig. 27.4(b) can be neither negative nor uncharged?

PROBLEM 27.8. Explain stages (a) and (b) in Problem 27.7 in terms of the modern conceptual scheme, according to which only the negatively charged electrons can move around freely in a solid metal.

27.5 Decline of the effluvia theories. Faraday and the concept of field.

Earlier we noted that many of the ancient Greek philosophers regarded the concept "attraction at a distance" as occult and reminiscent of magic, and that they were led to conceive of an electrified object as emitting a sort of material cloud or effluvium that extended out and in some way made connection with the attracted object (Section 26.2). In 1600 this still-prevalent notion was adopted by Gilbert and, in the light of his experiments, rendered more specific; for example, he pictured the effluvia to be like "material rods" that provided rigid connections between attracting and attracted objects. During the century and a half following Gilbert, his theory underwent various modifications to meet new discoveries, but the basic notion of material effluvia continued to prevail.

A drift away from the notion of effluvia started about the middle of the 18th century. By this time the Newtonian view of gravitational forces acting through empty space was gaining general acceptance. Franklin and his successors were now successfully picturing the electric fluid as made up of electrical particles that remain in the bodies themselves during attraction and repulsion, and nothing material was pictured as issuing from them. Instead, the particles were thought to exert forces on one another and on other particles *through distance*, without the help of any intervening medium. Moreover, when the inverse-square law became recognized as valid for electricity, it was seen that a force, though it might be a very small one, must exist between charged objects even when they are at very great distances apart. This could hardly be explained by the interaction of two supposedly small clouds of effluvia emanating from the electrified objects.

With the abandonment of the effluvia theory near the end of the 18th century, scientists had to view electrostatic forces simply as acting through space in a manner which provided or demanded no further explanation. But this view proved to be as uncomfortable and ultimately unacceptable to many of them as it had been to the earlier thinkers. It was soon replaced by a new formulation, principally the work of Faraday (Fig. 27.5).

FIG. 27.5. Michael Faraday (1791–1867).

Michael Faraday, a blacksmith's son, started in 1804 as an errand boy in a bookstore, to help support his family, and a year later he was apprenticed to his employer to learn the art of bookbinding. Faraday used his spare time to read books on chemistry and electricity, by Boyle and others, and to perform those of the simpler experiments they described "as could be defrayed in their expense by a few pence per week." By 1812 he had also been able to attend a dozen lectures on natural philosophy and, at the Royal Institution, four lectures by its director, Humphry Davy. Faraday applied to Davy for a job, and was made a demonstration assistant in the Royal Institution in 1813. There he worked for nearly half a century, having soon risen to the directorship of the laboratory. Davy eventually was able to boast that of his many discoveries in science the greatest was Michael Faraday.

Although his first work was mainly in Davy's field of chemistry, Faraday soon launched on the highly original electrical researches that were to occupy much of his scientific career. His research notes make fascinating reading; it is as though one watched him as he makes a sure path through a marvelous unexplored forest, stopping from time to time to lift up from the ground a dazzling flower or a brilliant jewel. Brightest among these was the concept of *field*, which he applied to both electric and magnetic phenomena.

More than two centuries earlier, Gilbert had shown that elongated iron filings sprinkled around a magnet on a table tend to arrange themselves in a definite pattern; each bit of iron aligns itself in the direction of the net magnetic force at that point (Fig. 27.6). Pieces of thread or sawdust around an electrified body likewise assume definite positions. Such phenomena led Faraday to suggest that the space around a magnet may be thought of as filled with *lines of magnetic force*, and similarly that the region around an electrified object may be considered to be filled with *lines of electric force*. To Faraday these lines existed as mechanical structures in the surrounding medium and could exert force on appropriate objects placed therein. For him the Coulomb equation [Eq. (26.2)] was not sufficient; it makes possible the calculation of the electrostatic force but does not explain the action of the force in terms of a *mechanism*, and this was unsatisfactory to Faraday.

We are reminded here of Gilbert's "material rods." Indeed, Faraday's theory is a direct descendant of the effluvia picture, although it involves important changes. No longer are effluvia thought of as issuing from bodies. Instead, it is the *medium* between two electric charges that transmits the force and accordingly becomes the seat of an *electric field*, and since an electrostatic force can act through a vacuum as well as through air and other substances, we must conclude that what we ordinarily think of as empty space somehow can serve to support such a field.

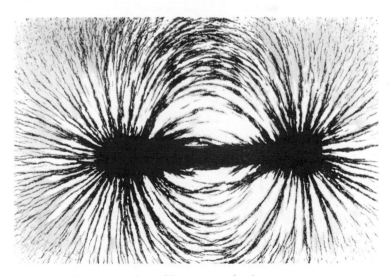

FIG. 27.6. Iron filings around a bar magnet.

Another change was the more definite and varied ways in which Faraday could describe any electric field and connect the description with experiment. Thus suppose that a small test charge q is placed at any point in the region near one or more other charges. The individual forces exerted by these charges on the test charge q can be *computed* with the help of Eq. (26.2), *provided* we know the magnitudes and signs of all the charges involved, and also their distances and directions from the test charge; the net force **F** on q is then the vector sum of the individual forces. But it is possible also to *measure* this net force **F** on the test charge directly, without having to know anything about the magnitudes, signs, or locations of the charges responsible for it, and this is why we come to think of the force as a property of the particular field point at which we have placed the test charge. If the net force on the test charge q is measured and recorded for each of a number of points scattered throughout the field, a map of the whole field is obtained, still without our having to know anything at all about the charges producing the field (Fig. 27.7).

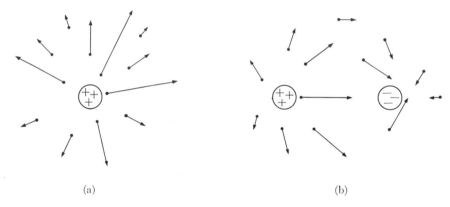

(a)   (b)

Fig. 27.7. Force vectors on a small positive test charge placed at selected points near (a) one fixed charge, (b) two fixed charges.

It is important to note that the test charge used in mapping an electric field must be kept small, so that it will not appreciably change the locations of the other charges or induce polarization in nearby objects; otherwise the field actually mapped may differ appreciably from the one we wanted to map. This illustrates a general principle of measurement: any measuring instrument should be so designed as to affect as little as possible the quantity that it is intended to measure. As an obvious example, in determining the temperature of a small amount of liquid, we should not insert into the liquid a large thermometer that will appreciably warm or cool it.

27.6 Electric field intensity. Suppose that some particular electric field has been mapped with the help of a probe made by attaching a small object to the end of a thin nonconducting handle and giving the object a very small test charge of known value q. The magnitude and direction of the force $\mathbf{F}$ on the test charge q placed at a point in the field will depend not only on the nature and distribution of the charges producing the field, but also on the magnitude and sign of the charge q. It might therefore seem that to describe a particular field, we would need a different map for each different test charge used. However, Coulomb's electrostatic force law tells us that the force on the test charge is directly proportional to this charge. For example, if a positive test charge q is replaced by one twice as large, $2q$, the force at every point will be doubled but will still have the same direction; and in general, if a positive test charge n times as large is used, the force at every point will be n times as large and in the same direction as before. This proportionality of force $\mathbf{F}$ to test charge q at any particular point means that *their ratio* $\mathbf{F}/q$ *has a constant value for that point;* this value does not depend at all on the magnitude of the test charge used to explore the field, but only on the nature of the field itself. So $\mathbf{F}/q$, *the electrostatic force per unit positive test charge* at any particular point P, provides a useful and economical way to describe an electric field. It is therefore given a special name, *electric field intensity* (or *electric field strength*), and is denoted by $\mathbf{E}$. Thus, by definition,

$$\mathbf{E} \text{ (at point } P) = \frac{\text{Net force } \mathbf{F} \text{ on any small positive charge } q \text{ at } P}{q}.$$

$$(27.1)$$

Note that the field intensity $\mathbf{E}$ at point P is a vector quantity (and, of course, is not to be confused with the concept *energy* for which the symbol E was used in earlier chapters). Its direction, by convention, is the same as that of the force on any *positive* test charge placed at P. The opposite convention, involving negative test charges, could equally well have been chosen, but having agreed on the present one, we must use it consistently. In diagrams like Fig. 27.8, the arrow may be drawn to represent, not the force $\mathbf{F}$ on some particular test charge placed at point P, but the field intensity $\mathbf{E}$, or force per unit positive charge at point P. The totality of such $\mathbf{E}$-vectors drawn for all points in a given region serves as a "map" of the electric field for that region.

From Eq. (27.1) we see that the mks unit of electric field strength $\mathbf{E}$ is the newton per coulomb.

Fig. 27.8. Representation of the electric field strength $\mathbf{E}$ at a point P.

PROBLEM 27.9. Which of the following statements is preferable, and why? (a) **E** at P is the force per unit positive charge on a test charge placed at P. (b) **E** at P is the force on a unit positive charge placed at P.

PROBLEM 27.10. When a positive test charge of 2×10^{-8} coul is placed at a certain point P, the electrostatic force on it is found by measurement to be 4×10^{-3} new in an eastward direction. Show that the field intensity at P is 2×10^5 new/coul eastward.

PROBLEM 27.11. At a certain point P, the field intensity is known to be 100 new/coul and directed vertically upward. If a small object bearing a negative charge of -10^{-5} coul is placed at P, show that the electrostatic force on it will be 10^{-3} new vertically downward.

As was pointed out earlier, there is another way to find the value of **E** at any point P, provided the nature and distribution of the charges responsible for the field are known; this consists of using Eq. (26.4) to compute the contribution made to **E** by each point charge Q at its particular distance r from P, and then adding these contributions vectorially. Such a set of calculations is usually involved and complicated, the exceptions being cases in which only a very few charges are responsible for the field. For example, it is particularly simple when the field is due to a single particle of charge Q or to a single sphere upon which Q is uniformly distributed. In either case the *magnitude* of the field intensity at any point P at a distance r from the particle or center of the sphere, in view of Eqs. (27.1) and (26.2), is

$$E \text{ (at } P) = \frac{F \text{ (at } P)}{q} = \frac{CQq/r^2}{q} = \frac{CQ}{r^2}, \qquad (27.2)$$

where F is the magnitude of the force on the test charge q placed at P.

In a somewhat more complex case, point P might lie at one corner of a triangle, with charges Q_1 and Q_2 at the other two corners. In that case, the electric field intensity at P is found by first finding the field intensity due to Q_1, then that due to Q_2, and obtaining the resultant or total field intensity at P by vectorial addition of the two components.

PROBLEM 27.12. Show that the field intensity at a point P, 0.1 m distant from a small sphere having a charge of 10^{-7} coul, is 9×10^4 new/coul in a direction radially away from the sphere.

PROBLEM 27.13. (a) In the preceding problem, what is the field intensity at a point 1 m distant from the sphere? (b) Find the field intensity at the position of q_1 in Problem 27.2, but before charge q_1 is placed at that point.

PROBLEM 27.14. A positive test charge of 2×10^{-9} coul is placed 0.3 m from a small sphere bearing a charge Q. Measurement shows that the force on the test charge is 2×10^{-4} new toward the sphere. Find the magnitude and sign of Q.

PROBLEM 27.15. The concepts of *field* and of *field intensity* have wide applicability in physics, for we may speak not only of electric fields, but of magnetic fields, gravitational fields, and so on. For example, the gravitational field intensity at any point P is defined as the net gravitational force $\mathbf{F}_{grav}$ per unit *test mass m* placed at the point, or $\mathbf{E}_{grav} = \mathbf{F}_{grav}/m$. (a) Using this definition, show that the magnitude of the earth's gravitational field intensity at any point outside the earth and at a distance r from its center is given by $E_{grav} = Gm_E/r^2$, where m_E ($= 5.98 \times 10^{24}$ kgm) is the mass of the earth. (b) Show that E_{grav} at the earth's surface ($r = 6.38 \times 10^6$ m) is 9.8 new/kgm.

27.7 Electric lines of force.

We can imagine at each and every point in an electric field an arrow indicating the magnitude and direction of the electric field intensity at that point, but obviously one cannot draw a diagram showing every one of the arrows. So today we still make use of Faraday's lines of force to provide an intelligible and vivid map of a field. Figure 27.9 shows three such maps. Each line of force, together with its arrow, shows the path that a positive test charge q would tend to follow if placed anywhere on the line, provided the test charge was under no appreciable influence other than the electrostatic force. At every point along each line, the electric field intensity $\mathbf{E}$ is tangential to the line and in the direction of the line's arrow.

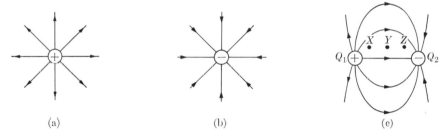

(a)   (b)   (c)

FIG. 27.9. Schematic diagram of the electric field near (a) a positively charged object, (b) a negatively charged object, and (c) two objects with equally large charges of opposite sign. For each case, all the space is to be envisaged as filled with lines of force, of which only a few are shown in these drawings.

No single line of force gives any indication of the magnitude of the field intensity at any point on it. But when a number of lines are drawn, as in Fig. 27.9, it is seen that the lines are close together in regions where $\mathbf{E}$ is large (near charged bodies) and show a larger spread elsewhere. For example, notice how the lines in parts (a) and (b) of the figure diverge as the distance from the charged sphere increases, and that in (c), point X is in a more intense field than point Y.

PROBLEM 27.16. (a) Why is it that a line of force that starts on a positive charge either terminates on a negative charge or goes to infinity? (b) Draw some lines of force to indicate in a general way the electric field in the region of two positive charges that are fairly close to each other.

PROBLEM 27.17. Is the electric field about a charged body real, or is it fictional? How about the lines of force? In scientific discourse, what is meant by the phrase "real"?

PROBLEM 27.18. For the two oppositely charged parallel conducting plates shown in Fig. 27.10, experiment shows that in the central portion of the air gap between the plates, such as at points X and Y, the electric field intensity **E** is uniform; that is, **E** everywhere has the same magnitude and is directed perpendicular to the plates. Only at points near the ends, such as at Z, does the field intensity vary somewhat in magnitude and direction from point to point. (a) On the basis of this information, draw some lines of force to show the nature of the field at various points between the plates and near the ends. (b) If the distance between the plates is s, show that the work that must be done on a positive test charge q to transfer it across the gap from the negative to the positive plate is equal to $E \times q \times s$.

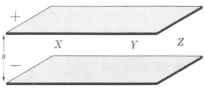

FIGURE 27.10

27.8 Electric potential difference. The concepts of work and energy, which had begun to play an important part in mechanics and heat in the early part of the 19th century, were now introduced into electrical science, where they gradually assumed the basic roles they have today. Evidently, when charged bodies are displaced relative to one another, work must be done either against or by the mutual electrostatic forces. In computing this work, we must specify that the velocities of displacement of the charged bodies are to be kept small, so as to keep negligible the additional magnetic forces that come into play whenever charges are in motion relative to the observer.

In Fig. 27.9, for example, work clearly must be done by some external agency on a positive test charge q to push it in a direction opposite to the direction of any line of force along which it is being moved. As this work is done, say by the hand of the experimenter, the test charge gains potential energy; if he releases the test charge, it moves back in the direction of the line with increasing kinetic energy. This is similar to the way in which water tends to flow from a point of higher altitude, where it has more potential energy, to a lower point where it has less, and also similar to the ways in which heat tends to flow from a point of higher temperature to one of lower temperature.

In describing the electric field at a point in space, we found it advantageous to deal primarily, not with the force **F** experienced at that point, but with the field intensity **E**, which is the force per unit positive charge located at the point. Similarly, we shall find it useful to deal primarily, not with the work W_{AB} done in moving a charge q from a point B to another point A, but with W_{AB}/q, the work done per unit positive charge during this operation. This quantity is known as the *electric potential difference*, V_{AB}, between points A and B. The term "potential difference" is simply an abbreviation for the expression, "the difference in potential energy, per unit positive charge, between the two points." Thus if a positive charge has a higher potential energy when it is at point A than when at some other point B, *the potential difference* V_{AB} *between A and B is the work done, per unit charge, in slowly moving a positive test charge q from B* (the point of lower potential energy) *to A*, or

$$V_{AB} = \frac{W_{AB}}{q}. \tag{27.3}$$

Since W_{AB} and q are scalar quantities, W_{AB}/q also is a scalar quantity. The mks unit of potential difference, as can be seen from Eq. (27.3), is the joule divided by the coulomb, or 1 j/coul. For the sake of brevity, this unit is called the *volt*.

PROBLEM 27.19.   In Fig. 27.9(c), suppose it is found by actual trial that 6.0×10^{-5} j of work must be done *on* a positive test charge of 3.0×10^{-6} coul to push it from the point Y to the point X. Using Eq. (27.3), show that the potential difference V_{XY} is 20 j/coul, or 20 volts. Then give in your own words an operational definition of "potential difference between two points, X and Y." Use a simple sketch to illustrate your statement.

EXAMPLE 27.3.   How much work must be done on a charge of 0.60 coul to move it from point B to point A if the potential difference V_{AB} is 110 volts?

Solution. From Eq. (27.3), we obtain $W_{AB} = V_{AB} \cdot q = 110$ volts $\times$ 0.60 coul = 66 volt·coul = 66 (j/coul)·coul = 66 j.

Measurements of potential differences can be made with various types of instruments called *electrometers*, some of which are simply modified forms of the leaf electroscope (Section 27.3). Formulas for computing potential differences are also available, but only for fields that are due to very simple arrangements of charges.   We shall consider only the simplest possible case, that of a uniformly charged sphere or a particle bearing a charge Q and situated at a fixed position in air or in a vacuum (Fig. 27.11).   For such a field, it turns out that the potential difference V_{AB} between any pair of points is given by the formula

$$V_{AB} = \frac{CQ}{r_A} - \frac{CQ}{r_B}, \quad (27.4)$$

where C ($=9.0 \times 10^9$ new·m²/coul²) is the constant of Eq. (26.2). This will now be proved.

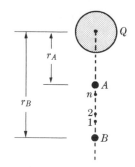

FIG. 27.11. The potential difference between points A and B is $V_{AB} = CQ[(1/r_A) - (1/r_B)]$.

27.9 Derivation of the equation for potential difference. Suppose that Q in Fig. 27.11 is positive, so that work must be done *on* a positive test charge q to transport it from B toward A against the repulsive force of Q. From Coulomb's law, the force on q when it is at point B is CQq/r_B^2, and the force on it when at point 1, on the way to point A, is CQq/r_1^2. The smaller the distance between points B and 1, the more nearly is the *average* force in this interval equal to $CQq/r_B r_1$, where $r_B r_1$ is a compromise between r_B^2 and r_1^2, being the square of the geometric mean distance of the interval $\overline{B1}$ from Q. Multiplication of this average force by the distance $r_B - r_1$ yields the work W_{1B} done in moving q from B to 1; that is,

$$W_{1B} = \frac{CQq}{r_B r_1}(r_B - r_1) = CQq\left(\frac{1}{r_1} - \frac{1}{r_B}\right).$$

Thus the potential difference V_{1B} between points 1 and B is W_{1B}/q, or

$$V_{1B} = CQ\left(\frac{1}{r_1} - \frac{1}{r_B}\right).$$

If charge q is now pushed to point 2 on its way toward point A, and if points 1 and 2 are very close together,

$$V_{21} = CQ\left(\frac{1}{r_2} - \frac{1}{r_1}\right),$$

and similarly for V_{32}, V_{43}, and so on, until q has been pushed up to point n and finally to point A. By adding all these quantities, we obtain V_{AB}, the total work per unit charge in moving q the whole distance from B to A; that is, $V_{AB} = V_{1B} + V_{21} + V_{32} + \cdots + V_{An}$, or

$$V_{AB} = CQ\left[\left(\frac{1}{r_1} - \frac{1}{r_B}\right) + \left(\frac{1}{r_2} - \frac{1}{r_1}\right) + \left(\frac{1}{r_3} - \frac{1}{r_2}\right) + \cdots\right.$$
$$\left. + \left(\frac{1}{r_A} - \frac{1}{r_n}\right)\right]$$
$$= CQ\left(\frac{1}{r_1} - \frac{1}{r_B} + \frac{1}{r_2} - \frac{1}{r_1} + \frac{1}{r_3} - \frac{1}{r_2} + \cdots + \frac{1}{r_A} - \frac{1}{r_n}\right)$$
$$= CQ\left(\frac{1}{r_A} - \frac{1}{r_B}\right),$$

since all the other terms cancel. Thus we obtain Eq. (27.4); incidentally, this derivation could have been carried out more simply and quickly if we had resorted to the methods of the infinitesimal calculus, but the result would be the same.

Note that Eq. (27.4) gives the potential difference only in the region about a single charged pointlike particle or uniformly charged sphere. Also, in our derivation we assumed that points A and B were located along a radial line pointing directly to Q, so that the angle between the displacement and applied force was always zero.

But actually it is unnecessary that A and B lie along a radial line. Equation (27.4) gives correctly the potential difference between *any* two points in the region near Q. The proof is strikingly simple. Consider Fig. 27.12, where points B and A are not on a radial line to Q. By definition, V_{AB} remains the work done per unit positive charge in transferring a test charge from B to A; to evaluate it in the same manner as for the case of Fig. 27.9 would give us difficulty because the direction of the force on the test charge would continuously vary as we go directly from B to A. But we may also reach A by way of the circular arc $\overparen{BX}$ and line $\overline{XA}$.

Because the electric lines of force intersect the circular arc $\overparen{BX}$ everywhere at right angles, the work done in transporting a charge along $\overparen{BX}$ is zero; therefore the only work done is in going along the radial line $\overline{XA}$, and V_{AB} $(=V_{AX}) = CQ[(1/r_A) - (1/r_X)]$. An experimental determination would show that this last equation gives the correct value for the work done per unit charge on traveling from B to A by either path.

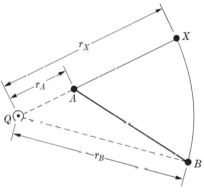

This discussion has implied an important property of the electrostatic field, namely, that the work done in transferring a given charge between any two points A and B

Fig. 27.12. The work done per unit positive test charge in transferring a test charge from B to A is the same whether the path is $\overline{BA}$ directly or $\overparen{BX} + \overline{XA}$.

in any field due to fixed charges is determined solely by the location of the points relative to the fixed charged objects and does not depend at all on the form and length of the path followed. In Sections 18.6 and 18.7 we noted that gravitational forces exhibit this same property; for example, the work done against gravity in pushing an object up an inclined plane depends on the vertical height reached and not at all on the length of the path traveled along the incline. Any force having the property that the work done against it or by it depends only on the locations of the endpoints of the path and not on the particular path followed is known as a *conservative force*. On the other hand, frictional forces are nonconservative, for the work done against friction in moving an object from one point to another is in general different for each particular path that may be followed (Section 18.4).

PROBLEM 27.20. A fixed conducting sphere of radius 0.2 m is insulated from its surroundings and given a charge of 10^{-6} coul. (a) Use Eq. (27.4) to show that the potential difference V_{AB} between two points B and A in the surrounding air that are 6 and 2 m respectively from the *center* of the sphere is 3×10^3 new·m/coul, that is, 3×10^3 volts. (b) Show that the work needed to move a positive test charge of 10^{-8} coul slowly from B to A, following any path whatever, is 3×10^{-5} volt·coul, that is, 3×10^{-5} j. (c) How much work would an externally applied force have to do on the test charge of part (b) if that charge were *negative?*

PROBLEM 27.21. Show that if a charged particle is moved slowly over any closed path in the electrostatic field of another fixed particle, the *total* work that one must do on the particle against the electrostatic force is zero.

27.10 Parallel conducting plates.

Recall from Problem 27.18 that the electric field intensity **E** has the same magnitude and direction at all points well within the air gap between two oppositely charged parallel plates A and B (Fig. 27.10). As a consequence, an amount of work $W = Eqs$ (where E is the magnitude of the field intensity and s is the distance between the plates) must be done on a positive test charge q to transfer it from the negative plate to the positive plate. But this work is also given by $W = V_{AB}q$, where V_{AB} is the potential difference between the plates. Equating these two expressions for W, we have $Eqs = V_{AB}q$, or

$$E = \frac{V_{AB}}{s}. \tag{27.5}$$

Since V_{AB} is usually a fixed quantity for each type of freshly prepared electric cell (it may be given on the label of the battery of cells used to maintain the potential difference between the plates) and since the distance s is easy to measure, Eq. (27.5) provides a practical means for computing E in the uniform field between the plates. The fact that the field is uniform and that its magnitude and direction are simple to compute makes the parallel-plate arrangement important in the design of electrical equipment.

EXAMPLE 27.4. Suppose that the two plates in Fig. 27.10 are spaced 0.020 m apart and are connected to a 90-volt battery. Compute the electric field intensity for any point in the central part of the air gap.

Solution. $E = V_{AB}/s = 90$ volts/0.020 m $= 4500$ volts/m $= 4500$ (j/coul)/m $= 4500$ (new·m/coul)/m $= 4500$ new/coul $= 4.5 \times 10^3$ new/coul. The direction of **E** is vertically downward.

PROBLEM 27.22. Two parallel metal plates are mounted horizontally in a vacuum at a distance 0.020 m apart (Fig. 27.10). They are connected to a source that maintains between them a potential difference of 10 kv (10 kilovolts or 10,000 volts). The upper plate is positive and the lower plate is negative. A negatively charged droplet of oil, which is known from other measurements to have a mass of 10^{-9} kgm, is in the space between the plates. Evidently the droplet tends to rise because of the electrostatic force on it, and to fall because of its weight. (a) Compute the weight of the droplet. (b) If the drop is observed to remain motionless, neither rising nor falling, what must be the magnitude of the upward electrostatic force on the droplet? (c) Compute the charge on the droplet in this example.

27.11 Electric potential. The last field concept we shall define is called the *electric potential V* at a given point. The term electric potential is merely a short name for "potential energy per unit positive charge at a given point." The difference between the terms *electric potential difference between points A and B* as developed in Section 27.8 and the new term *electric potential at point A* is simply that the former is the difference of potential energy per unit positive test charge *between two specified points A and B*, whereas the latter is the difference of potential energy per unit positive charge *between the specified point A and any point which has zero potential energy per unit charge*. These distinctions are now to be developed in more detail.

As was shown in Section 18.6 in connection with gravitational fields, the potential energy at a point must always be reckoned or described with respect to some arbitrarily selected reference point. This applies also in the case of an electric field. For example, in Fig. 27.9(c), we would have to do work *against* the electrostatic forces to move a positive test charge *q* from *Z* or *Y* to *X*, thus increasing the potential energy of the test charge. So we say that the potential energy, and therefore the potential, is more positive or "higher" at *X* than at *Z* or *Y*. On the other hand, *Z* is said to be at a negative or "lower" potential than *X* or *Y*, for when a positive test charge moves to *Z* from *X* or *Y*, all the work on it is done *by the electrostatic forces* rather than by an external agent.

From these considerations, we can see that the potential V_A at any point *A* is the potential difference between *A* and some reference point *B* that is taken to have zero potential. For point *B* actually to have zero potential, it would have to be at an infinite distance from all electric charges. However, for most practical purposes the earth may be used as a reference body, and then one speaks of the surface of the earth or "ground" as having zero potential. In symbols, $V_A = V_{AB}$ if *B* is ground or at ∞. (Incidentally, the colloquial term "voltage" is sometimes employed instead of potential or potential difference, but this usage is not recommended.)

For the special case of the field due to a single particle or a uniformly charged sphere bearing a charge *Q*, a formula for the potential at any point in the field can easily be obtained from Eq. (27.4). The potential

V_A is, by definition, the potential difference V_{AB} when B is at a very great distance from the field-producing charge Q. If r_B in Eq. (27.4) is made larger and larger, the term CQ/r_B becomes progressively smaller until finally it is negligible. Thus

$$V_A = \frac{CQ}{r_A}. \tag{27.6}$$

In arriving at Eq. (27.6), no restriction was placed on how close to a uniformly charged sphere the point A may be. It may even be right on the surface of the sphere, in which case Eq. (27.6) gives the potential V_S of the sphere itself; that is, $V_S = CQ/r_S$, where r_S is the radius of the sphere. Thus the larger the sphere, the smaller will be the potential V_S produced by a given net charge Q placed on it. On the larger sphere one can place a larger amount of charge for a given potential; it is therefore easier to charge and less likely to lose its charge to the surroundings. We can say that the larger the sphere, the larger is its *electric capacitance;* the quantitative measure of capacitance is the ratio of charge placed on the sphere to the potential produced on it.

These concepts of electrostatics furnish us with a valuable vocabulary for discussing a wide variety of questions, from the action of charges in motion, to which the next chapter is devoted, to the behavior of nuclear particles, which is the substance of Part IX.

ADDITIONAL PROBLEMS

27.23. (a) For the field described in Problem 27.20, show that the potential at any point 2 m distant from the center of the sphere is 4500 volts, while that 6 m from the center is 1500 volts. (b) How does the difference between these two "absolute" potentials compare with the potential difference computed in Problem 27.20?

27.24. Show that if a particle of charge q is placed in the field of a fixed charge Q at a point A a distance r_A from it, the electric potential energy of q is given by

$$\text{Potential energy of } q = V_A q = \frac{CQq}{r_A}. \tag{27.7}$$

27.25. A proton has a positive charge Q of about 2×10^{-19} coul, while an electron has a charge q_e of the same magnitude but of negative sign. Show that an electron has a potential energy of -7×10^{-18} j when it is in the field of a proton and at a point A 0.5×10^{-10} m distant from it. (That the potential energy at a point A is negative means that no external agent is needed to push the electron from a great distance to point A; on the contrary, it can move to point A under the action of the attracting electrostatic force, gathering more and more kinetic energy after starting from rest at a position at a great distance from A.)

FIG. 27.13. A Van de Graaff generator, with protective housing raised. Electric charges are taken from the bottom of the machine, where they are produced, to the sphere on top by an endless belt. Thereby the sphere can be given a potential of 3×10^6 volts, and a stream of charged particles can be accelerated downward along a vertical tube near the center of the supporting column. (Courtesy High Voltage Engineering Corporation.)

27.26. Show that if 10^{-3} coul of positive charge could be given to a steel sphere with a radius of 1 m, the resulting electric potential of the sphere would be 9 megavolts, that is, 9 million volts. (For practical reasons, a few million volts is the highest potential that ordinarily can be produced in this manner.)

27.27. A type of electrostatic generator of potential differences, known as the Van de Graaff generator (Fig. 27.13), has as one of its parts a large metal sphere that is mounted on an insulating stand and is charged by the operation of the machine to a high electric potential. This sphere is used to repel and accelerate charged atomic particles along an evacuated tube until they attain so much kinetic energy that, upon hitting a "target," they are capable of modifying or even "smashing" atomic nuclei. If the sphere is 1.0 m in diameter, how much negative charge must it bear in order for its potential to be -3 megavolts (-3 million volts)?

27.28. In atomic physics use is made of a unit of energy called the *electron volt* (ev), which may be defined as the work done on a particle having a net charge of the same magnitude as one electron (approximate charge -2×10^{-19} coul) in transferring it between two points of potential difference 1 volt. Show that 1 ev is approximately equivalent to 2×10^{-19} j.

27.29. Compute the potential energy, in both electron volts and joules, of an electron (approximate charge -2×10^{-19} coul) just as it begins to leave the sphere of Problem 27.26.

27.30. Use the outline of the modern theory of the "electric fluid" in Section 27.2 (a) to characterize the difference between conducting solids and nonconductors, and (b) to explain why an uncharged, nonconducting solid like wood or glass can be polarized by the presence of a charged body nearby.

27.31. Formulate operational definitions of (a) line of electric force, (b) electric field intensity, (c) electric potential difference, and (d) electric potential.

27.32. Figure 27.14 shows the steps for charging an electroscope by influence. Write a description of each of the steps, telling in words what the experimenter does and what he infers from the deflection of the leaves of the electroscope.

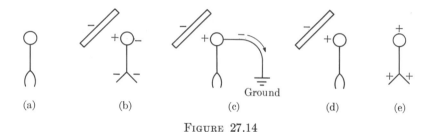

(a)   (b)   (c)   (d)   (e)

FIGURE 27.14

SUPPLEMENTARY READING

FARADAY, M., *Experimental researches in electricity* (originally 1839, often reproduced).

TAYLOR, L. W., *Physics: the pioneer science* (Houghton Mifflin, 1941), Chap. 43.

THOMPSON, S. P., *Michael Faraday* (Cassell, London, 1901).

TYNDALL, J., *Faraday as a discoverer* (Longmans, Green, 1868, and many later editions).

WHITE, H., *Modern college physics* (Van Nostrand, 3rd edition, 1956), Chap. 48.

CHAPTER 28

ELECTROCHEMISTRY AND ELECTROMAGNETISM

28.1 Electric current. When two charged conducting bodies A and B having different electric potentials are connected by a wire or other conductor, charge flows along the connector until the two bodies reach the same potential; then the flow stops. If the two bodies A and B are connected to the terminals of an electrochemical battery or some other type of electric generator that maintains a difference of potential between them, the flow of charge will be continuous (Fig. 28.1). This latter situation is somewhat like that of water in a pipe forming a closed circuit in which a continuous flow is maintained by a pump. The electric battery or other generator is analogous to the pump. And just as we often want to be able to speak of the rate of flow of water past a point in the pipe, expressing this current in units such as gallons per second, it often is useful to think of the rate of flow of charge past a point in a conductor. This possibility is provided by the concept of *electric current,* symbol I, defined by

$$I = Q/t, \tag{28.1}$$

where Q is the quantity of charge passing a point during the time t. The most widely used unit of current is the *coulomb per second;* it is called, for the sake of brevity, the *ampere,* after the French physicist André Marie Ampère (1775–1836). A current of, say, 2 amp means that charge is flowing at the rate of 2 coul/sec. If this current of 2 amp is maintained steadily for 4 sec, a total of 8 coul has passed the point.

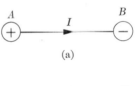

(a)

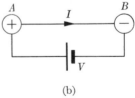

(b)

The direction of a current, by long-standing convention, is generally taken to be the direction in which *positive* charge would move in the circuit. Thus in Fig. 28.1(b) the electrostatic force would push a positive ($+$) charge along the wire in the direction A to B, from a point of higher potential to one of lower potential in the circuit. Actually, as it turned out, in metallic solids the flow is not that of positive charge

FIG. 28.1. (a) The current I in the connecting wire between A and B is transient. (b) When A and B are continuously maintained at different potentials by a battery or other generator, the current in the circuit is continuous.

511

but of negatively charged electrons (Section 27.2); therefore in a solid metal connected to a battery, negative charge moves from low potential to high potential, or from the negative pole toward the positive pole; but all phenomena can be equally well described by the time-honored tradition according to which an equally large amount of positive charge is considered to be flowing from high potential to low potential, or from the positive pole through the solid outside the battery to the negative pole.

The amount of current in a wire must be found indirectly in terms of some effect that the flow of electric charge produces, such as the heat it develops in the wire, the magnetic field it sets up around the wire, or the chemical action that occurs when the wire is broken and its ends are placed in an acid or salt solution.

PROBLEM 28.1. In Fig. 28.1(b), if the transfer of charge from A to B in 2.0 min is 180 coul, show that the average current in the wire during this time is 1.5 amp.

PROBLEM 28.2. If the current in a metallic wire has the steady value of 1 amp, show that at any point approximately 6×10^{18} electrons pass through the wire each second.

28.2 Conduction in liquids; electrolysis.

With the invention of the electric battery, means for maintaining a continuous current became available, and one of the first consequences was the discovery of the spectacular decomposing effect of an electric current on certain liquids. A current proved to be capable of breaking up, into their elements, dissolved or molten compounds that previously had resisted separation. It was by this process, which later came to be called *electrolysis*, that Humphry Davy in 1807 decomposed potash and soda (at that time still considered to be elements rather than compounds) and obtained from them the metallic elements potassium and sodium. Extending Davy's work, Faraday made a systematic study of the way in which electric charges pass through a conducting solution—or *electrolyte*, as he called it—such as water with some acid or a salt dissolved in it.

Faraday also reached *quantitative* conclusions of great importance. For example, as indicated in Fig. 28.2, he found that when electric charge passes through a molten sample of common salt (NaCl), two things happen: sodium metal collects at the pole forming the negative terminal or negative electrode (which he called *cathode*), and bubbles of chlorine gas appear at the positive electrode (which he called *anode*).

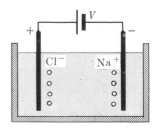

FIG. 28.2.   Schematic diagram of electrolytic decomposition of sodium chloride.

Specifically, Faraday found that for each coulomb of charge transferred between the two electrodes, 2.38×10^{-4} gm of metallic sodium is deposited on the negative electrode (cathode), and 3.68×10^{-4} gm of chlorine gas is liberated at the positive electrode (anode). It follows that for 1 gm-at.wt. (gram-atomic weight) of sodium (namely, 23.0 gm, where 23.0 is the atomic weight of sodium) to be deposited on the cathode, there must be a transfer of charge equal to 23.0 gm/$(2.38 \times 10^{-4}$ gm/coul), or 96,500 coul. As for the chlorine, it follows that the release of 1 gm-at.wt. of chlorine (namely, 35.457 gm) at the anode involves a transfer of charge equal to 35.5 gm/$(3.68 \times 10^{-4}$ gm/coul), which again is 96,500 coul. If twice this quantity of charge is transferred, the masses of the two elements yielded will be doubled, and so on. (Modern data have been used in this account.)

When a small amount of acid is added to water, the water molecules themselves can be broken down during electrolysis; in such experiments it is found that the passage of 96,500 coul will release 1 gm-at.wt. of hydrogen (1.008 gm) at the cathode but only $\frac{1}{2}$ gm-at.wt. of oxygen, namely 8.000 gm, at the anode. Hydrogen is a monovalent element, as is the case for sodium and chlorine, but oxygen is divalent (i.e., has a valence of 2). This suggests that the passage of 96,500 coul through a solution, the quantity of charge capable of releasing 1 gm-at.wt. of a monovalent element, will release only $\frac{1}{2}$ gm-at.wt. of a divalent element. Would it perhaps liberate only $\frac{1}{3}$ gm-at.wt. of a trivalent element? Experiments bore out these conjectures and enabled Faraday to formulate his *laws of electrolysis*. They may be summarized in modern terms by the single equation

Mass of element liberated at one electrode (gm) =

$$=\left(\frac{\text{charge passed (coul)}}{96{,}500 \text{ coul}}\right)\left(\frac{\text{no. of grams per gm-at.wt. of element}}{\text{valence of element}}\right).$$
(28.2)

The constant in Eq. (28.2), 96,500 coul of electric charge, has been appropriately given the name *faraday*.

PROBLEM 28.3. Predict what mass of each of the following elements would be liberated during electrolysis of a suitable solution by the passage of 1 faraday of charge between the electrodes: (a) copper, valence 2; (b) silver, valence 1; (c) antimony, valence 3.

PROBLEM 28.4. The element barium (at.wt. 137.36, valence 2) was discovered by Davy in an electrolysis experiment. Suppose that the experiment were carried out by maintaining a current of average value 1 amp for 1 hr in molten barium chloride ($BaCl_2$). What masses of barium and of chlorine would you expect to collect at the cathode and the anode, respectively?

PROBLEM 28.5. To silverplate a metal spoon, one may hang the spoon in a solution of silver nitrate and electrolyze the solution, using the spoon as the cathode. What mass of silver is deposited on the spoon by a current of 0.25 amp maintained for 20 min?

PROBLEM 28.6. An electrolysis apparatus is equipped with a removable cathode so that the mass of metal deposited on it can be determined by weighing. This apparatus is called a *coulometer*, for the weight of the deposit may be used to determine the charge that has flowed in an electric circuit during some specified interval of time. Suppose that a coulometer contains silver nitrate as the electrolyte. (a) What is the deposit of silver (in gm) when the current in the electrolyte is 1.00 amp for 30.0 min? (b) Use this information to suggest a definition for the ampere of current in terms of the measured mass of silver deposited per second in a coulometer. (c) In the same manner, suggest a definition for the coulomb of charge.

Today the hard-won conceptions of atoms and their constituents are so familiar to physical scientists that it is easy to visualize a mechanism for conduction in liquids and for explaining the main facts about electrolysis. For example, in the electrolysis of molten or dissolved sodium chloride (NaCl), the sodium atoms migrate to the negative electrode (cathode) and the chlorine atoms to the positive electrode (anode); therefore each sodium atom must somehow be positively charged, and each chlorine atom negatively charged. The conduction of electricity through the liquid is then accomplished by the movements of these charged atoms, or *ions* (from the Greek word for *to wander, to go*). Salt water, for example, is a good electric conductor because ordinary salt (NaCl), when dissolved in water, partially dissociates at once of its own accord into sodium and chlorine ions. On the other hand, sugar dissolved in water does not form ions, and hence sugar water is a poor conductor.

To complete the discussion, we shall make use of some other ideas and assumptions that were not completely developed for the better part of a century after Faraday. Sodium in the pure state is assumed to consist of atoms, each of which is electrically neutral because each atom has an equal number of protons and electrons. This is also true of chlorine in the pure state. When these atoms join to form solid salt, each sodium atom loses one of its electrons and each chlorine atom gains an electron. When the solid salt is then liquefied or dissolved in water, many of these charged atoms (ions) become free to move about. These ions are symbolized by Na^+ and Cl^- (Fig. 28.2). Similarly, when solid copper sulfate ($CuSO_4$) is dissolved in water, it dissociates partly into Cu^{++} and SO_4^{--} ions; here there has been a transfer of two electrons from each copper atom, and a gain of two by each sulfate radical.

An explanation of Faraday's laws of electrolysis as summarized by Eq. (28.2) now suggests itself. In Fig. 28.2, each Cl^- ion that reaches the anode gives up its excess electron to that electrode, becomes part of a neutral molecule of chlorine gas, and rises eventually in a bubble along with other chlorine gas molecules. At the same time, Na^+ ions reaching the cathode each pick up from it one electron and form neutral sodium metal. Thus for each pair of Na^+ and Cl^- ions which is neutralized at the electrodes, *one* electron moves through the circuit attached to the electrodes (i.e., through the battery or generator).

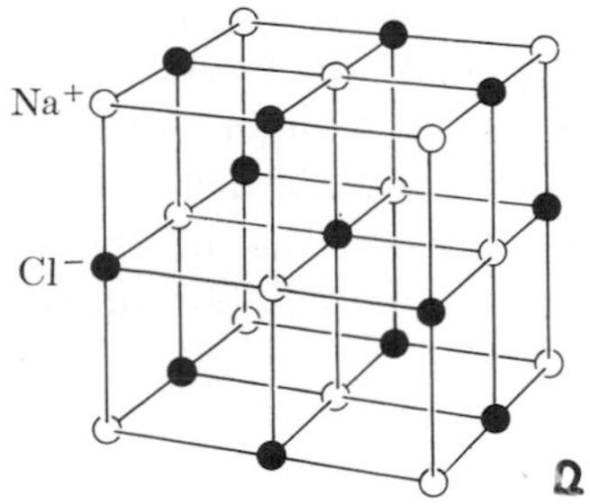

PROBLEM 28.7. Extend this physical argument to explain why in the electrolysis of water only $\frac{1}{2}$ gm-at.wt. of oxygen is released at the anode during the same time that 1 gm-at.wt. of hydrogen is released at the cathode.

FIG. 28.3. Solid sodium chloride has a simple cubic crystalline form. Notice that the ions have so arranged themselves that the attractions between ions of opposite sign exceed the repulsions between those of like sign.

28.3 The charge on the electron. The hypothesis of the previous paragraph leads at once to a computation of the charge q_e of an electron. We know that the passage of 96,500 coul releases 1 gm-at.wt. of a monovalent element at either electrode. This 1 gm-at.wt. consists of 6.02×10^{23} atoms, which is the Avogadro number N_0. If each atom transfers one electron, then the charge transferred by 1 gm-at.wt. is $N_0 q_e$. Thus $N_0 q_e = 96,500$ coul, or

$$q_e = \frac{96,500 \text{ coul}}{N_0}, \tag{28.3}$$

from which we get $q_e = 96,500 \text{ coul}/(6.02 \times 10^{23}) = 1.60 \times 10^{-19}$ coul. The confirmation of this value for q_e by a number of independent and entirely different experiments has given us confidence that the whole physical picture leading up to it is plausible.

Conversely, Eq. (28.3) together with a separate determination of the charge of an electron q_e enables us to compute Avogadro's number N_0. In fact, this is one of the important ways used today for determining N_0. It is therefore of interest to note briefly how q_e is measured. A precise method was developed in the 1900's by the American physicist and Nobel Prize winner, Robert A. Millikan, and his associates. He began by measuring the amount of electric charge Q on a small drop of oil; as the drop is sprayed out from an atomizer, it inevitably becomes charged by friction, and the charge it carries may be subsequently changed to a new value by ionizing the surrounding gases briefly with a beam of x-rays or rays from a radioactive substance. In every case, the amount of charge Q on the drop may be found *in principle* by putting the drop in the space between two horizontal plates (Fig. 27.10) to which a known potential difference V can be applied. The electric field intensity E, which by Eq. (27.5) is the ratio of potential difference V and the distance s between the plates, can then counterbalance the gravitational pull on the drop; if the drop with charge Q and mass m is seen to be in equilibrium when observed with a microscope, we know that

$$E \times Q = mg.$$

If we now let the same drop pick up different charges, and if we record the corresponding new values of E needed for equilibrium, the above expression can be used to compute the various values of Q which were on the oil drop during a long series of observations. Such a list shows directly that Q does not have any or every conceivable value, but *only whole multiples of one value*. For example, Millikan listed the 5 lowest values of Q he ever obtained as 1.60×10^{-19} coul, 3.20×10^{-19} coul, 4.80×10^{-19} coul, 6.40×10^{-19} coul, and 8.00×10^{-19} coul. Clearly, these are 1, 2, 3, 4, and 5 times 1.60×10^{-19} coul.

An interpretation follows naturally: the net electric charge on an oil drop (and presumably on anything else) can only be a whole multiple of a smallest, discrete unit of electricity, identified with the electron, and having a charge q_e of magnitude 1.60×10^{-19} coul. If, on other grounds, we have decided that the electron has a negative charge, then it is the excess of x electrons which gives the oil drop a *negative* charge $Q = x \cdot q_e$; and it is the deficit of x electrons which gives the oil drop a *positive* charge. Thus Millikan's oil-drop experiment gives a value for q_e which, together with the results of electrolysis in Eq. (28.3), permits us to calculate Avogadro's number N_0; and it will be remembered that the value for N_0 was needed in our previous chapters for solving such problems as the mass and size of atoms.*

Now we can return to the discussion of electrolysis and note that we had to use three important assumptions: (1) the atomicity of matter, (2) the "atomicity" of electric charges, i.e., that conduction in liquids is due to ions bearing 1, 2, 3, . . . electrons more or less than when the atoms are neutral, and (3) the assumption that electrons are ordinarily a part of atoms. But all three assumptions were far from evident at the time when Faraday phrased his laws of electrolysis in 1834. Atomicity of matter gradually became acceptable on other grounds (through chemistry, Chapter 22, and kinetic theory, Chapter 25), but the conception of dis-

---

*The details of the determination of q_e are far more complex than can be given here; see, for example, the books by R. A. Millikan and by O. Oldenberg referred to in the Supplementary Reading list at the end of this chapter.

crete charges called electrons began to take definite form only in the last
quarter of the 19th century, when it became possible to study beams of
electrons in cathode-ray tubes and eventually to determine their mass
and charge. The role that electrons play in atoms was then the next major
puzzle; its solution is the substance of an exciting portion of contemporary
science. To obtain the necessary concepts we turn first to two subjects of
great importance, magnetism and electromagnetism, which will lead us into
the study of optics and through it back to the nature of atoms.

28.4 Magnets and magnetic fields. Knowledge of magnets and their
effects had been accumulating for centuries and gradually grew into a
quite separate branch of physical science called *magnetism*. We shall be
content here merely with summarizing some basic phenomena and concepts of magnetism that are pertinent for our purposes.

(1) Loadstones are naturally occurring magnets; they usually consist
of the black oxide of iron called magnetite (Fe_3O_4).

(2) A few substances such as steel and certain alloys of metals become
fairly permanent magnets after having been held for some time close to a
loadstone. Soft iron is magnetized only while near a magnet.

(3) If a bar magnet is dipped into iron filings, the filings tend to cling
to it at certain places more than at others; these regions are usually at
opposite ends of the magnet and are called *magnetic poles*.

(4) If a magnet is suspended horizontally by a thread or floated on a
cork in water, it will rotate until one pole points northward and the other
pole southward. The north-seeking pole is called simply the *north pole* or
N-pole; the pole at the other end is the *south pole* or S-pole. These poles
always occur in pairs of opposite sign. While it is impossible to make a
magnet with only one pole, a single pole may be effectively isolated for
study by using a long thin magnet, so that one pole is remote from the
other.

(5) Poles of like sign repel each other; those of unlike sign attract each
other.

(6) Coulomb studied the forces between magnetic poles and arrived at
the Coulomb *magnetic* force law: the force F between two magnetic poles
of *pole strengths* p_1 and p_2 is directly proportional to the pole strengths and
inversely proportional to the square of the distance r between them, or

$$F \propto p_1 p_2 / r^2.$$

This relation may be used to define a unit of magnetic pole strength p,
much as we used the electrostatic force law (Section 26.14) to define a
unit of electric charge q. To cast the last proportionality into an equation,
we write

$$F = \kappa \frac{p_1 p_2}{r^2}, \tag{28.4}$$

where the constant κ (Greek *kappa*) is 6.32×10^4 new·m^2/(unit pole)^2 in the system of units used in this book.

(7) Figure 27.6 shows how the field of force about a magnet can be visualized with the help of iron filings. The needlelike filings become magnetized in the field, line up like compass needles to lie with their long dimensions along a line of force, and so tend to form chains extending from the N-pole to the S-pole. The direction of a line of magnetic force at any point in the field is, by definition, the direction in which the N-pole of a small compass needle would point when put at that place.

(8) The *magnetic field intensity* $\mathbf{H}$ at any point may be defined as the force per unit pole acting on an N-pole of strength p placed at the point; that is,

$$\mathbf{H} = \mathbf{F}/p. \tag{28.5}$$

PROBLEM 28.8. (a) Frame a definition, in words, of *unit pole strength*. (b) At a certain point in a magnetic field the field intensity $\mathbf{H}$ is known, by actual test, to be 2×10^{-4} new/unit pole, in the direction northeast. Show that if an S-pole of strength 100 units were placed at the point, the force on it should be 2×10^{-2} new southwest. (c) What operations would you carry out to check whether the given S-pole does indeed have a strength of 100 unit poles?

PROBLEM 28.9. List the similarities and differences between the magnetic and electrostatic concepts discussed so far.

William Gilbert, about 1580, had been among the first to emphasize the various striking ways in which magnetic and electrical phenomena differ from each other. Most important, all the evidence indicated that magnetic poles when at rest act only on one another, and that electric charges at rest act only on other charges, and that charges and poles at rest do not interact. Such clear distinctions were needed; indeed, part of the early successes in electricity and magnetism resulted because these two branches of physical science developed in the 17th and 18th centuries as separate disciplines. But while the phenomena were different, there were seen to be many close analogies between the concepts and laws found useful in electricity and in magnetism, and also in gravitation. That theories so alike in form should be applied to phenomena that were unrelated was a puzzling contradiction in the eyes of many scientists.

28.5 The magnetic effect of an electric current. A few 18th-century observations indicated the possibility, after all, of some interdependence of the above phenomena. For example there were several reports that pieces of iron were found to be magnetized after the nearby occurrence of a lightning stroke. But it was not until 1820 that a key discovery was announced, by Hans Christian Oersted (1777–1851), which really was to start the fusion of these hitherto separate disciplines into the branch of physics soon to be called *electromagnetism*. When Oersted held a wire in which there was an electric current over a compass needle, the needle rotated until it was at right angles to the wire (Fig. 28.4), and when he reversed the direction of the current in the wire, the magnetic needle reversed its direction also, but again came to rest at right angles to the wire.

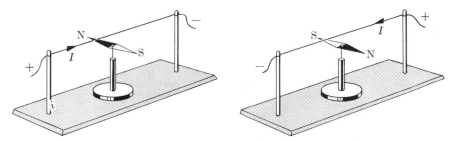

FIG. 28.4. Oersted's experiment.

This discovery was in a sense accidental but, as was said later by Pasteur in referring to it, "in the field of experimentation, accident favors the prepared mind." Just why Oersted performed the experiment is not known; one tradition is that he had intended to demonstrate the supposed *lack* of an interaction between an electric current and magnetic poles. But certainly he was prepared to notice and to seize upon what he actually did see, for he was an experienced observer with a special interest in possible connecting links among electrical, magnetic, and chemical phenomena, a subject on which he had written a paper a few years earlier.

Oersted's discovery may be described from a more modern viewpoint as follows. An electric charge always exerts force on other charges, but it also exerts a force on a magnetic pole *when in motion relative to that pole*. Or, speaking in terms of fields, an electric charge always has an electric field associated with it, but when a charge is in motion relative to the observer, he will find that it has a magnetic as well as an electric field associated with it. In addition, and almost as startling, was Oersted's observation that his magnet set itself *perpendicularly* across the current-carrying wire (Fig. 28.4). In other words, the force between a current and a nearby magnetic pole is perpendicular to the line connecting the two. This seemed paradoxical indeed to physicists who previously had been dealing with forces between two masses, or between two charges at rest, or between two magnetic poles at rest—forces that in every case are directed along the line connecting the two particles rather than perpendicular to that line.

No wonder that many of the best
minds in physical science now rushed
into electrical research. Within a
matter of months it was shown that
the lines of magnetic force in the
field about a wire carrying current
are circles with centers at the wire,
and with each circle lying in a plane
normal to the wire (Fig. 28.5). This
means that a test pole placed anywhere in the field near the wire will
tend to move at right angles to a
radial line, i.e., in a circular path
about the wire. The direction of the
field can be remembered by means
of a convenient "right-hand rule":
grasp the wire with the fingers of
the right hand, thumb extended in
the direction of the current (from

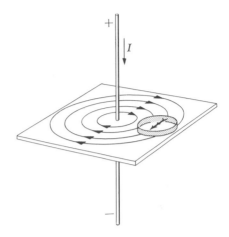

FIG. 28.5. Lines of magnetic force
around a current are circles, as made
evident by means of iron filings or a
small compass needle.

the + pole to the − pole of the battery); the fingers then curl and
point in the direction in which the magnetic lines of force encircle the wire
(Fig. 28.6). The magnitude H of the magnetic field intensity at any point
in the field of a *long straight* wire in which there is a current I was found by
experiment to be directly proportional to I and inversely proportional to
the perpendicular distance r of the field point from the wire; that is,

$$H \propto I/r. \qquad (28.6)$$

This relation does not hold if the wire is short or is curved; for such wires
special formulas for H must be derived.

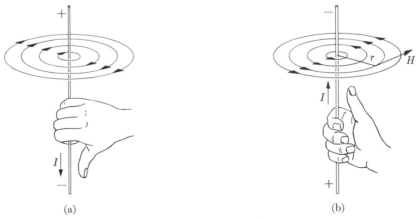

FIG. 28.6. The right-hand rule.

PROBLEM 28.10. A compass needle is placed underneath a straight wire that runs north and south. When a current is established in the wire, the needle is seen to rotate until it points eastward. What is the direction of the current?

28.6 The electromagnet. If a wire bearing a current is bent into a loop, the general pattern of its magnetic field is the same as that of a short bar magnet (Fig. 27.5). This follows from the right-hand rule; when the hand grasping the wire slides around the loop, the fingers always point through the loop in the same direction (Fig. 28.7). The side or face of the loop from which the magnetic lines of force emerge acts as an N-pole and the opposite face as an S-pole. With the addition of more turns, the coil has a proportionally more intense magnetic field. The intensity can also be increased markedly by inserting a bar of soft iron in the coil. Soft iron will lose most of its magnetism when the current is turned off. Such a device is called an *electromagnet*, to distinguish it from so-called permanent magnets.

If there is current in the coil of wire of Fig. 28.7, it can be detected and measured by placing a compass needle at the center of the coil. When there is no current, the needle points northward, owing to the earth's magnetic field. When there is a current, the needle tends to line up along the axis of the coil, and the larger the current the greater the deflection toward the axis. The angle of deflection can be read on a scale and is a measure of the current. Such an instrument is called a *galvanometer*, after Luigi Galvani (1737–1798), the Italian who paved the way for

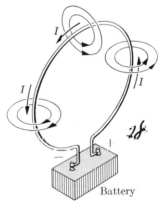

FIG. 28.7. Magnetic field of one loop of wire in which a current is established by a battery.

Volta's discovery of the electrochemical cell. A simple form of amperemeter, or *ammeter*, can be obtained by marking the scale to read amperes instead of degrees. To make this calibration, a series of different, steady currents are established in the coil, the deflection for each current is observed, and at the same time the current is independently measured with the help of, say, a coulometer and a watch (see Problem 28.6).

28.7 Force on a current in a magnetic field. If the moving charges constituting a current exert force on a nearby magnetic pole, we may reasonably ask whether the pole at the same time exerts force on the moving charge. This sort of question naturally arises, not because effects in nature are necessarily arranged symmetrically, but because our minds tend to be drawn to notions of symmetry. Symmetrical relations have an esthetic quality that make them pleasant and easy to think about. But when *forces* are involved, as here, the question is still more compelling. For if Newton's third law of motion is valid for forces of every sort, then the force of the moving charge on the pole must be accompanied by a force of the pole on the charge, and this pair of forces must be equal in magnitude although opposite in direction.

Experiment shows this to be so. Thus if the magnetic needle in Fig. 28.4 had been fixed so that it could not rotate, and the current-carrying wire had been loosely held, the wire would have been seen to turn into a position at right angles to the needle. Similarly, if the current-carrying coil in Fig. 28.7 were placed close to a fixed magnet, it would tend to rotate toward a position where its axis is parallel to the magnetic lines of force of the magnet. A spring may be attached to the coil so as to resist this

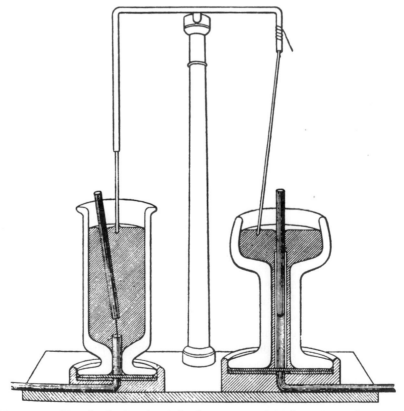

FIG. 28.8. Faraday's sketch of the bar magnet rotating about the current-carrying wire (left) and the wire rotating about the magnet (right).

twisting force, and the angle through which the coil turns, as indicated by a pointer and scale, is a measure of the current in the coil. Galvanometers and ammeters of this *moving-coil type* are more commonly used than are those of the fixed-coil type described in Section 28.6.

The symmetry of the effect between a magnet and a current was beautifully shown in 1822 by Michael Faraday with the equipment shown in Fig. 28.8. At the left, charge is sent to a vessel filled with a conducting liquid (mercury) through a wire at the bottom, and leaves through the wire at the top. A bar magnet is tilted so that the top pole finds itself in the circular magnetic field surrounding the current in the wire, and is thereby forced to rotate about the wire. At the right, it is the wire which is free to rotate about a central bar magnet. Clearly, both arrangements show that the interaction of currents and magnetic fields can be made to produce mechanical rotation. Therefore these arrangements constitute a first approach toward the electric motor.

But the detailed analysis of the second case above yields also a new physical principle of great interest. We may seek the reason why the wire turns, not merely in the symmetry of the effect between current and magnet, but more specifically by noticing that in both arrangements the charges in the current-carrying wire are made to move *across* the lines of magnetic force, in the horizontal plane, set up by one of the poles of the bar magnet. The force making the wire rotate with constant speed about the magnet (despite friction) must always be tangential, i.e., at right angles both to the direction of the current in the wire and to the magnetic field of the bar magnet. Therefore we may propose now to explain the motion by postulating the new principle that *whenever charges move across magnetic lines of force, the charges are acted on by a force in a direction perpendicular both to the current and to the magnetic field.*

This effect, first found by Faraday on Christmas Day 1821, can be simply demonstrated by placing a straight portion of wire into a more or less homogeneous field in the gap between the poles of a magnet, as in Fig. 28.9. As soon as a battery is connected and current is produced in the wire, a force F springs up to act on it as shown, tending to pull the wire out of the gap. Neither the direction nor the magnitude of the force was predicted. By test,

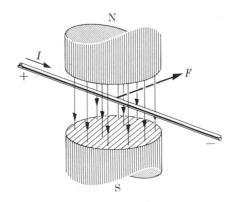

FIG. 28.9. The force experienced by the current-carrying conductor is here away from the observer, perpendicular both to the current and to the magnetic field.

the direction is away from the observer in this case (but toward him if the current is reversed). This suggests that the wire tends to be pushed in the direction of the weaker total field, for the circular magnetic field (not shown) that is set up by the current I itself, by the right-hand rule, is in a direction opposite to, and therefore diminishes, the effective field of the magnet just behind the wire in Fig. 28.9.

The magnitude of the force F, sometimes called the *magnetic side thrust*, was found to be proportional to the current I in the wire, the original magnetic field H set up by the magnet, and the length of wire l which is actually in the magnetic field. Thus $F \propto HIl$, or

$$F = \mu_0 HIl, \tag{28.7}$$

where μ_0 is the constant of proportionality, called the *permeability of free space*. As would be found by experiment, μ_0 has the numerical value 12.57×10^{-7} if the other quantities are expressed in mks units. [We note parenthetically that $\mu_0 = 1/4\pi\kappa$, where κ is the constant of Eq. (28.4).]

If a particle with charge q moves a distance l, with speed v, through a magnetic field H (in a vacuum), we may consider the moving charge as constituting a current $I = q/t$, where the time taken to traverse l is $t = l/v$. Substituting for I in Eq. (28.7), we obtain the force on a single charge moving across the lines of force of the magnetic field:

$$F = \mu_0 HIl = \mu_0 H(q/t)l = \mu_0 H \left(\frac{q}{l/v}\right) l,$$

or

$$F = \mu_0 Hqv. \tag{28.8}$$

In Sections 36.3 and 37.2, Eq. (28.8) will assume great importance, for it will help us to find the speed, the charge, and the mass of single charged particles such as electrons and ions.

PROBLEM 28.11. A vertical antenna wire at the earth's equator has a current surging upward; in which direction will the wire experience a force due to the earth's magnetic field? If, a moment later, the current surges downward, what is the direction of the force now? If this antenna is transferred to the earth's magnetic North Pole, what are the forces then?

28.8 Induced currents. Following Oersted's discovery in 1820 that an electric current can produce magnetic effects, many investigators began to look for a possible reverse effect, namely whether a magnet can be used to produce an electric current. In the circuit of Fig. 28.10 there is no battery, and hence no current. The present question is whether a current can be produced in the wire with the help of, say, a bar magnet. In 1824 Faraday

began such experiments but was unable to detect any current when he
put the bar magnet near or into the
loop of wire. After numerous such
attempts he put this work aside, but
he returned to it in 1831, and in
August of that year was successful.
However, he found that the way to
produce the current in the loop was
different from what he had earlier
envisaged. Merely to have a stationary wire in a constant magnetic field
is not enough. The field must move
with respect to the wire, or the intensity of the magnetic field must be
changing. True, in earlier experiments

FIG. 28.10. A closed circuit consisting of a loop of wire connected
to a galvanometer.

he had tried moving the bar magnet through the loop, thus changing the
magnetic field about it. But, as he later saw, to detect the current produced
in this manner he needed a coil of wire of many turns connected to a more
sensitive galvanometer, and a stronger magnet. In one of the earliest
successful experiments in 1831 he was using an electromagnet instead of
a bar magnet, with results that he described in these words:

> Two hundred and three feet of copper wire in one length were coiled around
> a large block of wood, another 203 feet of similar wire were interposed as a
> spiral between the turns of the first coil, and metallic contact everywhere was
> prevented by twine. One of these helices was connected with a galvanometer,
> and the other with a battery of 100 pairs of plates 4 inches square . . .
>
> When the contact was made, there was a sudden and very slight effect at
> the galvanometer, and there was also a similar slight effect when the contact
> with the battery was broken. But whilst the voltaic [battery] current was
> continuing to pass through the one helix [making it into an electromagnet
> with a constant magnetic field], no galvanometrical appearances nor any
> effect like induction upon the other helix could be perceived, although the
> active power of the battery was proved to be great . . .
>
> Repetition of the experiments with a battery of 120 pairs of plates produced
> no other effects; but it was ascertained, both at this and the former time, that
> the slight deflection of the needle occurring at the moment of completing the
> connexion, was always in one direction, and that the equally slight deflection,
> produced when the contact was broken, was in the other direction.

These were the clues that put Faraday on the successful path. In
Fig. 28.11 the two coils are shown separately. Upon connecting the battery to the electromagnet, coil A, the current in A increases quickly, but
not instantly, to its steady value, and the magnetic field of this current

increases in intensity at every point in the region in direct proportion to the growing current strength; during this period, current is "induced" in the coil of the separate circuit B. After the current in A reaches a steady value, its magnetic field ceases to change, and no current is induced in B. Upon disconnecting the battery, the current in A decreases to zero, and so does the magnetic field intensity at every point in the region; during this brief period, current is again induced in coil B. Most important, the current induced during stopping is opposite in direction to that induced during starting.

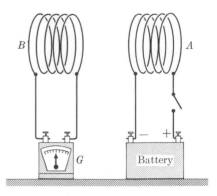

FIG. 28.11. Current is induced in the coil of circuit B while the current supplied by the battery in circuit A is increasing or decreasing; the currents induced in B in the two cases are in opposite directions.

Faraday extended his experiments. Keeping the current in A steady, he moved coil A toward coil B and also B toward A; during each motion, current appeared in B. It also appeared when he moved the coils apart, but now in the opposite direction from that observed when they were made to approach each other. After inserting a soft iron bar through the two coils, he repeated these experiments and found that the induced current was now stronger than before. Then, using only coil B, he thrust a bar magnet toward the coil and then withdrew it (Fig. 28.12). The results were the same when he held the magnet stationary and moved the coil toward and away from it.

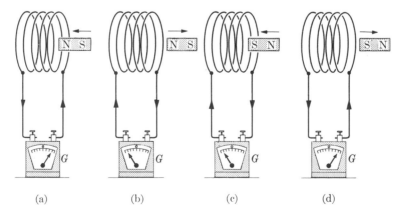

(a)   (b)   (c)   (d)

FIG. 28.12. Current induced in a coil by a moving magnet.

To explain these observations, Faraday made effective use of the idea of lines of magnetic force [Section 28.4 (7)]. *A current is induced in a conductor only while the conductor is in relative motion across lines of magnetic force.* For example, at the moment when coil A of Fig. 28.11 is first connected to the battery and while the magnetic field establishes itself, we may imagine circular lines of magnetic force originating at each wire of coil A and spreading out with increasing diameter and in greater numbers so long as the current in A is increasing, and these spreading lines may be envisaged as moving across each wire of coil B, thus inducing current in it. As soon as the current in A reaches a steady value, the magnetic field in this region ceases to increase, and lines of force no longer sweep across the wires of coil B; therefore the induced current in B is now zero. As the current in A is decreased, the magnetic field collapses and the lines of force shrink back toward the wires of A and again cut those of B, but in the direction opposite to that at starting; therefore the induced current now is in the opposite direction. Note how this picture also helps us to explain the observations symbolized in Fig. 28.12.

28.9 Henry's work on induced currents. Actually the phenomenon of induced currents had been discovered a year before Faraday by the American Joseph Henry (1797–1879), who at the time was teaching mathematics and natural philosophy (physics) at the Albany Academy. Henry apparently had suspected for some time that earlier failures to observe such currents could be attributed to lack of a magnet of sufficient strength. Having done pioneer work in the development of very strong electromagnets, he used one of them in the manner shown in Fig. 28.13. Across the two poles of the electromagnet he laid a soft iron bar, or *armature*, and around this wound a coil of insulated wire and connected its ends to a galvanometer. Lacking a switch, he started and stopped the current in the electromagnet by immersing the battery plates in the electrolyte and then withdrawing them. In his words:

At the instant of immersion, the north end of the [galvanometer] needle was deflected 30° to the west, indicating a current of electricity from the helix surrounding the armature. The effect, however, appeared only as a single impulse, for the needle, after a few oscillations, resumed its former undisturbed position . . . although the galvanic action of the battery, and consequently the magnetic power, was still continued. I was, however, much surprised to see the needle sud-

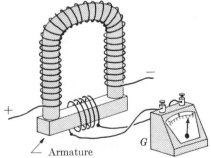

FIG. 28.13. A schematic drawing of Joseph Henry's apparatus for demonstrating induced currents.

denly deflected from a state of rest to about 20° to the east . . . when the battery was withdrawn from the acid, and again deflected to the west when it was re-immersed. The operation was repeated many times in succession, and uniformly with the same results . . .

This experiment illustrates most strikingly the reciprocal action of the two principles of electricity and magnetism . . .

Thus while the field in the armature was changing, current was induced in the coil around it. Unfortunately for Henry's place in the history of this discovery, he had to return to his heavy teaching duties at the end of the one-month summer vacation, without having published what he had found. Later, when he read the announcement of Faraday's discovery of the effect, he hastily made some additional experiments, and in July 1832 published a paper describing all his results. In it he was careful to give Faraday full credit for priority in publication.

If this were the end of the story, it hardly would be worth repeating, for Faraday certainly is to be regarded as the *effective* discoverer of induced current. However, Henry, in the last paragraph of his July 1832 paper, mentioned a major discovery that neither Faraday nor anyone else had described: while a current is increasing in a coil (for example after the coil has been connected to a battery) an opposite though smaller current is induced *in this same coil*, with the net effect that the time required for the net current in the coil to attain its steady final value is made longer than it otherwise would be. Conversely, while the current in a coil is decreasing, a forward current is induced *in the same coil*, its effect being to prolong the time required for the net current in the coil to fall to zero (Fig. 28.14).

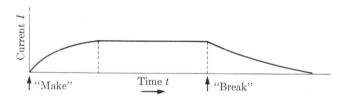

FIG. 28.14. Self-induction prolongs the time needed to increase or decrease current in a coil.

This important phenomenon has been given the name *self-induction* to distinguish it from the previously discussed *mutual induction*, where a changing current in one circuit induces a current in a separate, neighboring circuit. Self-induction is also explainable in terms of the cutting of lines of magnetic force: when a changing current in a coil generates a changing magnetic field around itself, the magnetic lines of force cut across the turns of the coil and induce a current in them.

Late in 1832 Henry accepted the chair of natural philosophy at Princeton University and there again, despite heavy teaching and administrative duties, carried on research that often was of fundamental importance. In 1846 he became the first secretary of the then new Smithsonian Institution in Washington, D. C., a post that he occupied for 32 years. In this position he became the prototype of the modern research administrator, whose important function is to facilitate and often help to plan and guide the researches of other gifted investigators.

28.10 Lenz's law. The fact that mutual induction was discovered independently and in the same period in England and America illustrates again that scientific development may be as much a product of the times as of the individual. The illustration here becomes even more convincing when we find that in Russia H. F. E. Lenz (1804–1865) was also simultaneously engaged in such studies. Working with only a partial knowledge of Faraday's discovery and with none about Henry's, he not only made similar studies but formulated a basic principle that had escaped both of them. Now known as *Lenz's law*, this principle permits prediction of the direction of an induced current in any circumstance. It is a basic principle in electrical theory, being indeed an application to electromagnetic induction of the principle of conservation of energy (Section 18.13).

Lenz reasoned in this way: Any electric current can do work, even one induced by a changing magnetic field, and therefore work must be done in producing this current. When an induced current, which represents energy, is produced in a coil, the agent responsible for the production of the induced current (for example, the hand bringing a magnet toward a coil) must bear the extra burden. Consequently, *the induced current must be in such a direction as to ensure that its own magnetic field will oppose the original action which produced the induced current.* For example, if the N-pole of a magnet is brought up to a coil [see Fig. 28.12(a)], the current induced in the coil must be in such a direction as to make the face of the coil nearer to the magnet equivalent to an N-pole also; the two N-poles will then produce mutual forces of repulsion, and this is the reason why the experimenter must do work to push them together. The work done on the magnet is the source of the energy of the current induced in the coil by the approaching magnet.

There is, clearly, no easy way of imagining how the work done by the hand on one object can turn up as energy of a current in a coil at some distance. However, this does not detract from the validity of the concept of induction of currents, but rather is symptomatic of the need to recognize the limitations of our imagination. Energy *does* get transferred "across" the space between magnet and coil, even though no simple and valid picture suggests itself to explain this transfer by some mechanical mediation. In analogy to Newton's decision in the case of gravitational action at a distance, we shall henceforth recognize that the existence of such energy in a given region of the electric and magnetic fields itself assures the possibility of transferring energy from one part of the region to another. The next chapter will provide a striking extension of the importance and generality of the field concept.

PROBLEM 28.12. (a) For each of the cases of Fig. 28.12, will the face of the coil nearer to the magnet act like an N-pole or an S-pole? (b) Using the right-hand rule (Section 28.5), verify that in each diagram the current does have the direction indicated by the arrows. (c) Show that the principle of conservation of energy would be violated if the current were in the direction opposite to that shown in Fig. 28.12. (d) Assume that the coils in Fig. 28.11 have only one loop each. What will be the direction of the current in coil B when the switch is closed in circuit A?

SUPPLEMENTARY READING

BLACKWOOD, O., and W. C. KELLY, *General physics* (Wiley, 2nd edition, 1953), Chaps. 31 to 35.

BONNER, F. T., and M. PHILLIPS, *Principles of physical science* (Addison-Wesley, 1957), Chap. 15.

BORN, M., *The restless universe* (Harper, 1936; Dover, 1951, 1957), Chap. 2.

CHALMERS, T., *Historic researches* (Morgan Brothers, London), Chap. 3.

FARADAY, M., *Experimental researches in electricity* (1839–1855; portions are given in No. 576, Everyman's Library).

HUMPHREYS, R. F., and R. BERINGER, *First principles of atomic physics* (Harper, 1950), Chaps. 13–15 and 17.

KNEDLER, J. W., *Masterworks of science* (Doubleday, 1947), pp. 445–502. Excerpts from Faraday's work.

MAGIE, W. F., *A source book in physics* (McGraw-Hill, 1935). Extracts from papers of Volta (pp. 427–431), Ohm (pp. 465–472), Oersted (pp. 436–441), Ampère (pp. 447–460), Faraday (pp. 473–489), Lenz (pp. 511–513), and Henry (pp. 514–519).

MENDENHALL, C. E., A. S. EVE, D. A. KEYS, and R. M. SUTTON, *College physics* (Heath, 4th edition, 1956), Chap. 34.

MILLIKAN, R. A., *Electrons* (+ *and* −) (University of Chicago Press, 1947, and many earlier printings).

OLDENBERG, O., *Introduction to atomic physics* (McGraw-Hill, 1954, and later editions), Chap. 7.

TAYLOR, L. W., *Physics, the pioneer science* (Houghton Mifflin, 1941), Chaps. 39, 41–45, and 51.

TYNDALL, J., *Faraday as a discoverer* (Longmans, Green, London, 1886).

SEMAT, H., *Fundamentals of physics* (Rinehart, 3rd edition, 1957), Chaps. 23–25.

WATERMAN, A. T., and A. L. KIMBALL, *College textbook of physics* (Holt, 1954), Chaps. 26, 34, and 35.

WHITE, H. E., *Modern college physics* (Van Nostrand, 3rd edition, 1956), Chaps. 51, 52, and 58.

CHAPTER 29

THE ELECTROMAGNETIC THEORY OF LIGHT

29.1 Maxwell. The work of Oersted, Faraday, and their contemporaries brought out an intimate relationship between electricity and magnetism: an electric charge and a magnetic pole can exert a force on each other, provided they are in relative motion. This fundamental postulate, phrased clearly by Faraday in terms of his lines-of-force model, became the point of departure for the electrical work of the British physicist, James Clerk Maxwell. Faraday's background (Section 27.5) and that of Maxwell were radically different. Maxwell came from a long line of distinguished persons, his parents had ample means, and he had received an excellent school and university education. While Faraday is to be regarded as one of the greatest experimentalists, Maxwell, although able in experimentation, ranks among the greatest theoretical physicists. Yet in his electrical work Maxwell was Faraday's intellectual heir, and in the preface to his *Treatise on electricity and magnetism* (1st edition, 1873), a work that can be ranked with Newton's *Principia*, Maxwell wrote:

> . . . before I began the study of electricity I resolved to read no mathematics on the subject till I had first read through Faraday's *Experimental Researches on Electricity*.

And later on in the preface he recommended that others read Faraday's book, since "It is of great advantage to the student of any subject to read the original memoirs on that subject, for science is always most completely assimilated when it is in the nascent state . . . "

Maxwell was much impressed by Faraday's explanations in terms of lines of force extending throughout the space around the interacting bodies. He said:

> As I proceeded with the study of Faraday, I perceived that his method of conceiving the phenomena was also a mathematical one, though not exhibited in the conventional form of mathematical symbols . . .
>
> For instance, Faraday, in his mind's eye, saw lines of force traversing all space where the mathematicians saw centers of force attracting at a distance; Faraday saw a medium where they saw nothing but distance; Faraday sought the seat of the phenomena in real actions going on in the medium, [whereas] they were satisfied that they had found it in a power of action at a distance impressed on the electric fluid.

Maxwell, like Faraday, could not accept the notion of a field devoid of a material existence of its own, though he was quite willing to admit that

531

the conception of action at a distance "may have been, and may yet be useful in leading to the coordination of phenomena."

Faraday, despite his desire to seek physical, mechanical pictures, had left open the question of how the lines of force themselves were constructed. However, he was ready to agree, without insisting on it, that these lines might be condensations of ether, for the notion of an elastic ether that filled all space was at the time a familiar conceptual device used to explain how light and the radiation from heated bodies could travel through a vacuum, for example through the vacuum that exists between our sun and other stars and the earth; even a vacuum supposedly was filled with the all-pervading ether. Faraday wrote: "It is not at all unlikely that, if there be an aether, it should have other uses than simply the conveyance of radiations," thus showing his characteristic predilection for the unification of separate fields of study.

Maxwell began by developing a clearer picture of how the lines of force functioned in transmitting electric and magnetic forces through the ether. Then, using this model as a basis, he proceeded to convert the descriptions of electric and magnetic phenomena into mathematical terms:

> When I had translated what I considered to be Faraday's ideas into a mathematical form, I found that in general the results of the two methods coincided, so that the same phenomena were accounted for, and the same laws of action deduced by both methods, but that Faraday's methods resembled those in which we begin with the whole and arrive at the parts by analysis, while the ordinary mathematical methods were founded on the principle of beginning with the parts and building up the whole by synthesis.

The set of *field equations* that Maxwell obtained by this "translation" are expressed in the language of the calculus. They can serve as postulates, and the phenomena for which they provide descriptions include the ones familiar to us from the preceding chapters. For example, consider a long, straight wire carrying an electric current. As we know, and as Maxwell's theory also predicts, there is in the surrounding space both an electric and a magnetic field—an *electromagnetic field*, as Maxwell called it. If the current in the wire is steady, its electromagnetic field will also be steady; at any point both the electric field intensity $\mathbf{E}$ and the magnetic field intensity $\mathbf{H}$ will be constant both in magnitude and direction, although the magnitudes will of course be smaller the more distant the point is from the wire.

Suppose next that we suddenly change the current in the wire to, say, a higher steady value. Then, as we know, $\mathbf{E}$ and $\mathbf{H}$ at a given point in the field increase proportionally in magnitude to new steady values. But what happens *while* the current is increasing, while the electric charges in the wire are undergoing acceleration? Here Maxwell's equations predicted something entirely new, i.e., that during the change in current, the accelerating charges will send out a *signal* in the form of a pulse of energy; moreover, the Maxwellian theory predicted that this pulse will spread out through the surrounding medium like the crest of a wave, with a speed equal to that of visible light!

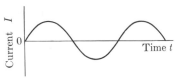

To see the further implications of this consequence of Maxwell's postulates, let us note what would happen if the current, instead of undergoing a single change, were made to oscillate (Fig. 29.1); that is, if the

FIG. 29.1. Oscillating current.

charges in the wire were made to surge back and forth periodically, each with a continuously varying acceleration similar to that of a pendulum bob. Here the prediction from Maxwell's theory was that a wave train, or succession of wave pulses, will continuously radiate from the wire in all directions, again with the speed of light. Mathematically speaking, the theory yielded equations which Maxwell recognized to be of the general type called the *equation of a wave*. Such an equation had long been in use to describe wave motions of various kinds—water waves, water ripples, sound waves, light waves. Every wave equation involves distance, time, and the speed of propagation of the wave, but the other variables entering it differ with the kind of wave being described. Thus for sound waves the variations of the pressure from the normal pressure in the medium may represent one variable. In Maxwell's equations for electromagnetic waves, the variables are the electric and the magnetic field intensities, **E** and **H**.

29.2 Some characteristics of any wave motion. In previous chapters, we saw how matter passing from one point to another may carry energy with it, as when a bullet having kinetic energy passes from gun to target, and when running water or the wind carries energy from point to point. In a wave motion, on the other hand, energy is transferred through a continuous medium without the passage of matter from one point to the other. What is propagated is solely a *state* or *condition* of the medium. For example, jiggling the end of a string once sends a kink, or *wave pulse*, traveling along the string; jiggling it periodically sets up a succession of similar pulses, or a *wave train* (Fig. 29.2). If the end of a clamped rod is struck once with a hammer, a wave pulse travels along the rod, and if it is struck periodically, a wave train results. Other examples are a mechanical oscillator touching the surface of water and setting up a succession of crests and troughs that spread out circularly over the surface, and the string and body of a musical instrument vibrating in air and producing minute variations of pressure that spread out spherically through the surrounding air.

One obvious characteristic of any wave is its *speed of propagation v*, the rate at which the disturbance traverses the medium. Its value depends both on the type of the wave and the nature of the medium. As examples, some speeds of sound waves are 332 m/sec for dry air at 0°C, 345 m/sec for dry air at 20°C, and 5130 m/sec for iron at 20°C.

Another important characteristic of a wave is the direction of the disturbance relative to the direction of propagation. If the disturbance takes place at right angles to the direction of propagation, the wave is said to be *transverse;* an example is the wave in the rope of Fig. 29.2. If the disturbance takes place in the direction of propagation, the wave is termed *longitudinal;* examples are the compressional waves that constitute sound, such as the sound waves set up in air by a vibrating tuning fork.

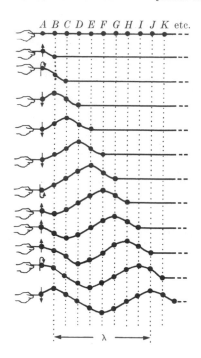

Fig. 29.2. Propagation of a transverse wave train along a rope.

In describing any periodic wave, two additional quantities are useful. One is the *wavelength,* denoted by the symbol λ (Greek *lambda*). It is defined as the distance, along the direction of propagation of the wave, between two successive points in the medium that are at any instant in precisely the same state of disturbance. For example, in Fig. 29.2 the distance between the adjacent crests B and J in the lowest of the 12 "snapshots" is one wavelength. The other useful quantity is the *frequency,* symbol ν (Greek *nu*), which may be defined as the number of complete waves that pass any given point per unit time. It is expressed in vibrations per second or cycles per second. The wave speed v, frequency ν, and wavelength λ are related by the equation

$$v = \lambda\nu. \tag{29.1}$$

In words, the speed of propagation, or distance traveled by the crest of the wave per second, is equal to the wavelength multiplied by the number of wave crests passing any point per second.

PROBLEM 29.1. (a) When a standard "A" tuning fork of frequency 440 cycles/sec was used to set up sound waves in carbon dioxide at room temperature, the wavelength was found to be 0.612 m. Show that these data yield a value of 269 m/sec for the speed of propagation. (b) Compute the wavelength in carbon dioxide for a frequency of 264 cycles/sec.

29.3 Electromagnetic waves. Maxwell's theory predicted that when charges oscillate they transmit energy into the surrounding region and that this energy spreads out from point to point, as in wave motion. To get a clearer picture of what happens in this fluctuating field, let us fix our attention on any one point P in the region. As time progresses, the electric field intensity E at this point will assume the values indicated by the arrows (vectors) in Fig. 29.3. Note that E periodically becomes zero.

FIG. 29.3. Variation of electric field intensity E, at a given point P, with time.

The magnetic field intensity H at the point will vary in magnitude in the same manner, but its direction remains perpendicular to that of E (Fig. 29.4). Compare the situation here with that in Fig. 29.2. In the string, any given particle bobs up and down as time progresses, whereas in an electromagnetic field it is not a material medium but the *values* of E and H that oscillate. However, if a wire containing electrons which are free to move is placed at the point P, these electrons will oscillate, for they are acted on by forces due to the fluctuating electric and magnetic fields.

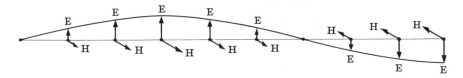

FIG. 29.4. Variation of field intensities, at a given point P, with time. The direction of propagation of the electromagnetic wave is perpendicular to E and H.

Having pictured what is predicted for any given point as time passes, let us now ask what is happening simultaneously at different field points 1, 2, 3, ... on any line in the direction of propagation of the electromagnetic wave. It is as if we could take an instantaneous photograph showing the values of the field intensities. Part (a) of Fig. 29.5 is one such "photograph." If, a moment later, we could take a second "photograph" (b), we would find that E no longer has the same values at the same points.

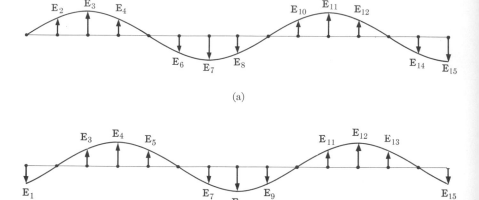

(a)

(b)

FIG. 29.5. Values of electric field intensities at different points for two successive instants.

For example, **E** is now maximum in magnitude at points 4, 8, and 12, instead of at 3, 7, and 11; it is zero at 2, 6, 10, and 14, instead of at 1, 5, 9, and 13. If we draw the line connecting the tips of the arrows in Fig. 29.5(a) and (b), it appears that the effect described above is the same as if waves were passing through the electric field; in the first "photograph," Fig. 29.5(a), the crests are at points 3 and 11, and a short time later, in Fig. 29.5(b), the crests have moved on to points 4 and 12.

In Fig. 29.5, the direction of propagation of the wave is toward the right. To picture the values of **H** as well as of **E** at the chosen points, we must resort to a sectional diagram such as Fig. 29.6. At every point, **E** and **H** are at right angles to each other and to the direction of propagation. To summarize: Maxwell's prediction was that in the neighborhood of an oscillating electric current the electric field and the magnetic field undergo

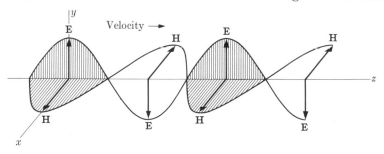

FIG. 29.6. Representation of the relation of electric field intensity and magnetic field intensity in an electromagnetic wave.

rhythmical fluctuations in synchronism with the oscillating current itself, but that these fluctuations in the magnitudes of **E** and **H** spread out like waves in a direction perpendicular both to the **E** and to the **H** vectors. He called the spreading disturbance in the electric and magnetic fields an *electromagnetic wave*, and as Fig. 29.6 implies, it is a *transverse* wave.

PROBLEM 29.2. (a) Give an operational definition for "electromagnetic wave." (b) What is the operational meaning of the statement, "when electric charges are accelerated, energy will spread through the surrounding medium"? (c) Give reasons in support of the statement that on the basis of Maxwell's theory an electron moving with constant speed in a circle should radiate electromagnetic energy and, moreover, do this at the expense of its own energy.

As was remarked earlier, the speed with which electromagnetic waves are propagated in any medium, as calculated on the basis of Maxwell's theory, turned out to be equal to the measured speed of light in the medium. For a vacuum (and in a gas such as air), this speed is about 3×10^8 m/sec, and is usually designated by the symbol c. There were other significant predictions—for example, that a metal object would reflect a beam of incident electromagnetic energy as a mirror reflects light, and that on entering glass, water, or any other substance, the path of the beam would be bent, as is true of a beam of light. The next step is clearly that of pursuing the inevitable suggestion that "light itself is an electromagnetic disturbance."

But we must remember that the existence of electromagnetic waves was at the time solely a prediction from theory. Maxwell had not *observed* that a fluctuating electric current gives rise to such waves, nor had he measured their speeds or shown that they are of the kind that our eye interprets as light. One obvious direct test suggests itself: set up an oscillatory current in a wire at a frequency equal to the known frequency of, say, green light and watch whether green light is actually released into the surrounding region. Even before the days of radios and microwaves, it was easy enough to produce electric oscillations in wires; indeed, as early as 1842, Joseph Henry had noticed that when the two plates of a so-called Leyden jar are charged oppositely until their potential difference is large and then are connected by a coil of low resistance, the discharge through the coil appeared to consist of "a principal discharge in one direction, and then several reflex actions backward and forward, each more feeble than the preceding, until equilibrium is restored." However, the frequencies obtainable by any such method were relatively low, and even today the frequencies producible with modern electronic circuits can hardly be pushed above 10^{12} cycles/sec, far below any of the frequencies for visible light, which range from about 4×10^{14} cycles/sec (red) to 8×10^{14} cycles/sec (violet). Consequently, a direct test of whether an oscillatory current would produce light seemed to be out of the question. Maxwell's theory, partly for this reason and partly because it was so radically new, failed to attract much attention for two decades to come.

29.4 Hertz's experiments.   In 1887–1888 the gifted experimentalist Heinrich Hertz (Fig. 29.7) set out to determine whether at least the main predictions of Maxwell's theory were valid, namely, whether electric charges undergoing acceleration actually do radiate detectable electromagnetic waves, and if so, whether these waves do have all the characteristics of light (except visibility).   Of course he had no expectation of being able to produce visible light with his oscillator, the frequency of which did not exceed about 5×10^8 cycles/sec.   But his confirmations of all of Maxwell's other main predictions were so brilliantly successful that hardly one important physicist remained unconvinced.

In essence, Hertz's experimental method was simple.   Two polished metal spheres were supported so that there was an air gap between them

Fig. 29.7. Heinrich Hertz (1857–1894).

(Fig. 29.8). A pair of wires connected the spheres to a device known as an induction or "spark" coil. This device built up large electric charges of opposite signs on the two spheres, and soon the potential difference of the spheres became so large that the air in the gap between them was ionized, thus providing a conducting path along which a spark occurred.

This spark, like the discharge described by Henry (Section 29.3),
was oscillatory; the ions in the gap
moved back and forth until equilibrium was again restored. Then,
with the air again rendered noncon-
ductive, the stage was set for the

FIG. 29.8. Hertz's spark gap.

next build-up of potential difference followed by another oscillatory spark. If Maxwell's arguments were right, an electromagnetic wave should be broadcast during the occurrence of each spark, and the frequency of oscillation of the charges should determine the frequency of the electro-magnetic wave.

To see whether the waves could be detected in the surrounding region, Hertz devised a receiver (antenna) made simply of a piece of wire with a small, polished sphere on each end, and bent into a circle so as to form a short spark gap between the spheres. If electromagnetic waves were spreading out and reaching the receiver wire, they should produce a current in it, alternating in direction with the oscillations of the trans-mitter. Hertz obtained an induced current, as observed by sparks across the receiver gap. This was a historic triumph—the transmission and detection of electromagnetic signals. Moreover, he was able to detect them even when his receiver was many meters away from the transmitter.

Extending his experiments, Hertz showed that electric conductors such as metals reflect the waves; that a large, concave metallic reflector brings the waves to a focus, as it would light waves; that electric non-conductors such as wood allow the waves largely to pass through them and bend their paths; and so on. The measured wavelength of the elec-tromagnetic waves in the air turned out to be 9.6 m when the frequency ν of the transmitter was 3×10^7 cycles/sec. Using Eq. (29.1), Hertz computed the speed v of the waves to be $v = \nu\lambda = (3 \times 10^7$ cycles/sec$) \times 9.6$ m $= 3 \times 10^8$ m/sec. This is the same as the speed c of light in air! In brief, Hertz was able to verify all of Maxwell's major predictions concerning the properties of electromagnetic waves.

This new invisible radiation produced by Hertz, still sometimes called "Hertzian waves," is of course identical in character with the now familiar radio waves. Such waves have some properties different from the higher-frequency waves identified as visible light; for example, Hertz himself showed that they will pass through nonconductors that are not transparent to light, which explains why an indoor radio antenna may work very well. Yet the Hertzian waves and light (as well as thermal radiation) had been shown to be so alike in fundamental properties as to leave little doubt that light also is electromagnetic in character. As Hertz expressed it: "The described experiments appear, at least to me, in a high degree suited to remove doubt in the identity of light, heat radiation, and electrodynamic wave motion."

An arresting prediction immediately followed: light too may well result from acceleration of charged particles, perhaps from the oscillation of particles in the atoms of the light emitter. In 1896, impressive, even sensational, support for this hypothesis was provided by P. Zeeman in Holland. He found that when a sodium flame is placed between the poles of a very strong magnet, the light emitted by the glowing gas undergoes small but measurable changes in frequency. Immediately, an explanation of this new phenomenon was given by the Dutch theoretical physicist, H. A. Lorentz. His analysis showed that when the electric charges in the atoms of the glowing sodium vapor are in the magnetic field, they are subjected to forces due to the field. These forces result in a change of the frequency of oscillation and of the emitted light. Moreover, the frequency change calculated from Maxwell's theory was found to be just equal to the observed change. From this known frequency change and the value of the magnetic field intensity H that Zeeman had used, Lorentz made a calculation which indicated that the oscillating charges producing the light have the charge of electrons.

This picture of light as electromagnetic waves emitted by submicroscopic electric oscillators, although still somewhat vague, was soon to afford explanations of many phenomena that long had been puzzling. We now turn to a brief account of some basic properties of light that were known at the turn of the 20th century, and then we shall see to what extent these explanations were satisfactory.

SUPPLEMENTARY READING

KOLIN, A., *Physics, its laws, ideas, and methods* (McGraw-Hill, 1950), Chaps. 25 (oscillatory motion) and 26 (wave propagation).

MAGIE, W. F., *A source book in physics* (McGraw-Hill, 1935), pp. 528, 538. Extracts from papers of Maxwell and Rowland.

MAXWELL, J. C., *A treatise on electricity and magnetism* (three editions, 1873, 1881, and 1891; third edition reprinted by Dover, 1954), especially Maxwell's preface.

TAYLOR, L. W., *Physics, the pioneer science* (Houghton Mifflin, 1941), Chap. 49.

Part VIII

THE QUANTUM PHYSICS OF LIGHT AND MATTER

THE QUANTUM PHYSICS OF LIGHT AND MATTER

To most scientists of the late 19th century, the physical world, despite all its superficial complexity, appeared to be endowed with a truly superb unity. The mechanics of Galileo and Newton explained the motion of all bodies—whether everyday objects or planets. Furthermore, the kinetic-molecular theory had triumphantly extended the reign of this mechanics into submicroscopic worlds by interpreting most phenomena of heat as the motion of atoms. Sound, too, had become a branch of mechanics, having been analyzed as a vibrating disturbance traveling among the molecules, according to those same classical laws of motion. Earlier there had been hope that even light might be dealt with as a mechanical wave motion traveling through a material fluid, but although this attractive picture had to be abandoned, its successor did not seem to be in contradiction with classical physics.

There were still many important unsolved problems, but in the 1880's and 1890's one could be confident that eventually the old mechanical concepts would provide the required solution. However, in 1900 there appeared a startling publication by Max Planck that threw doubt upon the most basic concepts. Other key contributions followed within the next few years, from the pens of Einstein, Rutherford, and Bohr. These four men were the standard bearers of a revolution that transformed physics fundamentally. What they did was to change completely the picture of the atom and particularly the way in which atoms absorb or emit the energy of radiation. The revised model gave us the new, larger unity, the new meeting ground of modern science. It not only resolved at one stroke some great problems and many minor puzzles of long standing, but, by providing a common mechanism basic to each of the physical sciences, it also brought together the work of such divergent groups as astrophysicists and industrial chemists. The growth of science became virtually explosive, the harvest in pure and applied knowledge unparalleled, the promise for future developments without limits.

How had this happened? Let us devote this section to that revolution. If our primary aim is again to study the facts and theories of physical science, we shall also find time here for some related tasks. It will become clear, for example, how the new concept of the atom differs from the old, what features in the older theories had all along hidden their own seeds of destruction, and what the experimental facts were which demanded a change in the model as well as in the outlook and methods in the physical sciences.

CHAPTER 30

SOME OPTICAL PRINCIPLES

30.1 Some early optical developments. Optics, like mechanics, is an old science—much older than the science of electricity and magnetism surveyed in the past several chapters. The concept of "rays" of light and the belief that such rays are straight lines in a uniform medium extend far back into antiquity. The Greeks knew that when a ray of light is reflected by a mirror the angle of reflection is equal to the angle of incidence. They knew that when a light ray passes from one transparent medium into another of different density, it will generally be bent or, as we now say, refracted. Aristotle, for example, described the apparent bending of an oar dipped into water. The astronomer Ptolemy reported experiments in which a narrow beam of light was directed from air onto water at a number of different angles of incidence θ_1, and the corresponding angles θ_2 of refraction were measured [Fig. 30.1(a)]. He described similar experiments with beams bent in passing from air to glass and from water to glass. Ptolemy concluded that for a given pair of media, the ratio θ_1/θ_2 of the angle of incidence to that of refraction is constant. That this rule is valid only for very small angles of incidence was pointed out much later, in the 11th century, by the Arabian scholar Alhazen. A book on optics written by Alhazen was to remain a standard authority on the subject up to the 17th century.

In the early part of the 17th century, Kepler, in addition to his astronomical work, was deeply and competently interested in such optical subjects as vision and refraction, including the refractive effects produced

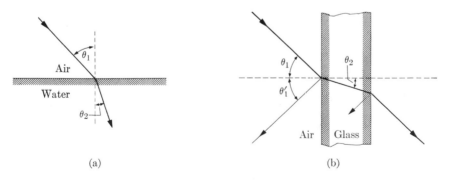

(a)   (b)

FIG. 30.1. Refraction of a light ray by a slab of glass. Some of the light is also reflected at each interface; note in (b) that θ_1 and θ_1' denote angles of incidence and of reflection, and θ_2 the angle of refraction.

543

by lenses of different sorts. Of the two books on optics that he published, the second (1611) contains important work that was stimulated by the discovery of the telescope.

Like Ptolemy and some of the medieval opticians, Kepler made numerous measurements of angles of incidence and corresponding angles of refraction for various pairs of substances but was unable to find a relationship between them that was valid for all angles. A few years later, in 1621, Willebrord Snell, a professor of mathematics at Leiden, formulated the relationship that still bears his name. Snell's law of refraction is now usually stated in the form,

$$\sin \theta_1 / \sin \theta_2 = \mu, \tag{30.1}$$

where θ_1 and θ_2 are the angles of incidence and refraction and μ (Greek letter mu) is called the *index of refraction* of the second medium with respect to the first. For example, measurements with a beam of visible light show that the index of refraction μ for water relative to air is about 1.3, and that for crown glass relative to air it is about 1.5. Incidentally, a relation of the form of Eq. (30.1) is useful for determining the refractive index of any type of wave, e.g., sound waves.

EXAMPLE 30.1. Suppose that a narrow beam of light passes from air into crown glass at an angle of incidence of 30°. Predict (a) the value of the angle of refraction, and (b) the angle through which the path of the ray is deviated as a result of the refraction.

Solution. (a) From Eq. (30.1), $\sin \theta_2 = \sin \theta_1 / \mu = \sin 30°/1.5 = 0.50/1.5 = 0.33$; therefore, from Appendix F, $\theta_2 = 19°$. (b) The angle of deviation is $30° - 19° = 11°$.

PROBLEM 30.1. (a) For the air-to-glass interface of Example 30.1, compute the angles of refraction for angles of incidence of 0° and of 45°. (b) The path of a beam of light in Fig. 30.1(a) is reversible, that is, light originating inside the water and incident at the surface at angle θ_2 is refracted away from the normal on leaving the water and proceeds at angle θ_1 in air. For such a beam, what is the angle of approach to the surface if, on emerging, the refracted beam just glances along the surface of the water?

PROBLEM 30.2. Show that for very small angles of incidence Snell's law of refraction reduces to the law proposed by Ptolemy.

PROBLEM 30.3. The index of refraction of air relative to vacuum is 1.00029. Show how the phenomenon of refraction may be used to explain why celestial bodies appear to us slightly higher above the horizon than they actually are.

This very brief account of some of the optical phenomena known and studied through the beginning of the modern period is intended mainly to render more meaningful several remarkable discoveries now to be recounted. The first of these, that light exhibits the phenomenon called *diffraction*, seemingly contradicted the ancient and highly useful rule that light, so long as it is in a medium having constant properties, always travels in straight lines.

30.2 Grimaldi's discovery of diffraction. Francesco Maria Grimaldi (1618–1663), professor of mathematics at the University of Bologna, described his extensive and highly competent optical researches in a book that was published in 1665, shortly after his death. Our interest now is in his discovery of diffraction. In one of Grimaldi's experiments a narrow beam of sunlight was entering through a small hole in the window shutter into a darkened room. Upon placing in the path of this beam an opaque screen containing a tiny hole, he observed that the area of light cast on the opposite wall was slightly larger than one would expect on the assumption that the light rays had passed through the hole in straight lines. In another experiment, Grimaldi put a tiny obstacle in the path of the beam and found its shadow on the wall to be smaller than that to be expected if the light had passed the edges of the object in straight lines. In both experiments, Grimaldi noticed that the edges of the spot of light and of the shadow on the wall were bounded by narrow fringes of color. He also observed that the amount that light bends from its straight path, or *diffracts*, is exceedingly small and is observable only if the aperture used in the experiment is small also.

Diffraction is characteristic of wave motions of all kinds, although the effect becomes appreciable only if the dimensions of the aperture or obstacle are not large compared with the wavelength involved. Thus in Fig. 30.2, water ripples are noticeably diffracted at an aperture having about the same width as the ripple wavelength, that is, the distance between the ripple crests. Water waves entering a harbor through a comparatively large opening in a breakwater similarly spread into the region behind the breakwater. Sound waves can be perceived behind an obstacle such as the trunk of a tree unless the frequency of the sound is extremely high and the wavelength therefore correspondingly small. But a very large object, such as a hill, will cast a sound shadow that is fairly definite.

Diffraction and refraction must not be confused. A ray will be refracted at a definite angle, and also partly reflected, at the interface between two media in which the speed of propagation is different. Diffraction, on the other hand, shows up as an un-sharp diffusion of energy into the geometric shadow, and it is not due to any change in the medium, but occurs upon the passage of a ray past the edge of an obstacle. This presents a puzzle which, as we shall see, was not solved for about 150 years.

PROBLEM 30.4. Assuming that diffraction becomes important only for wavelengths of the same order of magnitude as the width of the aperture, compute the maximum width of a rectangular slit that will produce appreciable diffraction

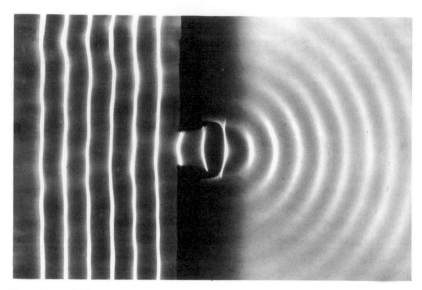

FIG. 30.2. Diffraction of water ripples. Beyond the aperture the ripples spread out in all directions just as if the aperture were now their source, as if a pebble, say, had been dropped into the water at the aperture. (By permission, from Webster, Farwell, and Drew's *General physics for colleges*, Appleton-Century-Crofts, Inc., 1923.)

of sound of frequency (a) 150 cycles/sec, which is in the region of predominant frequency components of the male speaking voice, and (b) 16,000 cycles/sec, which is about the upper limit of the audible range. (Take the speed of sound in air at room temperature to be 343 m/sec.)

30.3 Newton and the spectrum. How to explain the production of colors was another difficult problem for early investigators. Rainbows had always excited curiosity, and as early as the 14th century they were being ascribed to multiple refractions and reflections of sunlight in raindrops. Glass prisms as means for producing colors had also long attracted attention. Grimaldi, for example, made careful experiments with prisms.

Newton became interested in color theory while he was still an undergraduate, when he set out to construct an astronomical telescope. One of the troublesome defects of such an instrument was a colored border that always surrounded the image formed by the main telescope lens. It was perhaps in an attempt to understand this particular defect that he began his extensive study of color. In 1672 he published a theory of the nature of color in the *Philosophical Transactions*. It was his first scientific paper. To quote the opening paragraphs:

  . . . in the beginning of the year 1666 (at which time I applied myself to the grinding of optic glasses of other figures than spherical) I procured me a triangular glass prism, to try therewith the celebrated phenomena of colors. And in order thereto having darkened my chamber and made a small [round] hole in my window shuts, to let in a convenient quantity of the sun's light, I placed my prism at this entrance, that it might be thereby refracted to the opposite wall. It was at first a pleasing divertissement to view the vivid and intense colors produced thereby; but after a while applying myself to consider them more circumspectly, I became surprised to see them in an oblong form; which, according to the received laws of refraction, I expected should have been *circular* . . .

Comparing the length of this colored spectrum [sic] with its breadth, I found it about five times greater, a disproportion so extravagant that it excited me to a more than ordinary curiosity of examining from whence it might proceed.

The cylindrical beam of white light from the circular opening had passed through the prism and produced on the opposite wall an elongated, rather than a circular, patch of colored light which was violet at one end, red at the other, and with a continuous gradation of colors in between (Fig. 30.3). For such a pattern of colors, Newton invented the name *spectrum*.

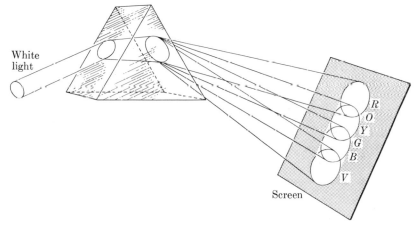

Fig. 30.3. Dispersion of white light by a prism.

But from where do the colors come, and why is the image spread out rather than circular? Seeking an explanation, Newton passed the light through different thicknesses of the glass, changed the size of the hole in the window, and even placed the prism outside the window. But he "found none of these circumstances material. The fashion of the colors was in all these cases the same." To test whether some unevenness or irregularity in the glass produced the phenomenon, he passed the colored rays due to one prism through a second prism turned in the reverse direction. If some irregularity in the glass was responsible, then the passage through the second prism should increase the dispersion still more. Instead, the second prism served to bring the colors back together to form a spot of *white* light, as if the light had not passed through either prism (Fig. 30.4). As Newton said, "whatever was the cause of that length [of the spectral image], it was not any contingent irregularity."

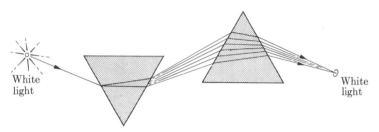

FIG. 30.4. When the spectral colors dispersed by the first prism are passed through a second prism, they combine to form a spot of white light.

By such a process of elimination, Newton convinced himself of a belief that he probably had held from the beginning: white light is composed of colors; it is not the prism that manufactures the colors. Instead, when white light passes through a prism, each of the component colors is *refracted at a different angle*, thus accounting for the dispersion or spreading out of the beam into an elongated spectrum. Figure 30.5 illustrates one of Newton's many tests of this hypothesis. In a screen upon which the spectrum from the prism fell he cut a small hole, so that a thin beam of essentially *monochromatic* (single-colored) light could pass through it. This beam continued on through a similar hole in another screen and then passed through a second prism. He then could note to what place on the wall this second prism would refract the beam. By slowly rotating the first prism, he caused monochromatic beams of the various colors to pass

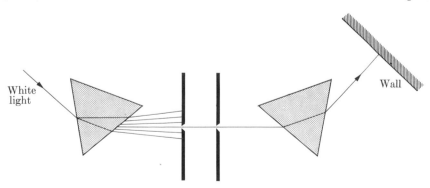

FIG. 30.5. Newton's *"experimentum crucis."*

through the pair of holes and, for each beam, noted the position of the colored spot on the wall. Thus he showed that for the same angle of incidence on the second prism, violet light was refracted the most and red the least. The elongated spectrum produced by a prism could therefore be thought of as an infinite number of overlapping circular spots, each of a different color, ranging from violet through blue, green, and yellow to red. Newton found that the amount of overlapping could be reduced by making the hole in the window shutter smaller. Later he replaced the circular hole by a rectangular slit, and found that when a prism is mounted so that its refracting edge is parallel to the slit, the spectrum formed is an infinite number of overlapping, colored rectangles. In modern work on resolving a beam of light into its color components, a slit is almost always used to define the beam.

In terms of Snell's law of refraction, Eq. (30.1), which Newton repeatedly used in his work, the discovery Newton had made was that the index of refraction μ of the prism glass has a slightly different value for each different color. Snell's law, which originally had been enunciated for white light as a whole, holds for each color individually, and is valid for all interfaces where refraction occurs. As an example, the index of refraction, relative to air, of a certain kind of crown glass is 1.538 for violet light and 1.520 for red light. For any transparent material, these indexes can be accurately measured by shaping a sample in the form of a prism and using a *spectrometer* (Fig. 30.6) to measure the angles of deviation of the refracted light. This important instrument is also used to study spectra and various other optical phenomena. When the telescope is arranged to record the spectrum on photographic film, the instrument is called a *spectrograph*.

PROBLEM 30.5. Suppose that a narrow beam of white light passes from air into a crown glass prism at an angle of incidence of 30°. Compute the angle of refraction into the prism for (a) violet light, (b) red light. (c) If the prism has 60° angles on all 3 sides, at what angles of deviation will the violet and the red beams emerge?

PROBLEM 30.6. For producing a spectrum, why is a prism better than a parallel-sided slab of the same kind of glass (Fig. 30.1)?

Although Newton himself was aware of the importance of his researches on colors, many contemporary scientists were slow in accepting or understanding the work, and some were even bitterly critical of it. This had the good effect that Newton, in preparing answers to these criticisms, found himself developing still further his views on the nature of light. On the other hand, his celebrated treatise, *Opticks*, in which he collected together nearly all of his work on light, was withheld by him from publication until 1704, many years after he had completed it, so as "to avoid being in disputes about these matters." Even a century later, his views on optics and on mechanics as well were still under attack, now mainly by a group of

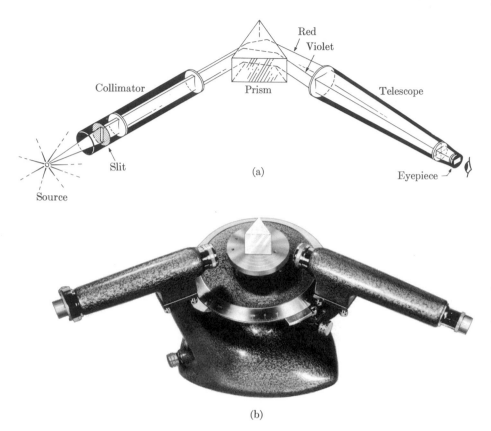

FIG. 30.6. Essential components of a simple prism spectrometer. The rays from the light source pass through the slit, are rendered parallel by the *collimator* lens, and then are refracted by the *prism*, which is mounted on a circular, graduated table that can be rotated. Finally, the rays pass through the first *telescope* lens, which forms an image of the spectrum at the cross hairs, and the observer views this image through the magnifying *eyepiece*. The telescope is mounted to rotate horizontally, so that the angles of deviation of the rays can be measured. (Courtesy of Ealing Corporation.)

philosophers in Germany, among them Schelling and Hegel, who were trying to develop a theory of nature on a foundation free of what they felt to be the taint of experimentation. This attempt was partly responsible for the separation between philosophy and science that to this day is still detrimental to the advance of both.

It should be said of Newton's *Opticks* that it described a far larger range of work than we have covered here, for example his studies of color pigments, colors produced by thin films, the phenomenon known as polarization of light, and finally, diffraction, for which he devised experiments more refined and of far greater variety than Grimaldi's. Although the book also contains all of Newton's theory of light, it is essentially an experimental treatise, recording dozens of experiments that he performed himself. This is in marked contrast with the *Principia*, in the many hundreds of pages of which Newton recorded only three groups of experiments of his own making. But in the *Principia* his concern was with unification of the very old fields of terrestrial mechanics and planetary motion (Chapters 4 and 11), and the observations and experiments which he needed to support this conceptual scheme were already available in the writings of his predecessors. Optics, too, was already an old field, but for the optical phenomena of most interest to Newton, such as color production and diffraction, he evidently felt that the experiments others had performed before him were not adequate for his purposes.

30.4 The particle and wave theories of light. The notion that light consists of tiny particles of matter emitted by the light source can be traced back to the Greek atomists (Section 21.1). Aristotle, who had rejected atomism, held that light is not made up of particles but is some kind of action occurring in a transparent medium filling the space between the eye and the object seen. Two millenia later, in the 17th century, something more than speculation became possible with the discovery of diffraction and a growing knowledge of such phenomena as color. Grimaldi's experiments led him to think that light has a periodic quality; for example, upon being diffracted light seemed to act as water waves do when they spread out upon passing an obstacle. In 1665 Robert Hooke, one of Newton's most bitter critics, spoke of light spreading out from a source like "the rings of waves on the surface of the water."

Any satisfactory theory of the nature of light must take into account the question whether light travels with a finite speed or whether it moves instantaneously from light source to observer—a question that had been debated since the time of the Greeks. A definite answer based on observation was not forthcoming until 1676, from the Danish astronomer, Olaf Roemer. He had assisted in making observations of the eclipses of the innermost satellite of Jupiter (Fig. 30.7), and he noted that the time interval elapsing between successive disappearances of the

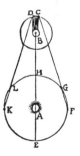

Fig. 30.7. Roemer's method for determining the velocity of light. Jupiter (at *B*) casts a shadow (*D* to *C*) lying across the path of one of its satellites. Observations of the period of the satellite are made when the earth is at different points in its orbit around the sun.

satellite behind Jupiter (or reappearances from Jupiter's shadow) seemed to be longer while the earth in its orbit was moving away from Jupiter than while it was approaching. The time from one eclipse to the next is observed to be $42\frac{1}{2}$ hours while the earth is not moving away from or toward Jupiter (at E and H in Fig. 30.7), but when the earth is moving away from Jupiter at its greatest relative speed, the apparent period is 14 seconds longer.

Roemer now showed that this observation could be accounted for by assuming that the speed of light is finite, for while the earth was moving away from Jupiter, each new "message" that an eclipse had again taken place had to travel farther and longer than the last previous message to catch up with the earth, but while the earth was approaching Jupiter, it would intercept this "message" earlier. Counting up the successive delays in receiving the "message" as the earth moves from a position nearest Jupiter to the opposite point on its orbit, Roemer could estimate that the total time needed for light to cross along a diameter of the earth's orbit was 22 minutes (the modern value is 17 minutes). Because this diameter is large, the indication was that the speed of light in empty space, although indeed finite, must be exceedingly large; its value is now known to be 2.99793×10^8 m/sec. Some of Roemer's contemporaries attacked his conclusions as implying a ridiculously large speed of light, whereas others continued to believe that the speed of light is infinite.

PROBLEM 30.7. (a) One of Roemer's colleagues, G. D. Cassini, determined the diameter of the earth's orbit to be about 180,000 mi (2.9×10^{11} m); show that this value, together with Roemer's 22 min for the passage of light, yields 2.2×10^8 m/sec as the speed of light in empty space. (b) Using present-day values for the speed of light in empty space and for the average diameter of the earth's orbit (see Appendix A), compute the time in minutes required for light to traverse this diameter.

In 1678, Christiaan Huygens cited Roemer's demonstration of the finite but extremely high speed of light as an argument against the hypothesis that light consists of particles, and proceeded to develop a theory in which light was pictured as a wave motion in an all-pervading ether. He assumed the waves to be longitudinal, as are sound waves (Section 29.2), and to be transmitted by means of the impact of one elastic "aether-molecule" upon another. Unlike sound waves, light in this scheme was not periodic, i.e., was not a regular sequence of equidistant wave pulses, but rather an irregular succession of isolated pulses. Although it was eventually established that light waves are transverse rather than longitudinal and are periodic in character, Huygens' theory nevertheless served to correlate and explain many of the optical phenomena known at that time. In particular, Huygens considered the refraction of a beam of light coming from air into glass or water as due to the slowing down of the waves in the latter media. To explain the refractive index of $\mu = 1.3$ for water, for example, he had to assume that the speed of light waves in water is 1.3 times smaller than in air. A direct measurement of the speed of light in water was, of course, not possible at that time, and the decisive test of this theory had to wait for nearly two centuries.

In the meantime, a rival theory of the nature of light arose out of the work of Newton. No one in the 17th century had contributed more to the theory of sound and water waves than had Newton, but in the case of light he held to the view that it consisted of streams of particles emitted by the light source rather than of waves. His chief objection to the wave theory was that it did not appear to explain why light travels in straight lines in any given medium. If light is a wave motion in the ether, should not rays of light show "a continual and very extravagant spreading and bending every way into the quiescent medium . . . ?" The answer seemed to be clearly "yes," and no refutation was forthcoming during Newton's lifetime.

Huygens, in his wave theory, had not covered color phenomena. To Newton, such phenomena provided the strongest evidence that light has a periodic character, and to account for this periodicity, he incorporated in his particle theory a postulate admitting the existence of waves—not of light waves, but rather of waves produced in the ether by the particles of light (1672):

> Assuming the rays of light to be small bodies, emitted every way from shining substances, those, when they impinge on any refracting or reflecting superficies, must as necessarily excite vibrations in the aether [inside the refracting or reflecting medium] as stones do in water when thrown into it.

Thus, to account for color sensations, Newton suggested that the various colored rays may produce vibrations of various "bignesses" (frequencies) and thus excite sensations of the various colors, "much after the manner that the vibrations of the air, according to their several bignesses, excite sensations of several sounds." As for diffraction, Newton well knew that this phenomenon is exhibited by sound and water waves. But to explain the relatively much smaller bending of light on passing near the edge of an obstacle, he suggested that the ether near the edge might be less dense than it is away from the obstacle, in which case the bending could be attributed to refraction rather than to diffraction.

As will be recalled, according to Huygens' wave theory light generally slows down upon entering a denser medium. Newton, on the other hand, considered his particles of light to be attracted by the denser medium and therefore accelerated upon entering it. For example, to Newton the speed of light in water should be equal to the speed in air *multiplied* (not divided) by 1.3. Although this immediately suggested a test between the wave and particle theories, a method sensitive enough to compare the speeds of light in different media was not forthcoming until 1850, when the French physicist J. B. L. Foucault, using newly developed and relatively costly equipment which he fortunately had the private means to acquire, succeeded in measuring the speed of light in water. Foucault found it to be smaller than the speed in air by a factor of 1.3. It seemed clear, therefore, that the wave theory had triumphed over the Newtonian corpuscular theory of light.

To Newton himself, this would not have been entirely unexpected. In replying to one of the many criticisms of his views by Hooke, Newton had said:

> Tis true, that from my theory I argue the corporeity of light; but I do it without any absolute positiveness . . . I knew, that the *properties*, which I declar'd of *light*, were in some measure capable of being explicated not only by that, but by many other mechanical hypotheses.

It is evident that Newton himself felt that acceptance of his experimental discoveries did not necessarily require that those who held to the wave theory had to abandon it. Nevertheless, the majority of his successors had attributed to him complete rejection of the wave picture and, supposing his authority to be wholly on their side, had tenaciously held to the particle theory.

30.5 Interference of light. Prior to Foucault's experiment the wave theory of light was revived in a fruitful manner by Thomas Young (1773–1829), physician, linguist, scientist in many fields, and one of the most erudite figures in the history of the sciences. While still in medical school, Young made original studies of the eye, and later developed the first version of what is known as the three-primary-color theory of vision. For his doctoral thesis, Young investigated the human voice, which led him into the physics of sound and sound waves. Turning to the study of physical optics, he carefully examined Newton's experiments and concluded that they were so completely explainable in terms of waves as to justify abandonment of any particle theory of light.

Young's most convincing evidence in favor of the wave picture centered on his discovery, first published by him in 1802, that light exhibits the phenomenon of *interference*. Newton himself had developed the idea of interference of waves to explain an anomalous tide effect in an ocean port where the tidal motion of the water comes from two directions, but apparently Newton did not think to apply the idea of interference to optics. Young, to illustrate his own conception of interference, in 1804 cited the example of two trains of water waves with the same wavelength or frequency traveling on the surface of a lake with the same speed, and meeting at the entrance to a channel leading out of the lake. If they meet in such a manner that the crests of one wave train coincide with the equally high crests of the other, and similarly for the troughs, the wave trains are said to be *in phase*, and the resultant wave train passing through the channel will have crests twice as high as the original crests, and troughs twice as deep. But if the two wave trains are directly out of phase, i.e., so meet that the crests of one coincide with the troughs of the other, they will cancel each other and there will be no wave train in the channel. The former effect is called *constructive interference* and the latter, *destructive interference*. For destructive interference to be complete, the two wave trains must not only be exactly out of phase when they meet, but they must also have the same amplitudes, i.e., their crests and their troughs must be of the same magnitudes.

Turning to optics, Young showed that interference of light waves can account for the color patterns observed by Newton when white light incident on a thin film is reflected to the eye. Examples familiar to everyone are the colors of soap bubbles and of films of oil on a water surface, which are explained as follows. The thin film reflects some light from the front surface and some light from the back surface, and these two beams arrive together at the retina. Now suppose that the difference of distance traveled from the two surfaces to the eye is effectively half a wavelength of red light or, using modern values, about $\frac{1}{2} \times (7 \times 10^{-5})$ cm; then the *red* component of light will not be seen because the "crests" of the wave coming from one surface are canceled by the "troughs" of the wave coming from the other, and vice versa. (In terms of the electromagnetic theory of light waves, developed much later, the "crests" can be taken to correspond to regions X and Y in Fig. 29.6, where the **E**-vectors have their maximum values, and the "troughs" correspond to regions P and Q, where the **E**-vectors have their minimum values. Destructive interference is therefore due to cancellation of the two fields.)

On the other hand, the difference of $\frac{1}{2} \times (7 \times 10^{-5})$ cm corresponds to a *full* wavelength of *blue* light, and therefore the blue component of the reflected white light from the same region where red light has destructive interference will appear to be fully reenforced (in terms of the electromagnetic theory, the **E**-vectors of light of the wavelength corresponding to blue light here coincide in phase, and therefore add their effects). For different film thicknesses, different components of light have destructive and constructive interferences, and so different hues can be observed to predominate over the whole surface. Conversely, if the thickness of the film in a given region is known by measurement, the wavelength of the predominant hue can be calculated on the assumption that interference is responsible for it. Using data on the colors of thin films recorded by Newton himself and supplementing them with measurements of his own, Young deduced the approximate wavelengths for several parts of the spectrum.

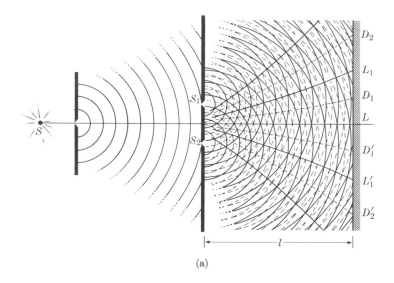

(a)

(b)

FIG. 30.8. Schematic plan of Young's double-slit experiment; not to scale. For the waves from either slit, S_1 or S_2, the distance between adjacent "crests" (solid half-circles) is grossly exaggerated. This distance, the wavelength, is actually about 5×10^{-5} cm for green light. Also, the distance l to the viewing screen has to be much larger than the separation between the double slits.

This brings us to the threshold of a truly spectacular achievement of physical science that will be fully appreciated in a quantitative discussion, namely the precise measurement, accurate to the highest degree, of as unimaginably small a distance as one wavelength of light. The method is exhibited in another experiment of Thomas Young's. Building on the general idea used above to explain the interference of two merging trains of water waves, he showed that when light from a common source is passed through two narrow and closely adjacent slits in a screen, the two beams emerging from the slits interfere where they partially overlap and form a pattern of alternate light and dark bands. In Fig. 30.8(a), S is a source of monochromatic light (light of a single wavelength or, for practical purposes, light from a very narrow portion of the whole spectrum). This light passes through the two narrow rectangular slits S_1 and S_2; as in Fig. 30.2, each slit acts as a new source of the light waves, and these spread out and overlap with the waves from the other slit. In Fig. 30.8, the continuous semicircles represent wave "crests"; the dashed semicircles, shown in (a) only, represent wave "troughs." Along the solid lines drawn from the slits to the viewing screen, "crests" coincide with "crests," and "troughs" with "troughs"; hence along these lines constructive interference occurs, and bands of light L, L_1, etc. appear on the screen, each brighter than either wave train alone could produce. But along the dotted lines, "crests" always coincide with "troughs," and destructive interference occurs; hence no light reaches the screen at the dark bands D_1, D_2, etc. On viewing the whole screen, the pattern is seen to consist of alternate light and dark bands (Fig. 30.9). Young, the first to demonstrate the "double-slit experiment," also pointed out that this interference pattern is immediately destroyed when either of the two slits is covered up.

The same phenomenon of interference can be demonstrated with waves other than those of light, for example with sound or with water ripples. In Fig. 30.10, the wave systems from two sources of ripples on the surface of water are seen to set up an interference pattern closely analogous to that in Young's double-slit experiment; along the lines of destructive interference, the water surface is seen to be not agitated.

Fig. 30.9. Photograph of an interference pattern of light from a double slit. (By permission, from Sears' *Optics*, Addison-Wesley, 1949.)

FIG. 30.10. Interference of two ripple systems on a water surface. (After Grimsehl, *A textbook of physics*.)

The double-slit experiment may be used to determine the wavelength λ of monochromatic light. Consider Fig. 30.11; the two slits S_1 and S_2 are equidistant from the source S, and thus the wave trains arrive at the slits in phase. The light waves from the slits that reach the center band L travel equal distances S_1L and S_2L and hence arrive at L in phase. The next bright band, to one side of L, is found to be at L_1 (or L_1'); to produce this bright band, the waves reaching L_1 from the two slits S_1 and S_2 must also be in phase. But here the two path lengths are unequal, differing by the amount $(S_2L_1 - S_1L_1)$, or CS_2. Hence, if crests (or troughs) from the two slits are to arrive in phase at L_1, the path difference CS_2 must be equal to the distance between successive "crests," or between successive "troughs," of either wave train. In other words, CS_2 must represent one wavelength λ:

$$\lambda = CS_2 = S_2L_1 - S_1L_1. \tag{30.2}$$

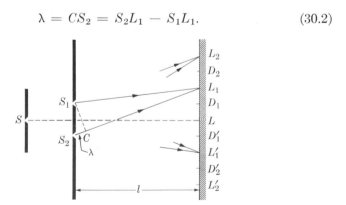

FIG. 30.11. Ray diagram for the double-slit experiment. (The distance S_1S_2 between the slits and the distances between the adjacent bright bands on the viewing screen are grossly exaggerated in order to make the diagram easier to examine.) S_2C is the difference between S_2L_1 and S_1L_1.

In principle, then, λ can be found by measuring the distances from the slits to the bright band L_1 (or L_1') and subtracting to obtain CS_2. However, a very great practical difficulty intervenes because the wavelengths of the visible colors are exceedingly small—of the orders of 10^{-4} to 10^{-5} cm. Thus CS_2 ($=\lambda$) is so small compared with the errors bound to occur in measuring S_1L_1 and S_2L_1 that Eq. (30.2) fails to yield meaningful values for λ. For a moment, this looks disappointing.

EXAMPLE 30.2. If the error in measuring lengths by a certain available method is 0.01%, what is the smallest difference between S_2L_1 and S_1L_1 that can be detected when these two lengths are each about 200 cm?

Solution. Each length can be determined to within about $0.01\% \times 200$ cm, or 0.02 cm. Thus S_2L_1 must exceed S_1L_1 by more than 0.02 cm if the difference between their measured lengths is to have any meaning. (This uncertainty in the measured lengths turns out to be 300 to 500 times larger than one wavelength of light.)

PROBLEM 30.8. In Example 30.2, what would be smallest detectable difference if the two lengths were each about 5 m?

PROBLEM 30.9. The wavelength for one of the colors in the violet region of the spectrum is 5×10^{-5} cm. In order to use Eq. (30.2) to determine this wavelength when S_1L_1 and S_2L_1 are each about 100 cm, how large a percentage error in measuring these distances would be allowable?

Although Eq. (30.2) cannot be used directly to determine wavelengths, there fortunately is a way to circumvent the difficulty. First we must note that in a typical double-slit experiment, the dimensions involved might be roughly these: distance d ($\equiv S_1S_2$) between the slits, 0.01 cm; distance x_1 ($=LL_1$) between the central and next bright band, 0.04 cm; distance l from slits to viewing screen, 100 cm. Thus l is always exceedingly large compared with d and x_1. Figure 30.12 shows what this implies geometrically. Because position L_1 is relatively so far from S_1 and S_2, no appreciable error will be introduced by treating the arc S_1C as a straight line that is

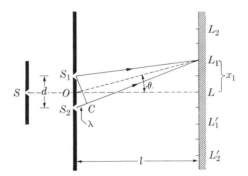

FIG. 30.12. Diagram for developing the formula for computing wavelengths.

perpendicular both to S_2L_1 and to OL_1. The small angles LOL_1 $(=\theta)$ and CS_1S_2 may therefore be regarded as essentially equal, for the pair of sides including the two angles are perpendicular to each other. This being granted, the two *right triangles* LOL_1 and CS_1S_2 are similar. In view of the geometric theorem that the ratios of corresponding sides of similar triangles are equal, we therefore have $\lambda/d = x_1/OL_1$. It follows that

$$\lambda = d \sin \theta. \tag{30.3}$$

If the angle θ is small, distance OL_1 can be replaced by the essentially equal distance l. So $\lambda/d = x_1/l$, or

$$\lambda = dx_1/l. \tag{30.4}$$

The distances d and x_1, although small, can be measured with little error by means of a microscope equipped with a scale, and if l is 1 m or more, it can be measured to 0.1% even with a meter stick.

Note how Eqs. (30.2) and (30.4) differ. The former expresses the wavelength λ as the *difference* between two large lengths. Even with a small percentage error in measuring these lengths, the error in their difference still corresponds to many wavelengths and so swamps the result to be obtained. It is as if one tried to measure the width of a north-south street in San Francisco by measuring the distance to each side of the street separately from New York and taking the difference. On the other hand, Eq. (30.4) involves ratios, not a difference; in such a case, the percentage error in the result is of the same order as in each of the factors. For example, if d, x, and l are each determined to an accuracy of 0.1%, the error in λ will also be of the order of 0.1% of one wavelength. In short, Eq. (30.4) shows that we can find the wavelength of light (a length far too small to be measured directly with such instruments as meter sticks or microscopes) with the aid of (a) a *theory* of light, and (b) a *combination of measurements*, each of the ordinary kind employing the ordinary instruments. This two-pronged attack is precisely the method by which nearly all of the "incredible" values in physical science are obtained, for example the huge values for the speed of light and for the number of molecules per mole, or the infinitesimal-sounding values for the mass and size of an atom. In the case at hand, the process for obtaining a value for λ of any color of light is further illustrated by means of the following problems.

PROBLEM 30.10. Monochromatic yellow light from a sodium vapor lamp falls on two parallel slits 0.010 cm apart. The distance between the central band and the first bright band is 0.47 cm when the viewing screen is 80 cm away. (a) Show that the wavelength in air is 5.9×10^{-5} cm. (b) Show that the frequency is about 5×10^{14} cycles/sec.

PROBLEM 30.11.   (a) Centering attention now on the *second* bright band L_2, beyond L, explain why the path difference $S_2L_2 - S_1L_2$ must be 2λ. (b) With the help of a diagram similar to Fig. 30.12, show that $2\lambda/d = x_2/l$ and therefore that

$$\lambda = dx_2/2l,$$

where x_2 ($=LL_2$) is the distance on the viewing screen between the central band and the second bright band beyond it.

PROBLEM 30.12.   If x_n ($=LL_n$) symbolizes the distance of the nth bright band from L, show that

$$\lambda = d \sin \theta / n, \tag{30.5}$$

or

$$\lambda = dx_n/nl, \tag{30.6}$$

if θ, the angle between the axis OL in Fig. 30.12 and the nth-order band, is small. The number n is known as the *order number* of the bright band. The central band is called the zeroth-order band; those at L_1 and L_1', to either side, are the first-order bands, and so forth.

PROBLEM 30.13.   Show that Eq. (30.6) embodies the experimentally verified fact that the bright bands on the viewing screen are evenly spaced (see Fig. 30.9).

PROBLEM 30.14.   In deriving Eqs. (30.3) and (30.4), we have made some approximations. Derive an equation for λ without approximations. Then solve Problem 30.10(a) with the aid of the new equation, and comment on the difference between the results obtained with the two equations.

PROBLEM 30.15.   Monochromatic red light from a cadmium vapor lamp illuminates a double slit of separation 0.0183 cm. On a viewing screen 100.0 cm away, the distance between the central band and the 4th bright band is found to be 1.40 cm. For this red light, compute (a) the wavelength in air, and (b) the frequency.

PROBLEM 30.16.   Review Sections 23.7 and 28.3 and then show that the mass of an individual atom has also been determined by (a) using a theory as a basis, and (b) combining a set of measured values, each of which can be obtained with ordinary instruments.

30.6 The grating spectrometer.   If we use sunlight rather than monochromatic light in the double-slit experiment, the central band L (Fig. 30.11) is white, because all the colors (wavelengths) inherent in the original beam of sunlight are superposed on one another at L. However, at each of the other bright bands, that is, at L_1, L_1', L_2, L_2', ..., the colors are not superposed on one another, but are dispersed into a spectrum. Consider, for example, the first-order band L_1 (or L_1'). As Eq. (30.4) shows, x_1 ($=LL_1$ or LL_1') is given by $\lambda l/d$, and so will be smallest for the shortest wavelength λ (at the violet end of the visible spectrum) and greatest for the longest wavelength (at the red end). This is true for the other bands, L_2 and L_2', etc. In each "order" except the central band, a spectrum is formed on the viewing screen; the colors in each band run from violet at the end nearer to the central axis to red at the farther end (where it may overlap with the beginning of the next order spectrum).

Thus the double slit and the prism can both disperse light into a spectrum, but with several important differences. First of all, the double-slit experiment enables us to obtain a value for the wavelength corresponding to each part of the spectrum, while this is possible with the prism only if the refractive index is known beforehand for each wavelength; in effect, we have to "calibrate" a prism spectroscope with light of known wavelengths, and these can be found only by the double-slit method or something equivalent to it. A second difference is rather incidental: the arrangement of the colors in each of the diffraction spectra is just the opposite from that in a prismatic spectrum (Fig. 30.3); in the former case, blue light is deviated less than red, in the latter case, red is deviated less than blue.

But a third difference between the action of prisms and of the double slit in producing spectra has serious practical implications. The amount of light that passes through one pair of narrow slits is small; moreover, in contrast with a prism, which disperses all of the incident light into a single spectrum, the pair of slits distributes it to form an undispersed central (zero-order) band and numerous higher-order spectra. Thus each band may be dim and difficult to observe. The intensity of the spectra improves if more than two parallel, equally spaced slits are used, as was shown by Joseph Fraunhofer (1787–1826). Fraunhofer stretched many very fine wires parallel to one another and showed that the light passing through the "slits" between the wires forms the same pattern on a viewing screen as does a single pair of slits, except that each colored band is brighter and more sharply defined. In essence, the effect of each pair of slits in the set is superposed on the neighboring pair. Fraunhofer, who had been using a prism spectrometer to obtain spectra, now replaced the prism with the set of wires, or *diffraction grating*, as a multi-slit arrangement is now called (Fig. 30.13). With this *grating spectrometer*, to which Eq. (30.5) applies without approximations, he determined wavelengths with an accuracy that had never before been attained in any kind of measurements. The field of spectroscopy helped to set a standard of high-precision instruments and techniques of measurement which became characteristic of physical science.

Nowadays diffraction gratings are made by ruling parallel, equidistant lines on a sheet of glass. This is usually done with a diamond point held in a "ruling engine," somewhat like a lathe, that advances the point the required distance sidewise between successive strokes. The unscratched strips of glass between the lines serve as the slits through which the light passes. The smaller the distance d between adjacent slits, the more spread

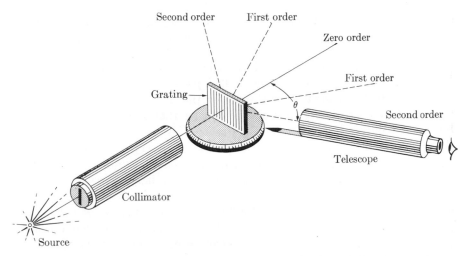

FIG. 30.13. Schematic outline of spectroscope employing a diffraction grating.

out (dispersed) the spectra will be; for this reason, gratings ruled with up to 10,000 lines per centimeter are in common use for research and industrial purposes. To rule a grating with so many fine lines, both uniform and evenly spaced, is a very difficult and expensive task. Hence, for most purposes, *replica* gratings are used; these are made by pouring collodion on an original grating, removing the film after it hardens, and placing it between two plates of glass for protection.

The precision obtainable with a fine grating spectrometer skillfully operated is superb; the accuracy is routinely better than 0.001%. A typical value obtained for a wavelength is $(5.88995 \pm 0.00004) \times 10^{-7}$ m, a result with six meaningful ("significant") digits. Values with eight significant digits are attainable with the best techniques.

PROBLEM 30.17. In a grating spectrometer, the light waves diffracted from two neighboring slits toward the first-order constructive interference band are one wavelength "out of step," as in Fig. 30.12; but the light waves leave S_1 and S_2 along parallel directions and are brought to a focus by means of a lens placed perpendicular to the incoming rays. Show that in this case Eq. (30.5) holds without approximations.

30.7 Polarization of light; the "elastic solid" theory. Young's announcement of his discovery of the interference of light and his revival of the wave theory initially aroused a storm of protests and even abuse on the part of those of his contemporaries who were holding to the Newtonian particle theory. Indeed, some of the attacks on Young were so effective that his reputation was marred for many years. Then, in 1815, a young French engineer, Augustin Fresnel (1788–1827), independently discovered the optical phenomena that Young had been studying, devised additional experiments, and coordinated all of this in a mathematical theory of wave motion.

In addition to diffraction and interference, Young and, especially, Fresnel investigated a third effect, called *polarization of light*, that also turned out to be of great importance for the development of the wave theory. There are many optical phenomena that involve polarization, but for our purposes it will suffice to discuss only one of them. Polarization is easily observable with certain transparent crystals, for example the mineral tourmaline (and also with the modern, synthetic material known commercially as Polaroid). If we look at a light source through a thin wafer cut from the crystal while rotating the wafer, we see no change in the character of the transmitted light. But if one such wafer is placed behind another, and one of the two is then rotated, we find that the intensity of the transmitted light varies from a maximum for one position to practically zero after a rotation of 90°.

An observation of this kind could not be satisfactorily accounted for in terms of either particles of light or of light waves so long as these waves were assumed to be longitudinal. In 1817, however, Young suggested a way out of this difficulty: light waves are not longitudinal, but transverse; the vibrations of the ether occur, not in the direction along which the light is traveling, but at right angles to this direction. This idea helped to explain the experiment with the two tourmaline crystals. In Fig. 30.14, the ordinary light from the source S is assumed to consist of ether vibrations occurring in all possible directions at right angles to the direction of propagation. This light is said to be *unpolarized*. The first tourmaline crystal is of such a structure as to permit only those vibrations that occur in one plane to pass through it. The light thus transmitted is said to be *plane polarized*. This plane polarized light will pass directly through the second tourmaline crystal when its polarizing axis is parallel to that of the first crystal, but if the axis of one crystal is turned 90°, so that the two axes are at right angles to each other, the light will not pass through the second crystal. Figure 30.15 shows a mechanical model that illustrates how transverse waves in a string can be polarized. It should be evident that longitudinal waves, such as sound waves, cannot be polarized.

Both Fresnel and Young recognized a great difficulty here: for light to consist of transverse waves in an all-pervading, elastic ether, this ether would have to be rigid, like a *solid*. A gas or a liquid will transmit longitudinal but not transverse elastic waves; in solids both types can be set up. Moreover, elastic waves travel through a medium with a speed that is proportional to $\sqrt{\epsilon/d}$, where ϵ is a measure of the elasticity of the medium and d is its density. For a speed as great as that of light, the "solid ether" would have to have both a very high elasticity and a very

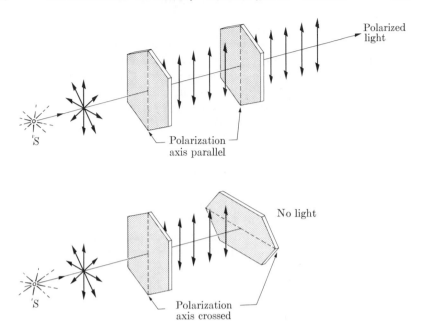

Fig. 30.14. The light polarized by one tourmaline crystal passes through the second crystal in one position (upper diagram) but is cut off when the second crystal is turned through 90° (lower diagram).

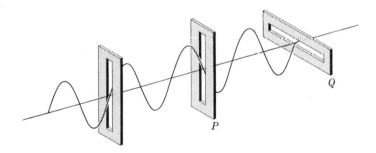

Fig. 30.15. A slot lets a transverse wave in a string pass if it is aligned in one direction (P), but cuts it off when rotated through 90° (Q).

low density. The requirement of a low density by itself did not create conceptual problems, for this would account for the well-known fact that the planets are not noticeably impeded in their motion through the ether. But even if the density d were close to zero, the great speed of light and hence the large value of $\sqrt{\epsilon/d}$ would still demand of this highly rarefied ether an elasticity far greater than that of steel.

Scientists of today, who more than their ancestors have grown up without feeling the need to account for phenomena by mechanical models, may find it more difficult to conceive of a medium with such contradictory properties than to think of light as propagated through space completely devoid of any material medium. Yet if light is a wave motion, what is it that waves? For most 19th-century scientists, in whose minds a mechanical conception of nature was firmly implanted, there seemed to be only one answer: the waves must occur in an all-pervading elastic substance; and since they are transverse waves, the substance must have properties that are possessed by solids. No wonder that this perplexing picture attracted the attention of some of the most brilliant theoreticians of the period, each trying to develop an improved or different elastic solid theory. Although all of these ether theories involved too many paradoxes to be satisfactory, the effort put on them simultaneously resulted in a great gain in another direction, namely, in the development of the mathematical theory of wave motions in solids. One modern application of this theory is to the transverse and longitudinal waves that spread out in the earth from the source of an earthquake.

It was in this period, before 1850, that Faraday worked out his conceptions of electric and magnetic fields in space (Section 27.5). Then, in the last half of the century, Maxwell, building on Faraday's work, brought forth the electromagnetic theory of light (Chapter 29), in which the mechanical quantities in the equations of the elastic solid theory were replaced by concepts such as the electric and magnetic field intensities, $\mathbf{E}$ and $\mathbf{H}$. Following Maxwell, others made additions to his theory until by 1896 it served to account for all the known phenomena connected with the *transmission* of light through space and through matter. The energy constituting light could be said with certainty to be propagated in the form of transverse electromagnetic waves.

Yet at this point a new difficulty arose; when attempts were made to explain the ways in which light is emitted and absorbed by matter, the wave theory, so useful to explain *propagation*, failed. Apparently light is not emitted or absorbed in the form of continuous waves. Light thus seemed to have a dual character—a perplexing notion that soon was to bring about a major revolution in physical thought.

ADDITIONAL PROBLEMS

30.18. Show how the paths of a ray of light can be traced through a prism when one knows the angle of incidence, the shape of the prism, and the index of refraction of the prism material.

30.19. Explain why: (a) celestial objects appear to us slightly higher above the horizon than they actually are; (b) these displacements may change with changes in the temperature of the atmosphere; (c) the sun and the moon, when near the horizon, appear to have a flattened rather than a circular shape.

30.20. View a distant light through a thin piece of silk or a window screen and explain what you see.

30.21. What considerations dictate the choice between a prism and a diffraction grating for use in a spectrometer?

SUPPLEMENTARY READING

BEYER, R. T., and A. O. WILLIAMS, *College physics* (Prentice Hall, 1957), Chaps. 15 and 18.

CREW, H., *The rise of modern physics* (Williams and Wilkins, 1935), Chap. 6.

DURBIN, F. M., *Introduction to physics* (Prentice Hall, 1955), Chap. 26.

FREEMAN, I. M., *Modern introductory physics* (McGraw-Hill, 1949), Chap. 13.

KOLIN, A., *Physics, its laws, ideas, and methods* (McGraw-Hill, 1950), Chaps. 28 and 29.

LITTLE, N. C., *Physics* (Heath, 1953), Chaps. 28–30.

MACH, E., *The principles of physical optics. An historical and philosophical treatment*, translated by J. S. Anderson and A. F. A. Young (Methuen, London, 1926; Dover, 1953).

MAGIE, W. F., *A source book in physics* (McGraw-Hill, 1935), pp. 265–278 (Descartes), pp. 283–294 (Huygens), pp. 294–298 (Grimaldi), pp. 298–308 (Newton), pp. 308–315 (Young), pp. 315–318 (Malus), pp. 318–324 (Fresnel), pp. 335–337 (Roemer), pp. 340–344 (Fizeau and Foucault).

MENDENHALL, C. E., A. S. EVE, D. A. KEYS, and R. M. SUTTON, *College physics* (Heath, 4th edition, 1956), Chaps. 46 and 50–52.

MICHELS, W. C., and A. L. PATTERSON, *Elements of modern physics* (Van Nostrand, 1951), Chap. 11.

MINNAERT, *The nature of light and colour in the open air*, translated by II. M. Kremer-Priest and K. E. Brian Joy (G. Bell, reprinted by Dover, 1954).

NEWTON, ISAAC, *Opticks, or a treatise of the reflections, refractions, inflections, and colours of light* (London, 4th edition, 1730; Dover, 1952).

SEARS, F. W., and M. W. ZEMANSKY, *College physics* (Addison-Wesley, 1948), Chaps. 46 and 47.

SEMAT, H., *Fundamentals of physics* (Rinehart, 3rd edition, 1957), Chap. 34.

TAYLOR, L. W., *Physics, the pioneer science* (Houghton Mifflin, 1941), Chaps. 29, 34, 36, 38.

WOOD, A., and F. OLDHAM, *Thomas Young* (University Press, Cambridge, England, 1954).

CHAPTER 31

CONTINUOUS SPECTRA. BIRTH OF THE QUANTUM THEORY

Even early in the 19th century it was known that the solar spectrum extended beyond the visible violet into what is called the *ultraviolet* and, at the other end, beyond the visible red into the *infrared*. After Hertz's experiments, which proved that electromagnetic waves exist and have all the main properties of visible light, it was clear that visible light is only one example of energy in the form of electromagnetic radiation. The radiation from our sun, for example, may be thought of as composed of an electromagnetic spectrum such as might be obtained when the radiation is passed through a suitable prism or diffraction grating, the visible portion between the red and the violet being extended on either side by ranges of invisible radiation. The approximate wavelength ranges in the spectrum, as obtained by experiment, are listed in Table 31.1. Note that these wavelengths are not given in meters or centimeters but, more conveniently, in multiples of 10^{-8} cm. This unit, used throughout spectroscopy, is called 1 angstrom (abbreviated A) in honor of the Swedish spectroscopist A. J. Ångström.

Table 31.1. Approximate ranges of wavelengths λ in vacuum (or air) for the visible and adjacent regions of the electromagnetic spectrum; $1 \text{ A} \equiv 10^{-8}$ cm.

Range	Wavelength range (A)
Near ultraviolet	1600 to 3800
Violet	3800 to 4500
Blue	4500 to 5000
Green	5000 to 5700
Yellow	5700 to 5900
Orange	5900 to 6100
Red	6100 to 7500
Infrared	7500 to 2×10^6 (or 0.02 cm)

In Section 29.4 we saw that the work of Hertz and others gave weight to the view that electromagnetic radiation is produced when submicroscopic electric particles in matter undergo accelerations. This hypothesis, if correct, should help to solve some long-standing puzzles about radiation and matter. For example, why are there marked differences in the radiation emitted and absorbed by different substances in varying circumstances? First we shall investigate the radiation found to be emitted and absorbed by heated solids and liquids, for the attempt to explain the features of this radiation eventually led to a momentous discovery.

31.1 Continuous spectra. When a solid piece of iron, say an iron poker, is slowly heated, it is found to emit infrared radiation while still not hot enough to emit an appreciable amount of visible light. This invisible infrared radiation may be detected by holding the hand near the iron, for our skin is sensitive to these long wavelengths; or, by using special infrared-sensitive film, the warm piece of iron can be photographed in a completely darkened room. As the temperature of the iron increases, radiation of shorter wavelengths from it becomes intense enough to be detected by the eye. At a temperature of 500°C to 550°C, a significant amount of visible light at wavelengths around 7500 A (red) is being emitted; the iron is now said to be "red hot." Further temperature increases bring out more short-wavelength radiation, and the color changes through orange and yellow to what is termed "white hot."

What has been said about iron is found to apply in a general way to the radiation from any solid or liquid. When the radiation is passed through a suitable prism or diffraction grating, a *continuous* spectrum is formed. There are no gaps in it, no missing wavelength bands or distinct "color" bands, even if measurements are carried into the ultraviolet and infrared regions. Since most kinds of glass strongly absorb both ultraviolet and infrared radiation, a prism spectrometer or spectrograph used to analyze these spectral regions must be equipped with prisms and lenses made of materials other than glass. For the ultraviolet range, quartz or fluorite is suitable; for the infrared, rocksalt.

Just as the eye is suitable for detection of radiation in only a limited portion of the spectrum, other instruments respond in restricted ranges only. For the visible and ultraviolet regions, the energy may be measured by observing the amount the radiation darkens a photographic film or the response it produces in a photoelectric cell. For the infrared region, either a thermocouple or a bolometer may be used. A bolometer is an instrument that utilizes the measurable increase in the electric resistance of a thin, blackened wire when this wire absorbs the radiation.

Figure 31.1 is a typical curve showing the relative amounts of energy associated with the different wavelengths in the radiation of a glowing solid having a temperature equal to that of the surface of the sun, 6000°K. Note the visible part of the spectrum; the peak of the curve falls in the green region. It is this distribution of energies that our eyes interpret as white light. As for the *total* energy emitted, the largest part is found to be in the infrared.

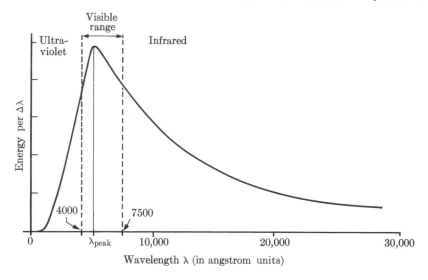

FIG. 31.1. Distribution of energy in radiation emitted by a body at 6000°K.

Figure 31.2 shows two additional features that all solid or liquid emitters have in common. With increasing temperature, more energy is associated with each wavelength region, as might be expected; what is perhaps surprising, however, is that the peak of the distribution curve shifts toward shorter wavelengths with increasing temperature.

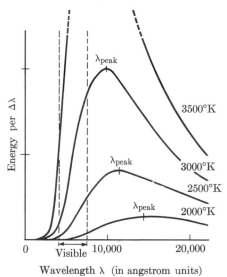

FIG. 31.2. Distribution of energy in the radiation emitted by a solid at each of four different temperatures.

It is most striking that the radiation from all solids and liquids is very similar, regardless of their chemical composition; this suggests the possibility of building a single theory of radiation that will be applicable to all of them. However, the dissimilarities that do exist make the start on a common theory difficult. Most important is the fact that the rate of radiation does not depend only on the temperature of the emitter, but also on the nature of its surface. For the same temperature, a solid object painted dull black will emit (and also will absorb) several times as much radiated energy per second as it will when coated with aluminum paint. Also, a rough surface is a better emitter and a better absorber (poorer reflector) than the same surface when polished. To complicate matters still more, the nature of a surface may change when it is heated. All this raises the question whether some "ideal" emitter might be found that always emits as efficiently as possible at every temperature and that is easy to construct for experimental purposes.

31.2 Ideal black surface (cavity) radiation. The first step toward the realization of an ideal emitter lay in a discovery made in 1859 by G. R. Kirchhoff that at any given temperature *the emitting power of a surface is directly proportional to its absorbing power.* Hence, if a surface could be found that always completely absorbs all radiation of all wavelengths falling on it, this surface would also be the best possible emitter of all wavelengths; the total radiation from it would depend solely on its temperature and not at all on its chemical or physical nature. As we shall see, this ideal surface has a special significance for the development of a theory of radiation.

The surface envisaged by Kirchhoff is called an *ideal black surface.* No such surface has been found; even lampblack absorbs only about 99% of the radiation incident on it. However, in 1895 an ingenious way to obtain the equivalent of an ideal black surface was proposed. A hollow ball or cylinder of some metal, which may or may not be coated on the inside with lampblack, has a single small hole drilled through its wall (Fig. 31.3). Radiation entering the hole from the outside is scattered inside and gradually absorbed during repeated reflections at the inside walls, so that the amount escaping back to the outside through the hole is negligibly small. The *hole* therefore acts as a practically perfect absorber, or ideal black surface. If this

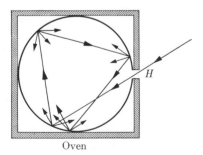

Oven

FIG. 31.3. The small hole H corresponds to an ideal black surface for the radiation passing through it.

device is put in an oven and its temperature raised, the inside wall radiates into the cavity, and the part escaping through the hole has the properties of black-surface radiation. Such radiation is also called *cavity radiation*.

Instead of using a prism or grating to analyze this radiation, the following method may be employed. With the walls of the emitter kept at a constant temperature, a filter that is transparent for only a very small band of wavelengths $\Delta\lambda$ is placed in front of the hole. The radiation from the cavity passing through this filter is allowed to fall on some energy-measuring device for a known interval of time t. If we divide the energy thus measured by t and by $\Delta\lambda$, we obtain the energy emitted per unit time and per unit wavelength range. The greater the cross-sectional area A of the hole, the larger is this quantity, but this variable can be eliminated by dividing the quantity by A. Thus we finally obtain what is called the *monochromatic emissive power* J_λ; it is the energy emitted per unit time, per unit wavelength range, and per unit area of the ideal black emitter. By using a series of filters, each of which transmits a different small band of wavelengths $\Delta\lambda$, we can determine J_λ for many different points in the total spectrum being radiated. These values of J_λ may then be plotted as a function of the wavelength λ; the shape of the curve is found to be the same as that in Fig. 31.1.

If the temperature of the emitter walls is changed to a new, constant value and the whole procedure repeated, a different curve is obtained. Thus a whole family of the J_λ versus λ curves can be plotted, one for each temperature (Fig. 31.2).

31.3 Two classically derived laws for cavity radiation. The discovery that a cavity emits ideal black-surface radiation made possible the experimental verification of two laws for such radiation that already had been derived theoretically. One of these is known as the *Stefan-Boltzmann law*. It asserts that the *total emissive power* J, or *total* energy of all wavelengths emitted per unit time and per unit area, is directly proportional to T^4, the fourth power of the absolute temperature of the surface, or

$$J = \text{a constant} \cdot T^4. \tag{31.1}$$

This relation had been derived from the known laws of heat and Maxwell's electromagnetic theory of radiation; the empirical verification of Eq. (31.1) was therefore a great triumph for the theory.

In 1893, Wilhelm Wien derived another law of ideal black surface radiation, also solely on the basis of physical principles well established at the time. As we have seen in Fig. 31.2, the wavelength λ_{peak} for which the radiation is most intense (i.e., where J_λ is largest) shifts toward shorter wavelengths with increasing temperature of the emitter. Wien showed that for cavity radiation a simple mathematical relation should hold between λ_{peak} and the absolute temperature T, that in fact one quantity is inversely proportional to the other, or

$$\lambda_{peak} = \frac{a\ constant}{T}.$$ (31.2)

This relation, called *Wien's displacement law*, was also found to be in accord with experiments on cavity radiation. When λ_{peak} is expressed in angstroms, the proportionality constant in Eq. (31.2) is found by experiment to be 2.898×10^7 A·°K. Applying this knowledge to an interesting problem, we can find the approximate surface temperature of an emitter such as our sun. Observations made at sea level show that λ_{peak} for sunlight is about 5000 A (in the far green region of the visible spectrum); Eq. (31.2) predicts that the temperature T of the sun's radiating surface is 2.898×10^7 A·°K/5000 A, or about 5800°K. This figure is somewhat too low, partly because the sun's radiation is absorbed by our atmosphere more effectively at the shorter wavelengths, so that the actual value of λ_{peak} is smaller than the value recorded by our instruments, and also because the sun is not an ideal black surface for which Eq. (31.2) accurately holds.

PROBLEM 31.1. Instruments carried by rockets *outside* the earth's atmosphere indicate that λ_{peak} for sunlight is 4650 A. (a) Compute from this datum the expected value for the temperature of the sun's radiating surface. (b) Will the actual temperature be higher or lower than this temperature, and why?

PROBLEM 31.2. Analysis of the radiation from the "hot" star Vega indicates that λ_{peak} for it is 2100 A, which is in the ultraviolet region of the electromagnetic spectrum. (a) Show that Wien's law yields 14,000°K as the surface temperature of Vega. (b) How should this prediction be qualified?

PROBLEM 31.3. Compute λ_{peak} (a) for the reddish star Antares, which has been estimated to have a surface temperature of 2500°K, and (b) for ice at 0°C. (c) Qualify each prediction.

PROBLEM 31.4. (a) Using Eq. (31.1) (the Stefan-Boltzmann law) show that when an ideal emitter is heated from 2000° to 3000°K, the total energy radiated by it per unit time increases fivefold. (b) For any J_λ versus λ curve (Fig. 31.2), the area between the curve and the abscissa is proportional to J, that is, to the total energy radiated per unit time and per unit area of the emitter when it is at the temperature indicated. Estimate the areas under the curves for emitters at 2000° and 3000°K, and compare the values so obtained for J at these temperatures.

PROBLEM 31.5. The value for the Stefan-Boltzmann constant in Eq. (31.1) is found by experiment to be approximately 5.669×10^{-12} (j/sec)/cm²·°K⁴. (a) If a small hole drilled in a furnace door is found to emit 96 (j/sec)/cm², what is the temperature of the interior of the furnace? (b) Does your answer need qualification? (c) If the furnace is allowed to cool to the temperature of its surroundings, what *net* amount of energy passes through the hole per unit time?

PROBLEM 31.6. What is the frequency of electromagnetic radiation that in vacuum has a wavelength of (a) 1600 A, (b) 2×10^6 A?

PROBLEM 31.7. According to Maxwell's electromagnetic theory and the discoveries growing out of it (Sections 29.3 and 29.4), the radiation from a heated cavity comes from oscillating electric charges in the cavity walls and has frequencies equal to the oscillatory frequencies. Starting with this picture, can you explain, at least in a semiquantitative way, (a) why the radiation emitted at any given temperature has a continuous spectrum of frequencies (and hence of wavelengths) instead of being just of one frequency, (b) why the values of J_λ are different at different frequencies, and (c) why the energy distribution varies with the temperature, as shown in Fig. 31.2? Defend your answers, but be frank about vague guesses.

31.4 The failure of classical radiation theory. The fact that both the Stefan-Boltzmann law (Eq. 31.1) and Wien's law (Eq. 31.2) could be derived from Maxwell's theory and the well-established principles of heat and mechanics provided an impressive victory for 19th-century physics. However, as soon became apparent, this was about as far as one could go with the concepts at hand. There remained in what is now called "classical" physics several important questions, apparently unanswerable. For example, classical physics did not yield a way to predict adequately the *shape* of the curve for any temperature, as in Fig. 31.2, unless the curve for some one temperature was known.

The general procedure for deriving the shape of the curve on theoretical grounds seemed evident: postulate some basic model of emission, compute from it the fraction of individual oscillators responsible for each range of emitted frequencies, and then add their individual contributions to obtain the over-all pattern. Various able theorists attacked this problem, but none with complete success. In Fig. 31.4 are shown the curves predicted on the basis of two classical models that differed from each other in some of the assumptions involved. These were the two most successful attempts. As can be seen, Theory I yielded a curve valid only for short wavelengths (high frequencies), while Theory II led to a curve useful only for very long wavelengths (very low frequencies).

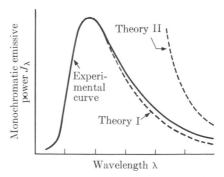

FIG. 31.4. The experimentally determined emission curve for a particular temperature compared with the curves for the same temperature predicted by two classically based theories.

FIG. 31.5. Max Planck (1858–1947).

31.5 Planck's semiempirical formula. Among those who had been trying, without success, to develop an adequate theory for the emission of continuous spectra was the German physicist Max Planck (Fig. 31.5). However, Planck was impressed by the fact that Theories I and II each led to an equation relating J_λ and λ that gave the correct curve for a part of the spectrum, one for short wavelengths, the other for very long wavelengths. Possibly an equation could be set up *empirically* that, so to speak, would be intermediate in form between those of I and II and that would combine the best features of both. This Planck succeeded in doing. For the first time there was now available a single formula which fitted the observed data for the complete energy-distribution curve at any cavity temperature. This formula, announced by Planck in October 1900 to the Deutsche Physikalische Gesellschaft, is

$$J_\lambda = \frac{C_1}{\lambda^5(e^{C_2/\lambda T} - 1)}, \tag{31.3}$$

where e denotes the base of natural logarithms, namely the number 2.718 . . . , and C_1 and C_2 are constant quantities that can be computed from the experimental data for cavity radiation and which have the same values for the whole family of emission curves, Fig. 31.2. To apply a quick method of checking qualitatively that Eq. (31.3) corresponds to the data plotted in Fig. 31.2 at least at the extreme portions of the curve, note that J_λ goes to zero both as λ goes to zero (because in that case $e^{C_2/\lambda T}$ in the denominator goes rapidly to ∞) and also when λ is given very large values (because in that case λ^5 in the denominator rapidly assumes very large values also).

Planck's method for obtaining his formula was not by searching blindly for an equation that would fit the data; as we saw, he was guided in part by the results of Theories I and II, which were based on two different classical models. But still, this was not an accomplishment that satisfied him; for after all, one can generally find some formula to represent any family of related curves. To take a simple example, in Fig. 31.6 the whole set of curves is given by the equation $y = c_1 x + c_2 T$; for each curve of this family there is a characteristic value for T, just as each curve in Fig. 31.2 corresponds to a specific value of T in Eq. (31.3).

PROBLEM 31.8. The family of straight lines in Fig. 31.6, which may be thought of as representing a set of experimental data, is much simpler than, but otherwise analogous to, the family of emission curves in Fig. 31.2. (a) In Fig. 31.6, use the numerical values corresponding to various points in the graph to test the assertion that each line of the family is represented by the equation given in the figure legend. (b) What are the values of c_1 and c_2?

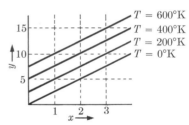

FIG. 31.6. The equation for this family of straight lines is $y = c_1 x + c_2 T$, where c_1 and c_2 are constants that have the same values for the whole family.

Finding Eq. (31.3), though useful, was to Planck no more of an explanation for the mechanism responsible for cavity emission than, say, the Bode-Titus Law was for explaining why the planets move in their present orbits. The big problem still was to find a single physical mechanism responsible for cavity radiation of all wavelengths and at all temperatures, in short, to find a single theory from which Eq. (31.3) could be derived. Planck later said of this problem that he had been impressed by the fact that the chemical composition of the cavity walls has no effect on the emitted radiation. This seemed to him to imply "something absolute, and since I had always regarded the search for the absolute as the loftiest goal of all scientific activity, I eagerly set to work."

At the very onset, Planck received unexpected encouragement when a colleague who had extended the measurements of cavity radiation beyond the range and accuracy previously attained reported that the results fully supported the validity of Planck's empirical formula. Planck tells us that, two months later, "after a few weeks of the most strenuous labor in my life, the darkness lifted and a new unimagined prospect began to dawn." His solution, which incorporated ideas that were to revolutionize physical science, was announced by him on December 14, 1900. This marks the birth of the quantum theory and the beginning of contemporary physics.

31.6 Planck's quantum hypotheses. Hertz's discovery of the electromagnetic waves emitted by oscillating charges (Section 29.4) had convinced Planck that the radiation of light originates in submicroscopic electric oscillators in the cavity walls. Each oscillator, he assumed, has its own fixed frequency ν and emits radiation of this frequency. All frequencies are represented in the enormous number of different oscillators, and hence all frequencies are present in the emitted radiation; the spectrum is continuous. While the oscillators are radiating, they must of course be losing energy, and thus the emitter will cool unless energy of some form, say heat, is continually supplied to it. This is the function of the oven around the cavity. The resulting kinetic energy imparted to the particles of the emitter, including the oscillators, is further distributed among them because of their incessant collisions. When any individual oscillator absorbs or radiates energy, only its amplitude of vibration changes, for its frequency is fixed. The higher its natural frequency and the greater its amplitude at the moment, the larger is the energy possessed by an oscillator.

Nothing in this picture of the oscillators is contrary to classical principles. But the classical views also imply two other postulates. One is that the energy E of an individual oscillator can be of any amount, from zero upward, and the oscillator can radiate or absorb any amount of energy, with its amplitude continuously changing while it does so; analogously, when an ordinary pendulum swinging in air loses energy because of friction, its amplitude is observed to decrease gradually and *continuously* from the initial value down to zero, when the pendulum will then be at rest. The other classical postulate is that since any electric charge emits radiation whenever it is accelerated, an electric oscillator must radiate all the time that it is vibrating. It was from these two classical predictions that Planck was now forced to break away in order to obtain a theoretical basis for Eq. (31.3). Because his ideas went through several modifications as he continued his work, as usually occurs while any important advance is under way, we shall state first his two new assumptions that continue to be of especial importance in present-day physics:

(1) *Each oscillator can have only certain definite energies.* These allowed energies are integral multiples of a quantity $h\nu$, where h is a new universal

constant now known as *Planck's constant,* and ν is the frequency of the oscillator. Thus the oscillator's energy E at any moment may be 0, 1 $h\nu$, 2 $h\nu$, 3 $h\nu$, or in general, $nh\nu$, where n is any integer, but the energy will never be 1.85 $h\nu$, or the like. In brief,

$$E = nh\nu, \tag{31.4}$$

where $h\nu$ is called the *quantum of energy* corresponding to the frequency ν. To put it another way, the total energy of an oscillator is "quantized" in lumps of energy of magnitude $h\nu$ each. It follows that any change ΔE in the energy of an oscillator must occur, not gradually and continuously, but suddenly and discontinuously, for example, from 3 $h\nu$ to 2 $h\nu$, or from 5 $h\nu$ to 6 $h\nu$. If the swinging pendulum in our example behaved according to this rule, its amplitude would decrease not smoothly but in discrete steps, and its energy while vibrating at each step would be an integral multiple of $h\nu$, where ν is the frequency of vibration of the pendulum.

(2) *An oscillator radiates only when it changes from one allowable energy value to the next smaller one,* and the energy ΔE that it loses with this sudden decrease in amplitude is emitted as a pulse of electromagnetic radiation of energy $h\nu$. Similarly, an oscillator can absorb a quantum of energy $h\nu$ of incident radiation, whereupon it changes immediately to its next higher allowable energy value. According to this assumption, an oscillator does not radiate so long as it remains in any quantum state $nh\nu$, even though, like the vibrating pendulum in our analogy, it is all the time undergoing acceleration.

At the time, these were indeed astounding proposals that did not agree with previous theory or with common-sense experience. For example, in addition to the pendulum, consider a vibrating tuning fork, another sort of oscillator, that loses energy by giving kinetic energy to the air molecules surrounding it. This energy appears to be imparted, not in spurts, but so as to produce a continuous train of sound waves in the air, and the amplitude of the vibrating prongs and of the air molecules decreases gradually as the fork radiates sound. But we must remember that Planck had to formulate the quantum hypotheses empirically and without guide from common-sense experience. In general, in passing from a familiar realm to a new one, as from the macroscopic to the submicroscopic, we must be prepared to revise our older hypotheses, perhaps radically.

A more graphic picture of the quantization of energy can be given in terms of the concept of *energy levels.* If any individual oscillator has a constant frequency ν, with only its amplitude changing, the allowable energy levels which it can reach at one time or another may be pictured as equally spaced rungs on a ladder (Fig. 31.7). At any moment the oscillator, so far as its energy content is concerned, is "located" on one or another of these energy levels, if it is not just then changing levels. Planck had little knowledge available to him about the precise nature of submicroscopic oscillators, or how they behave as time progresses. In such circumstances, the energy-level conception made further progress possible without having to picture prematurely the unknown physical situation.

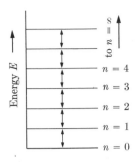

FIG. 31.7. Energy-level diagram for a single oscillator. The energy E corresponding to any level is $nh\nu$. Transitions are permitted between neighboring levels, as indicated.

31.7 Planck's theoretical law. Determination of the Planck constant.

With the help of his new assumptions Planck deduced the following expression for J_λ, the rate at which radiation of wavelength λ is emitted from a unit area of an ideal black surface of temperature T:

$$J_\lambda = \frac{2\pi hc^2}{\lambda^5(e^{hc/k\lambda T} - 1)}, \tag{31.5}$$

where h is Planck's constant, c is the speed of electromagnetic radiation in vacuum, and k is Boltzmann's constant (Section 25.8). The equivalence of this equation to the experimentally verified Eq. (31.3) is apparent, for we can identify the constant C_1 with $2\pi hc^2$, and C_2 with hc/k. Moreover, the values of C_1 and C_2 as computed from these theoretically obtained expressions are in agreement, within the experimental error, with their empirically determined values. How basic Planck's theoretical equation is in the theory of cavity radiation became evident when it was shown that various other laws of continuous spectra can be derived from it, for example, the Stefan-Boltzmann law (Eq. 31.1) and Wien's law (Eq. 31.2), both of which had been derived earlier from classical principles.

Although the details of Planck's mathematical argument leading to Eq. (31.5) cannot be given here, we can see in a general way that a possible approach would be first to develop an expression giving, for any temperature T, the value of the energies of all the oscillators having the same frequency ν, then to multiply this expression by another giving the number of active oscillators of this same frequency per unit volume of the emitter, and finally to reduce this result to one giving the amount of the radiation of the frequency that is emitted per unit time and per unit area of the emitter. For ν we may substitute c/λ, in view of Eq. (29.1), thus putting the final result in the form shown in Eq. (31.5). In this equation, Planck's constant h is the only unknown quantity, for c and k are known and

the value of J_λ for any particular wavelength λ and cavity temperature T can be found experimentally. Inserting these values in Eq. (31.5)
and solving for h, we obtain

$$h = 6.625 \times 10^{-34} \text{ j·sec.}$$

Although initially evaluated in the way just described, Planck's constant
has since made its appearance in many different physical theories. Therefore there are now several independent ways to calculate it; moreover, it
has achieved the same status as other universal constants, such as G
and N_0.

Indeed, the idea of quantization of energy is now recognized to apply
not only throughout the whole submicroscopic realm, but for any physical
system in which the energy is associated with a period of oscillation,
vibration, or rotation. Why then has its effect not been observed with
large-scale phenomena? Considering again our example of the pendulum,
suppose its constant frequency of vibration ν to be 1 cycle/sec. Because of
friction, its energy decreases, but the loss $h\nu$ in passing from any one
allowable energy value to the next smaller one, if Eq. (31.4) applies, is
6.625×10^{-34} j. The abrupt changes in amplitude corresponding to this
change in total energy are so small that they cannot possibly be observed;
conversely, the smallest observable change in amplitude corresponds to
such a large number of quanta that the effect of discreteness is lost, just
as the individuality of the molecules in the air around us does not come to
our notice if we deal with a quantity of air containing great numbers of
molecules. In short, *the small value of h assures that the effects of quantization of energy become significant only for submicroscopic systems in which
individual energy changes are correspondingly small.*

PROBLEM 31.9. (a) If a certain oscillator emits light of 7000 A wavelength
in vacuum, what is its frequency and what is the value of the quantum of energy
corresponding to this frequency? (b) Make these two computations for an oscillator that emits ultraviolet radiation of vacuum wavelength 2000 A.

PROBLEM 31.10. A pendulum bob has a mass of 1 kgm and a frequency of
vibration = 1 cycle/sec. At the topmost position of the first swing, it is 5 cm
above the lowest level. As the pendulum swings back and forth, its amplitude
is decreased by frictional losses. (a) What is the energy of the pendulum during
its first swing? (b) From what height does the bob start to swing after the pendulum has lost 1 quantum of energy? Can the difference in level be noticed?

PROBLEM 31.11. (a) By using the known values of the constants h, c, and k,
show that the theoretically predicted value of the constant C_2 in Eq. (31.3) is
1.4 cm·°K when wavelengths are expressed in centimeters, or 1.4×10^8 A·°K
when they are expressed in angstroms. (b) Similarly, show that C_1 is $3.7 \times
10^{-12}$ (j/sec)·cm^2 when λ is expressed in centimeters, or 3.7×10^{20} (j/sec)·A^4/
cm^2 when it is expressed in angstroms.

PROBLEM 31.12. The constant h is given in joules $\times$ seconds; the physical quantity *energy* $\times$ *time* is often called *action*. Some years ago a writer on popular science cited the fundamental role of the action concept in present-day physics as one piece of evidence for his contention that biological conceptions are beginning to permeate physics. Comment on this assertion.

31.8 The reception of Planck's work. Planck himself was deeply disturbed by the radical character of the hypotheses that he was forced to make, for they set aside some of the most fundamental conceptions of 19th-century science. Later he wrote that he spent many years trying to save physics from the notion of discontinuous energy levels, but that the quantum idea "obstinately withstood all attempts at fitting it, in a suitable form, into the framework of classical theory." That many of Planck's contemporaries also thought his view too radical to be satisfactory is not surprising. This is another example of initial opposition to radically new views which is both the necessary defense of the scientist against being blown about by the winds of mere speculation, and his challenge to the innovator to prove his case fully. This attack went to a very deep root. Most physicists of the time, including Planck, were still fundamentally convinced that natural processes are continuous; as Newton had expressed it, *natura non saltus facit*. Indeed, both the ancient faith in a sequence of cause and effect and even the usefulness of the mathematical calculus itself seemed to depend on the proposition that natural phenomena do not proceed by jumps.

There were also some specific reasons for skepticism concerning Planck's theory. His initial treatment involved ambiguities. He accepted Maxwell's wave theory as the correct description of the way in which radiation is propagated through space, spreading out continuously and in all directions from the source, but at the same time he had to assume, in contradiction to the Maxwell theory, that the oscillators making up the source do not radiate all the time they are oscillating, but only when their amplitudes of vibration suddenly change. Also, if the radiation after leaving the oscillators is assumed to spread out through space over an ever-expanding and continuous wave front, how can another oscillator in its path gather together the quantum of energy $h\nu$ needed if it is to change to its next higher energy level? In brief, absorption of radiation would appear to be impossible. Lastly, there was no detailed model of the oscillators that would explain, for example, why the radiation from solids and liquids differs in important respects from that emitted by gases (Chapter 33).

Some of these difficulties were gradually corrected by Planck himself, but others still remained. To most physicists of the time, the notion of quantization was regarded as providing perhaps a clever way to account for the phenomena for which it was devised, but as probably lacking in any fundamental and general significance (a response rather reminiscent of the original reception of Copernicus' work). This was the situation until 1905, when Albert Einstein extended Planck's conception to the explanation of another phenomenon, the photoelectric effect, and so laid bare the full power of the quantum hypothesis.

SUPPLEMENTARY READING

BLACKWOOD, O. H., T. H. OSGOOD, and A. E. RUARK, *An outline of atomic physics* (Wiley, 1955), Chap. IV, on black body radiation and quantum theory.

BUCKLEY, H., *A short history of physics* (Methuen, 1927), Chap. X.

TAYLOR, L. W., *Physics: the pioneer science* (Houghton Mifflin, 1941), pp. 539–543, 808–810.

CHAPTER 32

THE PHOTOELECTRIC EFFECT. EINSTEIN'S PHOTON THEORY

32.1 The photoelectric effect. Ironically, the first hint leading to the discovery of the photoelectric effect, and through that eventually to the recognition that the classical theory of light needed fundamental revision, was an incidental observation recorded by Hertz, and this during the same experimental research that at the time furnished the most convincing proof in favor of Maxwell's classical electromagnetic theory (Section 29.4): Hertz noticed that an electric spark would jump more readily across the air gap between the metal spheres in his receiving circuit if they were well polished. It was quickly established that ultraviolet radiation (as from the spark of the transmitter) had the effect of expelling negative electric charges from the clean surface of a metal, and that it was these charges that helped to maintain the current between Hertz's spheres. Indeed, some substances, notably the alkali metals, were found to show the same effect even with visible light. That the air around the metal is not involved was demonstrated by the experiment illustrated in Fig. 32.1. Here two metal plates are sealed inside a well-evacuated quartz tube and are connected to a battery. If the surface of the negatively charged plate C (the cathode) is clean, it will, when illuminated, copiously emit charges that are then attracted to the positively charged plate A (the anode) and recirculated by way of the battery. The rate of flow of the charges so obtained is appropriately named the *photoelectric current*. The charges emitted from the cathode in the photoelectric effect were later shown to be ordinary electrons. More detailed studies by many investigators gave the following information.

(1) If the light incident on the cathode in Fig. 32.1 is monochromatic (of essentially one frequency), the number of electrons emitted from the metal per unit time, as measured by the current in the circuit, is found to be directly proportional to the intensity of the light. This is not unexpected, for the energy of the incident light must somehow be absorbed by the metal, and thus the number of electrons escaping per second could well increase as the rate of receipt of light energy is increased.

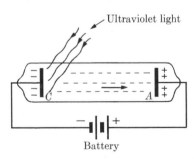

Fig. 32.1. When ultraviolet light falls on a negatively charged electrode in an evacuated quartz tube, a photoelectric current is set up in the gap between the electrodes.

(2) The electrons, each of mass m_e and charge q_e, emerge from the metal with kinetic energies $\frac{1}{2}m_e v^2$. To determine these energies, we reverse the battery connections, as in Fig. 32.2. Then the electric potential difference between the plates, V_{CA}, will *retard* the motion of the negatively charged electrons (Section 27.8). By Eq. (27.3), the work done by the electric field on each electron passing from C to A is $V_{CA}q_e$. Suppose that we increase V_{CA} until the photoelectric current is found to become zero.

Then even those electrons emitted from C with the highest speed, $v_{\max}$, just fail to reach A. Equating the maximum kinetic energy to the work done by the retarding field in stopping an electron of this energy just before it reaches A, we have

$$\tfrac{1}{2}m_e v_{\max}^2 = V_{CA}q_e. \quad (32.1)$$

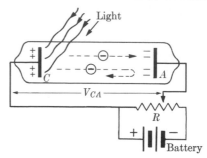

The *stopping potential difference* V_{CA} can be measured, q_e is known, and therefore the maximum kinetic energy with which the electrons emerge from C can be computed. This leads to a surprising result.

FIG. 32.2. Method of measuring the kinetic energy of the fastest electrons freed by the light. The potential difference V_{CA} of the plates can be varied by changing the point on R to which the anode A is connected.

Suppose that we vary the intensity of the monochromatic beam of light falling on C, to discover how this affects the maximum kinetic energy. Let us first think through what might be expected. An electron in the metal may absorb some of the light energy and thus acquire kinetic energy. In escaping from the metal, the electron loses part of this energy in doing work against the forces that bind it to the surrounding positive ions in the metal. It emerges with its remaining kinetic energy. This energy will be maximum for those electrons so situated on the metal that they can escape from it with the smallest loss of energy. If the light beam is made more intense one might expect the electrons to absorb more energy than before and thus to emerge with larger energies. But experiment now shows *this is not the case*. No matter whether the beam of monochromatic light incident on the metal C is made feeble or strong, the maximum kinetic energy of the electrons, computed from Eq. (32.1), will remain unchanged. Increasing the light intensity increases the *number* of electrons emitted per unit time, but has no detectable effect on their *speeds*. This was totally unexpected.

(3) The photoelectric effect appeared to be even more mysterious when the color, i.e., frequency ν, of the light used in the experiment was changed. The higher the frequency, the larger is the maximum kinetic energy of

the electrons. When the frequency of the light is gradually reduced, this energy gradually becomes smaller, until a critical frequency ν_0 is reached for which the kinetic energy of the emerging electron becomes zero (Fig. 32.3). In other words, light of frequency equal to or smaller than ν_0 cannot free electrons from the metal, *no matter how intense the beam of light may be.* This critical frequency ν_0 is called the *photoelectric threshold frequency* for the metal.

(4) Suppose that experiments are next carried out with different metals used as the cathode C. For each different metal, the threshold frequency ν_0 turns out to be different. For most metals, ν_0 is in the ultraviolet region. For some, including the alkali metals used in commercial photoelectric cells, it is in the visible region; for example, ν_0 is about 4.4×10^{14} cycles/sec for a sodium surface, which corresponds to a wavelength of about 6800 A, in the red part of the light spectrum. On the other hand, the angle of inclination and hence the *slope* of the line in Fig. 32.3 turn out to be the same for all metals; thus, if the curves for different metals were plotted together as in Fig. 32.3, they would form a family of parallel, straight lines, with each line meeting the abscissa at a different point ν_0, the threshold frequency for that metal.

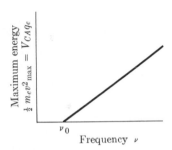

FIG. 32.3. By experiment, the maximum energy of the emitted electrons varies linearly with the frequency of the incident light if it is above ν_0.

(5) Finally, it was observed that whereas no amount of light of frequency ν_0 or less will free electrons from a particular metal surface, when the frequency exceeds ν_0 even the feeblest intensity suffices to release electrons *without any sensible delay.* Precise experiments have shown that if there is any time lag at all between arrival of light at the metal surface and the starting of the photoelectric current, it is less than 3×10^{-9} sec. Such a result is entirely contrary to expectations if we hold to the classical wave theory, according to which the energy of electromagnetic radiation is distributed continuously and uniformly over the advancing wave front. Indeed, calculations indicate that light of low intensity spread out in this way would have to fall on a metal for many seconds before any one electron accumulated sufficient energy to emerge from the metal. Thus the classical theory fails here, as well as in the attempts to explain why the maximum energy of the electrons varies with the frequency of the light and not with its intensity.

PROBLEM 32.1. State concisely the several empirical generalizations found to hold for the photoelectric effect.

PROBLEM 32.2. In 1902 P. Lenard, in an experiment with a metal on which the ultraviolet portion of sunlight was falling, found that a potential difference of 4.3 volts was needed to reduce the photoelectric current to zero. (a) Show that the maximum kinetic energy with which electrons emerged from the metal was 6.9×10^{-19} j. (b) Compute the speed of the fastest photoelectrons in this experiment.

32.2 Einstein's photon theory.

32.2 Einstein's photon theory. The resolution of these problems came in 1905 in a paper by Einstein, entitled modestly, "On a heuristic point of view concerning the generation and transformation of light."* Einstein (Fig. 32.4) began by paying tribute to the wide usefulness of Maxwell's theory of light: it "has proved itself excellently suited for the description of purely optical phenomena [reflection, refraction, interference, polarization, and so on], and will probably never be replaced by another theory" for this purpose. However, the classical theory was designed and tested primarily with reference to the *propagation* of light, its progress through space and matter as measured over relatively large time intervals. Therefore, Einstein continued, one should not be surprised if contradictions with this experience arise when the investigation turns to problems where everything is contingent on a *momentary* interaction between light and matter, as in the emission and absorption of radiation by oscillators and in the transformation of the energy of radiation into the kinetic energy of electrons in the photoelectric effect.

Einstein now proposed the hypothesis that *the energy of light is not distributed evenly over the whole wave front, as the classical picture assumes, but rather is concentrated or localized in discrete small regions*—in "bundles" or "lumps" of energy, so to speak. To gain some feeling for what this hypothesis implies, suppose that it were applicable to the energy of water waves on a pond where driftwood is floating everywhere on the surface. Then we should expect a passing wave to move pieces of driftwood up and down (impart energy to them) only at certain spots or small portions along the wave front; at all other places the passing wave would leave the pieces of wood undisturbed.

The difficulty of conceiving of a wave passing a floating object without setting it into oscillation dramatizes the difficulty of comprehending in common-sense terms Einstein's hypothesis that the energy of light is localized rather than being spread out evenly over a wide front. However, we can see the roots of Einstein's idea in Planck's work (Section 31.6).

Heuristic = furthering investigation, serving as an aid in the advancement of a conceptual scheme, but without necessarily being in final form or excluding alternative explanations. It is curious to note that Newton, in communicating to the Royal Society in 1672 the view that light consists of particles, explained that this hypothesis was heuristic.

FIG. 32.4. Albert Einstein (1879–1955), photographed in 1912. (*Copyright* Lotte Jacobi.)

Planck assumed, we will recall, that an oscillator can radiate or absorb energy only in quanta of amount $h\nu$, where ν is the frequency of the oscillator and also of the radiation emitted or absorbed. But in advancing his new conceptions, Planck retained that part of the classical view that concerned the nature and propagation of radiation after the moment of emission. This raised certain conceptual problems; for example, if an oscillator can change energy only in steps $h\nu$, how can it absorb radiation in which the energy is thinly distributed? If the oscillator cannot absorb energy by gradually increasing in amplitude, which is inconsistent with the quantum hypotheses, how can it store up the stream of incident energy until the amount $h\nu$ is available? Even if a storage mechanism could be imagined, the experiments showing the lack of any appreciable time delay in the emissions of electrons in the photoelectric effect [Section 32.1, (4)] indicate that no appreciable storage actually occurs.

According to Einstein's conception, a quantum of energy $h\nu$ lost by an emitter does not spread out over an expanding wave front, but *remains intact as a quantum of radiation of energy $h\nu$*. To this quantum of radiation the name *photon* later was given. Each wave front emerging from a glowing object, say the sun, is to be thought of as studded with photons, somewhat like little dots on a balloon that is expanding with the speed of light. As the wave expands, the light energy per unit area of the wave front decreases because the distance between the photons increases. The beams of light ordinarily used in experiments on reflection, refraction, polarization, and the like have so many photons on each wave front that the individuality of these photons is masked and the energy appears to be distributed continuously, just as any ordinary object appears to us to consist of continuous matter rather than of individual atoms or molecules. But in the absorption and transformation of light energy by an individual submicroscopic particle, as in the photoelectric effect, the finer "structure" of the light wave becomes important. Thus the classical theory remains valid and appropriate for dealing with most problems of optics, but the quantum theory must be used to understand the interaction between radiation and individual particles of matter.

32.3 Einstein's photoelectric equation. This new picture of light leads at once to a quantitative explanation of the photoelectric effect. A quantum of radiation (a photon) meeting an electron may or may not give it enough energy, all in one "bundle," to free it from the metal. If the photon's energy *is* sufficient, the electron can free itself despite the work it must do as it moves out against the electrostatic forces binding it to the metal. If the photon's energy is less than the work needed, the electron will not emerge. This at once explains why photoelectric emission, if it takes place at all, is instantaneous. Moreover, the significance of the threshold frequency ν_0 is now also clear. For any electron that is at the surface of the metal, where the binding energy is smallest, the photon energy $h\nu$ needed to free it must be at least equal to $h\nu_0$, a quantity called the *work function* of the metal. Furthermore, since different metals differ chemically and structurally, we would expect the work function $h\nu_0$, and therefore ν_0, to vary from one metal to another, as in fact it does.

For light of frequency higher than ν_0, each photon has an energy $h\nu$ that is larger than $h\nu_0$, so that the electron still has some kinetic energy left when it emerges from the metal. Because light can penetrate beneath the topmost layers of atoms of the metal, the transfer of energy from photon to electron may take place some distance below the surface, and such electrons will emerge with comparatively small speeds. But an electron that is at the surface will emerge with the maximum speed v_{max}. For any such electron we may write

$$h\nu = h\nu_0 + \tfrac{1}{2}m_e v_{max}^2. \tag{32.2}$$

This is *Einstein's photoelectric equation*, and it is an application of the principle of conservation of energy as well as of the quantum conception. This equation agrees with and expresses in algebraic form the experimentally reached generalization that the maximum kinetic energy with which electrons are emitted in the photoelectric effect increases linearly with the frequency of the emitted light, but not with its intensity [Section 32.1, (2) and (3)]. Moreover, because a larger intensity means that more photons are incident on the metal per unit time, the number of electrons set free per unit time should increase with the intensity, as is also observed [Section 32.1, (1)]. Thus Eq. (32.2) summarizes simply and beautifully all the basic features of the photoelectric effect.

Precise and reproducible photoelectric measurements are difficult to make; for example, roughness of the metal surface or the slightest amount of some impurities may greatly affect the experimental values obtained for ν_0 and v_{max}. Indeed, at the time when Einstein proposed Eq. (32.2), the experimental data were often merely semiquantitative and so incomplete that the equation could not be adequately tested. Only later, when the validity of the equation was fully borne out by the results of many refined experiments, did the photon theory come to be regarded, no longer as a "heuristic point of view," but as a fundamental part of physical theory. It was nominally for this work on the quantum theory of radiation that Einstein was awarded the Nobel Prize for physics in 1921.

In 1916, the American physicist Robert A. Millikan (Fig. 32.5) was the first to obtain the precise experimental data from which the straight-line graphs like the one shown in Fig. 32.3 were plotted for various metals. The theoretically predicted Eq. (32.2)—clearly having the right form for

FIG. 32.5. Robert A. Millikan (1868–1953).
(Courtesy Dr. Clark B. Millikan.)

a straight-line graph—was thus verified. The experimental curve for a particular metal immediately gives, by the intercept on the axis of abscissas, the value of its threshold frequency ν_0. Most important, the *slope* of the lines, which is the same for every metal, is seen to be equal to h, the Planck constant. This is obvious at once if we write Eq. (32.2) in the form $\frac{1}{2}mv_{\max}^2 = h\nu - h\nu_0$, to show the analogy with the simple equation for a straight line, $y = mx + b$, where b is the y-intercept. Millikan showed from his experimental curves that h has the same value, within the experimental error, as that obtained by Planck by a very different method (Section 31.7).

PROBLEM 32.3. When the experimental data for potassium are plotted as in Fig. 32.3, the threshold frequency ν_0 is found to be about 4.6×10^{14} cycles/sec (red region). Using the known value for the Planck constant h, (a) show that the work function for potassium is 3.0×10^{-19} j, and (b) compute the maximum kinetic energy of an electron freed from potassium by radiation of frequency 1.06×10^{15} cycles/sec (near ultraviolet).

PROBLEM 32.4. For a certain metal, the *threshold wavelength* λ_0 ($\equiv c/\nu_0$) is found to be 3000 A (near ultraviolet). Compute the work function, expressing it both in joules and in electron volts (see Problem 27.28).

PROBLEM 32.5. (a) Show that Eq. (32.2) may be written in the alternative form $h\nu = h\nu_0 + V_{CA}q_e$, where V_{CA} is the stopping potential difference when radiation of frequency ν is incident on the metal. (b) In Fig. 32.3, show that the slope of the line is equal to $V_{CA}q_e/(\nu - \nu_0)$.

PROBLEM 32.6. In a low-precision measurement made with the apparatus of Fig. 32.2, the threshold frequency of the metal forming the cathode C was found to be 10^{14} cycles/sec, while the stopping potential difference when light of frequency 5×10^{14} cycles/sec was incident on this cathode turned out to be 2 volts. What is the slope of the line in Fig. 32.3 in these experiments? Find h from this.

PROBLEM 32.7. In Fig. 32.2, suppose that the cathode metal has a threshold frequency of 10^{14} cycles/sec. What retarding potential difference, in volts, must be applied to keep all the electrons from reaching the anode A when the frequency of the light incident on the cathode is (a) 10^{14} cycles/sec, and (b) 10^{15} cycles/sec?

PROBLEM 32.8. In a tube like that in Fig. 32.1, a platinum cathode with a smooth, clean surface was illuminated with monochromatic radiation of wavelength 2100 A (400 A shorter than λ_0). Separate experiments showed that this radiant energy was falling on the platinum surface at the rate of 1.2×10^{-7} j/sec, but that about 90% of it was reflected by the surface. (a) Assuming that each photon absorbed by the metal resulted in the emission of an electron, compute the number of electrons emitted per second. (b) If the potential difference between A and C and the geometric arrangement were such that all these electrons reach A, what was the photoelectric current in amperes?

32.4 The photon-wave dilemma. Einstein's photon theory was soon found fruitful in explaining other phenomena, including some puzzling observations that had been made in photochemistry and on the specific heat capacities of solids, two topics to which Einstein himself made contributions. By adopting the conception that the energy of radiation is quantized, Einstein also contributed directly toward the acceptance of Planck's original quantum theory, then still without general support. But, similar to Dalton's repudiation of the work of Avogadro (Section 23.2), Planck expressed grave doubts about Einstein's proposal. If the photon theory were accepted, Planck wrote in 1910, "the theory of light would be thrown back by centuries" to the time when the followers of Newton and Huygens fought one another on the issue of the particle *versus* the wave theory of light. All the fruits of Maxwell's great work were threatened if quantization of radiant energy was accepted "for the sake of a few still rather dubious speculations."*

In truth, the photon conception presented many very real difficulties. Photons cannot be thought of as material particles having kinetic energy, for they cannot be stopped without being destroyed. In this they differ from the Newtonian conception of particles of light, leaving only a faint analogy between them. But our minds tend to cling to ideas that can be clearly visualized, and considerable self-control is needed to visualize a quantum of radiant energy without bringing in some matter to which to attach it. It was a little easier to think, with Maxwell, of radiant energy as spread evenly over a wave front.

There were other questions even more perplexing. What could be the meaning of "wavelength" or of "frequency" if a beam of radiation is a procession of photons? Yet it is the frequency ν that determines the energy $h\nu$ of a photon, and this frequency is computed by measuring the wavelength λ, on the assumption that radiation consists of waves, and then using the relation $\nu = c/\lambda$. Again, what is the cross-sectional area of the "spot" on the wave front where the photon is located? How about the phenomenon of interference, which only a wave theory seemed capable of explaining? And how does an electron absorb a photon's energy to become a photoelectron?

For a time, these conceptual difficulties forced physicists to retain the two separate theories, applying the wave theory to such phenomena as interference and polarization, and the photon theory to photoelectricity and other phenomena involving momentary interactions between radiation and matter. Indeed, in most practical situations it is still found simplest to apply one theory or the other as required by the problem. But for the theorist this is of course unsatisfactory, since his task is to find a general theory applicable to all the known phenomena in the field and perhaps capable of predicting entirely new phenomena as well.

The solution, which was reached comparatively recently, involves combining both views, and assuming that photons are distributed over the wave front in a statistical way and are not to be thought of as localized at particular points. For our purposes here, the main thing to see is that many of the perplexing questions raised earlier stemmed from attempts to transfer conceptions gained from experience with large-scale bodies to

---

*It is of interest to note that the work of Thomas Young over a hundred years earlier, which revived and further developed Huygens' wave theory and later provided an essential basis for Maxwell's theory, was generally attacked at the time by the proponents of the then current particle theory of light on the ground that the wave theory, as one critic put it, "can have no other effect than to check the progress of science and renew all those wild phantoms of the imagination which . . . Newton put to flight from her temple."

submicroscopic phenomena. Thus the concept of "size" as it has been developed for pebbles or projectiles should not necessarily be expected to have the same meaning when applied to photons. Furthermore, photons, and subatomic particles as well, differ from large-scale entities in that we cannot perform various experiments with one and the *same* subatomic entity. We can select, say, a particular stone and, in series of experiments, measure its weight, volume, velocities while in motion, and so on, and all this time be dealing with the same unchanged stone. But a photon, when it is absorbed by a detector such as a photographic emulsion, gives up its energy and ceases to exist. Moreover, a beam of radiation never discloses all its characteristics at one time in one set of experiments. Whether it reveals its photon or its wave property in a particular experiment depends on the nature of the experiment. As the physicist Max Born has said:

> The ultimate origin of the difficulty lies in the fact (or philosophical principle) that we are compelled to use the words of common language when we wish to describe a phenomenon, not by logical or mathematical analysis, but by a picture appealing to the imagination. Common language has grown by everyday experience and can never surpass these limits. Classical physics has restricted itself to the use of concepts of this kind; by analyzing visible motions it has developed two ways of representing them by elementary processes: moving particles and waves. There is no other way of giving a pictorial description of motions—we have to apply it even in the region of atomic processes, where classical physics breaks down.
>
> Every process can be interpreted either in terms of corpuscles or in terms of waves, but on the other hand it is beyond our power to produce proof that it is actually corpuscles or waves with which we are dealing, for we cannot simultaneously determine all the other properties which are distinctive of a corpuscle or of a wave, as the case may be. We can therefore say that the wave and corpuscular descriptions are only to be regarded as complementary ways of viewing one and the same objective process, a process which only in definite limiting cases admits of complete pictorial interpretation . . . (*Atomic physics*, 1946)

We note that the difficulties arise only if we insist on viewing the world solely through the eyes of everyday common sense, only if we want "pictures appealing to the imagination" rather than a workable theory couched in mathematical terms. The acceptance of the photon-wave duality also reveals a very powerful way of dealing with any two apparently incompatible theories or phenomena when both have sound claims for acceptance: what originally may have seemed to be two equally necessary but contradictory points of view can be brought together by adopting the *complementarity* point of view, by which the disparate phenomena are seen to be merely different responses of one system to different situations. In terms of a simple analogy, a child may behave sometimes like an angel and at other times like an imp; in fact, however, he is neither angel nor imp, but something combining both, and the particular circumstances merely reveal one or the other of these two complementary aspects, depending on the situation.

32.5 Applications of the photon concept. No matter what difficulty we may have in picturing the wave-photon duality, the photon theory stands on its own proven power to explain, to predict, and to stimulate new discoveries—the ultimate tests of the value of a scientific theory (Section 8.3). We can illustrate the strength of the photon theory by brief references to three examples.

(a) *Fluorescence.* A material is said to be *fluorescent* if it immediately emits radiation when subjected to an agency often invisible, such as a stream of electrons or ultraviolet light. When due to the action of incident radiation, the emitted fluorescence generally is found to be of a frequency equal to or *lower* than that of the incident radiation (Stokes' rule). This was once a disturbing puzzle, but the quantum theory of light gave an immediate explanation. When an incident photon of energy $h\nu$ is absorbed by an oscillator in the fluorescent material, the oscillator changes to one of the higher energy levels. Oscillators tend to remain only briefly at higher energy levels; each will quickly return to a lower level and thus reradiate the energy. An oscillator may do this in one transition, thus emitting a photon of the same energy $h\nu$ as the one it absorbed, or, if other energy levels exist between the original and final levels, it may return to its original level in two or more steps; in the latter case it will emit two or more photons in succession, each of lower frequency, but with the sum of their energies equal to that of the absorbed photon. It will be noted that this explanation involves the assumption that an oscillator is able to undergo energy changes from one energy level to any other, whether it is adjacent or not, but the changes must still take place in discrete jumps on the energy-level diagram.

PROBLEM 32.9. In rare cases the radiation absorbed by a fluorescent material is reradiated at a higher *frequency*. Suggest a way for explaining this phenomenon.

(b) *X-ray photons.* In 1895, W. K. Röntgen had discovered that a beam of what were then called cathode rays (soon identified as a stream of electrons) gave rise to a new type of radiation when they hit an obstacle such as the glass of the tube. In time these *x-rays*, a name given to them by Röntgen, were shown to be very high-frequency electromagnetic radiation of the same fundamental nature as radio waves, visible light, and other radiations (see Table 32.1); they are now usually all listed as part of one general spectrum.

Table 32.1. Spectrum of electromagnetic radiation.

Name of radiation	Approximate wavelength range
Gamma rays	Less than 0.5 A
X-rays	0.1 A to 500 A
Ultraviolet radiation	100 A to 3800 A
Visible light	3800 A to 7500 A
Infrared radiation	7500 A to 0.1 mm
Microwaves	A few millimeters to meters
Radio waves	A few meters and up

Nowadays, x-rays are generated in an evacuated tube by bombarding a metal target forming the anode with electrons emitted by a heated cathode (Fig. 32.6). In a sense, this is the reverse of the photoelectric effect: instead of electrons freed from a substance by incident photons, as in Fig. 32.1, we here have photons emitted when a substance is bombarded by electrons. We may provisionally imagine that at the target (anode) the kinetic energy of an incident electron is re-emitted as a photon after some interaction between the electron and the atoms in the anode. Therefore we may expect the energy of the x-ray photon to be at best equal to the kinetic energy of the incident electron, or $h\nu = \frac{1}{2}mv^2$. But the kinetic energy acquired by the electron during its acceleration from cathode to anode is $V_{AC}q_e$, by Eq. (27.3). Thus, finally,

$$h\nu = V_{AC}q_e. \tag{32.3}$$

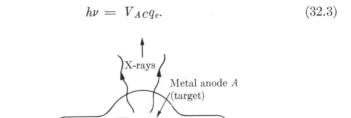

FIG. 32.6. An x-ray tube. The current due to source B heats the tungsten filament C to a temperature where it emits electrons copiously. When the potential difference V_{AC} is large, the electrons are attracted to and hit the anode A with high speeds, generating x-rays.

This equation is found to predict the frequency of x-rays correctly, but only the *maximum* frequency of the x-rays emitted by a given tube; in addition to the maximum frequency given by Eq. (32.3) there is a continuous spectrum of lower frequencies. But we should have expected this. Before an electron can interact with atoms in a way to cause photon emission, several other processes can be imagined to occur which will take some share of its kinetic energy. For example, electrons can be slowed down by various amounts by collisions with the atoms of the anode; indeed, the anode becomes so hot in an x-ray tube that it usually has to be cooled to prevent its deterioration or destruction. The kinetic energy of the free electron, not being associated with a periodic or oscillatory phenomenon, is *not* quantized, and therefore can be lost by the electron in driblets as well as in one lump.

PROBLEM 32.10.   In the tube of Fig. 32.6, suppose that the anode-cathode potential difference is made 50,000 volts. (a) Show that each electron reaches the anode with a kinetic energy of 8.0×10^{-15} j. (b) What is the maximum frequency of the emitted x-rays?

PROBLEM 32.11.   In an x-ray tube, V_{AC} is made 60,000 volts. Find (a) the speed with which the electrons reach the anode, and (b) the shortest wavelength represented in the continuous x-ray spectrum emitted by the target.

PROBLEM 32.12.   When the x-rays of Problem 32.10 were allowed to fall on a potassium cathode in a photoelectric cell (Problem 32.3), the maximum speed of the freed photoelectrons was found to be equal, within the experimental error, to the speed of the electrons that produced the original x-rays. Is this observation in accord with the expectations based on the photon theory of light?

PROBLEM 32.13.   X-ray experiments provide an independent method for determining Planck's constant h. In experiments with a 40,000-volt tube, measurements showed the value of the shortest wavelength present in the emitted x-rays to be 0.31 A. (a) Use the given data and the known values of c and q_e to compute h. (b) Name two other independent methods for evaluating h.

(c) *Momentum of photon.*   Another historic example of the use of the photon concept involves the interaction between a beam of negatively charged electrons and positively charged atomic nuclei. When a high-speed electron passes a nearby nucleus, the mutual forces of electrical attraction can deflect the electron strongly from its path in exactly the same manner as the sun affects a passing comet (Fig. 32.7). It would be expected that the change of momentum of the electron, $\Delta \mathbf{M}_e$, is compensated exactly by a corresponding and opposite $\Delta \mathbf{M}_n$ of the nucleus.

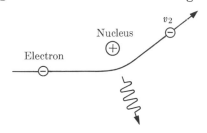

FIG. 32.7.   Radiation owing to deflection of an electron.

On checking experimentally, we find that the latter change is too small to account for ΔM_e. Is this not evidence that here at last the treasured principle of conservation of momentum breaks down?

We should be loath to accept this position without looking first for an explanation elsewhere. We remember well that the irregularities in the motion of the planet Uranus also offered such an alternative: either to consider a failure of the old law (of universal gravitation), or else to search for an explanation of the puzzling behavior by a bold hypothesis; it was the latter course which triumphantly proved to be correct and led to the discovery of Neptune.

Here also: does nothing else happen to carry away some momentum? During the deflection of the electron a flash of light is released, although of a frequency so far beyond the visible that instruments other than the eye are needed to detect it. If we could say that light has momentum, and assign it the missing quantity, all would be well and the principle saved. But surely that is not so easily permissible! How can one conceive of momentum, *mass* times *velocity*, where there is nothing but disembodied wave motion, radiant energy?

While some of the quantitative argument must be delayed to Part IX, there was other evidence that light exerts pressure and can produce changes of momentum, most spectacularly the observation that the material in the tail of a comet always is directed away from the sun at every point along the comet's path. (The suggestion that it was the sun's light which pushed the comet's tail was first made by Kepler.) Modern and most delicate measurements around 1900 showed clearly that light waves bring with them momentum, although the quantities are ordinarily small. Moreover, and most importantly, the amount of momentum in a given light beam can be predicted from simple assumptions in the classical theory of light, and does indeed coincide with these measured values to better than 1% despite the serious difficulties in experimentation.

The conception that a flash of light waves has associated with it a momentum became of importance subsequently in several other independent contexts; for example, in 1923 the American physicist A. H. Compton discovered that a beam of x-rays can collide with electrons and will bounce off with slightly less energy in another direction while each electron "recoils" as though it were one billiard ball hit by another (Fig. 32.8). Compton found that the observable momentum of the recoil electron was numerically just equal to the change of momentum of the x-ray photon (as will be seen in Chapter 38) by the same relation needed to fulfill the

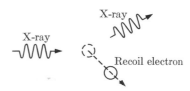

FIG. 32.8. Scattering of x-ray photon by an electron.

conservation law in Fig. 32.7. In this way, the conservation principle was borne out, and at the same time the nature of light itself became better understood.

32.6 Quantization in the sciences. In the period between 1808 and 1905, biology, chemistry, and physics saw the introduction of some remarkably similar conceptions. In each of these fields it was found fruitful to assume the existence of certain fundamental, *discrete* entities or quantities. Thus Dalton (1808) proposed that matter consists of atoms which maintain their integrity in all chemical reactions. In biology, Schleiden for plants (1838) and Schwann for animals (1839) proposed the theory of cells, by the various combinations of which living tissues were assumed to be built. Gregor Mendel's work (1865) led to the immensely fruitful idea that the material governing heredity contains a structure of definite entities, or genes, which may be transmitted from one generation to the next without change.

Meanwhile, heat, electricity, and light, which were the parts of physics that the 18th century had visualized largely in terms of the actions of imponderable fluids, were being rephrased in a similar manner. In Joule's kinetic theory (1847), sensible heat was identified with the motions of discrete atoms and molecules. In electricity, the electron, a particle with the smallest unit of negative charge, was discovered (1897). Finally, the energy of the sources of radiation and then of radiation itself was found to be quantized (1900 and 1905). In short, it was as if these new views in the sciences stemmed from a similarly directed change of the mental model used to comprehend phenomena—a change in which the guiding idea is no longer a *continuum*, but a particle or *quantum*. In part, this change can be ascribed to the development of new and better instruments and techniques that opened up new realms to observation. On the other hand, such technical improvements frequently were stimulated by the proposal of an idea that they later helped to fortify. To understand this conjunction of similar conceptions, each of which revolutionized its region of application, one must allow also the possibility of a change of tone and orientation in the whole field of the sciences, of a general conceptual trend not related to any single cause.

We shall see further results of this orientation toward quantization and discrete structure as we turn now to an examination of the radiation emitted and absorbed by *gases*. We shall also see that the attempts to explain this radiation leads to a model for the internal structure of atoms.

SUPPLEMENTARY READING

BLACKWOOD, O. H., T. H. OSGOOD, and A. E. RUARK, *An outline of atomic physics* (Wiley, 1955), Chap. IV.

BUCKLEY, H., *A short history of physics* (Methuen, 1927), Chap. X.

EINSTEIN, A., and L. INFELD, *The evolution of physics* (Simon and Schuster, 1938), Part IV.

FRANK, P., *Einstein, his life and times* (Knopf, 1947).

GLASSER, O., *Wilhelm Conrad Röntgen* (Springfield, Illinois, 1934).

MICHELS, W. C., and A. L. PATTERSON, *Elements of modern physics* (Van Nostrand, 1951), Chap. 23.

OLDENBERG, O., *Introduction to atomic physics* (McGraw-Hill, 1954), Chap. 8.

TAYLOR, L. W., *Physics: the pioneer science* (Houghton Mifflin, 1941), pp. 808–814.

WATSON, E. C., "The discovery of x-rays," *American Journal of Physics*, v. 13 (1945), pp. 281–291. Facsimile reproductions, together with English translations, of Röntgen's first two papers on x-rays.

CHAPTER 33

SPECTRA OF GASES

Our study of spectra up to this point has been confined to the continuous spectrum of radiation found to be emitted by every glowing solid and liquid, and incidentally also by gases at those extreme conditions of density and temperature found in the sun and other stars. We saw how the temperature of such a source can be found by observing the wavelength λ_{peak} for which the radiated energy is a maximum (Fig. 31.2). But as to *chemical composition*, we found no clue offered, for the quantity and quality of the emitted radiation depends solely on the temperature of the source and on the physical nature of its surface. Turning now to the radiation emitted by gases under ordinary conditions, we find a very different state of affairs.

33.1 Line emission spectra. It had long been known that light is emitted by gases or vapors when they are "excited" in any one of several ways: by heating the gas to a high temperature, as when some volatile substance is put into a flame; by an electric discharge, as when the gas is between the terminals of an electric arc or spark or, in nature, when a lightning discharge occurs in the atmosphere; by a continuous electric current in a gas at low pressure (Fig. 33.1), examples being the familiar "neon sign" and, in nature, the beautiful aurora, produced in the rarefied upper atmosphere by streams of charged particles coming presumably from the sun.

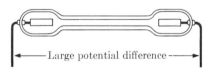

← ——— Large potential difference - - ——— →

Fig. 33.1. Gas under low pressure in the tube emits light when an electric current is maintained in the gas.

The pioneer experiments on light emitted by various excited gases were made in 1752 by the Scottish physicist Thomas Melvill. By putting one substance after another in a flame, and "having placed a pasteboard with circular hole in it between my eye and the flame . . . , I examined the constitution of these different lights with a prism." Melvill found the spectrum of light from a hot gas to be startlingly different from the continuum of rainbow colors in the spectrum of a glowing solid or liquid. It consisted, not of an unbroken stretch of color continuously graded from violet to red, but of individual circular spots, each having the color of that part of the spectrum in which it was located, and with dark gaps (missing colors) between the spots. Later, when more general use was made of narrow slits through which to pass the light (Fig. 30.6), the spectrum of a gas was seen, of course, as a set of *lines* (Fig. 33.2). Thus the spectrum of light from a gas came to be called a *line emission spectrum,* or a *bright-line spectrum.* From our general theory of light and of the separation of light into its component colors by a prism, we may infer that light from a gas is a mixture of only a few definite colors or wavelengths of light.

Melvill went further. He noted that the colors and locations of the bright spots formed by the prism were different when different substances were put in the flame. For example, with ordinary table salt in the flame, the predominant color was "bright yellow" (now known to be characteristic of the element sodium). In fact, the line-emission spectrum is markedly different for each chemically different gas. Each chemical element has its own *characteristic* pattern of wavelengths throughout the whole observable spectrum (Fig. 33.2). In looking at a gaseous source without the aid of a prism or a grating, the eye synthesizes the separate colors and perceives the mixture as reddish for

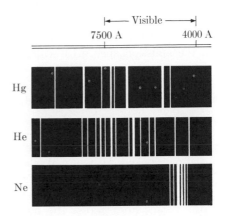

FIG. 33.2. Part of the line emission spectrum of mercury vapor, of helium, and of neon. (Redrawn from photographic records.)

glowing neon, pale blue for nitrogen, yellow for sodium vapor, and so on.

For some of these gases, the spectrum is found to be relatively simple. Thus sodium vapor shows only two prominent lines in the visible part of the spectrum, and modern measurements show that they correspond to the wavelengths 5889.953 A and 5895.923 A. These lines are so close together that only a good spectrometer can resolve them clearly, and therefore we usually speak of them as a sodium "doublet" at about 5890 A. Some gases or vapors, on the other hand, have exceedingly complex spectra. The radiation from iron vapor, for example, has some 6000 bright lines in the visible range alone. This great variety of spectral patterns, a different one for each elementary gas, seemed to be quite unaccountable. Why should an excited gas show discrete lines rather than a continuous spectrum, and why should closely related elements (such as He and Ne in Fig. 32.2) have line spectra of such different patterns?

In 1823 the British astronomer J. Herschel suggested that each gas could be identified from its unique line spectrum, and it has since been found that this can be done as surely as a person can be identified or traced by means of his characteristic fingerprints. Here was the beginning of the important branch of physical science known as *spectrum analysis*. By the early 1860's, the physicist Gustav R. Kirchhoff and the chemist Robert W. Bunsen at the University of Heidelberg, regarded as the inventors of the spectroscope, had jointly discovered two new elements, rubidium and cesium, by noting hitherto unreported emission lines in the spectrum of the vapor of a mineral water. This was the first of a brilliant series of such discoveries and marked the development of a technique that has made possible the speedy chemical analysis of small samples by routine spectroscopy. Another spectacular achievement that caught the imagination of the time was the spectroscopic analysis of meteorites. Observation of the emission spectra of vaporized meteorities showed that these consisted only of elements that are also present on our earth—a confirmation of the unity of the terrestrial and celestial realms that would have gladdened the hearts of Galileo and Kepler.

33.2 Line absorption spectra. In 1802 the English scientist William Wollaston saw in the spectrum of sunlight something that hitherto had been overlooked, although Wollaston's means of forming a spectrum with a slit and prism was no better than that which Newton had used in some of his experiments. Wollaston noticed a set of seven sharp, irregularly spaced *dark* lines across the continuous solar spectrum, but he did not comprehend their meaning and did not carry the investigation further. A dozen years later, Fraunhofer, the inventor of the grating spectrometer, noticed this same peculiarity in the spectrum of sunlight and, with improved instruments, he counted many hundred such dark lines (now, with still better instruments, we know of some 15,000, a small proportion being in the visible spectrum). To the most prominent dark lines, Fraunhofer assigned the letters A, B, C, . . . (Fig. 33.3). In the spectra of several other bright stars, he found similar dark lines, many of them, although not all, being in the same positions as those in the solar spectrum.

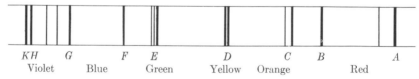

FIG. 33.3. The Fraunhofer dark lines in the visible part of the solar spectrum. Only a few of the most prominent lines are represented here.

It is noteworthy that Fraunhofer's interest in these dark lines was initially a practical one. He was designing lens systems for telescopes, and the dark lines were just what he needed to provide reference lines (markers) for specifying the parts of the spectrum for which he had measured the indexes of refraction of different kinds of glass used for lenses. But here, as often is true, the skills of the craftsman and the needs of technology eventually brought to the notice of scientists a new natural phenomenon and techniques for dealing with it.

The key observations toward a better understanding of both the dark-line and the bright-line spectra of gases were made by Kirchhoff in 1859. By that time it was known that the two prominent yellow lines in the emission spectrum of heated sodium vapor had the same wavelengths as the two prominent dark lines in the solar spectrum to which Fraunhofer had assigned the letter D. It was also known at the time that the light emitted by a glowing solid forms a perfectly continuous spectrum that shows no dark lines. What Kirchhoff now demonstrated was essentially

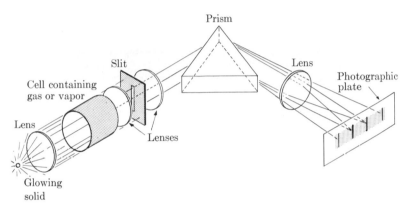

FIG. 33.4. Diagram of a spectrograph set up for recording an absorption spectrum of a gas or vapor.

that if the light from a glowing solid, as in Fig. 33.4, is allowed first to pass through sodium vapor having a temperature lower than that of the solid emitter and then is dispersed by a prism, the spectrum does exhibit two prominent dark lines at exactly the same place in the spectrum as the D-lines of the sun's spectrum. As Kirchhoff said, "the [dark] D-lines of the solar spectrum have been artificially produced in a spectrum in which they do not naturally occur." When this experiment was repeated with other, chemically different gases placed between the glowing solid and the prism, each was found to produce its own characteristic pattern of dark lines. Evidently each gas in some way absorbs light of certain wavelengths from the passing "white" light; hence such a pattern of dark lines is called a *line absorption spectrum*, to differentiate it from the bright-line emission spectrum which the same gas would send out at a higher temperature. Most interesting of all, Kirchhoff showed that the wavelength corresponding to each absorption line is equal to the wavelength of a bright line in the emission spectrum of the same gas. The conclusion is that a gas can absorb *only* light of those wavelengths which, when excited, it can emit (Fig. 33.5).

Lastly, Kirchhoff pointed out that the Fraunhofer lines in the solar and stellar spectra could be explained by assuming that the sun or other star is surrounded by an atmosphere of relatively cool gases which absorbs certain wavelengths from the continuous spectrum of the radiation emitted by the hot interior (except that a few additional dark lines in the spectrum are known to be caused by the passage of the radiation through the atmosphere of our earth). Consequently, these dark lines are clues to the chemical compositions of the stellar atmospheres. For example,

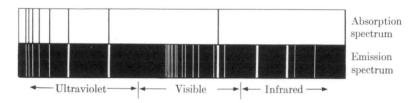

Fig. 33.5. Comparison of the line absorption spectrum and the line emission spectrum of sodium vapor.

Kirchhoff was able to identify certain of the dark solar lines as due to absorption by sodium and potassium; on the other hand, he remarked that "there is no dark line in the solar spectrum coinciding with the red line of lithium, [therefore] it seems probable that lithium either is not present in the sun's atmosphere or is there in relatively small quantity." Since Kirchhoff's day almost all the lines in the absorption spectra of the sun and many other stars have been identified; as one result, more than 60 of the elements known on the earth have now been also "found" on the sun.* Kirchhoff, by beginning the equivalent of a chemical analysis of a stellar atmosphere, thus laid the basis for modern astrophysics.

PROBLEM 33.1. Suggest experiments that would serve to show which of the Fraunhofer lines in the spectrum of sunlight are due to absorption in the sun's atmosphere rather than to absorption by gases in the earth's atmosphere.

PROBLEM 33.2. How might one decide from spectroscopic observations whether the moon and the planets shine by their own light or by reflected light from the sun?

---

*In the case of the element helium (from *helios*, Greek for sun), its existence was first suspected when some absorption lines in the solar spectrum could not be correlated with any element then known.

33.3 An astrophysical application.   Kirchhoff posed the question of what happens to the energy when a gas absorbs radiation of its own characteristic wavelengths from the passing beam of white light. We may quickly understand the essence of his argument in terms of an analogy. Suppose that a beam of *sound* involving many different frequencies is directed toward a mounted and silent tuning fork whose natural frequency, say, is 440 cycles/sec. Sound of this particular frequency, after reaching the fork, will not simply pass by it as does the rest of the beam.   Instead, being "in resonance" with the fork, sound energy at that frequency will be absorbed as it sets the prongs vibrating, and in principle a distant listener in the path of the beam might therefore notice that this one frequency component reaches him with less than full energy.   True, the tuning fork is now vibrating and therefore does send out again this sound energy that is initially absorbed by it, but it is emitted in *all* directions, not just along the original direction of the incident beam.   The amount of the absorbed sound energy that happens to be reradiated *toward* the observer is very small compared with the total energy absorbed and reradiated.

Turning now to optical absorption, our analogy leads to the following argument. A gas, after absorbing light of its own characteristic frequencies, may reradiate it in all directions, generally with the same frequencies. Therefore we should expect to see the gas, while it is absorbing light, reradiate some light of the same frequencies even if we view it at 90° to the direction of propagation of the original beam. For example, the absorbing layer of the sun's atmosphere should be reradiating light with a spectrum consisting of bright lines that are in the same positions as the dark Fraunhofer lines in the sun's directly observed spectrum. During the few moments of a total eclipse, while the blinding, full light of the sun is screened off by the moon, and all that can be seen of the sun is the light reradiated toward us by the outer edges of the absorbing layer, we expect to find that this light forms a line emission spectrum. This prediction was first and spectacularly fulfilled during observations made in 1870, and similar observations have since been made in the laboratory (Fig. 33.6). It also follows incidentally from our argument (and can be confirmed by observation) that each dark line in an absorption spectrum is not completely dark, but appears to be so because of the much greater intensity of the "background" of unaffected radiation on either side of the absorption line.

Among the many other applications of line absorption spectra to astrophysics we may very briefly mention the *Doppler effect*. In 1842 the Austrian physicist Christian Johann Doppler predicted, on the basis of the wave theory, that the frequencies comprising a beam of light will appear to an observer to increase if the light source and observer are in relative motion toward each other, and will appear to decrease if they are in

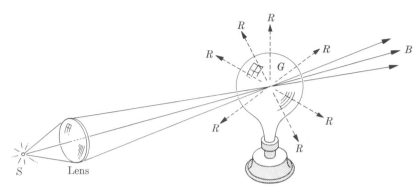

FIG. 33.6. A laboratory demonstration: *S*, high-temperature source of white light; *G*, glass bulb containing gas or vapor under low pressure; *B*, beam from source, but lacking light of certain wavelengths; *R*, reradiated light of those wavelengths.

relative motion away from each other. Qualitatively we are familiar with the analogous case of sound, namely the very noticeable rise or drop in *pitch* (not merely in loudness) heard when a jet plane or a locomotive with whistle blowing is rapidly approaching or receding from us; indeed, the effect was first successfully tested with sound waves. The explanation, for light and for sound, lies in the effect of relative motion on the perceived wavelength: if, for example, the emitter is in motion away from the receiver during the period between emitting successive wave fronts, the wavelength is effectively made longer and the frequency correspondingly lower.

For the light from a moving star, the Doppler effect should be observable as a shift of the dark absorption lines toward the red (to lower frequency) if the star is receding from the earth (Fig. 33.7), and toward the violet (to higher frequency) if it is approaching the earth. (Of course, those few Fraunhofer lines that result from absorption of the stellar light in the earth's atmosphere should not shift in position.) Observations confirming these predictions for stars were made in 1868.

Evidently, the shift should be more pronounced for higher relative speeds; indeed, Doppler gave the precise quantitative relation between the shift in frequency or wavelength and the relative speeds of source and receiver. Conversely, the *observed* shift in wavelength can be used to calculate the relative

FIG. 33.7. Dark lines in the spectrum of a star in relative motion away from the earth are seen to be shifted toward the red end of the spectrum in comparison with the absorption spectrum of a stationary source.

speeds, at least the component of relative motion along the line of sight between star and earth ("radial speed"). In this way we find that the stars in our galaxy have relative radial speeds toward or away from us of the order of 0.1 to 100 km/sec, and that all the more distant galaxies beyond ours appear to be in headlong flight away from us. The farther away they are, the faster they appear to be going; relative speeds up to $\frac{1}{3}$ the speed of light have been calculated for the most distant ones. Thus the observed "red shift" of the spectral lines from distant galaxies, if explained as a Doppler effect, leads to the conclusion that our universe is expanding. Indeed, Wollaston's puzzling observation has matured into an argument with grandiose conclusions!

33.4 Early attempts to find regularities in spectra. Following the work of Kirchhoff and Bunsen in the 1860's, experimental spectroscopy soon was pursued so widely and vigorously that almost uncountable numbers of lines in the emission and absorption spectra of various gases were being discovered and reported. The avalanche of data on wavelengths and intensities of these lines seemed to bury theorists in chaos. By 1880 no satisfactory progress had been made in their main task, that of finding a physical mechanism to explain why gases emit and absorb radiation in the way they do. In fact, there was not even much evidence of empirical regularities or order among these spectra: the lines in the spectrum of any particular gas did not appear to be spaced according to any definite pattern, nor could definite similarities between the spectra of different gases be detected. The only hints of possible simplicity were of this kind: it was noted that pairs of lines occur in various parts of the spectrum of sodium vapor and that these pairs become more numerous toward the short-wavelength end of the spectrum. Also, the wavelength difference between adjacent lines for some parts of the sodium and the zinc spectrum is constant, and certain patterns of spacings seem to recur in spectra of different elements.

This was a period of almost obsessed searching for some hint of numerical relations among the wavelengths of the tantalizing lines—for some mathematical key to decode the message that spectroscopists felt must be hidden in these observations. It is as if we watched again the contemporaries of Plato trying to reduce the offensive disorderliness of planetary motion to a series of circular motions, or Kepler trying to find relationship between the radii of planetary orbits and the times of revolution. And, most prominently, we recall chemists from Döbereiner to Mendeléeff trying to find order in the list of chemical elements. We are here observing a vital process in the advance of science.

33.5 Balmer's formula. In 1885 a Swiss school teacher, Johann Jakob Balmer (1825–1898), published a paper entitled simply "Note concerning the spectral lines of hydrogen," which contained the first important break in this problem—by an achievement quite analogous to that of Kepler, or of Planck at the beginning of his work. Balmer had found an *empirical relation* among the data for the wavelengths of the hydrogen emission lines. Earlier, Ångström had made and published quite accurate measurements of the wavelengths for the four prominent lines in the visible part of the emission spectrum (Table 33.1), but what Balmer had hit upon was a simple formula that would express these observed wavelengths, namely,

$$\lambda = b \left(\frac{n^2}{n^2 - 2^2} \right). \tag{33.1}$$

Here b is a constant that Balmer determined empirically and had found to be equal to 3645.6 A, and n is a whole number, different for each line. Specifically, n must be 3 for the first (red) line of the hydrogen emission spectrum (named H_α); $n = 4$ for the second (green) line (H_β); $n = 5$ for the third (blue) line (H_γ); and $n = 6$ for the fourth (violet) line (H_δ). Table 33.1 shows the excellent agreement (within 0.02%) between the values Balmer computed from his empirical formula and Ångström's previously measured values. With the sublime self-confidence of a numerologist, Balmer commented that the agreement was "A striking evidence for the great scientific skill and care with which Ångström must have gone to work."

Balmer had no inkling of a physical explanation why his empirical formula worked. But he was sure that the formula could be used to compute values of wavelength other than those for the four known lines simply by inserting it in other values of n. Using $n = 7$ for a hypothetical fifth line H_ϵ, and finding the expected wavelength to be 3969.65 A, he wrote:

> I knew nothing of such a fifth line, which must lie [barely] within the visible part of the spectrum . . . , and I was compelled to assume that the temperature relations in the hydrogen source were not favorable to the development of this line or that the formula was not generally applicable.

But then, he continued, a colleague mentioned that more hydrogen lines had been found, both for a hydrogen source and in stellar absorption spectra. Not only did a fifth line indeed exist, but it had the predicted wavelength! In a postscript to his paper, Balmer wrote that just then he had received word of the measured wavelengths of nine more hydrogen lines in the ultraviolet region of stellar spectra, and they all fitted his predictions to within 0.1% or better. His formula seemed completely vindicated.

Increasingly improved techniques in spectroscopy soon made it possible to record more and more of the ultraviolet region, as, for example, by photographing the line emission spectrum of the gases in the sun's atmosphere

Table 33.1. Data on hydrogen spectrum (as given in Balmer's paper).

| Name of line | n | Wavelength λ (A) | | Difference |
		From Balmer's formula	By Ångström's measurement	
H_α	3	6562.08	6562.10	$+0.02$
H_β	4	4860.8	4860.74	-0.06
H_γ	5	4340	4340.1	$+0.1$
H_δ	6	4101.3	4101.2	-0.1

during an eclipse. Of 35 consecutive lines in the "Balmer series for hydrogen" so recorded, all have been found to be in good agreement with the formula. Figure 33.8 is a spectrographic record of the hydrogen emission lines; it shows the correctness of another prediction inherent in Eq. (33.1): that the lines must crowd closer and closer together as n becomes larger. The shortest wavelength possible on the basis of the formula is 3645.6 A (if n is taken to be ∞). This predicted value for H_∞, which has come to be called the *series limit* or *convergence limit* of the Balmer series, also turned out to be in good agreement with observation.

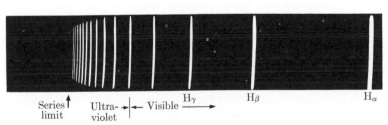

FIG. 33.8. The Balmer series of lines in the emission spectrum of hydrogen. (Redrawn from a photograph made with film sensitive to ultraviolet as well as to visible light.)

PROBLEM 33.3. (a) Check Balmer's computation for the fifth line, H_ϵ. (b) Compute λ for the Balmer line corresponding to $n = 1000$.

PROBLEM 33.4. Check Balmer's computation for the wavelength of the series limit, H_∞, of his series of lines. *Hint:* Note that $n^2/(n^2 - 2^2)$ may be written in the form $1/[1 - (2^2/n^2)]$.

33.6 Other hydrogen series. In his paper of 1885, Balmer also speculated on the possibility that there might be additional series of hitherto unsuspected lines in the hydrogen spectrum, and that their wavelengths could be found by replacing the 2^2 in the denominator of his Eq. (33.1) by other numbers such as 1^2, 3^2, 4^2, and so on. This suggestion, which stimulated many workers to search for such additional spectral series, also turned out to be fruitful. However, the formula was found to need still another modification before it would correctly describe the new series.

To use modern notation, we first rewrite Balmer's formula, Eq. (33.1), in a perfectly equivalent but more suggestive form:

$$\frac{1}{\lambda} = R_{\mathrm{H}}\left(\frac{1}{2^2} - \frac{1}{n^2}\right). \tag{33.2}$$

In this equation, which can be simply derived from Eq. (33.1), R_{H} is an empirical constant, equal to $4/b$. It is called the *Rydberg constant for hydrogen*, in honor of the Swedish spectroscopist J. R. Rydberg who, following Balmer, made great progress in the search for various spectral series. The value of R_{H}, as given by comparatively recent measurements, is $109{,}677.58$ (± 0.01) cm^{-1}.

If we now follow Balmer's speculative suggestion of replacing 2^2 by other numbers, we obtain the possibilities

$$\frac{1}{\lambda} = R_{\mathrm{H}}\left(\frac{1}{1^2} - \frac{1}{n^2}\right), \qquad \frac{1}{\lambda} = R_{\mathrm{H}}\left(\frac{1}{3^2} - \frac{1}{n^2}\right), \qquad \frac{1}{\lambda} = R_{\mathrm{H}}\left(\frac{1}{4^2} - \frac{1}{n^2}\right),$$

and so on. Evidently, all these possible series of lines can be summarized in one formula:

$$\frac{1}{\lambda} = R_{\mathrm{H}}\left(\frac{1}{n_f^2} - \frac{1}{n_i^2}\right), \tag{33.3}$$

where n_f is an integer that is fixed for any one series for which wavelengths are to be found (for example, it is 2 for the Balmer series), and n_i denotes integers that take on the values $n_f + 1$, $n_f + 2$, $n_f + 3$, ... for the successive individual lines in a given series (thus, for the first two lines of the Balmer series, n_i is 3 and 4, respectively). As for the Rydberg constant R_{H}, it should have the same value for all of these hydrogen series.

So far, our discussion has been merely speculation. No series, no single line fitting the formula in Eq. (33.3), *need* exist (except for the Balmer series, where $n_f = 2$). But when we now look for these hypothetical lines—we find that they do exist.

In 1908, F. Paschen in Germany found two hydrogen lines in the infrared whose wavelengths were correctly given by setting $n_f = 3$ and $n_i = 4$ and 5 in Eq. (33.3), and many other lines in this Paschen series have since been identified. With improvements of experimental apparatus and techniques, new regions of the spectrum could be explored, and then

to the Balmer and Paschen series others gradually were added. In Table
33.2, the name of each series is that of its first observer or proponent.

Table 33.2. Series of lines in the hydrogen emission spectrum.

Name of series	Date of discovery	Values in Eq. (33.3)		Region of spectrum
Lyman	1906–1914	$n_f = 1,$	$n_i = 2, 3, 4, \ldots$	Ultraviolet
Balmer	1885	$n_f = 2,$	$n_i = 3, 4, 5, \ldots$	Ultraviolet-visible
Paschen	1908	$n_f = 3,$	$n_i = 4, 5, 6, \ldots$	Infrared
Brackett	1922	$n_f = 4,$	$n_i = 5, 6, 7, \ldots$	Infrared
Pfund	1924	$n_f = 5,$	$n_i = 6, 7, 8, \ldots$	Infrared

PROBLEM 33.5. Compute the wavelength (a) of the third line (always counting
from the longest wavelength) in the Lyman series, and (b) of the series limit for
that series.

PROBLEM 33.6. Draw a long line and divide it into 20 equal intervals, each
of about 1 cm. Let this whole line represent a wavelength scale from 0 to 80,000 A.
On this scale mark the positions of the first, second, third, and last line (series
limit) of each of the five series listed in Table 33.2. Do these series overlap?
Of how many series could one conceive between $\lambda = 0$ and $\lambda = \infty$? How
many lines in all?

PROBLEM 33.7. Derive Eq. (33.2) from (33.1).

PROBLEM 33.8. Balmer's suggestion had been that formulas for additional
hydrogen series might possibly be obtained simply by changing his Eq. (33.1) to
$\lambda = bn^2/(n^2 - 1)$, $\lambda = bn^2/(n^2 - 3^2)$, $\ldots$, $\lambda = bn_i^2/(n_i^2 - n_f^2)$. Show that
the series limits for the various hydrogen series, when computed from these
formulas, are *not* in accord with experiment.

33.7 Spectral series for other gases. Balmer had also expressed the
hope that his formula might indicate a pattern for finding series relationships in the spectra of other gases, and this suggestion bore fruit even sooner
than the one concerning additional series for hydrogen. Rydberg and
others now made good headway in finding series formulas for various
gases. A discovery of unusual interest was made in 1896 by the American
astronomer E. C. Pickering, who observed in the absorption spectrum of
a star a series of previously unknown lines that virtually coincided in
wavelengths with the Balmer series for hydrogen except that an additional
line existed between every couple of Balmer-type lines. The whole set of
wavelengths fitted the empirical relation

$$\frac{1}{\lambda} = R_H \left[\frac{1}{(n_f/2)^2} - \frac{1}{(n_i/2)^2} \right], \tag{33.4}$$

where $n_f = 4$ and $n_i = 5, 6, 7, \ldots$ (Later, other series of this type were found, for example, one with $n_f = 2$, another with $n_f = 3$.) The thought was voiced at first, not unnaturally, that this was evidence for some celestial modification of ordinary hydrogen. The solution to this intriguing puzzle, as we shall soon see, was one of the earliest triumphs of the new model of the atom to which the historical development here is gradually leading us.

While Balmer's formula did not serve directly in the description of spectra of gases other than hydrogen, it inspired formulas of similar mathematical form that were very useful in discerning some order in portions of a good many complex spectra. The Rydberg constant also reappeared in such empirical formulas. More and more it became clear that somehow the *same basic physical mechanism* must be at work behind the variety of spectroscopic observations, and that this mechanism must be very intricate if it was to explain the great variety and number of spectral lines even in the simplest atom, hydrogen. But clearly, physical science *had* to uncover this mechanism in order to *understand* the spectra of gases instead of merely describing them with the aid of empirical formulas. However, as we now know with the wisdom of historical hindsight, no satisfactory progress in explaining the line emission and absorption spectra of gases was really possible for a generation after Balmer's paper, because the two key pieces for the construction of the necessary conceptual scheme were not then available. One of them was an understanding of the nature of light, as provided in Planck's conception of the quantization of energy (1900) and Einstein's photon theory (1905), and the other was a model of the structure of the atom. That is the subject to which we now turn.

Supplementary Reading

Blackwood, O. H., T. H. Osgood, and A. E. Ruark, *An outline of atomic physics* (Wiley, 1955), Chap. III.

Lenard, P. *Great men of science* (Macmillan, 1934). Contains brief biographies of Fraunhofer, Kirchhoff, and Bunsen.

Magie, W. F., *A source book in physics* (McGraw-Hill, 1935), pp. 360–365. A translation of Balmer's paper.

Taylor, L. W., *Physics: the pioneer science* (Houghton Mifflin, 1941), pp. 533–548.

CHAPTER 34

THE ATOMIC MODEL OF RUTHERFORD AND BOHR

34.1 Preliminary notions of atomic structure. By the beginning of the 20th century, the concept *atom* had taken on a much deeper meaning than it had possessed in Dalton's day, a century earlier. It was now known that electrons could be obtained from many different substances, and this suggested the notion that they are a part of the atoms themselves. But electrons are negatively charged, whereas atoms ordinarily are electrically neutral. Thus the presence of electrons in an atom requires the presence also of an equal amount of positive charge. The English physicist J. J. Thomson, for instance, suggested an atomic model in which each atom was pictured as a globule of positively charged fluid with the electrons embedded in it, somewhat like seeds in a watermelon.

Let us take the simplest example, an atom having a single electron. This electron should be at the center of the atom if it is to remain at rest, for only there will it be attracted equally in all directions by the positive charge of the globule. Suppose now that the electron is momentarily displaced to one side by a force due, perhaps, to another charged particle passing close to the atom. Then the electron, because there is more positive fluid on one side of it than on the other, will be attracted back toward the center. With the momentum thus acquired, the electron will move on through the center, and since the force on it is now in the opposite direction, it will slow to a stop and move back toward the center once more. In brief, the electron will have been set into oscillation; and an oscillating electric charge, according to Maxwell and Hertz, will radiate electromagnetic energy. For an atomic system with many electrons, each electron would find its position of equilibrium and execute oscillations in a similar manner when disturbed. Here then was a model that might account for the emission of light by atoms.

In this model, Thomson could compute the frequency of the oscillating electron, which gave him the frequency of the light that such an atom would emit on the basis of the "classical," Maxwellian theory of light. The result was encouraging in that the predicted frequency fell into the visible region of the spectrum. But neither this model nor others proposed at the time could account for the emission of light of frequencies in specific and discrete spectral series, as exemplified by the Balmer formula for hydrogen.

34.2 Rutherford's nuclear model of the atom. A new basis for all such speculations was provided in 1909–1911 by Ernest Rutherford (Fig. 34.1),

FIG. 34.1. Lord Rutherford (1871–1937).

a New Zealander who had already shown a rare virtuosity as an experimentalist at McGill University, Montreal, Canada, and who had moved in 1907 to Manchester University in England, where he headed a most productive research laboratory. Rutherford was particularly interested in rays emitted by radioactive substances, for example α-particles (alpha particles). As we shall see later, these have the same properties as positively charged helium ions: they are ejected with high speeds and, although exceedingly small, have a much larger mass than electrons. Rutherford had noted that on passing through a thin film of mica or metal a stream of α-particles was somewhat broadened, or scattered, by its encounters with the atoms comprising the film. This was an interesting effect, for the amount of scattering might supply information on the disposition of an atom's mass, then generally thought to be fairly evenly distributed, as in Thomson's globule of positive fluid. Later Rutherford wrote:

> . . . I had observed the scattering of α-particles, and Dr. Geiger in my laboratory had examined it in detail. He found, in thin pieces of metal, that the scattering was usually small, of the order of one degree. One day Geiger came to me and said, "Don't you think that young Marsden, whom I am training in radioactive methods, ought to begin a small research?" Now I had thought that, too, so I said, "Why not let him see if any α-particles can be scattered through a large angle?" I may tell you in confidence that I did not believe that they would be, since we knew that the α-particle was a very fast, massive particle, with a great deal of [kinetic] energy, and you could show that if the scattering was due to the accumulated effect of a number of small scatterings, the chance of an α-particle's being scattered backward was very small. Then I remember two or three days later Geiger coming to me in great excitement and saying, "We have been able to get some of the α-particles coming backward . . ." It was quite the most incredible event that has ever happened to me in my life. It was almost as incredible as if you fired a 15-inch shell at a piece of tissue paper and it came back and hit you. On consideration, I realized that this scattering backward must be the result of a single collision, and when I made calculations I saw that it was impossible to get anything of that order of magnitude unless you took a system in which the greater part of the mass of the atom was concentrated in a minute nucleus. It was then that I had the idea of an atom with a minute massive center carrying a charge.
> (*Background to modern science*, Macmillan, 1938)

This was the origin of the modern conception of the nuclear atom. Let us look at the experiments more closely to see why Rutherford felt driven to the idea that the atom is not filled with a positive fluid, but must have its mass largely concentrated at the center, thus forming a nucleus about which the electrons are clustered.

The α-particles, with speeds of about 2×10^7 m/sec, impinged in a narrow beam on a metal foil, for example a sheet of gold only 4000 A $(4 \times 10^{-5}$ cm) thick. Since the approximate diameter of an atom was known (for example, see Section 23.7), it could be estimated that a foil of this thickness contains about 1000 layers of gold atoms. Most of the α-particles emerged from the foil on the other side without being deviated, suggesting that the atom is after all not to be compared to a solid billiard ball, as might have seemed plausible on the basis of kinetic theory. True, there are many electrons in each atom, but encounters with them cannot be made to account for those few α-particles that are scattered so drastically as to return almost along the path by which they came. Each α-particle will swerve only slightly toward an electron in passing it, for an α-particle is about 7500 times more massive than an electron. Even for a head-on collision with an electron, the effect on the velocity of the α-particle is almost negligibly small, as small as the action of one grain of sand on the motion of a fast-rolling ball. In thousands of successive encounters with electrons, the probability is vanishingly small that an α-particle will undergo successive small deviations from its original direction which are so predominately *in one sense* that the net result is an actual turning back.

A more promising explanation of the observed scattering is that there exist in the foil much more substantial objects (positively charged nuclei) which are each so massive that an α-particle heading directly toward one of them is stopped and turned back, as a ball would bounce back from a rock but not from a cloud of dust particles. Figure 34.2 is based on one of Rutherford's diagrams in his paper of 1911 that may be said to have laid the foundation for the modern theory of atomic structure. The α-particle *A* is heading directly toward a nucleus *N*. Because of the electrical repul-

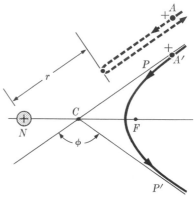

FIG. 34.2. Paths of two α-particles *A* and *A′* approaching a nucleus *N*. [Based on Rutherford, *Philosophical Magazine*, vol. 21 (1911), p. 669.]

sive force between the two (Coulomb's law), *A* is slowed to a stop at some distance *r* from *N*, and then moves directly back. At *A′* is another α-particle that is not headed directly toward the nucleus *N*; it swerves away from *N* along a path *PP′* that calculation showed must be a hyperbola. The deflection is indicated by the angle φ. Most of the α-particles do not pass so close to any nucleus and do not undergo such extreme deflections (see Fig. 34.3).

Rutherford considered the effects of important factors on the α-particles—their initial speed v_α, the foil thickness *t*, and the quantity of charge *Q* on each nucleus. On the assumption that the scattering occurs by single encounters with nuclei, he found that the number of particles scattered through a given angle should be proportional to *t* and to Q^2, and inversely proportional to v_α^4.

The verification of these predictions was undertaken by Geiger and

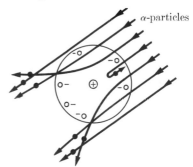

FIG. 34.3. Paths of α-particles passing through an atom of carbon. The large circle indicates the "boundary" of the atom. The tiny circles represent electrons.

Marsden with the apparatus shown schematically in Fig. 34.4. The lead box B contains a radioactive substance (radon) that emits α-particles. The particles emerging from the small hole in the box are deflected through various angles ϕ in passing through the thin metal foil F. The number of particles deflected through each angle ϕ is found by letting the particles strike a small zinc sulfide screen S. On it each incidence produces a scintillation (a momentary pinpoint of fluorescence), and these scintillations are observable and countable through the microscope M; S and M can be moved together along the arc of a circle up to $\phi = 150°$. In later experiments, the number of α-particles at any angle ϕ were counted more conveniently by replacing S and M by a Geiger counter (Fig. 34.5).

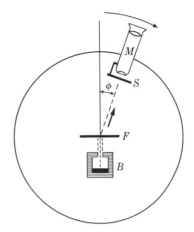

Fig. 34.4. Scintillation method for verifying Rutherford's theoretical predictions for α-particle scattering. The whole apparatus is placed in an evacuated chamber so that the α-particles will not be slowed down by collisions with air molecules.

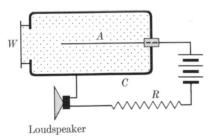

Loudspeaker

Fig. 34.5. A Geiger counter (1928). It consists essentially of a metal cylinder C containing a gas under reduced pressure and a thin axial wire A that is insulated from the cylinder. A potential difference slightly less than that needed to produce a discharge through the gas is maintained between the wire (anode A) and cylinder (cathode C). When an α-particle enters through the thin mica window W, it frees a few electrons from the gas molecules, leaving the latter positively charged. The electrons are accelerated toward the anode, freeing more electrons along the way by collisions with gas molecules. The avalanche of electrons constitutes a sudden surge of current which may be amplified to produce a click in the loudspeaker. The high resistance R quickly dissipates the energy of the current, and the counter is then ready to register the next α-particle.

PROBLEM 34.1. The following two scattering experiments were made with the apparatus of Fig. 34.4. The source of the α-particles was radon, and the scintillations were always counted for the same period of time. For each experiment, show to what extent the observed numbers of scintillations n are in accord with Rutherford's theoretical predictions. (a) For a certain angle ϕ, n was 210 when silver foil of thickness 4.0×10^{-4} mm was used as the scatterer, and n was 317 when silver foil of thickness 6.0×10^{-4} mm was used. (b) With gold foil as scatterer and $\phi = 75°$, $n = 200$. When the speed of the incident α-particles was reduced to one-half its former value (by placing a mica absorbing screen of suitable thickness between the source in B and the foil F), n was 3200 at $\phi = 75°$.

34.3 Nuclear charge and size. One of Rutherford's predictions still remained unverified: there was at the time no direct way to determine just how the path of an α-particle was affected by the charge Q on each nucleus of the scattering foil, for Q could not be obtained directly by independent measurements. However, the scattering experiments had confirmed the other predictions of Rutherford's theory, and we have repeatedly seen examples of what is done in such cases: it is assumed that the partial confirmation of the theory tentatively justifies the belief in that theory as a whole. On the hypothesis that the fraction of α-particles scattered through a particular angle *is* directly proportional to the square of the nuclear charge, the experimental data obtained with scattering foils of different materials can be used to compute Q for various atoms. This was done by Rutherford and his co-workers for carbon (in a sheet of paraffin wax), and for aluminum, gold, and other metal foils. For these materials the positive nuclear charge was roughly equal to $\frac{1}{2}$ at.wt. $\times q_e$, where q_e here represents the numerical value of the electronic charge, 1.6×10^{-19} coul. Values so obtained for Q were 6 q_e for carbon, 13 or 14 q_e for aluminum, 78 or 79 q_e for gold, and so on.

This was an important piece of information about the atom. If the nucleus has a positive charge of roughly $\frac{1}{2}$ at.wt. $\times q_e$, then the number of electrons surrounding the nucleus must also be $\frac{1}{2}$ at.wt. (6 for carbon, 13 or 14 for aluminum, etc.) since the atom as a whole is electrically neutral. Earlier experiments on the scattering of x-rays and of beams of electrons had in fact independently suggested that the number of electrons per atom is about $\frac{1}{2}$ at.wt. But soon it was noticed that the approximate relation between nuclear charge and half the atomic weight is not as important as another relationship, that between the values found for the nuclear charge and the *atomic number* Z, the ordinal number of the element in the periodic table (Appendix D). The data showed that *each nucleus has a positive charge Q numerically equal to Zq_e*—not approximately, but precisely. It is an astonishing fact that for most elements, $\frac{1}{2}$ at.wt. has about the same value as Z; thus for carbon $Z = 6$ and $\frac{1}{2}$ at.wt. $= 6.005$; for aluminum, $Z = 13$ and $\frac{1}{2}$ at.wt. $= 13.49$. This coincidence helped initially to hide the fact that the fruitful relationship is not $Q \doteq \frac{1}{2} \times$ at.wt. $\times$ q_e, but $Q = Zq_e$.

The suggestion that the number of positive charges on the nucleus and also the number of electrons around the nucleus are equal simply to the atomic number Z at once made the picture of the atom more precise. The hydrogen atom ($Z = 1$) has in its neutral state one electron outside the nucleus; a helium atom ($Z = 2$) has in its neutral state two electrons outside the nucleus; a uranium atom ($Z = 92$) has 92 electrons, and so on. This simple scheme was made all the more plausible when additional experiments showed that it was possible to produce singly ionized hydrogen atoms, H^+, and doubly ionized helium atoms, He^{++}, but never H^{++} and He^{+++}, evidently because a hydrogen atom has only one electron to lose, and a helium atom only two. And suddenly, the whole periodic table of elements assumes a new meaning; it is not only an ordering of the elements according to increasing atomic weight and progressively changing valence number to result in the proper grouping of chemical families, but it is also a *listing of elements according to the progressively increasing number of electrons around the nucleus or the number of (positive) units of charge in the nucleus.*

A second important consequence of the scattering experiments concerned the *size* of the nucleus, which Rutherford estimated by making use of the reasonable assumption that the kinetic energy of an α-particle headed directly toward the nucleus (A, Fig. 34.2) is transformed into electrical potential energy as the particle slows and stops before returning. On this basis (see Problem 34.2 below), he found the distance r of closest approach of the α-particle to the nucleus to be approximately 3×10^{-14} m, or 3×10^{-12} cm. This distance must be at least equal to the sum of the radii of the α-particle and nucleus—surely not less. Compared with the over-all diameter of an atom ($\sim 10^{-8}$ cm), the nuclear diameter is roughly 10^{-12} cm, that is, less than 1/10,000 times as large! Now the total mass of the electrons in any atom is almost negligibly small compared with the mass of the atom as a whole. Most of an atom's mass is therefore concentrated in a diameter which bears to the total atomic diameter a relation similar to that of the sun and the whole solar system, or of an i-dot on a sheet 10 times as large as the page of this book. An atom's outer "boundary," and hence its effective diameter, presumably is delineated by the orbits of the electrons moving around the nucleus at relatively large distances from it. Thus we arrive at a picture of the atom as being mostly empty space, as indeed it must be to account for the ease with which beams of α-particles or of electrons penetrate through thousands of layers of atoms in metal foils or in a gas.

While this model of the nuclear atom was fully able to deal with α-particle scattering and provided stimulating insight into such other problems as the general structure of atoms and the meaning of the periodic table, it also raised new issues: How are the electrons arranged around the nucleus? What keeps the electrons from falling into the nucleus because of electrical attraction? What is the structure of the nucleus? What keeps the nucleus from exploding by mutual repulsion of its components if it is endowed with charges of positive sign only? Rutherford was aware of these problems and drew attention to the inability of his model (which had not been developed for this purpose) to solve them. As we shall see, he himself and his many gifted associates soon began to contribute toward their solution. The remainder of this chapter will deal with the first problem and the solution offered by Niels Bohr, a young physicist who joined Rutherford's group just as the nuclear model was being announced.

PROBLEM 34.2. Compute the distance r of closest approach to the nucleus of a gold atom by an α-particle with speed $v_\alpha = 2 \times 10^7$ m/sec and positive charge $Q_\alpha = 2q_e$. (Note that the initial kinetic energy of the α-particle is $\frac{1}{2}m_\alpha v_\alpha^2$, where $m_\alpha = 6.6 \times 10^{-27}$ kgm, and that its potential energy, by Eq. (27.7), is $CQ_N Q_\alpha/r$, where Q_N is the charge of the nucleus.)

PROBLEM 34.3. If the atoms in a gold foil are assumed to be so close as to touch one another, with a distance of about 3×10^{-10} m between their nuclei, and if the diameters of gold nuclei and α-particles are for this rough calculation each taken to be 6×10^{-14} m, calculate the probability of an α-particle approaching a nucleus virtually head-on in any one layer of gold atoms. (*Hint:* Divide the diameter of a gold atom into segments, each equal to the diameter of the α-particle; then assume that the α-particle has the same chance of approaching any one segment as any other.)

34.4 The planetary model of the atom. If an atom consists of a positively charged nucleus surrounded by a cloud of negatively charged electrons, how can it continue to exist? What keeps the electrons from falling into the nucleus, i.e., from being pulled in by the Coulomb force of attraction? This question must have been immediately reminiscent of the analogous case of the solar system. The planets do not fall into the sun because they are revolving around the sun, and the gravitational attraction between the sun and each planet furnishes just sufficient centripetal force to keep the planet in its orbit. A "planetary atom" with the electrons revolving around the nucleus is an inviting and suggestive conception. Of course, the analogy is not complete; since the revolving electrons are undergoing centripetal acceleration, they must be expected to emit light according to classical electromagnetic theory.

Because of the importance of the planetary model, we must examine each of the implications carefully. Let us center attention on the simplest kind of atom, that of hydrogen, which, according to our model, consists of a single electron of mass m_e and charge $(-)q_e$, moving about a nucleus of charge $(+)q_e$. The assumption is that the electron is moving with a constant speed v in a circular orbit of radius r (Fig. 34.6). It must therefore be undergoing a continuous centripetal acceleration v^2/r, by Eq. (5.10), and hence must be continuously acted upon by a centripetal force $F_c = m_e v^2/r$. This force is furnished by the electrical attraction between the electron and the nucleus, and by Eq. (26.4), which is Coulomb's law of electrostatic attraction, it is given by $C q_e q_e/r^2$, where C ($=9.0 \times 10^9$ new·m²/coul²)

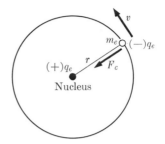

FIG. 34.6. An electron moving with constant speed in a circular orbit about the hydrogen nucleus.

is a constant whose value depends only on the units used. Equating these two expressions for the force, we have $C q_e^2/r^2 = m_e v^2/r$, or

$$C \frac{q_e^2}{r} = m_e v^2. \tag{34.1}$$

Consider next the energy possessed by the electron. Its kinetic energy E_k is $\frac{1}{2} m_e v^2$, which, in view of Eq. (34.1), may be expressed as

$$E_k = \tfrac{1}{2} m_e v^2 = C \frac{q_e^2}{2r}.$$

But the electron, because it is in the electric field of the nucleus, also has potential energy E_p which is equal to the electric potential V at a distance r from the nucleus (namely $C q_e/r$, by Eq. 27.6) multiplied by the electronic charge $(-)q_e$, or

$$E_p = \frac{C q_e}{r} \cdot (-q_e) = -C \frac{q_e^2}{r}.$$

If the presence of the negative sign seems curious, we should remember that this is simply a consequence of the way in which zero potential energy is defined. For example, if *gravitational* potential energy is taken to be zero at the surface of the earth, then the potential energy of an object of mass m at a height h above the surface has the positive value mgh. But for an object below the surface (say, a chunk of coal in a mine), h is negative and the potential energy mgh is negative; this means that the potential energy is less than it is at the arbitrary zero level, namely the surface, and hence that work must be done on the object to raise it to the surface. For an electron the potential energy is taken to be zero when it is at a very large (or infinite) distance from the nucleus; hence the negative value of the potential energy here also means that work must be done on the electron to move it away from the nucleus to the zero level of potential energy.

We may now write the expression for the *total* energy of the electron at any distance r from the nucleus:

$$E_k + E_p = C\,\frac{q_e^2}{2r} - C\,\frac{q_e^2}{r} = -C\,\frac{q_e^2}{2r}. \qquad (34.2)$$

PROBLEM 34.4. (a) Show that the total energy of the electron in a hydrogen atom is -23×10^{-19} j if the diameter of its electron orbit is 10^{-10} m. (b) Show that the orbital speed of an electron is $v = \sqrt{Cq_e^2/m_e r}$, and compute the speed for an orbit of diameter 10^{-10} m.

We see from Eq. (34.2) that the energy of the electron in a hydrogen atom depends upon the radius of the orbit; the larger the orbit, the greater (i.e., the less negative) is the energy. Now we know on the basis of kinetic theory that a molecule of hydrogen (H_2) has a diameter of about 2×10^{-10} m, and so we take the diameter of the hydrogen atom to be about 1×10^{-10} m. If this dimension is identified as the orbital diameter of the single electron of a hydrogen atom, and is substituted for $2r$ in Eq. (34.2), its total energy is about -23×10^{-19} j (see Problem 34.4); for a diameter four times as large the energy would be increased to about -5.6×10^{-19} j, and for an infinitely large orbit, as Eq. (34.2) shows, the energy is zero. Thus to move the orbital electron away from the hydrogen nucleus requires that energy be supplied to it, that is, that work be done. This is intuitively quite reasonable; as the electron is being moved away, the force of attraction toward the nucleus must be over-come. To move the electron completely away, its energy must be increased by about 23×10^{-19} j, that is, from -23×10^{-19} j to zero. In short, 23×10^{-19} j is the energy that should be needed to *ionize* a hydrogen atom.

This prediction may at once be subjected to experimental test by bombarding hydrogen gas with electrons. In schematic outline, the apparatus used is a sealed glass container (Fig. 34.7) filled with hydrogen gas, and containing a cathode C, a wire-mesh grid G, and an anode A. The electrons from the heated cathode are accelerated toward the grid by a potential difference V_{GC}. Some of these electrons may strike hydrogen atoms, either before or after passing through the grid, and may give up all or part of their kinetic energy to them.

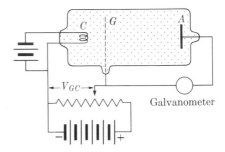

FIG. 34.7. Apparatus for measuring the ionization potential of hydrogen.

But an electron that does not lose energy by a collision prior to reaching the grid arrives there and passes through toward the anode with a maximum kinetic energy equal to $V_{GC}q_e$.

The electric current resulting from those electrons that reach the anode A is registered by the galvanometer. It can be observed that as the potential difference between the grid and cathode is increased, a sudden and large increase occurs in the galvanometer current when $V_{GC} = 13.6$ volts. This experimental fact may be accounted for in terms of the planetary model. An electron from the cathode, having acquired kinetic energy, may strike a hydrogen atom and cause its orbital electron to move into a new orbit in which it is farther away from the nucleus. The energy of the orbital electron must thereby increase, according to Eq. (34.2), and this additional energy is provided by the kinetic energy of the bombarding electron. If now the kinetic energy of the bombarding electrons is sufficient to knock orbital electrons completely away from the nucleus, these electrons join the swarm moving to the anode and an increase in galvanometer current results. On this model we may therefore explain the data by the statement that the hydrogen atoms are undergoing ionization when the value of V_{GC} has been increased to 13.6 volts and the kinetic energy of the bombarding electrons has a consequent maximum value of $V_{GC}q_e = 13.6$ volts $\times 1.60 \times 10^{-19}$ coul $= 21.8 \times 10^{-19}$ j. This is in remarkably good agreement with our previous prediction (Problem 34.4) that roughly 23×10^{-19} j should be required to ionize the atom.

The quantity 13.6 volts is called the *ionization potential*, and 21.8×10^{-19} j, or 13.6 ev, is called the *ionization energy* of the hydrogen atom.

The planetary model of the atom is thus becoming plausible; it is a nuclear model, as Rutherford cogently believed it must be, and the ionization energy of the electron, computed in terms of the model, is experimentally verifiable. At the same time, the defects of the planetary model are too great to be ignored for long. First, if light is indeed emitted by the orbital electron in its periodic motion, the principle of conservation of energy demands that the radiation result in a reduction of the total energy of the electron. By Eq. (34.2) such a decrease of energy (i.e., the total energy assuming larger negative values) means that the radius of the orbit decreases. The steadily radiating electron therefore steadily spirals in toward the nucleus. The model is self-destructive.

The second major defect of the planetary model is that even if it could account for the emission of light, there is nothing about the model that could account for the radiation of light of *discrete frequencies*, i.e., a line spectrum. The planetary model of the hydrogen atom thus (a) cannot remain nuclear for long and (b) does not predict emission of light as observed for hydrogen gas. It was at this point that Niels Bohr entered the picture.

34.5 Bohr's problem. Niels Bohr, born in 1885, the year of Balmer's publication on the hydrogen spectrum, had just received his doctorate in Denmark when he went to England in 1911. After a few months as a visiting researcher with J. J. Thomson at Cambridge, Bohr went to Manchester and joined Rutherford's group. The work there was just bringing conviction of the validity of the nuclear model, yet the deficiencies of that model were already apparent. As Rutherford said later, "I was perfectly aware when I put forward the theory of the nuclear atom that according to classical theory the electron ought to fall into the nucleus ... " Bohr saw that the problem was to join the new idea of the nuclear atom with another great new conceptual scheme, namely the quantum theory, which Planck and Einstein had shown to take the place of the classical electromagnetic theory for events on an atomic scale. But it should be clear that at the time this was a daring combination of controversial novelties. We must remember that Millikan's experimental confirmation of Einstein's equation for the photoelectric effect and the measurement of h was not given until 1916. Commenting on the state of the subject in 1912, the English physicist Arthur Eddington wrote later: "At that time, quantum theory was a German invention which had scarcely penetrated to England at all. There were rumors that Jeans had gone to a conference on the continent and been converted; Lindemann, I believe, was expert on it; I cannot think of anyone else."

According to classical electromagnetic theory, the orbiting electron should radiate at all times; according to the quantum theory, radiation is emitted in the form of photons of definite energy, one photon at a time, during occasional changes in energy level of the atom. Bohr postulated that classical electromagnetic theory, although verified by Hertz for radiation by large electric circuits, is not applicable to atomic phenomena.

From the viewpoint of this postulate he considered an atom of hydrogen. It has a nucleus of charge $(+)q_e$, circled by a single electron. Bohr postulated that the orbiting electron *normally does not radiate energy.* This was necessary to explain why the electron-nucleus system does not always radiate and so destroy itself. Radiation from hydrogen gas is therefore expected only in certain circumstances. For example, in an electric discharge tube containing hydrogen, moving electrons and ions bombard the gas atoms and transfer energy to them. Now suppose that in the bombardment the orbital electron receives sufficient energy to move it to a larger-sized orbit—not enough energy to ionize the atom, but merely enough to leave it in an "excited state." Bohr suggested that the electron may at a later time "fall" or jump back from an outer orbit into its original orbit, with a consequent decrease in energy. If E_i is the energy in the initial, larger orbit and E_f is the energy in the final, smaller orbit, the energy available for emission is given by

$$\Delta E \equiv E_i - E_f.$$

Bohr assumed *that this energy is radiated as a photon of energy* $h\nu = \Delta E$ *and therefore of frequency* $\nu = \Delta E/h$.

If the electron is able to go to any orbit, arbitrarily large or small, it should give rise to any frequency; however, we know that gases radiate light of only specific frequencies. Therefore Bohr postulated that when an orbital electron is moved out to orbits of larger energies, *there are only certain orbits that it may occupy.* Let us designate the successively larger radii of the "allowed" orbits by r_1, r_2, r_3, . . . and the energies of the electron in those orbits by E_1, E_2, E_3, . . . Then an electron moving or "jumping" from, say, orbit 3 into orbit 2 will radiate a photon of energy $h\nu = \Delta E = E_3 - E_2$. Thus this qualitative model now has a mechanism which might account for the observation that hydrogen gas emits light of only certain frequencies, that is, a *line spectrum.*

The success of the whole model depends now on finding the "allowed" orbits for the electron of the hydrogen atom. And if they can be determined, do all the energy differences that become available during the transitions from more distant orbits to those nearer the nucleus correspond quantitatively and exactly to the energies of the photons in the observed line spectrum of hydrogen? It would seem hardly possible even to start on these problems, for where is one to look for a guide to the allowed orbital layout of the atom?

34.6 The correspondence principle. It is precisely at this point that Bohr's genius asserted itself most strikingly. He found a systematic way of deducing radii of the allowed orbits in the hydrogen atom by a consideration of the following type.

When an atom is strongly excited, its electron should be moving in an orbit with a large diameter. But *for a sufficiently large orbit,* we must expect that the classical electromagnetic theory of Maxwell and Hertz applies; in that case the circulating current (here only one electron) should radiate light *at a frequency equal to the frequency of the orbital motion.* At the same time, Planck's quantum postulate should hold for this as for any system with periodic motion, so that the energy changes of the orbiting electron should proceed in smallest intervals of value $h\nu$. Here is a place where classical and quantum physics join, and we may assume that they overlap without leaving a discontinuous transition. *In this region the quantum physics and classical physics merge into each other, and their predictions must correspond.* This point of view, this *correspondence principle,* has, however, an astonishing consequence.

In Fig. 34.8, r_i and r_f refer to the orbits of the electron just before and just after it has decreased its energy by one quantum, $h\nu$. Both orbits are assumed to be relatively large, therefore $r_i - r_f(\equiv \Delta r)$ is relatively small. The decrease of energy ΔE of the atomic system is, by Eq. (34.2),

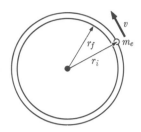

$$\Delta E \equiv E_i - E_f = -\frac{Cq_e^2}{2}\left(\frac{1}{r_i} - \frac{1}{r_f}\right)$$

$$= \frac{Cq_e^2}{2}\left(\frac{1}{r_f} - \frac{1}{r_i}\right).$$

(34.3)

FIG. 34.8.   Transition from orbit with radius r_i to orbit with smaller radius r_f, when r_i and r_f are both very large.

Our first point is now to show that the last expression reduces to $\Delta E = (v/r)\,\Delta(m_e r v)$, by making plausible but important assumptions. We replace r_f and r_i in Eq. (34.3) by $m_e v_f^2 r_f^2/Cq_e^2$ and $m_e v_i^2 r_i^2/Cq_e^2$, as permitted by Eq. (34.1). Therefore

$$\Delta E = \frac{(Cq_e^2)^2}{2}\left(\frac{1}{(m_e v_f^2 r_f^2)} - \frac{1}{(m_e v_i^2 r_i^2)}\right)$$

$$= \frac{(Cq_e^2)^2}{2m_e}\left(\frac{(m_e v_i r_i + m_e v_f r_f)\cdot(m_e v_i r_i - m_e v_f r_f)}{(m_e v_f^2 r_f^2)(m_e v_i^2 r_i^2)}\right).$$

Since $\Delta r(\equiv r_i - r_f)$ is assumed to be very small compared to r_i or r_f, we can write, to a first approximation, $r_i = r_f \equiv r$. Similarly, for this small change of the electron's orbit, $v_i = v_f \equiv v$ to a first approximation. Thus

$$\Delta E = \frac{(Cq_e^2)^2}{2m_e}\left(\frac{(2m_e v r)\cdot\Delta(m_e v r)}{m_e^2 v^4 r^4}\right).$$

On replacing v^4 by $(Cq_e^2)^2/m_e^2 r^2$, from Eq. (34.1), and canceling, we obtain

$$\Delta E = \frac{v}{r}\,\Delta(m_e v r).$$

Using $v = 2\pi r \nu_{\text{rot}}$ (see Eq. 5.4), where ν_{rot} is the frequency of orbital rotation of the electron, we can write $\Delta E = 2\pi\nu_{\text{rot}}\,\Delta(m_e v r)$. But by Bohr's assumption, ΔE is the energy radiated as a photon of energy $h\nu$, where ν is the frequency of the emitted light. Hence, $2\pi\nu_{\text{rot}}\,\Delta(m_e v r) = h\nu$. And now we invoke the correspondence principle and say that for sufficiently large orbits the system we are dealing with will obey the classical laws. If so, the frequency ν of emitted radiation should be numerically equal to the frequency ν_{rot} of the circulating electric charge. With $\nu_{\text{rot}} = \nu$, the last expression can be written

$$\Delta(m_e v r) = \frac{h}{2\pi}. \tag{34.4}$$

This is extremely important: The *change* in the quantity $(m_e v r)$ of the orbiting electron as a result of a postulated very small decrease in its orbital radius is discovered to be a *universal constant*, namely 1.054×10^{-34} j·sec. This at once invites the speculation that the whole quantity $m_e v r$ of the electron* anywhere in its orbit be thought of as an integral multiple of a smallest permitted value given by Eq. (34.4); that is, we are tempted to postulate that $mvr = n \cdot \Delta mvr$, and by Eq. (34.4)

$$mvr = n \frac{h}{2\pi}, \quad \text{or} \quad r = \frac{nh}{2\pi mv}, \tag{34.5}$$

where n is an integer $(1, 2, 3 \ldots)$. Analogously, if we note that the smallest unit by which our bank account can change is one penny, we may regard our total deposit, no matter how large or how small, as an integral multiple of one penny. In this way, each orbit is characterized by a value for n, just as a deposit of \$5.20, viewed as an assembly of the smallest quanta of money having the magnitude 1 cent each, is characterized by the number 520.

Having already made several imaginative assumptions in this purely hypothetical argument, we now make the last one. Our derivation of Eq. (34.5) depended on assuming very large electron orbits; our calculations were directed to the orbital electron in the twilight zone where both classical and quantum physics are equally prominent. Nevertheless, let us see whether we have not turned up a universally applicable conclusion. What consequences follow if we apply this result to the electron orbits even in the normal or only slightly excited atom? From Eq. (34.1) we know that the speed v in any orbit of radius r is given by

$$v = \sqrt{\frac{C q_e^2}{m_e r}}.$$

Therefore Eq. (34.5) becomes

$$r = \frac{nh}{2\pi m_e} \sqrt{\frac{m_e r}{C q_e^2}}.$$

Squaring both members of this equation and solving for r, we obtain

$$r = n^2 \cdot \frac{h^2}{4\pi^2 C m_e q_e^2}. \tag{34.6}$$

---

* In mechanics, the quantity mvr of a small particle of mass in orbiting at radius r and speed v is called the angular momentum of the particle. Eq. (34.4) says that the *change* in angular momentum which we discussed is not arbitrarily small, but is given by $h/2\pi$, a quantity often written as $\hbar$.

This is a remarkable result, because the "allowed" orbital radii are given as multiples of a constant value, since all factors to the right of n^2 are fixed quantities known by independent measurement! The value of $h^2/4\pi^2 C m_e q_e^2$ comes to 0.52×10^{-10} m or 0.52×10^{-8} cm by straightforward substitution of these values, and so we can write

$$r = (0.52 \times 10^{-8} \text{ cm}) \times n^2, \qquad (34.7)$$

where n is a positive integer, namely 1 for the smallest possible orbital radius, 2 for the next possible one, 3 for the third, etc. So we find that the "allowed" orbits are spaced out in accord with a scheme in which whole numbers appear prominently. In short, these considerations, which started with assuming a correspondence of results in the region between classical and quantum physics, have yielded a prediction that *the possible radii of the hydrogen atom's electron are quantized according to Eq. (34.7);* hence n may be called the *quantum number* associated with each orbit.

This is the kind of rule we had hoped to find for determining which radii are possible and where they lie. The big question is now obviously whether Eqs. (34.6) and (34.7) correspond to experimental fact, whether the real hydrogen atom has any resemblance to the hypothetical model which we have been here constructing.

PROBLEM 34.5. (a) State the correspondence principle in your own words. (b) When the electron of a hydrogen atom in a very excited state changes from $n = 1000$ to $n = 990$, find the energy $h\nu$, and show that the frequency of the light which is radiated is approximately the same as the frequency of the orbital motion of the electron (as expected also in classical theory).

34.7 The explanation of atomic size and of line emission spectra. Although Niels Bohr derived Eq. (34.6) with the aid of the correspondence point of view, he preferred in his first paper on this problem, entitled "On the constitution of atoms and molecules" (July 1913), to treat the result as if it were in the nature of a postulate justified mainly by the successful use which he could later make of it. As a first proof of its plausibility, Bohr drew attention to the fact that Eq. (34.6) or (34.7) was in accord with at least one well-known datum: on the basis of experiments interpreted with the aid of the "classical" kinetic theory of matter, the radius of the hydrogen atom in its "normal" or "natural" (unexcited) state, as in a gas at ordinary temperature, was known to be about 0.5×10^{-8} cm. And the predicted value which Eq. (34.7) yields as the smallest orbital radius for the hydrogen atom, i.e., where $n = 1$, is 0.52×10^{-8} cm! Thus the size of the hydrogen atom in the model is in accord with measurement; moreover, now one could see "why" the normal hydrogen atom had this particular radius: because the quantum number corresponding to the normal state has the lowest possible value, namely $n = 1$.

The assumption that the possible quantum numbers are integral numbers (starting at 1) was for Bohr not merely a convenience, nor even merely a necessity; it corresponded to a deep predilection of the type with which we dealt in the discussion on motivations for scientific work (Section 14.4). For many philosophers and scientists, from Pythagoras to this day, *numbers*, and particularly integers, represent the last level of explanation: as Niels Bohr said later, "The solution of one of the boldest dreams of natural science [is] to build up an understanding of the regularities of nature upon the consideration of pure number."

In our model, if the hydrogen atom is in an excited state, n has a value larger than 1, and the electron orbit is at a larger distance, given by Eq. (34.7); note that $r \propto n^2$. Figure 34.9 presents schematically the first few allowed orbits corresponding to the first few values of n.

PROBLEM 34.6. Show that Eq. (34.7) follows from Eq. (34.6). Use constants given in Appendix A.

PROBLEM 34.7. (a) Using the result of Problem 34.6, compute the radii of the first five orbits of the hydrogen atom, according to the Bohr theory. Make a diagram to scale. (b) Using the result of (a), compute the total energy of the electron when it is in each of the first five orbits of the hydrogen atom. Enter these values on the diagram of (a).

Now the mechanism for absorption and emission of photons by the atom becomes clear. If the electron receives energy from some external source, it shifts into a larger orbit of a size compatible with Eq. (34.7). The now "excited" atom contains more energy than normal. The electron will at some future time "fall" or jump back into a smaller orbit, with a consequent decrease ΔE in energy, this difference being radiated as a photon. Since only orbits of certain definite radii $r_1, r_2, r_3, \ldots$ are allowable, the electron can have only certain definite energies $E_1, E_2, E_3, \ldots$, and ΔE can have only certain definite values. The model thus predicts the emission of photons of only certain energies $h\nu$ and therefore certain frequencies ν. We can now deduce *what these possible frequencies should be* on the basis of the Bohr model. [We know already *what they are in fact*,

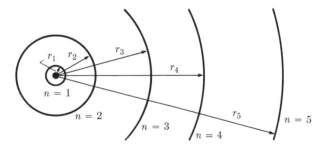

FIG. 34.9. First few allowed electron orbits for a hydrogen atom.

for all the known wavelengths are given by the extension of Balmer's formula, by the empirical equation (33.3).]

The total energy E_n of the electron in the nth orbit is, by Eq. (34.2),

$$E_n = -\frac{Cq_e^2}{2r}.$$

Substituting the value of r from Eq. (34.6), we obtain

$$E_n = -C^2 \cdot \frac{2\pi^2 m_e q_e^4}{n^2 h^2}. \tag{34.8}$$

A transition from an initial orbit of radius r_i to a smaller one of radius r_f (from the n_ith orbit to the n_fth orbit) results in a decrease in the electron's energy given by

$$\Delta E = E_i - E_f = -C^2 \cdot \frac{2\pi^2 m_e q_e^4}{h^2} \left(\frac{1}{n_i^2} - \frac{1}{n_f^2} \right)$$

or

$$\Delta E = C^2 \cdot \frac{2\pi^2 m_e q_e^4}{h^2} \left(\frac{1}{n_f^2} - \frac{1}{n_i^2} \right).$$

The photon radiated as the result of this transition has the energy $h\nu = \Delta E$, and therefore the frequency is

$$\nu = \frac{\Delta E}{h} = C^2 \cdot \frac{2\pi^2 m_e q_e^4}{h^3} \left(\frac{1}{n_f^2} - \frac{1}{n_i^2} \right).$$

To express the result in terms of wavelength of the light emission expected, we use $c = \nu\lambda$, where c is the speed of light, and convert the foregoing expression to

$$\frac{1}{\lambda} \left[= \frac{\nu}{c} \right] = C^2 \cdot \frac{2\pi^2 m_e q_e^4}{ch^3} \cdot \left(\frac{1}{n_f^2} - \frac{1}{n_i^2} \right). \tag{34.9}$$

Here we note with delight that this formula for predicting the wavelengths to be expected from the model *corresponds with the form of the empirical equation* (33.3). The ratio before the parenthetical term in Eq. (34.9) contains only constants, and may be quickly computed. It turns out to be 1.097×10^7 m^{-1} = 1.097×10^{-3} A^{-1}. *But this is the value of the empirical Rydberg constant R_H* (see Section 33.6). Thus Eq. (34.9) becomes, finally,

$$\frac{1}{\lambda} = R_H \left(\frac{1}{n_f^2} - \frac{1}{n_i^2} \right). \tag{34.10}$$

This *derived* expression is identical with Eq. (33.3), which is the *empirical* formula for the hydrogen spectrum. From his model, Bohr thus deduced an expression predicting the emission of light having precisely the wavelengths of the light actually emitted by hydrogen gas!

Moreover, the model also gives us a picture of the process of light emission, helpful for understanding the meaning of what previously had been a numerological formula. For example, in Eq. (33.3) all Lyman lines were obtained if $n_f = 1$ and $n_i = 2, 3, 4 \ldots$ in succession. Now we see that this means that the Lyman lines are emitted when the electrons in a large number of excited hydrogen atoms jump back to the lowest or normal state ($n = 1$) from any of the excited states ($n = 2, n = 3, \ldots$). Similarly, the Balmer lines are explainable as light emitted when the

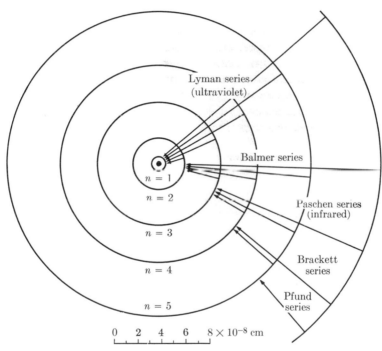

FIG. 34.10. Schematic presentation of some possible transitions of an electron in the Bohr model of the hydrogen atom.

electrons in excited hydrogen atoms jump from the orbits for which $n_i = 3, 4, 5, \ldots$ to the orbit for which $n_f = 2$. Figure 34.10 summarizes the possible transitions between the first few allowed orbits and the corresponding line emitted for each case; for example, the jumps corresponding to Balmer lines all end in the second possible orbit ($n = 2$), which we may call the "ground state" for the Balmer series.

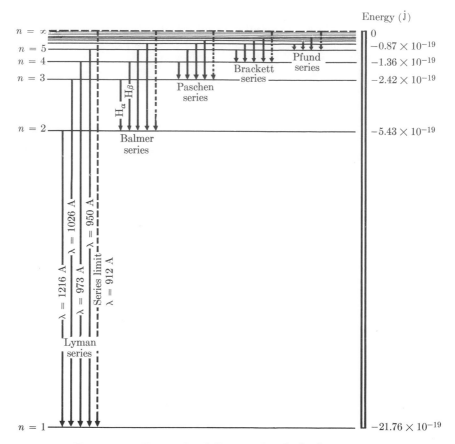

FIG. 34.11. Energy-level diagram for the hydrogen atom.

Such a picture is useful at the start, but it also has the danger of being too concrete. For instance, it leads us to visualize emission in terms of "jumps" of electrons between orbits, of which we can surely know very little. An alternative presentation of Bohr's theory, which yields the same facts but does not commit us too closely to a physical model, concentrates on possible energy states, which are all given by Eq. (34.8). In terms of this *mathematical* model, the atom is normally unexcited, its *energy* then being E_1, or -22×10^{-12} j. Absorption of energy can place the atoms in an excited state, with a larger energy. The excited atom is then ready to emit light, with a consequent reduction in energy. But the energy absorbed or emitted must always shift the energy of the atom to one of the values specified by Eq. (34.8). We may thus, if we wish, represent the hydrogen atom by means of an energy-level diagram (Fig. 34.11) in which the values were calculated from Eq. (34.8).

PROBLEM 34.8. Use Fig. 34.11 to show (a) that the first Lyman line has more energy per emitted photon than any of the Balmer lines, and (b) that (ν of the second Lyman line) $=$ (ν of the first Lyman line) $+$ (ν of the first Balmer line). (c) Formulate a general law relating the frequencies of lines in any two neighboring series.

PROBLEM 34.9. When a completely ionized atom of hydrogen captures an electron, the latter may conceivably cascade toward the nucleus by jumping successively from one permitted orbit to the next. (a) If we could watch the light emitted by this single atom, to what lines of the complete hydrogen spectrum will the last four jumps correspond? (b) Why will the electron of the hydrogen atom not jump from the innermost orbit ($n = 1$) to the nucleus?

PROBLEM 34.10. With proper techniques, the line $\lambda = 9500$ A may be found in the hydrogen spectrum. Attempt to identify the series to which the line belongs, and fix the numbers of the orbits (the quantum numbers) involved in the particular transition.

PROBLEM 34.11. (a) Examine the postulates of Bohr's theory, as we have seen them in this section, in the light of Newton's Rules of Reasoning (Section 11.3). (b) Compare the "physical" model for the hydrogen atom which utilizes electron orbits, with the "mathematical" model utilizing energy levels. What are the advantages of each? What are the disadvantages?

SUPPLEMENTARY READING

BEHRENS, C. E., "Atomic theory from 1904 to 1913," *American Journal of Physics*, v. 11 (1943), pp. 60-66; "The early development of the Bohr atom," *ibid.*, pp. 135–147.

BORN, M., *The restless universe* (Dover, 1957). Largely qualitative, but authoritative.

GREGORY, J. C., *A short history of atomism* (A. and C. Black, London, 1931), Chaps. XII–XV.

HECHT, S., *Explaining the atom* (Viking, 1954), Chaps. I–III.

NEEDHAM, J., and W. PAGEL, editors, *Background to modern science* (Macmillan, 1938), pp. 61–74. A lecture by Rutherford on "The development of the theory of atomic structure."

CHAPTER 35

FURTHER SUCCESSES OF BOHR'S THEORY OF ATOMIC STRUCTURE

The derivation of the empirical hydrogen spectrum formula from Bohr's postulates was a spectacular achievement, reminiscent of the derivation of Kepler's empirical laws from Newton's law of universal gravitation. And as Newton's theoretical structure had further wide application, illuminating such problems as the inequalities of the moon's motions, the motion of comets, the tides, etc., so also was Bohr's theory extended to a greater range of problems. This wide applicability, the hallmark of an important conceptual scheme, was manifest in Bohr's first paper; some of the topics he discussed there follow.

35.1 Absorption of radiation. Experiment shows that hydrogen atoms normally absorb only those frequencies that correspond to the lines of the Lyman spectrum ($n_f = 1$, $n_i = 2, 3, 4, \ldots$, in Table 33.2); to absorb light of frequencies corresponding to the Balmer lines, the hydrogen atoms must initially be heated or otherwise put in an excited state. These observations are now explained by making the assumption, consistent with the whole Bohr model, that an atom can absorb a photon only if the energy $h\nu$ so absorbed brings the orbital electron exactly into a higher, permitted orbit. Unexcited hydrogen atoms are in the most stable (the normal) state corresponding to $n = 1$. The energy differences between that level and all the others correspond to the energies of the photons giving rise to the Lyman lines (see Fig. 34.10). Any photon of less energy (and this includes all those having frequencies corresponding to the Balmer lines) cannot be absorbed by an unexcited atom because it cannot make the electron go from the innermost orbit even to the second one. Only if the gas is initially in an excited state will sufficient atoms be present in the ground state of the Balmer series ($n = 2$) to absorb photons having Balmer series frequencies.

On the same model, another puzzle was solved. It was known that *all* frequencies of the incident light above a certain "threshold" value are absorbed by hydrogen atoms; in other words, above this threshold frequency the absorption spectrum is *continuous* rather than consisting of lines. For unexcited hydrogen atoms, this threshold frequency is found to be equal to that of the Lyman series convergence limit ($n_f = 1$, $n_i = \infty$). The explanation is now easy. Let ν_L represent the frequency of the Lyman series limit. A photon of frequency ν_L is one that, if absorbed, has just the right amount of energy $h\nu_L$ to *ionize* the hydrogen atom by carrying the electron from the level $n = 1$ to $n = \infty$. This electron is no longer bound to the atom, but is free. If the absorbed photon has an energy $h\nu$ larger than the amount $h\nu_L$ needed just to free the electron, then the excess energy $h\nu - h\nu_L$ will be given to the emerging electron as kinetic energy $\frac{1}{2}m_ev^2$. Upon comparing this equation with Eq. (32.2), we realize that what we are dealing with here is the photoelectric effect as applied to a gas, ν_L being the threshold frequency and $h\nu_L$ the work function for unexcited hydrogen gas. As Bohr said, "Obviously, we get in this way the same expression for the kinetic energy of an electron ejected from an atom by the photoelectric effect as that deduced by Einstein . . ."

PROBLEM 35.1.   A sample of hydrogen gas is illuminated from a source emitting monochromatic light of wavelength 1026 A (corresponding to the second Lyman line). If the hydrogen atoms re-emit the energy absorbed, what *three* wavelengths can one expect to find in the light radiated by the sample?

PROBLEM 35.2.   (a) Compute the photoelectric work function $h\nu_L$ for unexcited hydrogen atoms.   (b) How does its value compare with the ionization energy of the hydrogen atom?

PROBLEM 35.3.   According to the kinetic theory of gases, the average kinetic energy *per molecule* is given by Eq. (25.8), namely, $\bar{E}_k = \frac{3}{2}kT$, where k is the Boltzmann constant and T the temperature in degrees Kelvin. Assume that if any two atoms of monatomic hydrogen collide inelastically, their kinetic energies may be absorbed by throwing the orbital electron of one of them into a higher energy level. (a) Show that if the hydrogen were at a temperature of 40,000°K, the electrons in most of the atoms would be in the energy level $n = 2$ and hence the gas would strongly absorb incident light of frequencies corresponding to the Balmer series. (b) Suggest an apparatus that, in principle, would permit the measurement of extremely high gas temperatures. (c) Why is it that even at a temperature much lower than 4×10^4 °K, some light of Balmer frequencies is found to be absorbed?

35.2 Spectrum of ionized helium.   As will be recalled, E. C. Pickering had found lines in a stellar spectrum that at the time were ascribed to some celestial modification of hydrogen (Section 33.7). In 1912, A. Fowler found these same lines in the spectrum from a discharge tube containing a mixture of hydrogen and helium. Their wavelengths were given by the empirical equation (33.4). Bohr now pointed out that his model does not provide for these lines. However, he continued, they can be accounted for by ascribing them to singly ionized helium atoms He^+. A neutral atom of helium, according to the Rutherford-Bohr model, would consist of a nucleus of charge $(+)2q_e$, surrounded by two electrons. But if one of the two electrons is stripped off through the violence either of an electric discharge or of mutual atomic collisions in a hot star, the resulting helium ion He$^+$ is like a hydrogen atom *except* for its doubly positively charged nucleus. The frequencies of the radiation emitted by transitions of the single remaining electron can be calculated at once.

The centripetal force on this remaining electron is again equal to the electrostatic force of attraction to the nucleus, and so is given by

$$F_c = m_e v^2/r = C \cdot 2q_e \cdot q_e/r^2,$$

from Eqs. (5.12) and (26.2). Therefore when this electron is in any stable orbit, $v^2 = C \cdot 2q_e^2/m_e r$. From Eq. (34.5), which is Bohr's postulate that defines the permitted orbits, we have $v^2 = n^2 h^2/4\pi^2 m_e^2 r^2$. By equating these two expressions for v^2 and then solving for r, we obtain

$$r = \frac{n^2 h^2}{4\pi^2 C m_e \cdot 2q_e^2}. \tag{35.1}$$

Note that this expression for the radii of the electron orbits for He$^+$ differs from Eq. (34.6) for hydrogen by the factor 2 in the denominator. Next we write the expression for the energy when the electron is in any permitted orbit n of He$^+$:

$$E_n = E_k + E_p = \frac{1}{2} m_e v^2 + C \cdot \frac{2q_e \cdot (-q_e)}{r}$$

$$= \frac{1}{2} m_e \left(\frac{C \cdot 2q_e^2}{m_e r} \right) - \frac{C \cdot 2q_e^2}{r} = -C \cdot \frac{q_e^2}{r}. \tag{35.2}$$

Using in Eq. (35.2) the expression for r in Eq. (35.1), and going by the same steps as from Eq. (34.8) to Eq. (34.9), we obtain

$$\frac{1}{\lambda} = \frac{\nu}{c} = \frac{E_i - E_f}{ch} = C^2 \cdot \frac{2\pi^2 m_e \cdot 2^2 q_e^4}{ch^3} \cdot \left(\frac{1}{n_f^2} - \frac{1}{n_i^2} \right). \tag{35.3}$$

In connection with Eq. (34.9) we saw that the constant factor

$$C^2 \cdot \frac{2\pi^2 m_e q_e^4}{ch^3}$$

is equal to R_H, the Rydberg constant for hydrogen, namely, 1.097×10^7 m^{-1}. Thus, with rearrangement, Eq. (35.3) can also be written

$$\frac{1}{\lambda} = R_H \left[\frac{1}{(n_f/2)^2} - \frac{1}{(n_i/2)^2} \right]. \tag{35.4}$$

But this equation is identical with the empirical equation (33.4)! Bohr said: "If we put $n_f = 3$ and let n_i vary, we get a series which includes two of the [lines] observed by Fowler . . . If we put $n_f = 4$, we get the series observed by Pickering . . . " The source of these lines was therefore not hydrogen, but singly ionized helium atoms—an exciting interpretation of an old puzzle.

Clearly, Eq. (35.3) differs from Eq. (34.9) only by the factor 2^2, which enters because the nucleus of the helium atom has twice the charge of the hydrogen nucleus. Now the number of positive charges on any nucleus is equal to the atomic number Z, and for helium $Z = 2$. Thus we may replace the 2^2 in Eq. (35.3) by Z^2:

$$\frac{1}{\lambda} = C^2 \cdot \frac{2\pi^2 m_e Z^2 q_e^4}{ch^3} \left(\frac{1}{n_f^2} - \frac{1}{n_i^2} \right). \tag{35.5}$$

Note that this equation holds for hydrogen, H, when Z is made 1, and for singly ionized helium, He^+, when Z is made 2. Moreover, if the atom of any other element were stripped of all electrons except one, Eq. (35.5) should apply to its spectrum when the appropriate value of Z is inserted. Such ions have been produced by means of violent electric discharges, not only in helium but also in the gaseous forms of each of the elements up to oxygen ($Z = 8$), and the line spectra of these ions are indeed found to be correctly predicted by Eq. (35.5).

To this point, Bohr's concern had been only with single-electron systems, such as hydrogen and singly ionized helium. Now, in ending the first paper on his theory (July 1913), Bohr indicated a possible method of attack on the problem of multi-electron systems, and in subsequent papers (September and November 1913), he developed the method in detail and also extended it to explain how atoms combine with one another to form molecules. This work, we shall see, dealt not only with line spectra, but also laid the basis for explaining the chemical properties of the elements.

PROBLEM 35.4. Draw an energy-level diagram for singly ionized helium, analogous to Fig. 34.11.

PROBLEM 35.5. By following steps similar to those used for singly ionized helium, He^+, *derive* the equations for r and for $1/\lambda$ which hold for doubly ionized lithium vapor, Li^{++}, where $Z = 3$.

PROBLEM 35.6. List the available contemporary experimental facts and conceptual schemes useful to Bohr in the formulation of his models for the hydrogen atom and other single-electron systems.

35.3 The periodic table and the shell structure of atoms. In the Rutherford-Bohr scheme, the atoms of the different elements differ essentially in the charge and mass of the nuclei, and in the number and arrange-

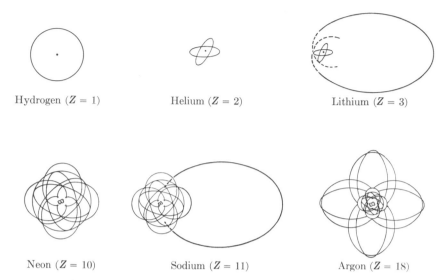

Hydrogen ($Z = 1$)   Helium ($Z = 2$)   Lithium ($Z = 3$)

Neon ($Z = 10$)   Sodium ($Z = 11$)   Argon ($Z = 18$)

FIG. 35.1. Schematic representation of electron orbits of various atoms, drawn approximately to scale, as used by Bohr in his lectures. [From *Die Naturwissenschaften*, v. 11 (1923).]

ment of the electrons about the nucleus. Recall that the charge of any nucleus is $(+)Zq_e$, and the number of orbital electrons is Z, where Z is the atomic number of the element. As for the arrangement of the electrons, Bohr came to picture the electronic orbits as in Fig. 35.1, though not as a series of coplanar concentric rings but as tracing out patterns in three dimensions. For example, the orbits for the two electrons of He in the normal state are indicated as circles at about 60° with respect to each other. In addition to circular orbits, elliptic ones with the nucleus at one focus could also be considered. But again a note of warning: These pictures are taken to be conceptual aids rather than quantitative models. It is neither necessary nor correct to think that the atoms "really" look like the pictures.

To relate the Bohr model of atoms with the chemical properties by a necessarily very qualitative argument, we may begin with the observation that the elements hydrogen ($Z = 1$) and lithium ($Z = 3$) are much alike chemically. Both have valences of 1. Both enter into analogous compounds, for example hydrogen chloride, HCl, and lithium chloride, LiCl. Furthermore, there are some similarities in their optical spectra. All this suggests that the lithium atom has some salient resemblance to the hydrogen atom. Bohr conjectured that two of the three electrons of the lithium atom are relatively close to the nucleus, in orbits like those of the helium atom, while the third is in a circular or elliptic orbit outside the inner system. Since this inner system consists of a nucleus of charge $(+)3q_e$ and two electrons each of charge $(-)q_e$, its *net* charge is $(+)q_e$. Thus the lithium atom may be roughly pictured as having a central core of charge $(+)q_e$, around which one electron revolves, somewhat as for a hydrogen atom.

Helium $(Z = 2)$ is a chemically inert element, belonging to the family of inert gases; it does not form compounds and, moreover, is monatomic. Its ionization potential is high, 25 ev as compared with 13.5 ev for hydrogen. All this indicated that the helium atom is highly stable, having both of its electrons closely bound to the nucleus. It seemed sensible to regard both electrons as moving in the same innermost *shell* around the nucleus when the atom is unexcited. Moreover, because of the great stability and the chemical inertness of the helium atom, one may reasonably assume that this shell, which came to be called the K-shell, cannot accommodate more than two electrons. The single electron of hydrogen is also in the K-shell when the atom is unexcited. For lithium, two electrons are in the K-shell, thus filling it to capacity, and the third electron starts a new one, called the L-shell. To this single outlying and loosely bound electron must be ascribed the strong chemical affinity of lithium for oxygen, chlorine, and many other elements.

Sodium $(Z = 11)$ is the next element in the periodic table that has chemical properties similar to those of hydrogen and lithium, and this suggests that the sodium atom also is hydrogenlike in having a central core about which one electron revolves. Moreover, just as lithium follows helium in the periodic table, so does sodium follow another inert gas, neon $(Z = 10)$. For the neon atom, we may assume that 2 of its 10 electrons are in the first (K) shell, and that the remaining 8 electrons are in the second (L) shell; and these 8 electrons may be expected to fill the L-shell to capacity because of neon's great stability and inertness. For sodium, then, the 11th electron must be in a third (M) shell. Passing on to potassium $(Z = 19)$, the next alkali metal in the periodic table, we again have the picture of an inner core consisting of a nucleus of charge $(+)19q_e$ and 2, 8, and 8 electrons occupying the K-, L-, and M-shells, respectively, and revolving around this core is the 19th electron, in a fourth (N) shell. The inert argon atom just ahead of it in the periodic table $(Z = 18)$ again represents a distribution of electrons in a tight and stable pattern, with 2 in the K-, 8 in the L-, and 8 in the M-shell.

These qualitative considerations have led us to the conception that the electrons are arranged in groups, or shells, concentric about the nucleus. The arrangement of electrons for the inert gases can be taken to be particularly stable and preferred, and each time we encounter a new alkali metal in Group I of the periodic table, a new shell is started with a single electron around a core which resembles the pattern for the preceding inert gas. We may expect that this outlying electron will easily come loose under the attraction of neighboring atoms, and this corresponds with the facts. The alkali metals in compounds or in solution (as in electrolysis) spontaneously form ions such as Li^+, Na^+, and K^+, each with one positive net charge $(+)q_e$. In the solid state, the outer electrons are relatively free to move about, which accounts for the fact that the alkali metals are good electrical conductors.

Turning now to Group II of the periodic table, we would expect those elements that follow immediately after the alkali metals to have atoms with two outlying electrons. For example, beryllium $(Z = 4)$ should have 2 electrons in the K-shell, thus filling it, and 2 in the L-shell. If the atoms of all these alkaline earths have two outlying electrons, they should be chemically similar, as indeed they are. Moreover, they should fairly easily form ions such as Mg^{++} and Ca^{++}, each with two positive charges, $(+)2q_e$, and this is also found to be true.

As a final example, consider those elements that immediately *precede* the inert gases in the periodic table. For example, fluorine atoms $(Z = 9)$ should have 2 electrons filling the K-shell but only 7 electrons in the L-shell, which is one less than enough to fill it. If the fluorine atom should capture an additional electron, an ion F^- with one negative charge $(-)q_e$ would result. The L-shell would then be filled, as it is for neutral neon $(Z = 10)$, and thus we would expect the F^- ion to be stable. This prediction is in accord with observation. Indeed, all the elements immediately preceding the inert gases in the periodic table tend to form stable negative ions in solution. In the solid state, we would expect these elements to be lacking in free electrons, and all of them are in fact poor conductors of electricity.

Altogether there are seven main shells, K, L, M, ..., Q, and each divides in as many parts, or *subshells*, as is indicated by the ordinal number of the shell on counting from the nucleus. Thus the first shell, K, is one shell without substructure; the second shell, L, consists of two subshells; and so on. The representation for a gold atom $(Z = 79)$ is given in Fig. 35.2; in this method of indicating electron orbits, only a very general indication of the grouping of orbits remains. The first subshell in any shell can always hold up to 2 elec-

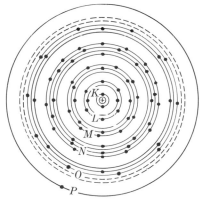

Fig. 35.2. Schematic representation of the electrons in an atom of gold $(Z = 79)$, showing shells and subshells.

trons, the second up to 6, the third up to 10, the fourth up to 14, and so on. Electrons that are in different subsections of the same shell differ very little in energy as compared with electrons that are in different shells. For all the elements up to and including argon ($Z = 18$), the buildup of electrons proceeds quite simply. Thus the argon atom has 2 electrons in the K-shell, 8 in the L-shell, then 2 in the first M-subshell and 6 in the second M-subshell. But after argon, there may be electrons in an outer shell before an inner one is filled. The arrangement of the electrons in any unexcited atom is always the one that provides greatest stability for the whole atom. The chemical phenomena generally involve only the outermost electrons of the atoms.

35.4 Formation of molecules. The extension of Bohr's model for hydrogen to account for the properties of other elements also opened the way to an explanation of chemical combination and of the concept of valence. Of importance in this connection are three rules, the first two of which we have already encountered: (1) Any physical system tends to assume the most stable configuration, the one requiring the most energy to change it. (2) The atoms of the inert gases have especially stable electronic configurations (He, 2; Ne, 2 + 8; A, 2 + 8 + 8; Kr, 2 + 8 + 18 + 8; . . .). (3) Atoms will tend to combine to form a molecule whenever their electrons can thereby redistribute themselves into patterns similar to those of the inert gas atoms.

Consider the lithium hydride molecule, LiH. When an Li-atom with its three electrons and an H-atom with its one electron combine to form a molecule, one may assume that the four electrons redistribute themselves around the two nuclei into two heliumlike patterns (Fig. 35.3), and since this leaves the two atoms with opposite net charges, $(+)q_e$ and $(-)q_e$, they mutually attract each other and are bound together as a molecule. As another example, a sodium chloride molecule, NaCl, presumably is formed by an Na atom losing its single outlying electron and a neighboring Cl atom capturing this electron; the result is an Na^+ ion with a neonlike electron structure bound by an electric force to a Cl^- ion with an argonlike electron structure. A similar explanation applies to the formation of such molecules as $CaCl_2$ and $MgCl_2$.

In the latter case, for example, each of the two chlorine atoms takes up one of the two outlying electrons from the magnesium atom; the result is an Mg^{++} ion with a neonlike pattern bound by electric forces to two Cl^- ions having argonlike patterns.

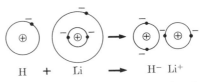

H + Li → H⁻ Li⁺

Fig. 35.3. Formation of a molecule of lithium hydride with transfer of one electron from a lithium to a hydrogen atom.

Compounds whose molecules are formed by the *transfer* of one or more electrons from one atom to another are called *electrovalent* or *ionic* substances. When an electrovalent compound solidifies, it may form a crystal consisting of a three-dimensional lattice of positive and negative ions that are relatively close to one another, bound by strong electric forces. The common salt crystal of Fig. 28.3 is an example.

PROBLEM 35.7. With the help of diagrams similar to Fig. 35.3, describe the formation of the molecules (a) NaF, (b) KBr, (c) CaCl₂, and (d) CaO.

PROBLEM 35.8. (a) What is the relationship between the number of electrons in an element's outermost electron shell and the charge transferred per ion by this element in electrolysis? (b) Why is it that sodium ions Na^+ can continue to exist and move around in water, as they do in electrolysis, whereas neutral sodium reacts vigorously with water, forming sodium hydroxide and releasing hydrogen according to the reaction equation $2Na + 2H_2O \rightarrow (2Na^+ + 2OH^-) + H_2$?

The foregoing scheme of electron transfer does not explain the formation and structure of all molecules. With molecules such as H_2, O_2, and Cl_2, there can be no question of a simple electron transfer from one of the two atoms to the other, because each partner in the molecule has the same "affinity" for electrons as the other. This difficulty of visualizing why two atoms of the same kind should be firmly bound together to form a molecule was indeed one of the most impressive points in the early arguments against Avogadro's molecular hypothesis (Section 23.2). However, a partial explanation may be obtained by introducing the notion of *electron sharing* (G. N. Lewis, 1916). In Fig. 35.4, the molecule H_2 is represented as sharing both electrons between the two nuclei, with the result that each atom of the molecule shares in a heliumlike configuration. In the molecule O_2, each O-atom continually shares two of its electrons with the other O-atom, so that each atom has $2 + 8$ electrons, or a neonlike configuration. In Cl_2, each atom shares one electron with the other, and thus each acquires the $2 + 8 + 8$ electron configuration of argon. In

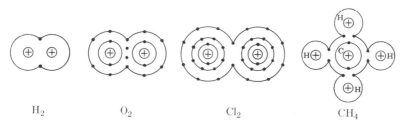

FIG. 35.4. Schematic representation of molecules of four covalent compounds formed by electron sharing.

none of these cases is there a permanent transfer of electrons from one atom to the other.

Numerous other molecules, including those of many of the organic compounds, involve bonds of this general type, in which electrons are continually shared between atoms. For example, in the methane molecule CH_4, the carbon atom shares its four outer electrons with the four hydrogen atoms, while each hydrogen atom in turn shares its single electron with the carbon atom (Fig. 35.4); this gives the carbon atom the $2 + 8$ electron configuration of neon, and each H-atom the configuration of helium. Here the general tendency to produce inert-gas configurations is again demonstrated. Compounds formed by the sharing process are termed *covalent*, and the bonds are called *covalent bonds*. When such a compound forms a crystalline solid, the crystal consists of a space lattice of atoms, not ions. The forces that hold the atoms of a covalent molecule or crystal together are thus not electrical in nature, and must be sought in entirely new developments of the theory of atomic phenomena.

There are many cases of chemical bonding that lie between the extreme electrovalent and covalent types. Thus in *polar* molecules, which form a subgroup of covalent molecules, the pairs of shared electrons are situated closer to one atom than to the other; the result is that one part of the molecule is negative with respect to the other. This is illustrated for HCl and H_2O in Fig. 35.5.

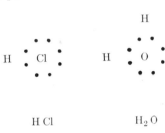

Fig. 35.5. Polar molecules. Only the outermost electrons are shown. The shared electrons are not located symmetrically between the atoms.

35.5 Valence. Our discussion of chemical combination has hinted at the broad outlines of an *electron theory of valence*. The "hooks," bonds, or coupling mechanisms between atoms in compounds referred to in the earlier discussion of valence (Section 23.7) begin to have physical meaning. We have seen that the atoms of some elements [for example, the alkali metals (Group I) and the alkaline earths (Group II)] tend to become positive ions by losing electrons in electrolysis or in forming electrovalent compounds; these are the so-called *electropositive* elements, and their valences are conveniently identified as *positive*. On the other hand, nonmetals such as oxygen and fluorine (Groups VI and VII) tend to form negative ions by gaining electrons to supplement their incomplete shells; these elements are designated as *electronegative* and their valence is identified as *negative*. The number of electrons transferred gives the numerical value of the valence. For example, magnesium and oxygen form MgO or, to use the structural formula, Mg=O, by the transfer of 2 of the 12 electrons from the magnesium atom to add to the oxygen atom's 8 electrons, leaving each with its electrons in a neonlike pattern; the transfer of 2 electrons corresponds to a valence of $+2$ for the magnesium and of -2 for the oxygen. Hydrogen is unique. Having only one electron to lose and needing only one to complete the shell, it may have a valence of $+1$ or -1, depending on the role it plays in the compound. Carbon, nitrogen, and other elements that stand approximately equally far from inert-gas configurations may also have positive or negative valences, depending on whether they combine with nonmetals or metals.

In the formation of covalent compounds, the valence of an element is determined by the number of electrons of the atom that participate in the sharing process. Thus for CH_4 (Fig. 35.4), carbon has a valence of 4 and hydrogen a valence of 1. For CO_2, the carbon atom shares its four outermost electrons and thus has a valence of 4, but the oxygen atom shares only two of its six outlying electrons and hence has a valence of 2.

When the periodic table is re-examined in the light of the theory of electron shells, we find an explanation for Mendeléeff's observation that the valences of the elements vary in periodic fashion (Section 24.3). For example, in the second period of the table, the number of outlying electrons beyond the K-shell increases by one as we move successively from lithium at the left end of the row to carbon in the middle; thus the main valence increases correspondingly from $+1$ to $+4$. At carbon we may say that the trend away from an inert-gas configuration reverses, for as we approach the full neon pattern, carbon may have the valence -4, nitrogen -3, oxygen -2, and fluorine -1, each corresponding to the number of "vacancies" in the pattern. Such a rise and fall in valence numbers occurs in each period, as the elements recede from one and approach the next of the inert-gas configurations.

PROBLEM 35.9. Decide on the electron configuration, valences, and, if possible, the type of bonding involved in the formation of each of the following molecules: (a) CCl_4, (b) SO_2, (c) KCl, (d) N_2, (e) NaOH.

PROBLEM 35.10. (a) Why should we expect to find that certain elements exhibit properties of both metals and nonmetals? Where should we look for them in the periodic table? (b) How can we account for the fact that the valence of an element may be different in different compounds?

35.6 X-ray spectra of heavy atoms. The foregoing picture of electron configurations, which we have based mainly on chemical evidence, also serves well in accounting for the line-emission spectra of the various elements. When any element is in the gaseous state and is properly excited, its atoms exhibit characteristic series of spectral lines with wavelengths lying in or fairly close to the visible region. These *optical spectra*, as they are sometimes called, may be attributed to the outlying electrons of the atoms, for example the single outer electron of lithium, sodium, or potassium, or the two outer ones of magnesium or calcium. Relatively little energy is needed to move one of these loosely bound electrons out from its normal position to some other allowable energy level E_i, and when it falls back to some lower energy level E_f, a photon of energy $h\nu$ is emitted in accordance with the Bohr postulate $h\nu = E_i - E_f$.

It was discovered in 1913 by the English physicist W. H. Bragg that the heavier atoms, when strongly excited, also exhibit characteristic lines lying in the x-ray region of the spectrum. In Section 32.5(b) we noted that an element mounted as the target in an x-ray tube and bombarded with high-speed electrons emits a *continuous* x-ray spectrum, the nature of which does not depend on the element forming the target. What Bragg now discovered was that there is superimposed on this continuous spectrum a line-emission spectrum with wavelengths *characteristic of the element* forming the target. In the same year, 1913, a systematic study of these "x-ray spectra" was begun by the young English physicist H. G. J. Moseley

Fig. 35.6. H. G. J. Moseley (1887–1915).

(Fig. 35.6). He found that the lines for any element used as the target in the x-ray tube formed two groups, to which the names K-series and L-series were given (Fig. 35.7). Later on, better equipment brought out more series, M, N, ..., and in each series, usually more lines.

These x-ray spectra, in contrast with the optical spectra of the same elements, revealed an astonishing simplicity. Moseley found that the x-ray lines progressively shift to shorter wavelengths as the atomic number Z of the target increases. This is evident in Table 35.1, where are listed the wavelengths of two prominent lines in the K-series, called the K_α and K_β lines, of five *neighboring* elements in the periodic table (recent values are used).

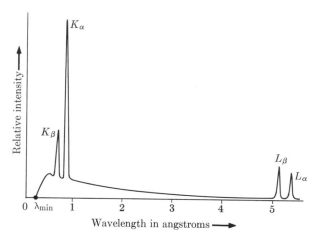

FIG. 35.7. Plot of the intensity of x-rays *vs.* wavelength, for a solid target.

Table 35.1. Wavelengths, in angstrom units, of the K_α and K_β lines in the x-ray spectra of several elements

Element	Atomic number Z	Atomic weight	Wavelength (A)	
			K_α	K_β
Manganese, Mn	25	54.93	2.10	1.91
Iron, Fe	26	55.85	1.94	1.75
Cobalt, Co	27	58.94	1.79	1.62
Nickel, Ni	28	58.69	1.66	1.48
Copper, Cu	29	63.54	1.54	1.39

It must be remembered that in 1913 the concept of *atomic number Z* was just beginning to reveal its importance in physics; the idea that $(+)Zq_e$ is the charge on the nucleus of an atom had just been advanced in connection with Rutherford's work. Indeed, Moseley seems to have been the first to have used the term "atomic number" explicitly. As Table 35.1 indicates with striking clarity, it is on the atomic number, not the atomic weight, that the progressive regularity in the wavelengths of the K_α lines depends. Note that the atomic weights of cobalt and nickel do not increase regularly with increasing ordinal number of the places of the elements in the periodic table, yet the wavelengths of the K_α lines do follow regularly. (The same point was established for the other inversions.) Here was comfort for the chemist who had initially been forced to make such inversions on the basis of chemical behavior and macroscopic physical properties: x-ray spectra hinted at some physical justification for having made these inversions.

From his initial observations of nine elements from calcium to copper, and from his further work in 1914 embracing elements between aluminum ($Z = 13$) and gold ($Z = 79$), Moseley showed that the frequency ν of the K_α line for each element can be computed from an empirical formula that may be written

$$\nu \text{ (cycles/sec)} = 2.48 \times 10^{15} \, (Z - 1)^2. \tag{35.6}$$

(An analogous formula was found for the L_α line.) Thus the frequency ν of any given line, say K_α, is proportional to $(Z - 1)^2$ in regular progression through the periodic table. This means that the x-ray spectra show none of the periodicity that is so strikingly evident in the chemical properties of the elements. Clearly then, x-ray spectra are not controlled by the outer parts of the atom, which reign over optical spectra and chemical phenomena and which are beset by the periodic filling and starting-anew of shells as we go from one element to the next down the list of elements in the periodic table. Rather, x-ray spectra must be generated in a region nearer to the nucleus, whose positive charge is the only physical quantity that increases linearly and nonperiodically with increasing atomic number Z.

But even before we try to explain Eq. (35.6), we can put it to interesting use. Moseley's formula stood up so well under tests with elements for which Z and the frequency of K_α were known that other elements could be identified by noting whether their K_α lines fitted properly between those of their immediate neighbors in the periodic table; conversely, whenever a large gap occurred between the wavelengths of K_α lines for neighboring elements, there, and only there, could one hope to find a yet-unknown element. For example, when the known elements were arranged according to increasing frequency for the K_α line, a gap had to be left at $Z = 43$, indicating the existence of an element (now called technetium) then unknown. Similarly, hafnium ($Z = 72$) was identified by means of its x-ray spectrum, thus filling a previously empty place in the periodic table.

Not only are the x-ray line spectra of the elements nonperiodic and similar for neighboring elements in the periodic table, but they differ from the visible and ultraviolet line spectra in other important ways. For example, the x-ray lines can be excited in an element when it is in the solid or liquid as well as in the gaseous state, and the x-ray line spectrum for any given element is the same for all three states.

Several months before Moseley's first paper appeared, Bohr had taken up a suggestion made previously by Thomson, namely that the x-ray lines should be ascribed to the "settling down" of the atoms after electrons in their *inner* rings have been completely removed from the atoms, say by the impact of a beam of high-speed electrons. Moseley, in his first paper, extended this argument in a beautiful way. He reasoned that if sufficient energy was supplied to the electron in the innermost or K-shell to remove it completely from the atom, a vacant place would be left. If an electron from some outer shell could drop into the vacancy, the result would be the emission of an x-ray photon. He assumed that a photon corresponding to the K_α line is emitted when, subsequent to the removal of an electron from the K-shell, one from the next (L) shell falls into its place; similarly, the second, or K_β, line of the K-series is ascribed to the fall of an electron from the M-shell into the K-shell, and so on. Similar considerations apply to the other x-ray series. For example, if an L-electron has either dropped into the K-shell or has been knocked out of the atom by an impinging electron, the vacancy thus left in the L-shell can be filled by, say, an M-shell electron, in which case the first line, L_α, of the L-series results.

With the x-ray lines thus attributed to the inner electrons lying in the strong field of the nuclear charge Zq_e, the dependence of the x-ray wavelengths on Z immediately becomes understandable. And since the inner electrons are "shielded" by those in the outer ring and are not affected by the presence of neighboring atoms, the fact that the x-ray spectrum of an element is independent of its state or of its binding in a compound is also explained. Incidentally, we now also can see why the *optical* spectrum of a glowing solid or liquid is continuous rather than consisting of lines (Chapter 31): there can be no distinct and characteristic energy-level scheme for the electrons in the outermost shells when the atoms and therefore these shells are close together.

Moseley reasoned that when an L-electron falls into a vacant place in the K-shell (radiates a K_α photon) it is faced with the positive charge Zq_e of the nucleus, diminished somewhat by the effect of the negative charge of whatever electron still remains in the innermost shell. He could disregard the effects of the electrons in the other shells in view of the theorem that there is no electric field inside a hollow charged sphere (Section 27.4). When it was later seen that the K-shell normally contains only two electrons, with just one remaining after the other has been removed, the assumption could be made that the net positive charge facing the "falling" L-electron is approximately $(Z - 1)q_e$. This suggests that an approximately correct expression for the wavelength λ of K_α can be obtained by replacing the Z in Eq. (35.5) by $Z - 1$ and setting $n_f = 1$ and $n_i = 2$, since the transition is to the innermost shell from the one next to it. The resulting prediction for λ is thus given by

$$\frac{1}{\lambda} = C^2 \cdot \frac{2\pi^2 m_e (Z - 1)^2 q_e^4}{ch^3} \left(\frac{1}{1^2} - \frac{1}{2^2} \right). \tag{35.7}$$

As an example, for the K_α line of copper ($Z = 29$) this expression yields a predicted wavelength of 1.55 A; this is in remarkably good agreement with the experimental value of 1.54 A (Table 35.1).

When Eq. (35.7) is converted to an expression for the frequency of K_α by using the relation $c = \nu\lambda$ and substituting modern values for the constant quantities, the result is

$$\nu \text{ (cycles/sec)} = 2.47 \times 10^{15} (Z - 1)^2,$$

which is in excellent agreement with the *empirical* equation (35.6). In addition to its many other accomplishments, the Bohr theory was thus also successful in predicting the frequency of the K_α lines.

PROBLEM 35.11. For scandium ($Z = 21$), a metal that was not available to Moseley as a target material at the time, experiments now give the wavelength of K_α as 3.03 A. What value does Moseley's empirical formula predict?

PROBLEM 35.12. Show whether our model for heavy atoms serves to account for these experimental results: (a) when electrons striking a target in an x-ray tube have sufficient kinetic energy to expel K-electrons from the atoms, the whole K-series and all the other x-ray series make their appearance; (b) the L-series, together with all the x-ray series of longer wavelengths, can be excited without simultaneously exciting the K-series; (c) the x-ray line spectrum of a solid target does not extend to wavelengths lying in the visible or ultraviolet region.

35.7 The anomalous heat capacity.   Here is a last example of the spectacular range of problems which the Bohr theory helped to solve directly or indirectly. We recall that the kinetic theory left us with an unresolved puzzle in the anomalous temperature dependence of the heat capacity of molecular hydrogen gas (Section 25.15). The question was, why do the rotational degrees of freedom begin to "freeze in" below about

60°K? Or to put it another way, why do thermal collisions of hydrogen gas molecules not begin to change their state of rotational motion until temperatures of above 40°K are reached (see Fig. 25.7)?

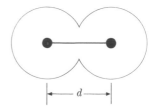

Consider a "dumbbell" molecule of H_2, and imagine it as in Fig. 35.8. The electron orbits are now of no interest, for virtually all the mass is contained in the two nuclei, each of mass 1.6×10^{-24} gm. Therefore the total mass of the molecule, m_{H_2}, is 3.2×10^{-27} kgm. The distance d

FIG. 35.8. "Dumbbell" model of a hydrogen molecule.

between these nuclei should be about 10^{-8} cm, and the distance r of each nucleus from the center of the system should therefore be about 0.5×10^{-10} m. The kinetic energy of rotation $(E_k)_{rot}$ for the whole system is $(m_{H_2} \times v^2/2)$. If we write this as $(m_{H_2}vr)^2/2m_{H_2}r^2$, we are reminded that in Eq. (34.5), the allowed values of the quantity mvr were restricted by the relation $mvr = nh/2\pi$, where n is an integer (1, 2, 3, . . .). Of course, Bohr postulated that the quantity mvr is quantized in whole multiples of $h/2\pi$ for the case of orbiting *electrons* only. But *if* we now extend this principle to *all* periodic systems, even those that constitute a rotating system of two atoms as in this case, then we may write, hopefully,

$$(E_k)_{rot} = \frac{(m_{H_2}vr)^2}{2m_{H_2}r^2} = \frac{n^2h^2/4\pi^2}{2m_{H_2}r^2} = n^2 \times 7 \times 10^{-22} \text{ j.}$$

In short, the kinetic energy of rotation is quantized, so that the least amount of kinetic energy of rotation $(E_k)_{rot}$ which the molecule can have (on this simple model) is 7×10^{-22} j, when $n = 1$.

Now is this quantity of energy available at low temperature by a transfer of $(\bar{E}_k)_{trans}$ into $(\bar{E}_k)_{rot}$? By Eq. (25.18),

$$(\bar{E}_k)_{trans} = \tfrac{3}{2}kT = 2.1 \times 10^{-23} \text{ (j/°K)} \times T. \qquad (35.8)$$

Not until T exceeds 33°K will this expression give values equal to or higher than 7×10^{-22} j, the amount needed for the lowest state of rotation of the H_2 molecule! We note that despite our rather crude approximations, the order of magnitude, > 33°K from theory, > 40°K from experiment, is in gratifying agreement. To summarize this much-simplified argument: at low temperatures, the available average energy is not sufficient to provide the smallest acceptable quantum of energy for rotational notion; only at higher temperatures does the rotational degree of freedom become active.

PROBLEM 35.13. How would the analysis in Section 35.7 be changed if molecules were found to have a fixed amount of kinetic energy of rotation even at the absolute zero of temperature; if, in other words, an unchangeable "background" of $(\overline{E}_k)_{rot}$ were to underlie all *changes* of $(\overline{E}_k)_{rot}$?

35.8 The new model. The successes of Bohr's fundamental approach, of which we have given only a relatively brief outline, has by no means been exhausted in this account. We might continue, as is done in some of the books recommended at the end of this chapter, to apply the theory and its subsequent modifications to solving such perplexing problems as the specific heats of solids, the relative intensities of the observed spectral lines, and much besides. But the fact is that Bohr's conceptual scheme, while today still indispensable and basic to an initial understanding of countless physical and chemical phenomena, has by now been overtaken by the relentless and swift progress of modern physical science. Some fundamental changes in theory have been needed to account for the wealth of phenomena not included even in so sweeping a synthesis as Bohr's. In essence, these changes have centered on the abandonment of the last vestiges of visualization of single events in the electron cloud surrounding the nucleus; the intuitively meaningful orbits, shells, and "jumps" of electrons had to be given up as being essentially meaningless from an operational point of view and, in fact, misleading for some purposes of prediction. The present-day atomic model, while still retaining the now familiar conception of energy levels and quantization, *quite intentionally no longer presents any simple picture to guide our imagination. It is a mathematical model*, a set of postulates and of equations. As Bohr himself said at the very beginning of this new development (1925):

> To the physicists it will at first seem deplorable that in atomic problems we have apparently met with such a limitation of our usual means of visualization. This regret will, however, have to give way to thankfulness that mathematics in this field, too, presents us with the tools to prepare the way for further progress.

The problem was attacked from many sides; the prominent names include Sommerfeld, Heisenberg, Schrödinger, de Broglie, Born, Jordan, and Dirac. While this work has not solved every problem that Bohr's scheme left unanswered, it has accounted for all the successes of the older model in a larger context, and it has confirmed Bohr's fundamental conception that one unified model of atomic structure can account for the whole range of questions in physical science, from optics to chemistry.

The task is by no means finished. Will it ever be? Can it ever be? We have followed the development of physical science from its infancy in ancient Greece to its flowering in our day, and have seen that every

Ptolemy is challenged by a Copernicus, that every Kepler and Galileo must be made meaningful by a Newton, that the insight of every Dalton eventually has to be transposed to a new plane by the work of a Mendeléeff or a Bohr; so we are now fully prepared to accept the view that science is an unending quest for wider horizons.

Even if Bohr's model of the atom in its original form had been the unassailable last word, there would still be a wide and fascinating range of problems which it did not settle, or rather was not designed to consider at all. Our investigation of atomic structure has given us a picture of the arrangement and behavior of the electrons surrounding the nuclei, and we have used it to great advantage to solve such old puzzles of physics and chemistry as emission spectra and valence. Indeed, this picture has pulled together many separate parts of physical science. As for the nucleus of the atom, we found that its charge is $(+)Zq_e$ and that its mass (practically the whole mass of the atom) is concentrated in a nuclear diameter only about $1/10,000$ as large as that of the whole atom. *But does the nucleus itself also have internal structure?* The question and the way to answer it both became first possible with the discovery of radioactivity in 1896. No development in science has contributed more to changes in our conceptions of the atom and of matter in general than this discovery, to which we shall now turn our attention.

ADDITIONAL PROBLEMS

35.14. List the various accomplishments of the Bohr theory of the atom.

35.15. Bohr was aware in 1913 of Rutherford's earlier observation that electrons sent with high speed through a gas "will lose energy in distinct finite quanta." Explain this observation in terms of Bohr's model.

35.16. The photon of smallest energy that a neutral lithium atom can absorb is one for which the wavelength is 6708 A. At what temperature will colliding lithium atoms have an average kinetic energy equal to this smallest quantum accepted by an unexcited lithium atom?

35.17. For each of the following atoms, draw a diagram showing the electron configuration: (a) sodium, (b) potassium, (c) magnesium, (d) calcium.

35.18. Decide on the electron configuration, valences, and, if possible, the type of bonding involved in the formation of each of these molecules: (a) $NiCl_2$, (b) CO_2, (c) MgS, (d) N_2, (e) Na_2O.

35.19. (a) Show that Eq. (35.7) may be expressed in the form $1/\lambda = \frac{3}{4}R_H(Z - 1)^2$, where R_H is the Rydberg constant for hydrogen. (b) For nickel ($Z = 28$), compute the expected wavelength of K_α on the basis of Bohr's model, and compare the result with the experimental value listed in Table 35.1.

35.20. By extending the argument that led to Eq. (35.7), compute the wavelength of the L_α line of copper, which is ascribed to the jump of an M-electron into a vacancy in the L-shell. Assume that the K- and L-shells, when filled, contain two and eight electrons, respectively. (The observed wavelength of L_α is 13.3 A.)

35.21. How can x-rays help us decide that there is no rare earth element after lutetium (Lu, $Z = 71$)?

Supplementary Reading

Behrens, C. E., "Further developments of Bohr's early atomic theory," *American Journal of Physics*, v. 11 (1943), pp. 272–281.

Cheronis, N. D., J. B. Parsons, and C. E. Ronneberg, *The study of the physical world* (Houghton Mifflin, 1955), Chaps. 28–33. A review of chemistry in terms of modern atomic structure.

de Broglie, L., *The revolution in physics* (Noonday Press, 1953), Chaps. 6–12.

Newman, J. R., *The world of mathematics* (Simon and Schuster, 1956), pp. 849–850. Excerpts from Moseley's paper.

Pauling, L., *General chemistry* (Freeman, 2nd edition, 1953), Chap. 8.

White, H. E., *Modern college physics* (Van Nostrand, 3rd edition, 1956), Chap. 68.

Zimmer, E., *The revolution in physics* (Faber and Faber, London, 1936), Chaps. IV–VIII. A good account of further developments.

Part IX
THE NUCLEUS

(1901–1954)

THE NUCLEUS

Nuclear physics today dominates the scene of physical science. Challenging and important work is, of course, being done in other fields of physics and other aspects of physical science, but in nuclear physics contemporary science has reached a remarkable climax of discoveries and insights. These heights have been taken in an assault led by a galaxy of great leaders of science. Moreover, the assault has gathered ever more speed and scope, from its origin in the lonely labors of the Curies just before the turn of the century to the nationwide mobilization of research teams in nuclear physics, chemistry, and technology in this country and abroad.

The main events are so recent that the conceptual order still follows largely the order of historical development. Starting with the discovery of radioactivity, these concluding chapters bring us to problems concerning nuclear forces, thermonuclear reactions, and other research lying on the frontiers of knowledge.

CHAPTER 36

RADIOACTIVITY

36.1 Becquerel's discovery. The discovery of radioactivity in 1896 by the French physicist Henri Becquerel (1852–1908) was another of those "accidents" that illustrate how the trained and prepared mind may be able to respond to unexpected observations beyond the range of initial interest. Becquerel's discovery came within less than two months after Röntgen's published announcement of the discovery of x-rays (Section 32.5). Röntgen had pointed out that the x-rays came from the spot on the glass tube where the beam of cathode rays (electrons) was hitting, and that this spot simultaneously showed strong fluorescence. It occurred to Becquerel and others that x-rays might in some way be related to fluorescence and phosphorescence.* Becquerel accordingly tested a number of phosphorescent substances to determine whether they emitted x-rays while phosphorescing. He had no success until he happened to test a compound of uranium. In his words:

> I wrapped a ... photographic plate ... with two sheets of thick black paper, so thick that the plate did not become clouded by exposure to the sun for a whole day. I placed on the paper a crust of the phosphorescent substance, and exposed the whole thing to the sun for several hours. When I developed the photographic plate I saw the silhouette of the phosphorescent substance in black on the negative. If I placed between the phosphorescent substance and the paper a coin or a metallic screen pierced with an open-work design, the image of these objects appeared on the negative. The same experiment can be tried with a thin sheet of glass placed between the phosphorescent substance and the paper, which excludes the possibility of a chemical action resulting from vapors that might emanate from the substance when heated by the sun's rays.
>
> We may therefore conclude from these experiments that the phosphorescent substance in question emits radiations which penetrate paper that is opaque to light, ...

Becquerel could have said at this point, more emphatically than he did, that x-rays actually seemed to be emitted by this substance while it phosphoresced. But almost immediately his conviction was shaken by a further event.

---

*A phosphorescent substance differs from one that is fluorescent (Section 32.5) in that it continues to emit light for a time *after* the exciting agency is removed; for example, it will glow in the dark after having absorbed sunlight.

... among the preceding experiments some had been made ready on Wednesday the 26th and Thursday the 27th of February [1896]; and, as on those days the sun showed only intermittently, I kept my arrangements all prepared and put back the holders in the dark in the drawer of the case, and left in place the crusts of uranium salt. Since the sun did not show itself again for several days, I developed the photographic plates on the 1st of March, expecting to find the images very feeble. On the contrary, the silhouettes appeared with great intensity. I thought at once that the action might be able to go on in the dark.

Further experiments verified this conjecture: the uranium compound, whether or not it was allowed to phosphoresce by exposure to light, continuously emitted something that could penetrate lightproof paper and even thicker materials. Becquerel tested other compounds of uranium, and finally uranium itself, and all showed this same spontaneous "activity." He found that the emission produced ionization in the surrounding air. Thus either the ionizing effect, as indicated by the rate of discharge of a charged electroscope, or the degree of darkening of a photographic plate, could be used to measure the intensity of the invisible emission. The intensity of the emission from any uranium compound Becquerel found to be directly proportional to the fraction by weight of the uranium in the compound.

These findings raised many questions. For example, the emission from the uranium was persistent and perhaps even permanent, and yet entirely spontaneous, requiring no energy from any external source to maintain it. Here was a phenomenon that was far more puzzling than that of x-rays. Yet, probably because of the current interest and excitement over x-rays, Becquerel's work received little attention for some two years following his discovery. But then, early in 1898, the Curies entered the picture.

36.2 Other radioactive elements are discovered. One of Becquerel's colleagues in Paris was the physicist Pierre Curie, husband of Marie Sklodowska Curie (Fig. 36.1), a young physical scientist of Polish birth. Marie Curie began a systematic examination of a large number of minerals and elements and soon found that the element thorium, Th, and its compounds show the "radiating activity," or *radioactivity*, as the Curies later came to call the phenomenon. (The same discovery was made independently in Germany, by G. C. Schmidt, at about the same time.) To find that thorium is radioactive was of great importance, for until this time it had been thought that the phenomenon was a unique property of just one element, uranium.

By this time Pierre Curie had laid aside his researches in other fields and was assisting his wife. The intensity of the emission from any thorium compound, they found, was directly proportional to the fraction by weight

Fig. 36.1. Marie Curie (1867–1934) and Pierre Curie (1859–1906).

of the thorium present, as Becquerel had similarly concluded for uranium compounds. But the Curies went further, pointing out that radioactivity is an *atomic process*, being affected neither by the physical state nor by the chemical combination of the radioactive atoms with other elements. They found one mineral, pitchblende (about 80% uranium oxide, U_3O_8), for which the emission, as measured by its effect in ionizing air, was several times more intense than that from an equal weight of pure uranium. This suggested that pitchblende must contain a new and unknown element more radioactive than uranium, for the other elements known at the time to be associated with it in pitchblende, such as bismuth and barium, had been found to be nonradioactive. The Curies therefore began a painstaking search for a radioactive part of pitchblende other than uranium; this involved laborious chemical treatments and separation processes. After each separation, the products were tested, the inactive part discarded, and the active part further analyzed. The final residue presumably consisted mainly of the unknown radioactive element. In July 1898 they reported to the French Academy of Sciences:

By carrying on these different operations we obtained products that were more and more active [per unit mass]. Finally, we obtained a substance whose activity is about 400 times greater than that of uranium . . .

We believe, therefore, that the substance which we have extracted from pitchblende contains a metal that has not yet been observed, related to bismuth in its chemical properties. If the existence of this new metal is confirmed, we propose to call it *polonium*, from the name of the native country of one of us.

Six months after this discovery of polonium (chemical symbol Po), the Curies tested another fraction separated from pitchblende, and found the emission from it so intense as to indicate the presence of another new element more radioactive even than polonium. The final fraction obtained had an activity per unit mass 900 times that of uranium, and was chemically entirely different from uranium, thorium, and polonium. Spectroscopic analysis of this fraction revealed spectral lines characteristic of barium and also a line in the ultraviolet region that did not seem to belong to any known element. They reported their belief that the residue, "although for the most part consisting of barium, contains in addition a new element which produces radioactivity and which furthermore is very near barium in its chemical properties." For this new element, so extraordinarily radioactive, they proposed the name *radium* (Ra).

A next step in making the evidence for the existence of the new elements more convincing was to determine their specific properties, especially the atomic weights. For both polonium and radium, the Curies had made clear that they had not yet been able to isolate the element or even to obtain a pure sample of one of its compounds. From the residue containing the strongly radioactive material they had separated a fraction consisting of barium chloride mixed with a presumably very small quantity of radium chloride. Additional fractionations gave an increasing proportion of radium chloride. An indication of the difficulty of this task is implicit in the Curies' remark that radium "is very near barium in its chemical properties," for it is the differences in properties that makes separation possible. Moreover, to obtain successive fractions in usable amounts, one must start with a very large amount of material.

With an initial 100-kgm shipment of pitchblende from which the uranium salt had been removed for use in the manufacture of glass (this "useless" residue was a gift from the Austrian government) the Curies prepared a "laboratory" at the School of Physics where Pierre Curie taught. Failing to obtain financial support, the Curies began their work without technical help in an abandoned wooden shed. Marie Curie wrote later

I came to treat as many as 20 kilograms of matter at a time, which had the effect of filling the shed with great jars full of precipitates and liquids. It was killing work to carry the receivers, to pour off the liquids and to stir, for hours at a stretch, the boiling matter in a smelting basin.

From the mixture of radium chloride and barium chloride only the *average* atomic weight of the barium and radium could be computed. At first an average value of 146 was obtained, as compared with 137 for the atomic weight of barium. After many additional fractionations that increased the proportion of radium chloride, the average atomic weight rose to 174. Continuing this tedious process for four years, during which she treated several tons of pitchblende residue, Marie Curie was able to report in July 1902 that 0.1 gm of radium chloride had been obtained, so pure that spectroscopic examination showed no evidence of any remaining barium. The atomic weight of radium could be computed on the reasonable assumption that radium is divalent, as are the chemically similar elements barium and calcium. The value obtained was 225 (the present-day value is 226.05).* In 1910, Marie Curie (her husband had died in 1906 as the result of a traffic accident) isolated radium metal by means of electrolysis of molten radium chloride. The activity of pure radium is found to be more than a million times that of the same mass of uranium; the yield of radium from one ton of high-grade uranium ore is about 0.2 gm by modern methods.

36.3 The nature of the radioactive emissions (α, β, γ-rays). While the early separation experiments were in progress, an understanding was slowly being gained of the nature of the spontaneous emission from the various radioactive elements. Becquerel thought at first that it was simply x-rays, but it was soon found that there are three different kinds of radioactive emission, now called α-particles, β-particles, and γ-rays. The α-particles, we now know, are positively charged particles of atomic mass, the β-particles are streams of high-speed (negative) electrons, and γ-rays are short-wavelength electromagnetic waves like x-rays. The radiations come from the nuclei of radioactive atoms. Methods for determining their characteristics will now be given briefly.

Figure 36.2 illustrates schematically a magnetic method for separating the three components of radioactive emissions. Some radioactive material is placed at the bottom of a long, narrow hole in a block of lead. A fairly parallel beam of the emission thus emerges from the hole, while the emission in all other directions is absorbed by the lead. A strong magnetic field, perpendicular to the direction of travel of the rays, causes the charged

---

*In 1903, the Nobel Prize for Physics was given jointly to Becquerel and the Curies for their work on the discovery of radioactivity. As a unique recognition Marie Curie also was awarded the Nobel Prize for Chemistry in 1911 for the discovery of the elements polonium and radium.

particles to be deflected sideways. The whole equipment is in an evacuated box to avoid absorption of any part of the radiation by the air. After separation, the beams may be intercepted by a photographic plate to provide a record.

The explanation for the observed deflection of α- and β-particles in the magnetic field is to be sought in Faraday's discovery that a force acts on a current in a magnetic field (see Section 28.7). Figure 28.9 and Eq. (28.7) give respectively the direction and the magnitude of the force on a conventional (positive-charge) current in a wire of length l. But the wire is not essential, for the force acts on the moving charges themselves. Consider a beam of charged particles, such as α- or β-particles, moving through a vacuum and entering a magnetic field H as shown in Fig. 36.2; since F is always perpendicular to the direction of motion, each α-particle experiences a constant deflection and so moves along the arc of a circle so long as it is in the field H. The same argument applies to the beam of β-particles, except that it is deflected to the other side, being of opposite charge. Indeed, from the direction of the deflection we can determine in each case whether a beam consists of positive or negative charges. This conclusion can be confirmed by directing the deflected beam into a collector connected to an electroscope and testing the charge that builds up on the leaves. This was done by the Curies in 1900 to confirm the negative charge of β-particles.

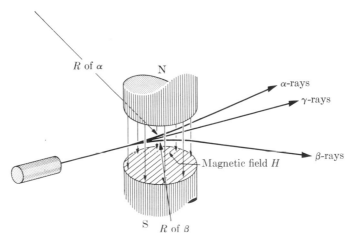

Fig. 36.2. Separation of the "rays" from a radioactive material by passage through a magnetic field. The magnetic lines of force are here downward in the plane of the diagram; while the α- and β-particles travel in this field, they are deflected along circular arcs in a plane perpendicular to the magnetic lines of force.

PROBLEM 36.1. A beam of cosmic rays travels to our earth, directly down toward the equator. How will this beam be deflected by the earth's magnetic field if it consists of positively charged particles?

PROBLEM 36.2. Gamma rays are never deflected by magnetic or electric fields, and the deflection of the path of α-particles can be observed only if considerably stronger magnetic fields are applied than suffice for the deflection of β-particles. Suggest explanations for both observations.

The experiment of Fig. 36.2 furnishes an even more important datum than the *sign* of the charges. Equation (28.8) gives the magnitude of the force on a single charge q moving with speed v across a magnetic field of strength H:

$$F = \mu_0 Hqv.$$

But the force is always perpendicular to the motion, and so curves the path of a free particle in a circular arc, acting as a centripetal force $F_c = mv^2/R$; here m is the mass of the particle (either α or β) and R is the radius of curvature of the path, easily obtained once the path is determined. It follows that $\mu_0 Hqv = mv^2/R$, or

$$\frac{q}{m} = \frac{v}{\mu_0 HR}. \tag{36.1}$$

While μ_0, H, and R are given or obtainable in the experiment, q, m, and v were, of course, not initially known for α- or β-particles. Thus Eq. (36.1) deals with three unknown quantities. Therefore Becquerel, investigating β-particles in 1900, had recourse to a separate experimental method for measuring v. The procedure was essentially the same as that used by J. J. Thomson in 1897 to obtain a reliable value for the ratio of charge q_e to mass m_e for the electron in cathode rays (thereby establishing quantitatively the existence of the electron): once the deflection owing to the magnetic field H has been recorded, a *compensating electric field* is established, to return the beam to the initial straight-line motion. In Fig. 36.3, path I would be taken by the negatively charged β-particles if the magnetic field H were applied alone, and path II would result if the electric field were applied alone; note that the electric field is perpendicular to the magnetic field. By Eq. (27.1), in the electric field E the particle experiences a force $F = qE$. Therefore at balance, when the straight path III is followed, $qE = \mu_0 Hqv$, or

$$v = \frac{E}{\mu_0 H}. \tag{36.2}$$

Applying Eq. (36.2) to the case of β-particles, Becquerel found their speeds to be about half the speed of light. Using this value for v in Eq. (36.1),

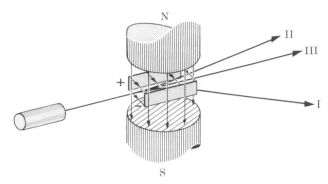

FIG. 36.3. The magnetic lines of force are vertically downward; the electric lines of force between the electrodes in the gap are at right angles to the magnetic lines of force.

he obtained a value of q/m for β-particles which was in close enough agreement with that found by J. J. Thomson for the electron to permit the deduction that the β-particles were electrons. Subsequent experiments produced a complete agreement of the measured values.

PROBLEM 36.3. In an experiment to measure the value of q/m and v of β-particles, the apparatus is set up as in Fig. 36.3. When a magnetic field of intensity $H = 900$ new/unit pole is applied, the radius of curvature R is 0.22 m; when an electric field is set up between the two plates, which are 2.50 cm apart, by applying a potential difference of 850 volts, the beam of β-particles returns to its straight-line motion. (a) Show that $q/m = (-)1.76 \times 10^{11}$ coul/kgm, and that the speed was in this case 3.0×10^7 m/sec. (b) Using the result of Millikan's experiment on the charge of the electron (Section 28.3), find the mass of a β-particle.

Establishing the nature of α-radiation was rather more difficult than to do so for β-particles. It was Ernest Rutherford who had originally made the distinction between these rays in 1899; he had placed layers of metal foil close to uranium and found that one part of the emission was able to penetrate only a few layers, whereas the remainder required many layers to be completely absorbed. He concluded that the emission consists of at least two components—one that is very easily absorbed and which he termed "for convenience, α-radiation," and the other, about 100 times more penetrating, which he called "β-radiation." (The γ-rays, identified later, were present too, and are about 100 times more penetrating than β-particles.) In 1903 Rutherford first deflected α-radiation in a strong magnetic field, as was schematically shown in Fig. 36.2. The best value for q/m of α-particles found in subsequent work was about $(+)4.8 \times 10^7$ coul/kgm—about 4000 times smaller than q/m for β-particles. This value explained the difficulty of getting a small enough radius of curvature with reasonable field intensities H, for $R \propto 1/(H \cdot q/m)$ by Eq. (36.1). And since q was not likely to be smaller than for β-particles, m would have to be much larger for the α-particle.

In fact, the value of q/m given above for α-particles is just one-half the value of q/m for a hydrogen ion. This would be explained in a reasonable way if the α-particle were like a hydrogen molecule minus one of its two electrons (H_2^+), or else were a helium atom, whose mass was known to be about four times that of a hydrogen atom, but missing both its electrons (He^{++}). Other possibilities might have been entertained—for example, bare nuclei of carbon, nitrogen, or oxygen would have about the same q/m ratio.

Rutherford hypothesized that of all possibilities the most probable was that the α-particle is a doubly-ionized helium atom (or a helium nucleus, as we would now put it). He knew that the gas helium was found as an inclusion in radioactive minerals and was liberated by some compounds of radioactive elements. In a series of experiments from 1906 to 1909 he succeeded in proving his hypothesis in several different ways. The last and most conclusive of these experiments was made in 1909 with T. D. Royds by constructing what Sir James Jeans later called "a sort of mouse trap for α-particles" (Fig. 36.4). Some of the radioactive element radon, Rn, was put in a glass tube having walls only one hundredth of a millimeter thick. This tube was sealed into a thick-walled glass tube equipped at the top with a capillary tube containing two electrodes. The space between the inner and outer tubes was then evacuated and the apparatus allowed to stand for about a week. During this time, α-particles from the radon passed through the thin walls of the inner tube, and a gas gradually accumulated in the previously evacuated space. This gas was compressed into the capillary tube by letting mercury enter through a side tube. When a large potential difference was applied to the electrodes, an electric discharge passed through the gas. When the resulting light was examined with a spectroscope, the spectral lines characteristic of helium were clearly seen. A separate experiment showed that neutral helium atoms could not have passed through the thin walls of the inner glass tube.

Now it was clear how to interpret these observations: Since there are

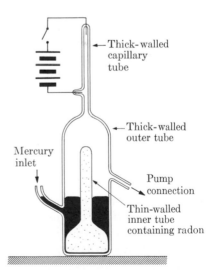

FIG. 36.4. Apparatus for showing spectroscopically that helium is formed from α-particles.

many electrons present even in a well-evacuated space, Rutherford could safely conclude that the gas collecting in the outer tube was due to α-particles passing into the outer tube and capturing electrons there. Hence the α-particles are doubly ionized helium particles. To be sure, this argument entailed the curious result that one element (here, radon) spontaneously emits, as an α-particle, a fragment of itself which corresponded to *another* element, helium. Time has accustomed us to this fact; and since a neutral helium atom ($Z = 2$) has only two electrons, we may now equally well say, in terms of Rutherford's nuclear model of atoms, that the α-particle is simply a helium nucleus.

PROBLEM 36.4. Describe an apparatus and procedure that could be used to determine the *volume* of helium gas, expressed for standard conditions of pressure and temperature, generated in a specific time interval by a selected sample of a radioactive substance.

PROBLEM 36.5. This problem illustrates the most direct of all methods for determining Avogadro's number, N_0. Experiment showed that a certain sample of a radioactive substance emits 5.3×10^8 α-particles per hour. (How could this be measured?) Observations made over a long period of time showed that this same sample yields helium gas at the rate of 1.96×10^{-11} cm^3/hr, this volume being that for standard conditions of pressure and temperature. The atomic weight of helium is 4.00 and its density is 1.8×10^{-4} gm/cm^3 under standard conditions. On the assumption that the emitted α-particles, after slowing down, each captured two electrons and became a neutral helium atom, compute N_0, the number of helium atoms per gram-atomic weight. [Helium being monatomic (on what evidence?), this is also the number of helium molecules per mole.]

Relatively little need be said here about the third type of radioactive emission. The French experimenter P. Villard had observed in 1900 that the emission from radium contains a highly penetrating component to which he gave the name γ-rays. Later these γ-rays were found in the emissions from other radioactive elements. They show no deflection whatever in passing through even the most intense magnetic or electric fields, which indicates that they consist of electromagnetic radiation. This has turned out to be true; for example, although their wavelengths are generally even shorter than those of x-rays, interference effects analogous with those obtainable with light waves and x-rays can be produced. Of course, as for all electromagnetic radiation, the interaction with matter shows γ-radiation to consist of photons, now referred to as γ-photons. The energy per photon, $h\nu$, is very high because ν is so large; hence when γ-rays impinge on a target to release photoelectrons, the latter come off with very high speeds. On the other hand, γ-rays passing through matter do not interact with as many atoms per centimeter of travel as does a stream of charged particles (β-particles and particularly α-particles), so they lose their energy less rapidly and are much more penetrating.

PROBLEM 36.6. When the γ-rays from the radioactive element called radium C are examined spectroscopically, they are found to form a line spectrum. The measured wavelength λ corresponding to one of the lines is 0.016 A. (a) Show that the energy of each γ-photon producing this line is 1.2×10^{-13} j. (b) How does this energy compare with that of an x-ray photon of wavelength 1.0 A?

PROBLEM 36.7. Show that an x-ray tube [Section 32.5 (b)] would have to be operated at a potential difference of about 750,000 volts to produce x-rays of the same wavelength as the γ-rays in Problem 36.6.

36.4 Radioactive transformations. It was almost immediately evident that the discovery of radioactivity required a re-examination of existing conceptions of matter and its structure. The emission of α- and β-particles was not in accord with the well-established principles and postulates of the highly useful atomic-molecular theory of chemistry. For example, it had been assumed (a) that a pure element is a collection of identical atoms, and (b) that atoms are indestructible and unchangeable (except for the temporary effects of ionization and excitation). Two of the most basic and useful postulates in physics also seemed threatened, namely (c) the principle of conservation of mass and (d) the principle of conservation of energy. These four generalizations needed review in the light of these two discoveries, namely that radioactive elements spontaneously and continually emit α-particles, β-particles, and γ-photons, and that α- and β-particles have computable masses and kinetic energies and γ-photons computable electromagnetic energies.

The contradictions are evident. Consider the relatively massive α-particles emitted from pure samples of elements such as radium: They must come from the atoms of the radioactive elements; there is no other source. Yet, by point (b) above, these atoms are unchangeable. Thus we have a picture of a radioactive atom expelling an α-particle of definite mass, but without the atom losing mass; this is in contradiction with (c). Similar considerations apply to the tremendous amounts of energy carried off by the emission from a radioactive element. By (d), the atoms initially must have at least as much energy as they give off. The energy released in ordinary chemical reactions is explained as due to a reduction in the potential energy as the result of rearrangements of the atoms to form different molecules, and the energy released, atom for atom, is of a much smaller magnitude than that involved in radioactive emissions. But radioactivity does not involve chemical changes in the ordinary sense of the term, for it occurs in samples of pure elements.

To resolve these impasses, Rutherford and Frederick Soddy, in 1902, published a bold and epoch-making solution, a *theory of radioactive transformation*. They proposed to discard postulate (b) insofar as radioactive atoms are concerned, and to assume instead that an atom which has emitted an α- or a β-particle is no longer an atom of the same original element. The emission of either type of particle constitutes a breaking up of the atom into two parts—the emitted particle, and a massive residue physically and chemically different from the original parent atom.

Powerful evidence for the new assumption was provided by observations of this sort: When a sample of pure radium was placed in a container which was then evacuated, later analysis revealed that an "emanation" was given off from the radium—a gas that turned out to be a new element, to which the name radon (Rn) was eventually given. And the mass of a radon atom was found to be less than the mass of a radium atom by just the mass of an α-particle. We may conveniently represent this disintegration of the radium atom symbolically in various ways; for example,

$$\text{Ra} \longrightarrow \text{Rn} + \text{He}^{++}, \quad \text{or} \quad \text{Ra} \overset{\alpha}{\nearrow} \text{Rn}.$$

This process is often spoken of as the "decay" or "transmutation" of radium into radon, with α-particle emission.

Radon itself turns out to be radioactive, each atom emitting an α-particle and thereby decaying to an atom of an element which was called radium A: $\text{Rn} \rightarrow \text{RaA} + \text{He}^{++}$. RaA is a solid, and is also radioactive. In fact, the original radium atoms experience a succession of transformations into new radioactive "daughter" elements until one is reached that is stable, or nonradioactive, namely lead. The chain beginning with Ra has 10 members, some of which emit β-particles rather than α-particles; γ-photons do not appear alone but along with an α-particle or a β-particle. Rutherford also suggested that since radium is always found in uranium minerals, it may be merely a member of a series starting with uranium as ancestor of all members. We now know this to be the case. Each uranium atom may in time give rise to successive daughter atoms, radium being the sixth generation and stable lead the fifteenth; this is shown in Table 36.1.

Each member, given a symbol as shown in Table 36.1, differs physically and chemically from its immediate neighbors, and so can in principle be separated from them. But the step from one to the next is taken by different atoms of the same element after different time intervals, and as a result the problem facing the experimentalist at this point was difficult: any radioactive substance, even though it initially consists of identical atoms, will eventually become a mixture of many different kinds of atoms; starting with pure, α-emitting uranium atoms, after a time there may be 14 other elements present in the sample, of which 13 contribute to the radioactive emission, each in its own way. (This is the reason why the sample in Fig. 36.2 was said to give off α-, β-, and γ-radiation at the same time.)

Table 36.1. The uranium-radium series.*

Symbol for element	UI	$\xrightarrow{\alpha}$	UX$_1$	$\xrightarrow{\beta,\gamma}$	UX$_2$	$\xrightarrow{\beta,\gamma}$	UII	$\xrightarrow{\alpha}$	Io	$\xrightarrow{\alpha,\gamma}$	Ra	$\xrightarrow{\alpha,\gamma}$	Rn	$\xrightarrow{\alpha}$	RaA
Half-life T	4.51×10^9 yr		24.1 days		1.18 min		2.48×10^5 yr		8.0×10^4 yr		1620 yr		3.82 days		3.05 min

Symbol for element		$\xrightarrow{}$	RaB	$\xrightarrow{\beta,\gamma}$	RaC	$\xrightarrow{\beta,\gamma}$	RaC′	$\xrightarrow{\alpha}$	RaD	$\xrightarrow{\beta,\gamma}$	RaE	$\xrightarrow{\beta}$	RaF	$\xrightarrow{\alpha,\gamma}$	RaG
Half-life T			26.8 min		19.7 min		1.64×10^{-4} sec		19.4 yr		5.0 days		138.4 days		(stable lead)

*In this and all other radioactive series, some points are reached where a small fraction of atoms decays in a manner other than as indicated here. For example, about 0.04% of the RaC atoms decay with the emission of an α-particle and a γ-photon to form atoms of RaC″, and these in turn emit a β-particle and form RaD. These cases of "branching" have been omitted from the table for simplicity.

To unravel this complexity and to ascertain the properties of each member of a series often requires the greatest experimental ingenuity. One method depends on the skillful purification of a particular radioactive substance, as the Curies had done. For example, suppose that a sample were obtained from which all the radioactive substances except radium had been removed. The radon gas which would immediately begin to be produced by the sample could be drawn off and its properties examined without delay before it became seriously contaminated by the disintegration of an appreciable number of its atoms into radium A. If this is done, it turns out that, on the average, a given number of radon atoms decays into polonium much faster than radium into radon. The *exact rate of decay* becomes now an important concept.

36.5 Decay constant; activity; concept of half-life. Not only do the various radioactive elements show great differences in the respective rates of decay, but each atom of a given element is likely to decay to the next stage at a different moment than another atom of the same element. However, for any given kind of radioactive atoms, *the fraction of the total number of atoms that will decay per unit time interval is characteristic, fixed and unchangeable*, being independent of all physical and chemical conditions, such as pressure, temperature, and chemical binding forces.*

This remarkable property merits our particular attention, both because it is easily misunderstood and because it leads to a fruitful concept. Let N_0 denote the number of atoms present in any pure radioactive sample at the start of an experiment (here N_0 need not be Avogadro's number); in a short interval Δt, we find that ΔN of the original atoms have decayed. Therefore $\Delta N/\Delta t$ is the *activity* of the sample at the start, that is, the number of atoms which disintegrate per unit time interval by the emission of either an α- or a β-particle (and perhaps also a γ-photon). Clearly, the ratio of $(\Delta N/\Delta t)$ and N_0, namely $(\Delta N/N_0)/\Delta t$, is the *fraction of the original number of atoms* that decay per unit time. This corresponds to, say, the death rate in a city—perhaps one person per 20,000 persons per day. Now suppose we wait some time t and measure the number of unchanged survivors N_t out of the original sample, and also the new activity $\Delta N_t/\Delta t$. The fraction which now decays per unit time, $(\Delta N_t/N_t)/\Delta t$ is, *by experiment*, found to be the same as before for that particular species of radioactive atom:

$$\frac{\Delta N}{N_0\,\Delta t} = \frac{\Delta N_t}{N_t\,\Delta t} = \text{constant.} \qquad (36.3)$$

---

*Only at extremely high pressures and for special cases of chemical binding has a slight modification of the rate of decay been found recently.

The value of this constant, called the *decay constant*, symbol λ (it has of course nothing to do with wavelength) can be found by experiment for each radioactive species; for radium, for example, it is $1.4 \times 10^{-11} \sec^{-1}$, that is, on the average, 1.4 atoms per 10^{11} radium atoms decay per second.

PROBLEM 36.8. (a) Strictly speaking, a minus sign should be placed before the constant in Eq. (36.3). Why? (b) Describe some other phenomenon to which an equation similar to Eq. (36.3) applies.

Since the ratio $(\Delta N_t / N_t)/\Delta t$ is constant, the activity $\Delta N_t / \Delta t$ must decrease in proportion to the number of unchanged survivors, N_t. Thus the "total lifetime" of a sample is indefinitely long, for the fewer atoms left unchanged in the sample, the fewer will disintegrate per unit time. If the number N_t of atoms left at the end of time t is plotted as a function of t, a curve such as that shown in Fig. 36.5 is obtained. The equation for this type of curve is

$$N_t = N_0 e^{-\lambda t}, \qquad (36.4)$$

where e is the number 2.718 . . . Hence Eqs. (36.3) and (36.4) are equivalent, and they can be shown to be derivable from each other.

The curve approaches the time axis asymptotically, which is another way of saying that we cannot assign any finite time at which the value of N_t falls to zero; hence "total lifetime" is not a useful notion. But

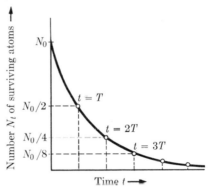

FIG. 36.5. Radioactive decay curve. After a time interval $t = T$, one-half the initial number of atoms has survived without radioactive decay ($N_t = N_0/2$).

it is possible to specify the time required for any particular fraction N_t/N_0 of a sample to decay. For convenience the fraction $\frac{1}{2}$ has been chosen. To the time T required for the decay of one-half the atoms of a sample, Rutherford appropriately gave the name *half-life*. Because each kind of radioactive atom has a unique decay constant λ, it also has a unique half-life T, and thus the half-life of a substance can be used to compare it with any other radioactive substance. As Table 36.1 shows, these half-lives are very different for different radioactive substances. Thus for the matriarch of the uranium series, namely UI (pronounced "U-one" or "Uranium one"), the half-life is 4.5 billion years, whereas for RaC' it is of the order of 1/10,000 of a second. Consequently the activity of RaC' is very strong and of UI very feeble. It is possible to speculate that some radioactive elements, present in great quantities eons ago, decayed so rapidly that no measurable traces are now left. On the other hand, many radioactive elements decay so slowly that during any ordinary length of experimentation their activities seem to be constant.*

The principal advantage of the concept of half-life lies in the experimental result implied in Fig. 36.5 that, no matter how old a sample with given half-life T is at a given moment, in an additional time T half of the atoms will still have survived. Thus the half-life is not to be thought of as an abbreviation for "half a life." If one-half the original atoms remain unchanged after a time T, one-fourth $[=\frac{1}{2} \times \frac{1}{2}]$ will remain after two consecutive half-life intervals $2T$, one-eighth after $3T$, and so on. Note how different the situation is for a population of, say, human beings instead of radioactive atoms. If we select a group of N_0 babies, half the number may survive the 60th birthday; of these $N_0/2$ oldsters, none is likely to celebrate a 120th birthday. But of N_0 radioactive atoms with a half-life of 60 yr, $N_0/4$ will have remained intact after 120 yr, $N_0/8$ after 180 yr, etc. In short, the probability of survival for atoms is unchanged by the age they have already reached.

We are not dealing here with the behavior of individual atoms, but with the behavior of a very large number. If a hundred thousand persons were to flip coins simultaneously just once, we could predict with good accuracy how many would obtain heads, namely one-half of them. But we could not predict that one particular person in this crowd would obtain heads. And even the prediction of 50% heads in the whole group might be considerably in error if the group is small. Similarly, from experiments in radioactivity we can predict that a certain fraction of a relatively large sample will survive in any given time interval, but not whether a particular atom will be among the survivors. And as the sample of survivors decreases in size owing to disintegrations, our predictions about the fraction of survivors become less accurate and finally, when only a few atoms remain intact, are no longer meaningful. In short, the disintegration law as expressed either by Eq. (36.3) or by Eq. (36.4) or by Fig. 36.5 is a *statistical* law, applicable only to large populations of the radioactive atoms and involving no special assumptions as to why the atoms disintegrate.

In developing the kinetic theory of matter (Chapter 25), it would have been a hopeless task to have tried to describe the zigzag path of each of the molecules involved, but one could determine quite well the average

---

*Of course, λ and T must be related to each other. Taking logarithms of both sides of Eq. (36.4), we have $\log (N_t/N_0) = -0.4343 \lambda t$. If $N_t/N_0 = \frac{1}{2}$, and consequently $t = T$ by definition, the last equation becomes $\log (\frac{1}{2}) = -0.4343 \lambda T$, or $\log 2 = 0.4343 \lambda T$. But $\log 2 = 0.3010$, therefore $T = 0.693/\lambda$. Thus for radium, where $\lambda \doteq 1.4 \times 10^{-11} \sec^{-1}$, $T \doteq 5.0 \times 10^{10}$ sec or about 1600 yr (more accurately, 1620 yr).

number of collisions of a molecule per unit time within the container, the average speed, and so on. Similarly, in radioactivity it is the complete inability to specify when each of the tremendous number of atoms will disintegrate that makes a statistical approach both necessary and rewarding. Many other examples of the usefulness of a statistical view of nature have since come to light as attention has shifted from the specifically predictable behavior of each of a small number of macroscopic bodies to the statistically predictable behavior of large numbers of submicroscopic entities.

ADDITIONAL PROBLEMS

36.9. Justify the statement that, for an initially pure sample of any given radioactive substance, N_0 and N_t can be compared by comparing the activities, or numbers of particles emitted per unit time, at the start and at the time t.

36.10. With the help of a Geiger counter it is found that the total number of β-particles emitted per unit time by an initially pure sample of a radioactive element decreases to one-half the initial value in about 25 hr. (a) What fraction of the original number of atoms is then still unchanged? (b) What fraction of the original number will have decayed in 50 hr? (c) What assumptions have you made? How might you check them?

36.11. If m_1 is the mass of an initially pure sample of radium E (see Table 36.1), what is the mass m_2 of the still unchanged portion at the end of 30 days?

36.12. Consider 1.00 gm of pure radium of atomic weight 226, having a half-life of about 1600 yr. (a) On the basis of the Avogadro hypothesis, show that 2.66×10^{21} atoms of radium initially are present in the sample. (b) Make a plot of N_t vs. time covering a period of about 8000 yr. (c) Show that 8.3×10^{19} atoms of radium still remain at the end of the 8000 yr. (d) From your graph, estimate the percentage of radium atoms still present at the end of 4000 yr.

36.13. If a sample initially contains N radioactive atoms of the same kind, show that the number of these atoms (a) surviving at the end of an integral number n of consecutive half-life intervals is given by $N/2^n$, and (b) decaying during this same time nT is given by $N(1 - 2^{-n})$. (c) Use this information to find what fraction of radium D atoms still survives at the end of 88 yr.

36.14. Given that the disintegration constant for uranium I is 4.9×10^{-18} sec^{-1}, find the number of UI atoms present in a sample at the moment when its activity is 1 disintegration/sec.

36.15. Is there any contradiction in the statement that the statistical conception of radioactive disintegration leads to the conclusion that the total lifetime is infinite, but that any finite amount of radioactive material must all disintegrate in a finite time?

36.16. The equation for decay curves like the one in Fig. 36.5 is given by Eq. (36.4), with $T = 0.693/\lambda$, as shown in the footnote on page 672. Therefore

$$N_t = N_0 e^{-0.693t/T}, \tag{36.5}$$

where t is the elapsed time of observation, e is 2.718 . . . (the base of natural, or Naperian, logarithms), and N_0 and N_t are the numbers of atoms of the original species at the start and at time t respectively. (a) Use this equation to compute the ratio N_t/N_0 for the times $t = 0$, $t = T$, $t = 2T$, $t = \infty$. (*Note:* As can be found by consulting a table of natural logarithms, $e^{-1.386} = 0.250$ and $e^{-0.693} = 0.500$.) (b) In a certain uranium ore it is found that for every 59 UI atoms there are 41 atoms corresponding to its daughter elements listed in Table 36.1. What is the age of the sample of uranium ore? What assumptions have you made? (*Note:* Values of e^{-x} are listed in tables, for instance in the *Handbook of chemistry and physics.*)

36.17. Explain each of these puzzling observations: (a) The Curies noted in 1899 that ordinary substances placed near a radium compound acquired an "induced" radioactivity. (b) William Crookes discovered in 1900 that on purifying a strongly radioactive uranium-containing compound, the uranium compound itself was left with a very much smaller activity, and the separated residue containing none of the uranium possessed strong radioactivity. (c) A year later Becquerel showed that in a case like (b) the uranium compound regains the original activity after some months, whereas the residue gradually loses much of its activity during the same time.

36.18. Cite the evidence and arguments for believing that the phenomena of radioactivity are controlled by the nuclei of atoms.

36.19. An example of branching is described in the footnote to Table 36.1. Write symbolic expressions for the transitions from RaC to RaD by way of RaC′, and then by way of RaC″.

36.20. The activity of any radioactive sample is often expressed in terms of a unit called the *curie*, which is defined as equivalent to 3.70×10^{10} disintegrations per second. (a) Given that 1.0 gm of pure radium consists of 2.66×10^{21} atoms and has an activity of 1.0 curie, compute the decay constant for radium. (b) Compute the decay constant for U^{238} (namely UI) from these data: number of atoms per gram, 2.5×10^{21}; activity of 1.0 gm, 0.33 microcurie.

36.21. During an experiment, radioactive contamination has escaped into the laboratory room at time $t = 0$, and the monitoring instrument registers an activity A_0. At $t = 1$ full day, the measured activity has decreased to A_1, and at $t = n$ days to A_n. What can you say about the relation between A_n and A_1?

Supplementary Reading

Editors of Scientific American, *Atomic power* (Simon and Schuster, 1955), pp. 69–82. On sources of uranium.

Glasstone, S., *Source book on atomic energy* (Van Nostrand, 1950, 1958), Chaps. V and VII.

Jauncey, G. E. M., "The early years of radioactivity," *American Journal of Physics*, v. 14 (1946), pp. 226–241.

Knedler, J. W., Jr., *Masterworks of science* (Doubleday, 1947), pp. 571-595. Excerpts from the Curies.

Magie, W. F., *A source book in physics* (McGraw-Hill, 1935), pp. 610–616. Excerpts from Becquerel and the Curies.

Needham, J., and W. Pagel, eds., *Background to modern science* (Macmillan, 1938), pp. 49–60. A lecture by Rutherford on the history of radioactivity.

Oldenberg, O., *Introduction to atomic physics* (McGraw-Hill, 1954, and later editions), Chap. 17.

CHAPTER 37

ISOTOPES

37.1 The isotope concept and displacement rule. The discovery of so many seemingly new radioactive elements presented a perplexing problem. As Table 36.1 shows, the "uranium-radium series" involves many substances that were at first given new names and symbols, such as UX_1, UX_2, and RaA. To add to the complexity, there is a similar but quite independent series that was traced back to thorium as the parent element (thorium series). The thorium series has 11 members, and ends with a stable substance to which the name thorium D was given, although it later was found to have the chemical properties of lead. A third series exists with 12 members, once thought to originate from actinium (actinium series). *Thus there was an embarrassing plentitude of seemingly new elements*, with far too few empty spaces in the periodic table then still available to handle them. (In addition to the members of these three *natural* series, many other radioactive species are now known, mostly produced artificially.)

To solve the puzzle, Soddy made a radical suggestion in 1910. The key observation was that some of the supposedly new elements had *chemical* properties identical with those of well-known elements, although their *physical* properties were different. For example, the great-granddaughter of UI, namely uranium II (or UII), was found to have the same chemical properties as UI itself. But they differ from each other in their physical properties; as Table 36.1 shows, UI and UII have quite different half-lives, and the mass of a UII atom must be smaller than that of a UI atom by at least the mass of one α-particle. Similarly, RaB and RaG turn out to have the same chemical properties as lead, as shown by the fact that if they are mixed with lead they cannot be separated from it by chemical means; yet RaB is radioactive and RaG stable, and their atomic masses evidently cannot be the same. Soddy's suggestion now was that a chemical element should be regarded as a *pure* substance in the sense that all of its atoms have the same chemical properties, but as a *mixture* in that the atoms of one element may fall into several groups having different radioactive behavior and different atomic masses. This meant the modification of still another fundamental postulate of Dalton's atomic-molecular theory, namely, the postulate that the atoms of a pure element are alike in all respects [Section 36.4(a)]. It is only in chemical properties that they are alike. Therefore the several physically different species of atoms comprising a particular element occupy the same place in the periodic table and have the same atomic number Z. Soddy referred to them as *isotopes* of the element (Greek, *isos* + *topos*, same + place).

Thus the many species of radioactive atoms in the three natural radioactive series were shown to be isotopes of one or another of the last 11 elements in the periodic table ending with uranium. At one stroke the complexity is resolved: By chemical test, UX_1 is found to be a species of thorium ($Z = 90$), as is also ionium (Io); UX_2 is now identified as an isotope of protactinium ($Z = 91$); and so forth. The series in Table 36.1 can be rewritten in terms of the chemical nature of the radioactive atoms as follows (the atomic number Z is here placed under the old symbol for each species):

Table 37.1. Uranium-radium series.

$$\text{uranium} \begin{pmatrix} UI \\ 92 \end{pmatrix} \xrightarrow{\alpha} \text{thorium} \begin{pmatrix} UX_1 \\ 90 \end{pmatrix} \xrightarrow{\beta,\gamma} \text{protactinium} \begin{pmatrix} UX_2 \\ 91 \end{pmatrix} \xrightarrow{\beta,\gamma}$$

$$\longrightarrow \text{uranium} \begin{pmatrix} UII \\ 92 \end{pmatrix} \xrightarrow{\alpha} \text{thorium} \begin{pmatrix} Io \\ 90 \end{pmatrix} \xrightarrow{\alpha,\gamma} \text{radium} \begin{pmatrix} Ra \\ 88 \end{pmatrix} \xrightarrow{\alpha,\gamma}$$

$$\longrightarrow \text{radon} \begin{pmatrix} Rn \\ 86 \end{pmatrix} \xrightarrow{\alpha} \text{polonium} \begin{pmatrix} RaA \\ 84 \end{pmatrix} \xrightarrow{\alpha} (\text{etc.} \ldots \text{to}) \longrightarrow$$

$$\longrightarrow \text{bismuth} \begin{pmatrix} RaE \\ 83 \end{pmatrix} \xrightarrow{\beta} \text{polonium} \begin{pmatrix} RaF \\ 84 \end{pmatrix} \xrightarrow{\alpha,\gamma} \text{lead} \begin{pmatrix} RaG \\ 82 \end{pmatrix}.$$

The next questions arising are these: what is the mechanism by which these changes of chemical nature are obtained; and what law, if any, determines and orders the sequence here presented?

Soddy and his co-workers answered both questions by formulating two important rules for dealing with radioactive decay series. In interpreting these rules it will be helpful to recall that by this time (1913) Rutherford's nuclear model of the atom was receiving general acceptance, and so a radioactive atom could be regarded as one having an unstable nucleus that eventually "explodes" and ejects either an α- or a β-particle. Also recall that every nucleus has a positive charge given by $(+)Zq_e$, where Z is the atomic number, and that the neutral atom is surrounded by Z electrons which determine the chemical behavior of the atom.

The rules, called *group displacement rules*, are now rendered as follows: (1) When a nucleus expels an α-particle (He^{++}, at.wt. about 4, $Z = 2$, positive charge $2q_e$), the mass of the atom decreases by about 4 atomic-weight units, and its atomic number Z decreases by two units; the resulting atom is therefore displaced two spaces backward in the periodic table. (2) When a nucleus expels a β-particle (an electron of negative charge q_e), the mass of the atom virtually does not change, but its atomic number Z increases by 1 unit; thus the resulting atom is displaced one space forward in the periodic table.

Inspection of Table 37.1 will show that these rules do apply to the uranium-radium series so far as Z is concerned. Moreover, in the light of the Rutherford-Bohr model of the atom it is now clear why a shift in chemical nature occurs as a result of α- or β-emission: An α-particle takes from the nucleus two positive charges, and the atom can now hold two less electrons than before; the rearranged electron cloud around the nucleus acts in chemical (and optical) events like an element with an atomic number 2 units smaller than for the original atom. So by α-emission, Z goes to $Z - 2$. In β-emission, a negative charge is sent out by the nucleus, leaving it necessarily more positive than before by one positive unit charge of magnitude q_e. Therefore the electron cloud around the nucleus can now capture and accommodate one more electron, and in chemical and optical events can act like an atom with an atomic number 1 unit larger than for the original atom. Thus by β-emission, Z goes to $Z + 1$. Problems 37.6 through 37.10 at the end of this chapter are designed to indicate further the power and scope of the simple group displacement rule.

Satisfying as the clarification furnished by the group displacement rule was, a truly dramatic proof of its soundness and therefore of the whole theory that radioactive atoms decay in a series of successive steps was given in 1914. Soddy knew that the stable end product of the uranium-radium series, RaG, was chemically lead, and that the end product of the thorium series (ThD) also was an isotope of ordinary lead. But he saw that RaG, ThD, and ordinary lead must all have different atomic weights. For if we neglect β-emission, which contributes virtually nothing to the change of atomic weight, RaG is derived from uranium (chemical atomic weight about 238) by the emission of 8 α-particles (He^{++}, relative weight about 4 units each); therefore RaG is expected to have an atomic weight of about $238 - (8 \times 4)$, or 206. On the other hand, ThD is derived from thorium, atomic weight about 232, after 6 α-emissions (and 5 β-emissions which we can neglect now); therefore its atomic weight should be about $232 - 24$, or 208. And a glance at the periodic table shows that for ordinary lead, the atomic weight has been found to be a little over 207. The lead extracted from the mineral thorite, in which thorium predominates and uranium is present only to the extent of 1% or 2%, may be presumed to be the final product of the thorium series. Comparing it with lead from uranium minerals such as pitchblende should show the marked difference of atomic weights.

Here was a *quantitative prediction* which could be checked; and it was confirmed in 1914 in a series of most thorough determinations, made in the laboratory of the American chemist Theodore W. Richards* and elsewhere. It was the first proof that isotopes of the same element have different atomic weights. Although one could guess on the basis of Table 36.1 or Table 37.1 that the uranium isotopes UI and UX_2 must have different atomic masses, this could not be confirmed experimentally at the time, for the isotopes were both present in any single sample and so could not be chemically separated. And note also that the three forms of lead which were compared here are all stable and nonradioactive. Thus the possibility suggested itself that other stable elements may have several isotopes. Evidence for this view came at this time also from an entirely different direction.

37.2 The mass-spectrographic separation of isotopes. In 1912, two years before these results were obtained, J. J. Thomson (Fig. 37.1) was engaging in a quite unrelated series of experiments when he chanced on an unexpected effect of great significance. His research will now be described in terms of the rather simpler and more precise apparatus developed later for this field of study.

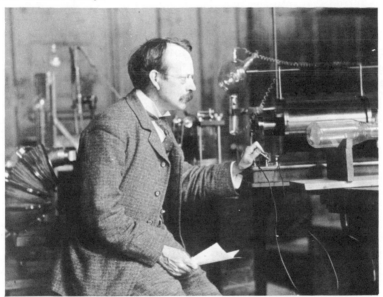

FIG. 37.1. J. J. Thomson (1856–1940). (Courtesy of Cavendish Laboratory.)

---

*Awarded the Nobel Prize for Chemistry, 1914, for his precise determinations of atomic weights for many elements.

The relative atomic weight of an element can, of course, be found by chemical means, as was shown in Section 23.5. But there is also a physical method. Recall that the ratio of charge to mass (q/m) of α- or β-particles can be found by observing their paths in electric and magnetic fields (Section 36.3); knowing the charge q in such a case will allow computation of the mass m of the particle. The same argument applies also to the positively charged atoms in a beam of ions such as passes through the narrow slit in the discharge tube described in Fig. 37.2. Deflecting fields

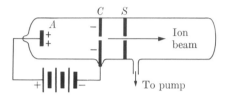

FIG. 37.2. Discharge tube for producing a beam of positive ions. The gas between anode A and cathode C is ionized during the electric discharge. After the ion beam has passed through the opening in the cathode and slit S, it moves in a good vacuum and is not influenced by the electric field between A and C.

can be introduced into the right-hand portion of the tube; for example, when the ion beam from a discharge tube passed through a magnetic *and* an electric field, as in Fig. 37.3, the deflecting forces produced by the magnetic field H (here shown to pass upward, as from an N-pole situated below the beam) and by the electric field E between plates P_1 and P_2 are respectively given by

$$F_{\text{mag}} = \mu_0 H q v, \qquad F_{\text{elec}} = q \cdot E,$$

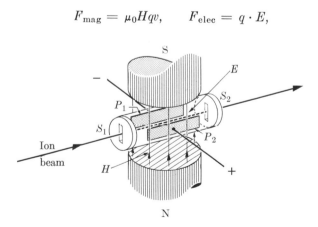

FIG. 37.3. Velocity selector for ions. The magnetic field H is upward, and perpendicular both to the electric field E between P_1 and P_2 and to the direction of travel of the ion beam.

where q is the charge on the ion. The two opposing forces must cancel for those ions that pass straight from slit S_1 to slit S_2; hence for them, $qE = \mu_0 H q v$, and

$$v = \frac{E}{\mu_0 H}. \tag{37.1}$$

An appropriate name for the arrangement in Fig. 37.3 is *velocity selector*, for it allows only those ions to pass through S_2 whose speed is given by Eq. (37.1).

The beam passing through S_2 may now be acted upon by a magnetic field only, usually from a magnet other than the one used to provide the magnetic field between S_1 and S_2. Now the deflecting force is uncompensated and acts as a centripetal force to curve the beam in a circular arc of radius R (see Fig. 37.4). Hence $mv^2/R = \mu_0 H q v$, and

$$\frac{q}{m} = \frac{v}{\mu_0 H R} = \frac{E}{\mu_0^2 H^2 R}. \tag{37.2}$$

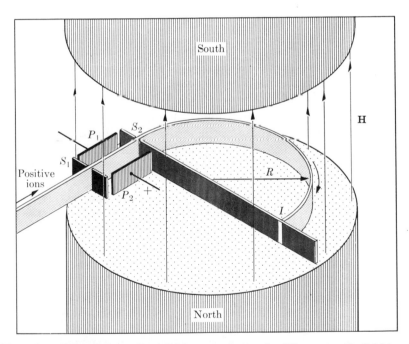

FIG. 37.4. Schematic outline of mass spectrograph. The magnetic field bends the ion beam beyond S_2 in a circular arc. For practical reasons separate magnets are generally used to provide the magnetic fields for the velocity selector (between S_1 and S_2) and for the space beyond S_2.

The radius R is readily measured by inserting a photographic emulsion perpendicular to the beam as it emerges from S_2. The beam will curve back to some position I, "photographing" itself as it hits the emulsion (see Fig. 37.5); the distance S_2I is the diameter of the semicircle traced out, and so $R = \frac{1}{2}S_2I$.

Once all quantities on the right side of Eq. (37.2) are known, the q/m value of the ion beam is found. Then it is easy to deduce m. The magnitudes of q can be only q_e or $2q_e$, $3q_e$, $4q_e$, . . . Thus a doubly ionized atom will trace out a path with half the radius of a singly ionized one, etc.; therefore the largest value of R in a series in which the values of R are as $1 : \frac{1}{2} : \frac{1}{3} : \frac{1}{4} : . . .$ belongs to the ion with $q = q_e$. And in any case, multiply ionized atoms are so much rarer than singly ionized ones that there may not be sufficient intensity for them to register at all on the plate.

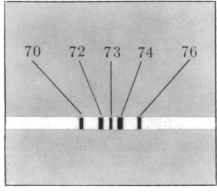

Fig. 37.5. The mass spectrum of germanium, showing the isotopes of mass numbers 70, 72, 73, 74, 76. (Courtesy of K. T. Bainbridge.)

We have thus been led to an *electromagnetic* method for measuring the mass of positively charged, singly ionized atoms; the mass of the neutral atom is larger than this by the known mass of one additional electron. This equipment, shown schematically in Fig. 37.4, is called a *mass spectrograph;* this particular version of the instrument is due to the American physicist K. T. Bainbridge (1930). When the beam at I is detected not by photographic but by electrical methods, the instrument is called a *mass spectrometer.*

The accuracy of mass determination with modern mass spectrometers, such as that shown on the frontispiece of this book, can be better than one part in a hundred thousand (i.e., below 0.001%). In J. J. Thomson's original instrument the accuracy was only of the order of 1%, but this was enough for Thomson to make an important observation. He had introduced neon gas into his mass spectrograph, for which the atomic weight was known to be 20.2. At about the expected place on the photographic plate in the mass spectrograph he obtained a record of the arrival of atoms of about this atomic weight, but in addition there was also present an unexpected faint "line" such as would correspond to the trace of a particle with atomic weight 22. This was very puzzling, for no chemical element or gaseous compound has this atomic or molecular weight.

Although no compound had ever been observed to be formed by the rare or "inert" gases, Thomson felt driven to consider that the line was evidence of a combination of the inert gas neon with two atoms of hydrogen (NeH_2). To separate this heavier admixture from "ordinary" neon, Thomson's associate F. W. Aston allowed the gas to diffuse many times through porous walls and, by the effect discussed for the separation of uranium isotopes in Section 25.10(b), obtained an "enrichment" of the proportion of heavy gas to such an extent that the chemical atomic weight of the final sample had increased by 5%, i.e., to a final value of nearly 20.3. The mass spectrograph now showed the faint line at mass 22 to be much more prominent, but when a discharge was passed through the sample, the same optical spectrum was obtained as for ordinary neon gas. This suggested strongly that the "heavy" component of neon differed only in weight, not in chemical and optical properties, from the rest of the sample. Thus, by another road than through radioactivity, we again encounter the idea of *isotopes*.

When Aston* improved the design of Thomson's mass spectrograph, he noted that no neon came to the place corresponding exactly to an atomic weight of 20.2; rather, the heavy trace was at 20.00, and the light trace at 22.00. The ratio of the intensities was found to be about 10:1, and so it became clear that the average atomic weight of neon, as determined by chemical means, had the value 20.2 because of the particular distribution of the two isotopes, for the weighted average is $(10 \times 20.00 + 1 \times 22.00)/11 = 20.2$. (A third isotope of neon with atomic weight 21.00 is now known to be also present, but in negligibly small amounts.) Similar results were soon obtained with other elements, and now that all the naturally occurring elements have been analyzed by means of this *electromagnetic method of isotope separation* with the mass spectrograph, some 320 natural isotopes have been found among them. Let us summarize briefly some other points of current interest concerning isotopes.

37.3 Some results of mass-spectrographic analysis. (a) About 20 of the 92 elements do not have naturally occurring isotopes (i.e., more than one species), each instead consisting of atoms of one mass only; examples are beryllium, fluorine, sodium, aluminum, gold. As a rule, the elements of odd atomic numbers Z have either few isotopes or only one species. Elements of even atomic number tend to have many isotopes, for example, 10 for tin and 9 for xenon.

(b) With the exception of some elements that have radioactive isotopes, and a few other, lighter elements, the fractional abundance of the isotopes constituting an element (Table 37.2) is constant within very narrow limits, no matter where the element is obtained.

---

*Awarded the 1922 Nobel Prize for Chemistry for his discovery of many nonradioactive isotopes, and for his "whole-number rule," referred to later.

Table 37.2. Natural isotopes of a few elements.

Element	Natural isotopes	Atomic mass of neutral atom* (amu)	Fractional abundance of atoms (percent)
Hydrogen	$_1H^1$	1.008142	99.985
	$_1H^2$	2.014735	0.015
Helium	$_2He^3$	3.016977	$\sim 1.5 \times 10^{-4}$
	$_2He^4$	4.003873	~ 100
Oxygen	$_8O^{16}$	16.000000 (standard)	99.759
	$_8O^{17}$	17.004534	0.037
	$_8O^{18}$	18.004855	0.204
Neon	$_{10}Ne^{20}$	19.998777	90.92
	$_{10}Ne^{21}$	21.000504	0.257
	$_{10}Ne^{22}$	21.998358	8.82
Uranium	$_{92}U^{234}$	234.1138	0.006
	$_{92}U^{235}$	235.1170	0.715
	$_{92}U^{238}$	238.1249	99.28

*Atomic mass as computed from mass-spectrometric measurements; probable error about 0.001% or less. 1 amu $= 1.65980 \times 10^{-24}$ gm.

(c) It has become desirable to have more specific symbols to represent the various atoms. These are obtained by writing the chemical symbol for the element to which the atom belongs, adding a subscript at the left to indicate the atomic number Z (and therefore the nuclear charge), and adding a superscript at the right to indicate the *mass number A*. Thus any atom X has a symbol of the form $_Z X^A$. By the mass number A is meant the integer nearest in value to the relative mass of the atom. For example, UI in Table 36.1 has the atomic number $Z = 92$ (being an isotope of uranium) and the mass number $A = 238$; hence its symbol is now given as $_{92}U^{238}$. Hydrogen has two natural isotopes, a light one with atomic weight of about 1 and a heavy one with atomic weight about 2; hence the symbols are $_1H^1$ and $_1H^2$ respectively. Aston's two isotopes of neon are, of course, $_{10}Ne^{20}$ and $_{10}Ne^{22}$.

(d) The standard of mass that has been adopted for expressing the atomic mass of any isotope is slightly different from that used for the chemical atomic weights. The *chemical scale* is defined by assigning the value 16.0000 atomic weight units (awu) to ordinary oxygen. But oxygen, long thought to consist solely of O^{16} atoms, was found in 1929 to contain minute traces of $_8O^{17}$ and $_8O^{18}$ atoms. So, for isotopic mass measurements, it is more convenient to assign the number 16.0000 to the most abundant isotope, $_8O^{16}$, and to use this as a standard. In other words, the *atomic mass unit*, 1 amu, is defined to be exactly 1/16 of the mass of a neutral $_8O^{16}$ atom. On this *physical scale*, the weighted average of the atomic masses of the three oxygen isotopes as found in nature is 16.0045 amu. Thus 16.0045 amu = 16.0000 awu, or 1 amu = 0.9997 awu. The difference in the standards used by the chemist and the nuclear physicist is only about 3 parts in 10,000.

(e) The atomic masses of the isotopes can be measured with great precision and, when expressed in atomic mass units, all turn out to be very close to whole numbers—always within less than 1% (see Table 37.2). This is called Aston's *whole-number rule*, and is the justification for using the mass number A in the symbols $_ZX^A$ for the atoms. The physical reason for this gratifyingly simple state of affairs is connected with the structure of the nucleus, the topic of the next chapter.

(f) The number of known *chemical compounds* has been greatly increased by the discovery of isotopes. Of special importance was the discovery of "heavy" hydrogen (R. T. Birge, D. H. Menzel, H. C. Urey, 1931); there is consequently a "heavy" form of water for which the molecular formula is $(_1H^2)_2O$. Heavy water differs from ordinary water in a number of physical properties; for example, its melting and boiling points are, respectively, 3.8°C and 101.4°C. Naturally occurring water contains traces of heavy water. A residue rich in $(_1H^2)_2O$ molecules, as compared with the ordinary $(_1H^1)_2O$ molecules, can be obtained by taking a large quantity of natural water and allowing most of it to evaporate or to be decomposed by electrolysis.

PROBLEM 37.1. At the National Bureau of Standards in 1932, a gallon of liquid hydrogen was prepared and slowly evaporated until only about 1 gm remained. The residue allowed the first experimental check on the existence of the "heavy" hydrogen isotope $_1H^2$. This isotope, which has been given the special name *deuterium* (from the Greek *deuteros*, second) and for which the symbol D is often used, was difficult to obtain because of its small relative abundance in hydrogen-containing natural substances. (a) With the help of the kinetic theory of matter, explain why evaporation will leave a residue of increased richness in the isotope of larger atomic mass. (b) Why should one expect the evaporation method of separation to be especially effective with hydrogen?

PROBLEM 37.2. By computing the weighted average of the atomic masses of the three oxygen isotopes (Table 37.2), show that the average atomic mass of oxygen is 16.0045 amu.

PROBLEM 37.3. (a) Use the data in Table 37.2 to compute the weighted average of the atomic masses of the isotopes of uranium. (b) Convert this value to atomic weight units (awu) and compare the result with the atomic weight of uranium as determined directly by chemical methods.

PROBLEM 37.4. Is it possible that the atomic masses of the isotopes might have come out to be exactly whole numbers if the unit of atomic mass (amu) had been chosen a little differently? For example, would taking the mass of $_1H^1$ as the unit result in whole numbers for all other isotopes? Or taking the mass of $_2He^4$ as exactly 4 units?

PROBLEM 37.5. In the formation of water molecules, various combinations of the two hydrogen and three oxygen isotopes are possible. (a) List them and give the molecular mass of several on the physical scale (amu). (b) Compute the molecular weight, on the chemical scale (awu), of "heavy water," that is, of water formed by the combination of $_1H^2$ atoms with the usual mixture of oxygen isotopes.

(g) With the concept of mass number (A) and the new notation for isotopes, we can economically handle the information previously presented on radioactive decay. For example, the three natural radioactive series are now recognized to stem from the following species: the uranium-radium series from $_{92}U^{238}$ (see Table 37.3 for the complete sequence from $_{92}U^{238}$ to $_{82}Pb^{206}$); the thorium series from $_{90}Th^{232}$ (ending with $_{82}Pb^{208}$); and the actinium series from $_{92}U^{235}$ (ending with $_{82}Pb^{207}$).

The decay of an atom may also be presented with this symbolism; for example, the first decay in the uranium-radium series is

$$_{92}U^{238} \rightarrow {}_{90}Th^{234} + {}_2He^4,$$

the α-particle being symbolized by $_2He^4$. This is a *nuclear reaction equa-*

Table 37.3. Uranium-radium series.

Original symbol	Revised symbol	Emission
UI	$_{92}U^{238}$	α
UX$_1$	$_{90}Th^{234}$	β, γ
UX$_2$	$_{91}Pa^{234}$	β, γ
UII	$_{92}U^{234}$	α
Io	$_{90}Th^{230}$	α, γ
Ra	$_{88}Ra^{226}$	α, γ
Rn	$_{86}Rn^{222}$	α
RaA	$_{84}Po^{218}$	α
RaB	$_{82}Pb^{214}$	β, γ
RaC	$_{83}Bi^{214}$	β, γ
RaC'	$_{84}Po^{214}$	α
RaD	$_{82}Pb^{210}$	β, γ
RaE	$_{83}Bi^{210}$	β
RaF	$_{84}Po^{210}$	α, γ
RaG	$_{82}Pb^{206}$	stable

tion analogous to chemical reaction equations; the subscripts on the two sides of the arrow must balance ($92 = 90 + 2$) because electric charge (on the nucleus) is conserved, and the superscripts must balance ($238 = 234 + 4$) to satisfy the principle of conservation of mass. From Table 37.3, we see that $_{90}\text{Th}^{234}(\text{UX}_1)$ disintegrates to $_{91}\text{Pa}^{234}(\text{UX}_2)$ with the emission of a β-particle. Because a β-particle, or electron, bears a charge $(-)q_e$ and has a practically negligible mass, a suitable symbol for it is $_{-1}e^0$. Thus,

$$_{90}\text{Th}^{234} \rightarrow {}_{91}\text{Pa}^{234} + {}_{-1}e^0.$$

ADDITIONAL PROBLEMS

37.6. Supply the missing data in these transformation equations:

(a) $_?\text{Pb}^{212} \rightarrow {}_?\text{Bi}^{212} + ?$; (b) $_?\text{Bi}^{212} \rightarrow ? + {}_{-1}e^0$; (c) $? \rightarrow {}_?\text{Pb}^{208} + {}_2\text{He}^4$.

37.7. The radioactive series originally called the actinium series is now known to start with the uranium isotope $_{92}\text{U}^{235}$ as the parent member and with each member emitting in succession the following particles: $\alpha, \beta, \alpha, \beta, \alpha, \alpha, \alpha, \alpha, \beta, \beta, \alpha$. This last disintegration yields $_{82}\text{Pb}^{207}$, which is stable. From this information, and by consulting the periodic table, determine the complete symbol for each member of the series and make a table similar to the second and third columns of Table 37.3.

37.8. As Table 36.1 shows, RaC' has a half-life too short to permit enough of the substance to accumulate for chemical or mass spectrographic analysis. How do we know RaC' exists at all? How can we be sure that it is an isotope of polonium?

37.9. In the following diagram of the thorium series, which begins with $_{90}\text{Th}^{232}$, the symbols used are those that were originally assigned to the members of the sequence. (a) Supply the missing data, and replace the original symbols by the revised ones; indicate where alternative possibilities (branchings) can exist.

$$_{90}\text{Th}^{232} \xrightarrow{\alpha} {}_?\text{MsTh}_1 \xrightarrow{?} {}_{89}\text{MsTh}_2 \xrightarrow{\beta} {}_?\text{RaTh} \xrightarrow{\alpha} {}_?\text{ThX} \xrightarrow{?} {}_?\text{Tn} \xrightarrow{?}$$

$$\longrightarrow {}_{84}\text{ThA} \xrightarrow{?} {}_?\text{ThB} \xrightarrow{\beta} {}_?\text{ThC} \xrightarrow{?} {}_{84}\text{ThC}'' \xrightarrow{?} {}_?\text{ThD}^{208} \text{ (stable)}$$

(b) Describe briefly what experiments might have been made to determine the data given in the foregoing diagram. (This example indicates the sort of interpolation that often must be used initially in determining the successive steps of a series.)

37.10. From $_{95}\text{Pu}^{241}$, an isotope of plutonium produced artificially by bombarding uranium in the nuclear reactor, a radioactive series has been traced for which the first six members are $_{94}Pu^{241}$, $_{95}Am^{241}$, $_{93}Np^{237}$, $_{91}Pa^{333}$, $_{92}U^{233}$, $_{90}Th^{229}$. The $_{90}Th^{229}$ atom emits an α-particle. (a) From this information, make a table similar to Table 37.3 for the first seven members. (b) The next to the last member of the whole series is $_{82}Pb^{208}$, which is a β-particle emitter; show that the final, stable member of the series is not an isotope of lead, but of another element.

37.11. For the uranium-radium series (Table 37.3), make a plot on graph paper of atomic number Z versus mass number A, indicating the position of each member of the series by a labeled dot. Draw a straight arrow between successive dots. (Such graphs are widely used to represent radioactive series.)

37.12. It follows from the way in which the atomic mass unit (amu) is defined that exactly 16 gm of the $_8O^{16}$ isotope of oxygen contains 6.02×10^{23} atoms (Avogadro's number). Show from this that 1 amu $= 1.66 \times 10^{-24}$ gm.

37.13. The mass of a neutral atom of helium is 4.0039 amu, and that of an electron is 0.00055 amu. Find the mass of the α-particle from these data in amu and in gm.

37.14. The neon isotope $_{10}Ne^{20}$ has been separated from the naturally occurring mixture of neon isotopes by allowing the mixture to diffuse through a porous barrier into an evacuated chamber, a number of successive diffusion stages being employed. By using Eq. (25.13) and data from Table 37.2, show that, in the first stage: (a) the numbers of $_{10}Ne^{20}$ and $_{10}Ne^{22}$ atoms escaping per second are *initially* in the ratio of about 11 to 1; (b) the fractional abundance of $_{10}Ne^{20}$ atoms in the diffused portion is thereby increased by about 4.4%. (The $_{10}Ne^{21}$ atoms in the mixture may be disregarded because of their small fractional abundance.)

37.15. Experiments show that the α-particles from $_{88}Ra^{226}$ atoms are each expelled with an energy of 4.791 Mev (million electron volts). With what speed do they emerge from the atoms?

37.16. In Fig. 37.6 are sketched the radioactive decay curves, N_t vs. t for three isotopes X^{A_1}, X^{A_2}, X^{A_3}, and for equal numbers of atoms (N_0) at $t = 0$ in each case. Supposing these isotopes to be mixed together in the ratios 6 : 3 : 2, derive graphically the shape of the composite decay curve.

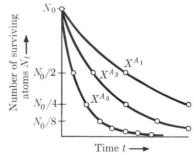

FIGURE 37.6

37.17. The natural isotopes of argon are $_{18}A^{36}$ (35.979 amu, 0.34%), $_{18}A^{38}$ (37.975 amu, 0.06%), $_{18}A^{40}$ (39.975 amu, 99.6%). It is by no means clear at present why the fractional abundances are distributed as they are. Compute approximately what the chemical atomic weight (awu) of the element argon would be if the abundances of $_{18}A^{38}$ and $_{18}A^{40}$ were interchanged. Consult the periodic table, and note whether this would have prevented the perplexing inversion in the case of argon and potassium.

37.18. One of the advantages of the mass spectrograph schematically shown in Fig. 37.4 is that it may be calibrated, say by introducing some oxygen gas into the source of ions. Suggest a sequence of operation for obtaining the atomic weight (in amu) of, say, neon without any other measurements than the distance from slit S_2 to the trace made on the photographic plate by the neon and the oxygen atoms.

37.19. The precision mass spectrometer shown in the frontispiece, based on the Mattauch-Hertzog design, is arranged approximately as in Fig. 37.7. The beam from the ion source passes first through the narrow gap (width d) between

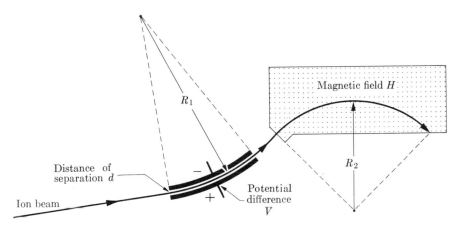

FIGURE 37.7

two electrodes (potential difference V) along a curve that is a circular arc of radius R_1. Hence the force due to the electric field can act as a centripetal force on the positively charged ions of mass m and charge q. (a) Show that only those ions can emerge from the curved channel whose speed is given by $v = \sqrt{VR_1q/dm}$. (b) On entering the magnetic field H, the ion beam is bent in an arc of determinable radius R_2. Show that the mass of the ions taking this path is $m = \mu_0^2 H^2\, dq R_2^2 / V R_1$.

Supplementary Reading

CHALMERS, T. W., *Historic researches* (Scribner's, 1952), Chap. XII on isotopes.

GLASSTONE, S., *Source book on atomic energy* (Van Nostrand, 1950, 1958), Chaps. V and VIII.

KAPLAN, I., *Nuclear physics* (Addison-Wesley, 1955), Chaps. 9 and 10.

NEEDHAM, J., and W. PAGEL, editors, *Background to modern science* (Macmillan, 1938), pp. 93–114. Lecture by Aston on isotopes and their separation.

CHAPTER 38

NUCLEAR STRUCTURE AND NUCLEAR ENERGY

The account of the discoveries of radioactivity and of isotopes, together with the description of the main facts of observation, must not obscure the lack of a theory to explain these phenomena. We shall now see the development of a model of the nucleus with a specific structure, designed to explain the main observations of radioactivity and isotopy somewhat as the facts of optics and chemistry are explained by the structure of the electron cloud around the nucleus.

38.1 The proton. The discovery that the atoms of radioactive elements emit α- and β-particles naturally first suggested that a model of the nucleus start with these building blocks. But even the nucleus of the ordinary hydrogen atom, $_1H^1$, cannot be so constructed, for it has only a single positive charge, $(+)q_e$, and only about one-fourth the mass of an α-particle. (The heavy isotope of hydrogen, $_1H^2$, was not known until 1932; but its mass is only about one-half that of an α-particle, and so its nucleus also could not be regarded as a combination of an α- and a β-particle.)

The nucleus of the ordinary hydrogen atom was accessible for observation in the form of H^+, the ionized atom whose single electron had been stripped off in the violence of an electric discharge or as the result of bombardment of hydrogen gas with high-speed electrons. The nucleus $_1H^1$ can be detected when it hits a scintillation screen or, having participated in a collision, leaves a track when speeding through a cloud chamber (Fig. 38.1). The name *proton* (Greek *protos*, first) was adopted for this particle about 1921, when it had become generally suspected that it could be an important constituent of the nuclei of all atoms. In addition to $_1H^1$, the symbol p is sometimes used to indicate the proton.

Fig. 38.1. Principle of the Wilson cloud chamber. The cylinder C contains a gas saturated with water vapor. When the piston P is rapidly lowered, the gas expands, and thus cools and becomes supersaturated. If charged particles traverse the chamber just before or during expansion, the water vapor condenses on them, forming cloud tracks that may be viewed or photographed through the glass window W.

690

38.2 The discovery of artificial transmutation. In 1919 Ernest Rutherford reported observing a very strange event. While bombarding nitrogen
gas with α-particles, he found that high-speed particles were produced in
the gas which could travel much farther in the nitrogen gas than do the
α-particles themselves; moreover, on hitting the scintillation screen, these
particles gave rise to brief flashes of light of the same intensity as would
be obtained if H^+ ions (protons) were intercepted. After detailed investigation, Rutherford proposed a bold explanation: When an incoming α-
particle collides with a nitrogen nucleus, the latter ejects a proton. The
α-particle itself is captured by the nucleus which it hit, so that the product
is a nucleus not previously present; for if we recall that the α-particle and
the proton have respectively the same structures as the nuclei of ordinary
helium, $_2He^4$, and ordinary hydrogen, $_1H^1$, we can write this nuclear
reaction in the usual symbolism:

$$_7N^{14} + {}_2He^4 \rightarrow {}_1H^1 + {}_8O^{17}. \tag{38.1}$$

The last term in the above expression requires the superscript 17 and the
subscript 8 if the equation is to balance, and so the product nucleus is
identified as an isotope of oxygen.

That protons actually were being ejected was confirmed by means of
magnetic deflection experiments, and by observing this reaction by means
of a cloud chamber (Fig. 38.2). Even with an intense α-beam there are,

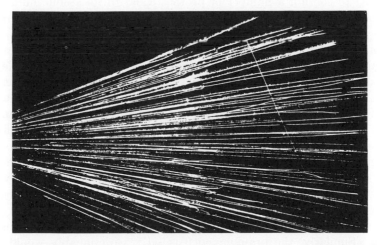

Fig. 38.2 Photograph of α-particle tracks in a cloud chamber filled with
nitrogen gas. One α-particle has hit a nitrogen nucleus; a proton is ejected upward toward the left, and the resulting oxygen nucleus recoils downward toward
the right. (After P. M. S. Blackett, 1925.)

however, not enough reactions of this type in a given sample to produce a sufficient quantity of O^{17} atoms for a direct mass-spectrographic check. Nevertheless, as Rutherford said, we must conclude "that the nitrogen atom is disintegrated under the intense force developed in a close collision with a swift α-particle," and that the hydrogen nucleus (proton) which is liberated formed a constituent part of the nitrogen nucleus. He added prophetically, "The results on the whole suggest that if α-particles or similar projectiles of still greater energy were available for experiment, we might expect to break down the nuclear structure of many of the lighter atoms."

Rutherford's conclusion was the fulfillment of the ancient alchemic dream in unexpected form—the first induced, or laboratory-controlled, transmutation of matter, although in a quantity too small to be directly recovered. The process was to initiate a whole new way of thinking in nuclear physics.

PROBLEM 38.1.   Following Rutherford's work with nitrogen, various other light elements were subjected to bombardment with α-particles, new nuclei being formed and protons simultaneously ejected. Write an expression similar to Eq. (38.1) for the nuclear reaction of this type in which the transmutation is (a) from $_9F^{19}$ to $_{10}Ne^{22}$, (b) from $_{13}Al^{27}$ to the nucleus of an atom which you are to identify, (c) from a potassium isotope to $_{20}Ca^{42}$.

38.3 An early hypothesis of nuclear structure. The problem of nuclear structure now seemed much nearer to its solution. Each nucleus may be assumed to contain a number of protons equal to its atomic number Z, for each proton has one unit of charge $(+)q_e$, and the total charge of $(+)Zq_e$ would account for the proper positive charge of the nucleus. But the proton has a mass of about 1 amu, and so the total number of protons accounts in general for only half the mass of an atom. For example, the nucleus of ordinary helium, $_2He^4$, has a charge of $(+)2q_e$, but a mass of about 4 amu (Table 37.2). A possible solution, considered by Rutherford and others, was to imagine a nucleus as consisting of a sufficient number (Z) of protons to account for its total charge, and in addition a sufficient number of *proton-electron pairs*, each pair having zero net charge but enough mass to make up the difference between the observed atomic mass and the atomic number. Thus a helium nucleus or an α-particle would consist of four protons and two electrons, giving a net charge of $(+)2q_e$ and a mass of about 4 amu (the mass of an electron is only about 1/1836 that of a proton and therefore contributes very little to the total nuclear mass). Similarly, the uranium nucleus $_{92}U^{238}$ presumably would have 92 un-neutralized protons and $238 - 92$ neutral proton-electron pairs.

This hypothesis had initially two other appealing features: it put some electrons in the nucleus, and this was in accord with the opinion that

high-speed electrons were thought to come from the nucleus during radioactive decay in the form of β-particles, and it also tied in well with the
explanation of why an element, after ejecting α- or β-particles, is found
displaced to a different position in the periodic table (Section 37.1). Since
the nuclear charge is equal to $(+)Zq_e$, the loss of an α-particle of charge
$(+)2q_e$ should reduce the nuclear charge to $(+)(Z - 2)q_e$, thus displacing
the element two spaces backward in the periodic table. And if the emission
of a β-particle is due to the splitting up of a neutral proton-electron pair in
the nucleus, the loss of a β-particle of charge $(-)q_e$ should increase the
number of effective protons by one; the nuclear charge would increase to
$(+)(Z + 1)q_e$, thus displacing the element one space forward. All this
was just as observed. However, despite these advantages, the hypothesis
was soon found to need modification.

38.4 The neutron. The hypothetical neutral pair, proton-electron,
began to be referred to by the name *neutron* in 1921. Many experiments
were made to see whether this proton-electron doublet could exist as a
distinct particle, for example, whether it was ever emitted when fast
α-particles collided inelastically with other nuclei. None of the many
experiments planned specifically for this purpose succeeded.

In 1930 it was reported in connection with a different investigation
that beryllium, when bombarded by fast α-particles from polonium,
emitted a radiation so penetrating that it was thought to consist of high-
energy γ-photons. Indeed, its penetrating power exceeded that of any
γ-radiation then known. In a historic experiment in 1932, the French
physicists Frédéric Joliot and his wife Irène Curie (daughter of the discoverers of radium) noted that this new radiation from beryllium could
in turn expel protons at very high speed from hydrogen-containing materials such as paraffin wax. Immediately after the publication of this
result, James Chadwick, who had worked with Rutherford, pointed out
that γ-rays could not have ejected the protons with the high speeds
observed unless the γ-rays differed in behavior from all other known
electromagnetic radiations and also had left the beryllium target with an
energy 10 times as large as that of the incident α-particles. In his paper,
"The existence of a neutron" (1932), Chadwick went on to show that these
difficulties disappear completely if the hypothesis is adopted that the
radiation coming from beryllium bombarded by α-particles consists, not
of photons, but "of particles of mass nearly equal to that of the proton
and with no net charge," that is, of particles each consisting of a proton
and an electron in close combination—the neutron discussed by Rutherford more than a decade earlier. Having no charge, these neutrons can
penetrate matter, even blocks of lead, without giving up their energy when
passing near electrons and nuclei as α- and β-particles do, and neutrons

can approach charged nuclei head-on without experiencing the strong force that deflects or repels charged particles. Moreover, in a head-on collision with a hydrogen nucleus of approximately equal mass, the neutron can transmit practically all its kinetic energy, so that the $_1H^1$ nucleus leaves the scene at high speed as a proton.

The nuclear reaction that led to Chadwick's discovery of the neutron can be expressed by the formula

$$_4Be^9 + {_2}He^4 \rightarrow {_6}C^{12} + {_0}n^1, \tag{38.2}$$

where $_0n^1$ is the symbol for the neutron, that is, for a particle of charge (and atomic number) zero and mass number one. Note that the other product of this nuclear reaction is considered to be the common isotope of carbon, $_6C^{12}$, here produced artificially by bombarding beryllium with α-particles; as in the transmutation of nitrogen into oxygen (Eq. 38.1), not enough of this substance is produced in the bombardment to obtain direct evidence of its existence, but it is inferred from the principles of conservation of charge and of mass, which require that the subscripts and superscripts in Eq. (38.2) balance.

The neutron has no net electric charge, therefore its mass could not be determined by deflection measurements in electric and magnetic fields. But Chadwick was able to estimate the mass of the neutron on the basis of supplementary experiments. In one of these a neutron beam from beryllium was sent through nitrogen gas and the maximum speed of those nitrogen nuclei that recoiled after collision with a neutron was recorded. If we designate the masses of the neutron and the nitrogen nucleus by m_n and m_N, the speeds of the neutron before and after collision by v_{n1} and v_{n2}, and the speed of recoil of the nitrogen nucleus by v_{N2}, then it follows from the principles of conservation of momentum and of energy that for a head-on collision between a neutron and a relatively stationary nitrogen nucleus

$$v_{N2} = \frac{2m_n}{m_n + m_N}\, v_{n1}. \tag{38.3}$$

Similarly, for a head-on collision between a neutron and a hydrogen nucleus of mass m_p, the speed v_{p2} with which the latter is ejected is

$$v_{p2} = \frac{2m_n}{m_n + m_p}\, v_{n1}. \tag{38.4}$$

Dividing Eq. (38.3) by Eq. (38.4), we find

$$\frac{v_{N2}}{v_{p2}} = \frac{m_n + m_p}{m_n + m_N}. \tag{38.5}$$

But v_{N2} and v_{p2} were known, the latter by measuring the maximum speed at which protons were leaving the sheet of paraffin wax in the Joliot-Curie experiment; also, m_p and m_N were known quantities. Therefore the only unknown, the mass of the neutron, m_n, could be computed. It came to somewhat more than the mass of the proton. Chadwick concluded that "such a value for the mass of the neutron is to be expected if the neutron consists of a proton and an electron, and it lends strong support to this view."

PROBLEM 38.2. (a) Derive Eqs. (38.3) and (38.4), and show that they lead to (38.5); state each of the assumptions you are making explicitly, and estimate how reasonable they are. (b) In Chadwick's paper, the experimental values given for v_{N2} and v_{p2} are 4.7×10^8 cm/sec and 3.3×10^9 cm/sec, respectively. Find the mass of the neutron (but note that more accurate measurements have since shown that $m_n = 1.00898$ amu).

Today we no longer think of the neutron as composed of a proton and an electron as Chadwick preferred; instead it is regarded as a fundamental particle in its own right. Also, it is now known that the neutron can disintegrate when freed from its parent nucleus; the free neutron eventually changes into a proton by emitting a β-particle (and also a neutrino; see Section 38.11), the half-life T for the decay being about 12 min. Inside the nucleus of a radioactive atom, the neutrons do not act as they do in the free state, but in certain of the radioactive transformations β-emission can be ascribed to a decay of a neutron. In this way no electrons need be accommodated inside any nucleus, and so we avoid many difficulties which this notion had raised.

PROBLEM 38.3. Many other reactions have since been found in which a nucleus captures an incoming α-particle and then disintegrates into a new nucleus by the emission of a neutron. Write an expression similar to Eq. (38.2) for the transmutations involving each of the following targets: (a) $_3Li^7$, (b) $_5B^{11}$, (c) $_7N^{14}$.

38.5 Composition of nuclei. With the proton and the neutron as building blocks, the composition of the nucleus became clear (W. Heisenberg, 1932) in a form that substantially corresponds to today's conception. For any particular element, the nucleus has Z protons to make up the proper nuclear charge $(+)Zq_e$; in addition, the nucleus has enough neutrons to bring the mass to the proper value. This number of neutrons is equal to $(A - Z)$, the difference between the mass number and the atomic number, because the masses of the proton and neutron are both nearly 1 amu. In Fig. 38.3, the contents of various nuclei are shown schematically. Thus for the "heavy" isotope of hydrogen (deuterium), 1 proton and 1 neutron are required in the nucleus, a combination referred

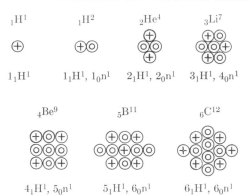

FIG. 38.3. Schematic representations of some nuclei.

to as a deuteron ($_1$H^2). For $_2$He^4, the helium nucleus (α-particle), 2 protons and 2 neutrons are needed, and similarly for the other nuclei.

PROBLEM 38.4. (a) Draw representations similar to those in Fig. 38.3 for $_8$O^{16}, $_8$O^{17}, $_8$O^{18}, $_{15}$P^{31}. (b) What is the composition of the nucleus of each of the naturally occurring isotopes of uranium listed in Table 37.1? (Do not draw.) Note that the nuclei of the isotopes of an element differ only in the number of neutrons present.

38.6 Particle accelerators. Up to 1932 the investigation of atomic nuclei proceeded first through the study of the naturally occurring spontaneous disintegrations of the very massive nuclei, such as those of uranium and thorium (Chapter 37), and second, through the observations of what happens when the high-speed α- or β-particles from these naturally radioactive elements bombard various other elements, as in Rutherford's transmutation experiment (Section 38.2). But now a third method was introduced, namely, bombardment with charged particles, such as protons ($_1$H^1) and deuterons ($_1$H^2), that have been given enormous speeds by artificial means. One of the great advantages of this method is that the bombarding particles are produced, and their speeds controlled, by the experimenter. The first to use the method successfully were J. D. Cockcroft and E. T. S. Walton, also in Rutherford's laboratory. Protons were produced in the form of hydrogen ions in a hydrogen discharge tube and accelerated by potential differences up to 600,000 volts. When the stream of protons was directed onto a lithium target (in 1932), particles were seen to be emitted that had all the appearances of α-particles, as seen by their scintillations, by their tracks in a cloud chamber, etc. This nuclear reaction is given by

$$_3\text{Li}^7 + {}_1\text{H}^1 \rightarrow {}_2\text{He}^4 + {}_2\text{He}^4; \tag{38.6}$$

that is, each lithium nucleus absorbs a proton and at once splits up into two α-particles, or helium nuclei.

Many different devices have since been invented for accelerating charged particles to be used in disintegration experiments. One of the most remarkable of these particle accelerators is the *cyclotron*, constructed in 1931 by E. O. Lawrence and M. S. Livingston at the University of California. In principle it is a round metal box cut in half along a diameter to form two hollow D-shaped sections A and B (Fig. 38.4); these sections are in an evacuated chamber between the poles of a large electromagnet. The two halves or "dees" A and B are connected to a high-frequency electric generator, so that the potential difference between the dees changes sign several million times per second. Near the center O is a source of positively charged particles—protons, deuterons, or heavier particles. If, at a certain moment, section A has a negative potential, a positively charged particle near O will be accelerated toward A and, owing to the magnetic field, will be deflected in a semicircular path; and if, on returning to the gap between A and B, the particle finds the potential difference reversed so that B now has the negative potential, the particle

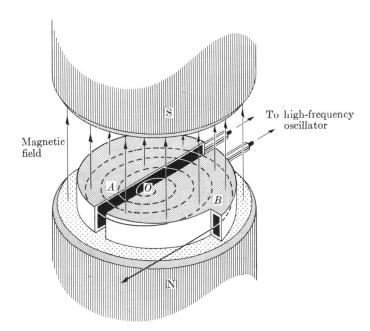

FIG. 38.4. Schematic diagram of a cyclotron. In the actual accelerator, the spiral path of the positive particles in the evacuated space between the magnet poles is several hundred feet, i.e., the spiral is very tightly wound, each full turn being very nearly a circle.

will receive additional kinetic energy while crossing the gap; and inside B it will describe a larger half circle since, by Eq. (36.1), for a given value of q/m and H, R is proportional to v. As the particle's speed increases with successive crossings of the gap, the particle describes larger and larger half circles until at last it reaches the periphery, where it either is allowed to hit a target or, with an auxiliary electric field, is deflected out through a thin window W.

The energy given to the particles at each crossing by the potential difference between the two dees A and B accumulates until the beam of a modern cyclotron finally emerges with total energies per particle of up to several hundred million electron volts, depending on the details of design. In comparison, particles from natural radioactive disintegrations have a kinetic energy of only a few Mev at most. Therefore, particle accelerators extend the range of possible experimentation many-fold. Figure 38.5 shows various stages in the development of the cyclotron.

PROBLEM 38.5. (a) Write the reaction formula for each of the following disintegrations produced by proton bombardment: $_4\mathrm{Be}^9$ into another beryllium nucleus and a deuteron; $_3\mathrm{Li}^6$ into the nuclei of the two naturally occurring helium isotopes. (b) Write the reaction formula for each of these deuteron-induced disintegrations: $_6\mathrm{C}^{12}$ into another nucleus and a proton; $_{11}\mathrm{Na}^{23}$ into another nucleus and a proton.

PROBLEM 38.6. In Fig. 38.4, a beam of positively charged particles of mass m and charge q is kept in a horizontal orbit by the vertical magnetic field H, and is accelerated by a horizontal electric field between the "dees." (a) Show that at any distance R from the center of the spiral, the velocity of the particles is given by $v = (q/m)\mu_0 H R$, i.e., is proportional to the radius of the turn. (b) Show that the frequency of the orbital motion of the particles is given by $f = (q/m)(\mu_0 H/2\pi)$, i.e., is *independent* of the distance R from the center.

38.7 Induced (artificial) radioactivity. The next advance in this unfolding story leading to the release of nuclear energy was made in an unexpected way in 1934. Irène Curie and F. Joliot were then studying the effect of α-particles from polonium on the nuclei of light elements. In the bombardment of aluminum, for example, neutrons were generated, evidently in a process analogous to Eq. (38.2), namely

$$_{13}\mathrm{Al}^{27} + {}_2\mathrm{He}^4 \rightarrow {}_{15}\mathrm{P}^{30} + {}_0\mathrm{n}^1. \tag{38.7}$$

But in addition to neutrons, another particle, namely a positively charged electron or *positron*, was also observed to come from the metal target.

The positron (symbol $_{+1}\mathrm{e}^0$), a particle having the same mass m_e as a negative electron and the charge $(+)q_e$, had been discovered in 1932 by C. D. Anderson; it had been produced in a cloud chamber by cosmic rays,

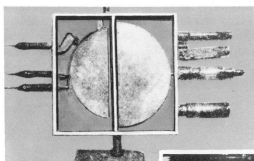

One of the earliest cyclotron chambers (cover removed). The apparatus, only 11″ wide, gave 1.2-million-volt protons in 1931.

E. O. Lawrence at the 27″ cyclotron (University of California) which he and M. Stanley Livingston constructed (1932). Protons and deuterons were accelerated by an effective potential difference of several million volts.

The 42″ cyclotron at Harvard University (1938). The beam of 12-million-volt deuterons was here allowed to emerge into the air.

The vacuum chamber of the 130-million-volt cyclotron (at Harvard University) is completely hidden by the accessories, shielding, and electronic gear around it. The diameter of the magnet poles is nearly 100″. The largest machine in the U. S. is at the University of California (184″).

FIG. 38.5. The growth of the cyclotron.

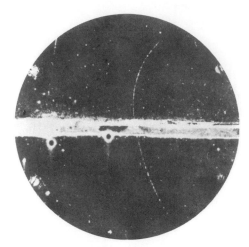

Fig. 38.6. Cloud chamber track of a positron moving in a magnetic field directed toward the reader. The positron originated in the lower right-hand part of the cloud chamber, passed through a lead plate of thickness 6 mm, and then continued on with decreased speed. This photograph, marking the discovery of the positron, was taken by C. D. Anderson in 1932.

and identified by the electronlike track and its curvature in the applied magnetic field (Fig. 38.6). Now the Joliots found positrons as a result of alpha bombardment. This in itself was far less interesting than the quite unprecedented observation that unlike the neutrons *the emission of positrons did not cease when the bombardment of the aluminum by α-particles was stopped.* "The foil remains radioactive, and the emission of the $[_{+1}e^0]$ radiation decays exponentially as for an ordinary radio-element." They pointed out that the $_{15}P^{30}$ isotope of phosphorus, required in Eq. (38.7) to explain the neutron emission and also identified by chemical analysis of the target, had never been observed in nature; it was therefore reasonable to suspect that once it was created it would be a short-lived radioactive material, spontaneously decaying with the emission of a positron. Such a reaction would have to be

$$_{15}P^{30} \rightarrow {}_{14}Si^{30} + {}_{+1}e^0.$$

By experiment, the half-life of this artificial radioactive isotope of phosphorus is 2.5 min; the daughter-product is a common isotope of silicon, and is stable.

Since all nuclei are assumed to consist solely of protons and neutrons, we must account for the emission of positrons in such cases. The present assumption is that a proton in the nucleus can break up into a neutron, which remains in the nucleus, and a positron and a neutrino (Section 38.11), which are at once expelled.

Following this discovery of *induced radioactivity*, many investigators began the production of radioactive isotopes by bombarding the different elements with various particles. As one example, E. O. Lawrence bombarded rock salt with high-speed deuterons and obtained radioactive sodium having a half-life of about 15 hr. The reactions were

and

$$_{11}Na^{23} + {}_1H^2 \rightarrow {}_{11}Na^{24} + {}_1H^1$$

$$_{11}Na^{24} \rightarrow {}_{12}Mg^{24} + {}_{-1}e^0.$$

The unstable nucleus $_{11}Na^{24}$ disintegrates with the emission of a β-particle. The resulting $_{12}Mg^{24}$ nucleus, incidentally, in turn emits a γ-photon.

In recent years, the number of radioactive isotopes artificially prepared has grown to about a thousand. Many of these find considerable use in research outside physics (see Section 39.7). For example, when mixed with an ordinary sample of sodium, the radioactive isotope $_{11}Na^{24}$ becomes a tracer which by its β- and γ-radiation reveals the presence and course of sodium in chemical or biochemical research in minutest quantities.*

PROBLEM 38.7. Express in ordinary language this example of induced radioactivity: $_{13}Al^{27} + {}_0n^1 \rightarrow {}_{12}Mg^{27} + {}_1H^1$; then $_{12}Mg^{27} \rightarrow {}_{13}Al^{27} + {}_{-1}e^0 + \gamma$-photon; $T = 10$ min.

38.8 Nuclear energy; exothermic and endothermic processes. We now come to what is perhaps the most challenging problem which the nucleus offers us—the release of nuclear energy. From the discovery of radioactivity onward, the relatively large energies emitted during radioactive decay were a source of excited speculation; for example, it was said in 1906 that if all the uranium atoms in one ton of uranium could be made to decay in one year, the energy of the α-particles so released would correspond to the energy supplied by all the electric power stations of a metropolis like London. Schemes for "unlocking the store of energy" in the atom were vigorously debated from the day when the Curies noted that a sample of radium maintained itself at a temperature higher than its surroundings (owing to the conversion into heat energy of the kinetic energy of α-particles absorbed while trying to pass out of the sample).

Of course, the possibility of energy release by itself was not at all new; for example, in ordinary combustion, energy is made available in the form

---

*Abundant examples of the use of radioactive isotopes in chemistry, medicine, industry, and agriculture are given in several of the books cited at the end of this chapter and Chapter 39.

of heat energy at the expense of the chemical energy or internal potential energy of the participating molecules. Hydrogen gas burning in oxygen to form water vapor sets free 58 kcal per mole of hydrogen, that is, 2.0×10^{-19} j per atom of hydrogen. In the burning of carbon, the value is 6.5×10^{-19} j per atom of carbon. But the striking feature of *nuclear* energy release lies mainly in the much larger amounts of energy obtained per atom; in the radioactive decay of uranium the α-particle carries away 4.2 Mev of kinetic energy from each atom of $_{92}U^{238}$, or 6.7×10^{-13} j. This is 10^6 times larger than the heats of combustion cited. Evidently, the rearrangement inside the nucleus can make available a far greater amount of energy than the rearrangement of electrons in the region around nuclei or of atoms in molecules.

These considerations apply not only to radioactivity but even more evidently to such nuclear reactions as transmutations. In Cockcroft and Walton's experiment, the α-particles obtained by bombarding lithium had a total of 2.8×10^{-12} j of energy, over 50 times greater than the kinetic energy of the bombarding protons which set off the reaction. In detail, the energies and masses involved in this reaction have the following values by modern measurements (see Table 38.1 for a useful list of mass values):

$$_3Li^7 \quad + \quad _1H^1 \quad \rightarrow \quad _2He^4 \quad + \quad _2He^4$$

Mass if at
rest (amu):   7.01822   1.00814   4.00387   4.00387   (38.8)

E_k (joules)   (0.000) 4×10^{-14} 1.4×10^{-12} 1.4×10^{-12}

A nuclear reaction is called *exothermic* (exoergic) or *endothermic* (endoergic) according to whether the total kinetic energy of the product particles (and the energy of the γ-photon, if any) is larger or smaller than that of the original participants in the reaction. The difference between these final and initial energies is called the energy balance or *nuclear reaction energy*, Q. In Eq. (38.8), which is for an exothermic reaction, the "Q-value" is $2 \times 1.4 \times 10^{-12}$ j $- 4 \times 10^{-14}$ j, which is about 2.8×10^{-12} j or 17.3 Mev. This computation assumes that the lithium atom in the target is stationary; in actual fact, it will of course move in Brownian or thermal vibration, with energy $\bar{E}_k = \frac{3}{2}kT$ (Eq. 25.8), but this amounts to less than 10^{-20} j at ordinary temperatures and is therefore negligible.

As an example of an endothermic nuclear reaction, consider Rutherford's experiment on the bombardment of nitrogen by particles (Section 38.2). We can rewrite Eq. (38.1), now placing under each symbol the modern values for the nuclear mass (in amu) of the particle at rest and also the observed kinetic energy of the particle:

$$_7N^{14} \quad + \quad _2He^4 \quad \rightarrow \quad _8O^{17} \quad + \quad _1H^1$$

Mass if at
rest (amu): 14.00752   4.00387   17.00453   1.00814   (38.9)

E_k (joules):   (0.000) 12.3×10^{-13} 0.9×10^{-13} 9.5×10^{-13}

The Q-value is seen to be -1.9×10^{-13} j, or -1.2 Mev, the negative sign indicating that the reaction is endothermic.

But how shall we *explain* the release of energy in exothermic reactions and the disappearance of energy in endothermic reactions? Unless we can envisage a mechanism to make plausible potential energy changes inside the nucleus, we may have to face the possibility of a violation of the principle of conservation of energy. And if we next compare the total mass of the particles before and after the interaction, we encounter an equally startling possibility: in Eq. (38.8), the mass of the products is *smaller* by 0.01862 amu compared to the total mass before the reaction, and in Eq. (38.9) the mass has *increased* by 0.00128 amu. This appears to be in violation of the principle of conservation of mass.

PROBLEM 38.8. When boron $_5B^{11}$ is bombarded with deuterons of 1.51-Mev energy, an α-particle is emitted with energy 6.37 Mev and the remaining nucleus recoils with 3.18-Mev energy. (a) Write the nuclear reaction equation. (b) Determine whether the reaction is endothermic or exothermic, and find the Q-value.

Table 38.1. Masses of some particles and neutral atoms (in amu).
Based in part on values quoted by I. Kaplan (1955).

Electron	0.000549	$_6C^{12}$	12.003804
Proton	1.007593	$_7N^{14}$	14.007515
Neutron	1.008982	$_8O^{16}$	16.000000 (standard)
Deuteron	2.014186	$_8O^{17}$	17.004534
α-particle	4.002675	$_8O^{18}$	18.004855
$_1H^1$	1.008142	$_{10}Ne^{20}$	19.998777
$_1H^2$	2.014735	$_{10}Ne^{21}$	21.000504
$_1H^3$	3.016997	$_{10}Ne^{22}$	21.998358
$_2He^3$	3.016977	$_{29}Cu^{63}$	62.94862
$_2He^4$	4.003873	$_{59}Pr^{141}$	140.959
$_3Li^6$	6.017021	$_{90}Th^{232}$	232.11034
$_3Li^7$	7.018223	$_{92}U^{233}$	233.11193
$_4Be^9$	9.015043	$_{92}U^{234}$	234.11379
$_5B^9$	9.016190	$_{92}U^{235}$	235.11704
$_5B^{10}$	10.016114	$_{92}U^{236}$	236.11912
$_5B^{11}$	11.012789	$_{92}U^{238}$	238.12493
$_5B^{12}$	12.018162	$_{94}Pu^{239}$	239.12653

(c) Use the atomic masses in Table 38.1 to find the excess or deficiency in mass of the products. (*Note:* 1 Mev $\equiv 10^6$ ev $= 1.602 \times 10^{-13}$ j.)

PROBLEM 38.9. When boron $_5B^{11}$ is bombarded with 1.51-Mev deuterons, one may also obtain from it protons of energy 2.37 Mev in a reaction having a Q-value of 1.14 Mev. (a) Write the reaction equation. (b) Find the energy of the product nucleus. (c) Use Table 38.1 to find the excess or deficiency in mass of the products. (d) In the nuclear reactions cited above, the masses used were those of the *neutral atoms,* in accord with current usage in nuclear physics. However, the particles involved are usually bare nuclei differing in mass from neutral atoms by the mass of the electrons. Does this vitiate our calculations?

38.9 The principle of conservation of mass and energy in restricted relativity theory. The results cited above would have been most perplexing, had not the way been paved for their explanation by the discovery of a principle of spectacular power and importance which had opened the way for reinterpretation of the conservation principles of mass and of energy. This new principle, one of the consequences of the *restricted* or *special theory of relativity,* was first fully revealed in a series of papers by Albert Einstein, beginning in 1905. The main features of this contribution will now be developed insofar as it refers to our topic, the release of nuclear energy.

(a) *The mass-velocity relationship.* Not long after the discovery of the electron by J. J. Thomson, it was shown experimentally by deflection experiments in magnetic and electric fields that the measured ratio of charge to mass, q_e/m_e, is not really constant, as we have implied to this point, but varies with the speed of the electron. More specifically, W. Kaufmann (1900 and later), A. H. Bucherer (1908), and others, using high-speed electrons in the form of β-particles, showed that q_e/m_e has the previously given value of 1.76×10^{11} coul/kgm only for relatively low speeds, and has smaller measured values the higher the speed of the electron. At $\frac{1}{10}$ the speed of light ($0.1c$) the decrease is only 0.5%, but at $0.5\ c$, the value of q_e/m_e is 15% lower, and it approaches zero more and more rapidly as the speed of the electron approaches the speed of light.

This change was expected on theoretical grounds, not because the charge q_e would *decrease* in any way with speed, but because the effective mass of a charged particle would *increase* with speed and so decrease the value of q_e/m_e. The precise relation between the measured mass and the speed was taken to be

$$m = \frac{m_0}{\sqrt{1 - (v^2/c^2)}}, \tag{38.10}$$

where m_0 is the mass of the particle at rest with respect to the observer, now called *rest mass,* and m is the mass of the particle measured while it moves with speed v relative to the observer, now called *relativistic* or effective mass. (This is the mass m determined, for instance, by using a magnetic field to apply a known centripetal force F and measuring the radius of curvature R of the path, i.e., from $F = mv^2/R$.) Furthermore, c is again the speed of light in vacuum, a constant with the value of nearly 3×10^8 m/sec.

If we accept Eq. (38.10), it is evident that at ordinary speeds, where v is very much less than c, the denominator $\sqrt{1 - (v^2/c^2)}$ is virtually 1, and $m = m_0$ within the experimental error of measurement. But if v is 10% of c, $m = m_0/0.990 = 1.005\ m_0$. The ratio m/m_0 goes up very rapidly as v/c goes beyond 0.8; see Fig. 38.7. This is, of course, the region of importance in nuclear physics, where β-particles from some naturally radioactive material reach speeds of over 95% of c, and product particles may be separating with similarly high speeds in many nuclear reactions.

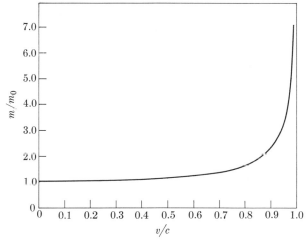

Fig. 38.7. Increase in relativistic mass with speed (m_0 = rest mass, c = speed of light).

The observed decrease of q_e/m_e was in full agreement with the increase of the mass of the electron expected according to Eq. (38.10), so that the observations can be taken to constitute an experimental verification of Eq. (38.10). But Einstein's conclusion went further. He postulated that Eq. (38.10) applied to the "tangible," ponderable mass of *any* object, whether charged like an electron or not. At first glance, this extension is likely merely to deepen the feeling of confusion which may well have been raised by our initial statement that the mass of a particle increases with speed. Surely a moving object does not suddenly have more molecules, more tangible, ponderable matter than before! If the inertia can increase without a corresponding addition of matter, mass cannot be simply a measure of the quantity of matter after all. And then the principle of conservation of mass would appear to be no longer strictly true. Such are the speculations to which we must now turn.

PROBLEM 38.10. Compute the ratio of relativistic mass to rest mass of (a) a rocket moving at 900 m/sec (about 2000 mi/hr), (b) an α-particle whose speed is 0.1 c, and (c) a β-particle with a speed of 0.98 c.

PROBLEM 38.11. How fast would you have to move before one could become aware of a change in your mass by measurement? (*Hint:* First describe the measurement and estimate the magnitude of the effect needed to show up on the instrument which is to be employed.)

PROBLEM 38.12. Bucherer found that at $v = 0.687\ c$, the measured ratio of charge to effective mass of β-particles was 1.283×10^{11} coul/kgm. Find the ratio of charge to rest mass. What conclusions do you draw from this calculation?

PROBLEM 38.13. What force would be needed to give even the smallest imaginable acceleration to an object that is assumed to be moving with the speed of light? (This may suggest a physical reason for the startling conclusion in Einstein's 1905 article: "Velocities greater than that of light have no possibility of existence.")

(b) *The mass-equivalence of energy.* Equation (38.10) may be written

$$m = m_0 \left(1 - \frac{v^2}{c^2}\right)^{-1/2}.$$

However, by the binomial theorem introduced into algebra by Newton, namely,

$$(1 + x)^n = 1 + nx + \frac{n(n-1)}{2}\,x^2 + \frac{n(n-1)(n-2)}{6}\,x^3 + \cdots,$$

it follows that, if

$$x = -\frac{v^2}{c^2} \quad \text{and} \quad n = -\frac{1}{2},$$

$$\left(1 - \frac{v^2}{c^2}\right)^{-1/2} = 1 + \frac{v^2}{2c^2} + 3\,\frac{v^4}{8c^4} + \text{other terms of still higher power.}$$

Now in the special case when v is considerably less than c (say 20% of c), v^2/c^2 is very small, and v^4/c^4 together with all higher terms is negligible. Therefore, for relatively low speeds, we can write Eq. (38.10) in the form

$$m = m_0 \left(1 + \frac{v^2}{2c^2}\right) = m_0 + \frac{\frac{1}{2}m_0 v^2}{c^2}.$$

This last result opens our eyes to an amazing physical interpretation of the increase in mass (Δm) with speed, for it points out directly that

$$m - m_0 = \frac{\frac{1}{2}m_0 v^2}{c^2} = \frac{E_k}{c^2},$$

or

$$\Delta m \; [\equiv m - m_0] = \frac{E_k}{c^2}. \tag{38.11}$$

In trying to understand the change in effective mass with speed, we are led to the conception that kinetic energy E_k added to a ponderable object *also adds inertia* in an amount E_k/c^2. Whether we say energy *has* mass or *is* mass or *appears as* mass is only playing with words and adds nothing to the interpretation of the last equation. The best way of expressing Eq. (38.11) is to say that the energy E_k has a *mass-equivalence* of E_k/c^2.

Although we have arrived at this result by an approximation, and for low speeds, the equation $E_k/c^2 = \Delta m$ is true in general. Only we must note that in such a purely mechanical situation *the kinetic energy of a fast-moving particle is redefined in line with Eq. (38.11) as*

$$E_k = \Delta m c^2 \tag{38.12}$$

and is not separately evaluated by $\frac{1}{2}m_0 v^2$; for the mass increases from m_0 with speed, and so more kinetic energy is required for equal changes in speed at the latter stages of reaching speed v than at the earlier stages.

The idea that it is the increase of energy which changes the mass can be extended further to include energies other than ordinary kinetic energy. Consider first a spring with a mass m_0 when limply extended. When we compress it and so give it elastic potential energy E_p, its mass increases to $(m_0 + E_p/c^2)$. A lump of metal likewise increases its observed mass when it is heated; here $\Delta m = $ (heat energy supplied)$/c^2$. In brief, the principle of mass-equivalence of energy has been extended to cover the increase (or decrease) of any type of energy; *for every unit (1 j) of energy supplied* to a material object, whether it be kinetic energy given to a bullet, gravitational potential energy acquired by the change in relative distance of two stars, or any other form of energy, *the mass of the system thereby increases by*

$$\frac{1 \; \text{j}}{(3 \times 10^8 \; \text{m/sec})^2} = 1.1 \times 10^{-17} \; \text{kgm,}$$

and we can generalize Eqs. (38.11) and (38.12) to read:

$$\Delta m \; [\equiv m - m_0] = \frac{\Delta E}{c^2} \tag{38.13}$$

and
$$\Delta E = \Delta m \cdot c^2, \tag{38.14}$$

where ΔE refers to the change of energy attended by the change of mass Δm. To repeat, this does not mean that there are more molecules in the system after energy has been added than before; what has changed is the observable inertia of the energy-enriched material.

Evidently the factor c^2 in Eq. (38.13) indicates that such changes in mass are beyond direct experience in ordinary mechanical experiments, and therefore we had no need to consider this point in the chapter on the conservation of mass. But in nuclear phenomena or in accelerators, where the masses of the particles involved are relatively small to start with and the energies are relatively large, the changes in mass may become very noticeable. If you prefer, *mass* does not measure the amount of tangible or ponderable matter in a system, it measures the amount of matter together with the mechanical energies, electrical energies, etc. Therefore we rewrite the principle of conservation of mass to read:

$$\text{In a closed system,} \quad \Sigma \left(m_0 + \frac{\text{Energy}}{c^2} \right) = \text{constant.} \tag{38.15}$$

In words: *in a closed system, the sum of rest masses and mass-equivalents of energy is constant.*

This extension of the principle of conservation of mass immediately explains the apparent discrepancies noted in connection with the nuclear reactions of Eqs. (38.8) and (38.9). In the former, the rest mass of the two product particles was found to be smaller by 0.01862 amu than the rest mass of the two initial particles, but the product particles had more kinetic energy than the initial particles by 2.8×10^{-12} j, and this energy has, by Eq. (38.13), a mass-equivalent of

$$\frac{2.8 \times 10^{-12} \text{ j}}{(3.0 \times 10^8 \text{ m/sec})^2} = 3.1 \times 10^{-29} \text{ kgm}$$

or

$$\frac{3.1 \times 10^{-29} \text{ kgm}}{1.66 \times 10^{-27} \text{ kgm/amu}} = 0.0186 \text{ amu.}$$

In short, *the mass-equivalent of the extra energy corresponds exactly to the "missing" rest mass;* therefore if we had compared the *relativistic* masses of the particles before and after the reaction instead of comparing *rest* masses, we should not have noted any deficiency or discrepancy. Similarly, in Eq. (38.9) the rest mass is smaller on the left side of the equation, but the kinetic energy is larger, and therefore the relativistic masses, namely rest masses plus mass-equivalents of energy, balance.

PROBLEM 38.14. Apply the extended principle of conservation of mass to the reaction in Eq. (38.9) and show that the relativistic mass is conserved in the system consisting of the particles involved.

PROBLEM 38.15. What general statement can we make about the rest masses of the particles if a nuclear reaction is (a) exothermic, (b) endothermic?

PROBLEM 38.16. When a deuteron absorbs an x-ray or γ-ray photon from a beam of proper frequency, it breaks apart into its constituent particles, namely a proton and a neutron. Use the masses given in Table 38.1 to compute the lowest energy and frequency of the radiation that can initiate this process (photodisintegration) in deuterons.

The examples given above for the mass-equivalence of energy have stressed events considered to take place in a "closed system," where the total rest mass decreases if the energy content increases, and vice versa, so that the total relativistic mass is constant. But if we now think only of a single particle, it must of course lose mass if it gives up energy, and gain mass if it gains energy. If a high-speed particle is slowed down, it gets "lighter" by an amount given as (loss of $E_k)/c^2$. After a nucleus has emitted a γ-photon, its new mass will be less than before by $h\nu/c^2$, where ν is the frequency of the radiation. In such cases it is again largely a matter of taste whether to say that matter has been destroyed while energy has been created, or that matter *is* energy, or has assumed the *form* of energy, etc. The physical facts behind such phrases are the same, as stated, for example, by Einstein in 1905:

> If a body gives off the energy ΔE in the form of radiation, its mass diminishes by $\Delta E/c^2$ . . . The mass of a body is a measure of its energy content; if the energy changes by ΔE, the mass [of that body] changes in the same sense by $\Delta E/c^2$ . . .

(c) *The energy-equivalence of mass.* In most subatomic phenomena only a small fraction of the mass of the system is transferred into an equivalent quantity of radiant or kinetic energy, as in the release of nuclear energy in exothermic reactions. But now the factor c^2 is favorable; by the relation $\Delta E = (\Delta m)c^2$, any small Δm results in a large ΔE. While the mass-equivalence of energy is detectable only in highest precision measurements, the *energy-equivalent of mass*, as expressed in Eq. (38.14), can be spectacular. For example, if by some exothermic process a mere 1-gm piece of ordinary matter could be "converted" into heat, the energy made available would amount to 9×10^{13} j—more than enough to operate a typical 10,000-kw electric power station for a full day.

Such a large-scale application became worth considering only recently, when the necessary exothermic processes were found, but long before that it was clear, on the basis of such reactions as Eq. (38.8), that the *principle of conservation of energy must be reformulated* if energy-mass conversions are to be included. One simple way of doing this is to consider every object in the system as a potential source for complete "annihilation," and therefore to assign to every rest mass m_0 a *rest energy* m_0c^2, a potential energy which in the course of events may be partly or completely converted into other forms of energy. Then we can safely say: in a closed system, the total amount of energy, namely, rest energy ($\Sigma m_0 c^2$) plus all *other* forms of energy (ΣE), is constant, i.e.,

$$\Sigma(m_0 c^2 + E) = \text{constant.} \tag{38.16}$$

Now this is not really an entirely new principle; Eq. (38.15), the extended principle of conservation of mass, read $\Sigma(m_0 + E/c^2) = \text{constant}$, and if Eq. (38.16) is divided through by c^2 on both sides we obtain the very same expression. Either equation tells essentially the same story. As Einstein himself pointed out:

> Pre-relativity physics contains two conservation principles of fundamental importance, namely, the principle of conservation of energy and the principle of conservation of mass; these two appear there as completely independent of each other. Through relativity theory they melt together into *one* principle.

This single principle, expressed by either Eq. (38.15) or Eq. (38.16), may be termed the *principle of conservation of mass-energy*. We may say that the concepts of mass and of energy also "melt together," as though they were two aspects of one physical reality.

PROBLEM 38.17. (a) Show that the speed v of a particle is given by $v = c\sqrt{1 - (m_0/m)^2}$. (b) Find the expression for v in terms of the kinetic energy of a moving particle. (c) The fastest particle emitted in natural radioactive decay is the β-particle from RaC ($_{83}Bi^{214}$), having an energy of 3.17 Mev. What is its speed?

PROBLEM 38.18. (a) If 1 amu of mass is "lost" in a nuclear reaction, how much energy is "created"? Express in joules and in Mev. (b) Comment on the appropriateness of the words "lost" and "created" in this context.

PROBLEM 38.19. In your own words, formulate the principle of conservation of mass-energy (a) for a closed system, (b) for an open system.

PROBLEM 38.20. Taking the average specific heat capacity of iron to be 0.2 kcal/kgm·°C, compute the change in mass of a 1-kgm iron ball when it is heated from 15°C to the melting point (1535°C).

38.10 Pair formation and annihilation. A striking example of the equivalence of mass and energy is furnished by the phenomenon called *pair formation* (Fig. 38.8). It is observed to occur when a γ-photon passes near an atomic nucleus, where the γ-photon may be transformed into two particles—an electron, $_{-1}e^0$, and a positron, $_{+1}e^0$. If the energy of the initial γ-photon is $h\nu$, then in accordance with Eq. (38.16),

$$h\nu = 2(m_e c^2) + E_{k1} + E_{k2}, \tag{38.17}$$

where $m_e c^2$ is the energy-equivalent of the (rest) mass of each of the particles having the mass m_e, and E_{k1} and E_{k2} are their respective kinetic energies when they are produced. Taking the mass m_e of an electron or positron to be 9.1×10^{-31} kgm, we find that $2(m_e c^2)$ is 1.6×10^{-13} j. Hence we can predict that if the energy $h\nu$ of a photon is less than this value, the photon cannot form an electron-positron pair. If $h\nu$ exceeds 1.6×10^{-13} j, the excess appears as the kinetic energies E_{k1} and E_{k2} of the newly formed particles. Both statements are in accord with observations.

FIG. 38.8. Pair formation in a cloud chamber. A γ-photon, having entered from above, is converted into an electron and a positron whose paths curve in opposite directions in the external magnetic field applied perpendicular to the plane of the page.

The converse effect, called *electron-positron annihilation*, is also observed. A slow positron may interact with an electron; the two particles, with a total energy equivalent of 1.6×10^{-13} j, disappear by giving rise to an "annihilation radiation" of two photons having 0.8×10^{-13} j energy each. The process of pair formation and that of electron-positron annihilation demonstrate in purest form the complete convertibility between matter and energy, and the applicability of the mass-energy conservation principle.

PROBLEM 38.21. An ionization chamber is sensitive only to charged particles, but it can be made to detect entering neutrons by lining the inside walls of the chamber with a substance containing boron or filling it with a gaseous compound of boron (BF_3). When a boron nucleus $_5B^{10}$ captures a slow neutron, an α-particle is emitted which can be detected by the ionization it produces. (a) Write the formula for the nuclear reaction involved. (b) Compute the change in mass resulting from this reaction and thus find whether the reaction is endothermic or exothermic. (c) Determine the Q-value of the reaction. (Refer to Table 38.1.)

PROBLEM 38.22. (a) Show that a photon must have a frequency of at least 2.5×10^{20} cycles/sec if it is to form an electron-positron pair. (b) What is the corresponding wavelength in angstrom units? Where does this fall in the electromagnetic spectrum? (c) What is the frequency of electron-positron annihilation radiation?

38.11 The neutrino problem. The principle of conservation of mass-energy should, of course, also be applicable to the case of radioactive decay. Consider first an α-emitter such as the uranium nucleus $_{92}U^{238}$, which spontaneously disintegrates into a thorium nucleus $_{90}Th^{234}$ by emitting an α-particle having a definite kinetic energy of 4.2 Mev or 6.7×10^{-13} j: the mass of the $_{92}U^{238}$ nucleus before disintegration is found to be accurately equal to the sum of the masses of the particles and mass-equivalents of the energies after disintegration, just as we now would expect.

But the situation is less simple when we analyze what happens during β-decay. Take, for example, the spontaneous disintegration of bismuth $_{83}Bi^{210}$ into polonium $_{84}Po^{210}$ (RaE to RaF in Table 36.1). We would expect the kinetic energy of every emitted β-particle to be 1.87×10^{-13} j or 1.17 Mev, which corresponds to the energy-equivalent of the difference between the mass of the $_{83}Bi^{210}$ nucleus and the total mass of the final particles. Experiment shows, however, that the β-particles from a sample of $_{83}Bi^{210}$ emerge with kinetic energies anywhere from 0 to 1.17 Mev, the majority having energies far below this maximum; indeed, the average energy for all particles is 0.34 Mev, less than $\frac{1}{3}$ of the expected full value, i.e., less than $\frac{1}{3}$ of the energy-equivalent of the mass deficiency of the products. What has happened to the rest of the energy? No other charged particle or photon is observed to be emitted along with the β-particle. The emission of a neutron is also ruled out, for the product nucleus $_{84}Po^{210}$ has the same mass number A as $_{88}Bi^{210}$. The same paradoxical situation applies to other β-emitters.

Because of this dilemma (and because the observations on emission are also in conflict with the principle of conservation of momentum), the Austrian-born physicist Wolfgang Pauli in 1931 and the Italian physicist Enrico Fermi in 1934 considered that the β-particle emerges from the nucleus along with another, undetected particle that has a very high speed and the "missing" energy, but no charge; as to its mass, Fermi wrote: "We come to the conclusion that the rest mass of the [particle] is either zero or at any rate very small compared to the mass of the electron." To this hypothetical particle, Fermi gave the name *neutrino* (Italian diminutive for neutron).

For about 20 years all attempts to find direct evidence for the existence of the neutrino failed; this was not entirely unexpected, for a particle without charge and virtually no mass would readily penetrate matter without giving away its presence by some interaction. But throughout this period, the value of the neutrino hypothesis was unquestioned. The principles of conservation of mass-energy and of momentum are so firmly embedded in present-day physical theory that it was almost inconceivable that it should fail in only one little corner of the whole matrix. Also, the neutrino not only served to "save" these tested and treasured principles of physical science, it also became more and more useful for the explanation of other anomalies in nuclear experiments.

Still, the lack of direct evidence was disturbing, and the analogy with the problem of the electromagnetic ether would have increasingly worried scientists if the neutrino had continued to remain completely undetectable except in explanations of discrepancies and in constructions of hopeful models. Therefore the news of the unambiguous "capture" of the neutrino in 1956 was greeted as a major break. It was achieved by a superb refinement of the techniques and instruments for initiating and recording the very rare interactions expected between neutrinos and ordinary matter.

38.12 The Compton effect. In 1923 the American physicist A. H. Compton discovered that the photons in a beam of x-rays can interact with electrons in a block of carbon (and, later, other materials) in the manner indicated in Fig. 32.7. Clearly, the momentum of the recoiling electron has been changed during the "collision" with the photon, and the principle of conservation of momentum, *if it is assumed to hold in this case as in every other tested so far*, demands that the photon experiences an equally large change of momentum in the opposite direction. But how may we assign a momentum to a photon?

The mass-equivalence of energy furnishes the required hint. The energy $h\nu$ of a photon has a mass-equivalent of $h\nu/c^2$ (though this is in no sense to be regarded as a *rest* mass).* If multiplied by the speed of the photons, c, this quantity has the units and meaning of *momentum*. Hence we assign each photon of frequency ν and wavelength λ a momentum $\mathbf{M}_{ph}$ with magnitude

$$M_{ph} = h\nu/c = h/\lambda. \tag{38.18}$$

We may now attempt to apply the usual momentum and energy relations to an interaction such as that shown in Fig. 32.7, namely,

$$(\mathbf{M}_{ph})_1 = (\mathbf{M}_{ph})_2 + m_e\mathbf{v}, \tag{38.19}$$

$$h\nu_1 = h\nu_2 + \tfrac{1}{2}m_e v^2. \tag{38.20}$$

And in fact, these equations yield predictions (such as those in Problem 38.24) which can be verified with great precision by experiment.

PROBLEM 38.23. What is the mass, momentum, and energy of an x-ray photon of wavelength 1 A?

PROBLEM 38.24. If we used x-rays of wavelength 1 A and watched those that are scattered from electrons in a direction at right angles to the incident path, we would find their wavelength after scattering is 1.024 A, while the electron re-

---

*If the photon had any rest mass m_0, what should be its observed mass at the usual speed of photons?

coils as shown in Fig. 38.9. (a) Explain why there is a change in wavelength. (b) Calculate the speed and direction of the recoiling electron. (It is assumed throughout that the electron was initially stationary and was not bound to an atom by any significant force.) (c) If the calculated speed and direction of the recoiling electron coincides with independently obtained experimental data, what can one say about the conception that photons have a momentum given by Eq. (38.18)?

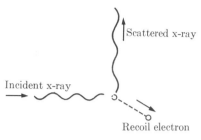

FIGURE 38.9

PROBLEM 38.25. If an electron and a positron are substantially at rest when they combine to form annihilation radiation, their total momentum is zero; then, by the principle of conservation of momentum, the total momentum of the resulting radiation must also be zero. Show that this cannot be true unless *two* photons are produced that have the same frequency and travel in opposite directions. Is this theoretical prediction in accord with the observations cited in Section 38.10?

38.13 The "uncertainty principle." Building on the Compton effect, we can deduce a form of the *uncertainty principle*, an important principle of fundamental significance for the physics of systems of atomic dimensions. In a "thought experiment," consider how one might observe the position of an electron (or a similarly small particle). To "see" the particle, even with the aid of instruments such as Geiger counters, we must illuminate it. Ordinary light, with a wavelength of the order of 5×10^{-5} cm, has too large a wavelength to be scattered by an object with a diameter of the order of 10^{-13} cm, just as ocean waves are not scattered by a small floating cork. The "light" chosen should have a very short wavelength; indeed, it will have to be high-frequency electromagnetic radiation in the gamma-ray range.

Let us analyze what happens when we use the hypothetical "gamma-ray microscope" to ascertain the position of a moving electron as it passes across the vertical axis of the microscope (Fig. 38.10). To see the electron, we send the beam of gamma rays across the axis as shown, in order to have some

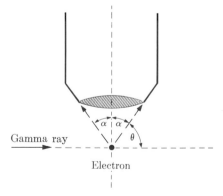

FIG. 38.10. A "gamma-ray microscope" used to determine the position of an electron by scattered gamma photons.

gamma photons scattered from the electron toward the lens of the microscope. After scattering, the gamma rays have a slightly different wavelength λ', owing to the Compton effect.

From the theory of optical instruments, let us now accept the result that for all optical systems the uncertainty Δx in the position of an object seen with light of wavelength λ' is approximately given by

$$\Delta x = \frac{\lambda'}{2\mu \sin \alpha}, \tag{38.21}$$

where μ is the index of refraction of the medium above the object ($\mu = 1$ here), and $\sin \alpha$ is one-half of the angular aperture of the lens. The momentum of the photon is h/λ before scattering, and h/λ' after scattering, where, by the Compton effect, $\lambda' > \lambda$. Also, during scattering, the original momentum $\mathbf{M}$ of the electron has been changed, but there is an uncertainty ΔM_x of magnitude $\Delta M_x = (2h/\lambda') \sin \alpha$ in the value of the x (horizontal) component of the momentum. The reason for this is as follows: When the scattered photon is observed at the eyepiece, it appears at the center axis of the instrument by being refracted to the axis with the superlenses of this supermicroscope. But note that the photon received at that position may originally have been scattered by the electron either straight up along the axis, or at an angle up to α to either side of the axis. The x-component of the momentum of the photon in the former case is zero; in the latter case it is $+(h/\lambda') \cdot \cos \theta$ [$= +(h/\lambda') \sin \alpha$] if the photon was scattered at angle α to the right of the axis, and $-(h/\lambda') \sin \alpha$ if to the left. So the total uncertainty in the value of the x-component of the photon's momentum is $(2h/\lambda') \sin \alpha$. By the principle of conservation of momentum, this is necessarily also the uncertainty in the value of the electron's x-component of momentum. Therefore

$$\Delta M_x = 2 \frac{h}{\lambda'} \sin \alpha. \tag{38.22}$$

Comparing Eqs. (38.21) and (38.22), we note that the uncertainty in the position is proportional to λ', whereas the uncertainty in momentum is inversely proportional to λ'. Therefore the product $\Delta M_x \, \Delta x$ is independent of λ', that is, independent of the wavelength of the photons used to observe the electron:

$$\Delta M_x \, \Delta x = \left(\frac{2h}{\lambda'} \sin \alpha\right)\left(\frac{\lambda'}{2 \sin \alpha}\right),$$

or

$$\Delta M_x \, \Delta x = h. \tag{38.23}$$

We also note that neither the dimensions nor the mass of the electron, nor the aperture angle of the equipment enters into Eq. (38.23). Therefore we generalize this argument to apply to any object under any condition: *The product of the uncertainties in momentum and position of an object is of the order of Planck's constant h.*

This statement is one form of the widely debated uncertainty principle or indeterminacy principle which Werner Heisenberg found in 1927 (on the basis of considerations other than these). Though far more sophisticated and general than our semiquantitative derivation suggests, some of its power and imaginative appeal are here reflected. It is important, however, to avoid the frequent mistake of assuming that the interconnected uncertainties of momentum or position are merely the result of difficulties in experimental design. While the principle has been here illustrated in terms of limitations on measurements in a specific thought experiment, the more profound view to take is that the very concepts of momentum and of position themselves do not permit a meaningful specification of simultaneous values with an arbitrary degree of precision.

PROBLEM 38.26. Determine the magnitude of the uncertainty in momentum and therefore in velocity for the following cases, and comment whether this uncertainty may be meaningful in terms of experimentally obtainable values of velocity:

(a) For an electron (mass about 10^{-30} kgm) in a system where the uncertainty in position is of the order of its diameter (about 10^{-15} m).

(b) For an atom (mass about 10^{-27} kgm) when the uncertainty in position is of the order of its diameter (about 10^{-10} m).

(c) For a small ball (mass about 10^{-1} kgm) passing through a hole whose diameter is the same as that of the ball to within 0.1 m.

PROBLEM 38.27. On the basis of the previous problem, comment on the opinion that the uncertainty principle does not apply to ordinary large-scale phenomena ("macrophysics") but is a principle specifically limited to small-scale phenomena ("microphysics").

38.14 The discovery of nuclear fission. In the 1930's the possibility that exothermic nuclear reactions might be powerful sources of energy was being debated more and more widely. Thus for the lithium-proton reaction of Eq. (38.6), the experiments showed the nuclear reaction energy Q to be 17.3 Mev, or about 2.8×10^{-12} j. Although this quantity sounds small, it is the energy surplus for each and every lithium atom disintegrated. A 10-mole or 70-gm piece of the isotope $_3Li^7$ contains 6.03×10^{24} atoms, and if all of them were disintegrated by proton bombardment, 1.7×10^{13} j would be released in the form of kinetic energies of the α-particles. Stopping these particles in some absorbing medium would ultimately provide about enough heat energy to operate a 10,000-kw electric power station for one day. Other nuclear reactions were found to be even more energetic. On the other hand, it had been found that in such reactions only between one and ten bombarding particles out of a billion could be expected to induce the reaction; therefore, on the whole, more energy has to be supplied than is gained. Also, the technical problems of efficiently sustaining the reaction and exploiting the energy released seemed almost insuperable.

The situation changed almost overnight with the publication on January 6, 1939, of some puzzling observations by two German physical chemists, Otto Hahn, formerly an assistant of Rutherford, and F. Strassmann. Their work originated in a problem first encountered by E. Fermi, E. Segré, and their co-workers, in 1934 in connection with the bombardment of uranium by fast neutrons. As a result of the neutron bombardment the sample gave evidence of a number of different induced radioactive processes with relatively short half-lives. Of particular interest were several different observed *beta* emissions, which Fermi had explained as the result of formation of *transuranic elements;* for in each β-decay, the atomic number Z is increased by one, to $Z + 1$. In this way, the formation of elements beyond uranium, up to $Z = 96$, had been proposed.

Chemical evidence appeared to support this hypothetical scheme. For when Fermi mixed with the neutron-bombarded uranium sample a quantity of, say, thorium, and chemically separated this "carrier" again from the rest of the material, the carrier could be tested to find whether or not it carried down the induced β-emitter as an impurity. If it did not, the unknown β-emitter clearly was chemically not related to thorium, but if it did, it was either the same element or one closely related. In this way, Fermi had ruled out that the β-emitters created in the sample by neutrons were isotopes of the elements for which $Z = 82, 83, 86, 87, 89, 90, 91$, and 92.

But in 1938, Hahn and Strassmann found in neutron-bombarded uranium evidence not only for transuranic elements but for elements with atomic numbers less than 92, namely actinium (89) and radium (88). These elements seemed to be formed both with fast and with slow neutrons. The sequence postulated by them was

$$_{92}U^{238} + {_0}n^1 \longrightarrow (_{92}U^{239}) \xrightarrow{\ \alpha\ } {_{90}}Th^{235} \xrightarrow{\ \alpha\ } {_{88}}Ra^{231} \xrightarrow{\ \beta\ }$$

$$\longrightarrow {_{89}}Ac^{231} \xrightarrow{\ \beta\ } {_{90}}Th^{231} \text{ (etc.).} \qquad (38.24)$$

Support for this view again seemed to be given by the chemical analysis of the sample. *One* of the many induced β-emitters present could be separated out from the neutron-bombarded uranium sample by means of a carrier of readily available barium (Ba), and a glance at the periodic table (Appendix D) shows that barium, an alkaline earth in Group II, stands directly above the next member of the chemical family, namely radium. Another β-emitter, having a $3\frac{1}{2}$-hr half-life, could be separated with a lanthanum carrier, lanthanum (La) being the chemically related lanthanide to be found directly above actinium (Ac) in the periodic table.

But this attempt to understand the appearance of radium and actinium in neutron-bombarded uranium was thrown in doubt by the immediately following publication of Irène Joliot-Curie and P. Savitch, who re-examined in more detail the chemistry of the supposed actinium carried down by lanthanum and found that if both actinium and lanthanum were added as carriers, the β-emitter formed in neutron bombardment of uranium chose to go with lanthanum rather than with actinium. This does not prove that the β-emitter is lanthanum, for other chemically related substances can behave in this way, but it did prove that the $3\frac{1}{2}$-hr β-emitter could not be actinium.

Hahn's and Strassmann's publication of January 6, 1939, was prompted by this dissent. They confirmed the findings of Joliot-Curie and of Savitch, and now saw that if their $3\frac{1}{2}$-hr β-emitter was not actinium but possibly lanthanum ($Z = 57$), the parent element in Eq. (38.24) could not be radium, but might be barium itself ($Z = 56$), even though it seemed initially "altogether too improbable." It does indeed—for how could uranium turn into barium? Not by successive α-decays; this would have to be attended by the appearance of at least 18 α-particle emissions and 17 different chemical elements, none of which was observed. Moreover, there were good theoretical grounds against this hypothesis, and the alternative, namely the emission of a whole barium nucleus by uranium during neutron bombardment, was quite as incredible. For in all the years of nuclear research, nothing bigger than an α-particle had been obtained from any nucleus, even with the strongest beams of incident radiations or accelerated particles. Also there appeared to be theoretical difficulties with such a hypothesis.

Nevertheless, when mixed with radium, the "radium" of Eq. (38.24) was not carried down with it; but when mixed with a carrier of barium, it followed barium during every step of the chemical separation process. Hahn and Strassmann prefaced this finding with the remark, "Now we must speak of a new investigation which we are publishing only with hesitation because of the strange results ... We come to this conclusion: Our 'radium isotopes' [they had thought that they had found four in the initial sample of bombarded uranium] have the properties of barium; as chemists we should really say that these new emitters represent not radium but barium."

Perhaps even the so-called transuranic elements previously thought to result from β-decay of $_{92}U^{239}$ might now turn out to be identical with some lighter elements in the middle of the periodic table. "After all, one could formerly not have thought of this. The sum of the mass numbers of $_{56}$Ba + $_{43}$Tc, for example 138 + 101, is 239!" And here, at the brink of the suggestion that in the bombardment of uranium by neutrons the heavy nucleus can split into two large parts, there follows the remark we referred to previously:

> On the basis of these briefly presented experiments, we must, as chemists, really rename the previously offered scheme and set the symbols Ba, La, Ce in place of Ra, Ac, Th. As 'nuclear chemists' with close ties to physics, we cannot decide to make a step so contrary to all existing experience of nuclear physics. After all, a series of strange coincidences may, perhaps, have feigned these results.

The step which Hahn and Strassmann could not bring themselves to make was taken on January 16, 1939, by two Austrian physicists, Miss Lise Meitner, formerly Hahn's colleague (Fig. 38.11), but at that time in Sweden as a refugee from Nazi Germany, and Otto R. Frisch. In their

FIG. 38.11. Lise Meitner and Otto Hahn (in 1925).

paper of that date, they proposed that the neutron initiated an explosion of the uranium nucleus into "two nuclei of roughly equal size," a process which they referred to as *nuclear fission*. The fragments were predicted to be endowed with great kinetic energy and to be radioactive, which would account for the β-emissions that previously had been interpreted by transuranic series or series like that given in Eq. (38.24). These predictions were quickly fulfilled by experiment.

Before the publication of Meitner's and Frisch's paper, Niels Bohr, who had been informed by them, announced their conclusions at a meeting of the American Physical Society in Washington, D. C., on January 26, 1939. Almost as soon as he had finished his remarks, confirmatory experiments were started. It occurred to many that when a few uranium nuclei were made to undergo fission, they could release neutrons which could in turn trigger the reaction in many more neighboring uranium atoms. Once started, a "chain reaction" would spread through a sample of uranium, setting free a large amount of energy in each nuclear fission. Here was the promise of a practical source of nuclear energy—and thus was born the nuclear age, with an unprecedented explosion of research interest.

As it turned out, slow neutrons such as used in some of the experiments of Fermi and of Hahn and Strassmann, cause fission not of $_{92}U^{238}$ but of $_{92}U^{235}$. Of the many ways in which a uranium nucleus can split up, the following is typical [and explains the data to which the erroneous Eq. (38.24) was directed]:

$$_{92}U^{235} + _0n^1 \rightarrow _{56}Ba^{141} + _{36}Kr^{92} + 3_0n^1. \qquad (38.25)$$

The nuclei $_{56}Ba^{141}$ and $_{36}Kr^{92}$ are not to be found in nature and are not stable, but they decay radioactively; for example, $_{56}Ba^{141}$ can become $_{59}Pr^{141}$ by successive emission of three β-particles, by the scheme

$$_{56}Ba^{141} \xrightarrow{\beta^-} _{57}La^{141} \xrightarrow{\beta^-} _{58}Ce^{141} \xrightarrow{\beta^-} _{59}Pr^{141}$$
$$\text{(18 min)} \qquad \text{(3.6 hr)} \qquad \text{(32 days)} \qquad \text{(stable)}$$

Similarly, $_{36}Kr^{92}$ can become $_{40}Zr^{92}$ by emission of four β-particles. Each of these β-decays has its own half-life, and this profusion of different β-emitters in a sample of neutron-irradiated uranium was the reason for the initial puzzle posed by the data.

The measured Q-value of the reaction in Eq. (38.25) is about 200 Mev, or 3×10^{-11} j. This can be predicted by noting that the total rest mass of the products on the right side of the equation is about 0.215 amu less than the total rest mass on the left side. Since 1 amu corresponds to 1.49×10^{-10} j, the 0.2-amu deficit of rest mass corresponds to the energy release of 3×10^{-11} j. As physicists everywhere quickly realized, no other nuclear reaction yields nearly as much energy per atom. We shall return in Sections 39.6 and 39.7 to the use of the energy and the neutrons released in fission for obtaining a self-sustaining chain reaction at explosive speeds (fission bomb) or under controlled conditions (nuclear reactor).

38.15 Fusion. Until recently it was difficult to conceive of a mechanism for explaining how the sun and other stars could have continued to pour out such enormous quantities of energy over a period of billions of years. If the source were any chemical reaction, all of the material would have been consumed after a few thousand years. Even nuclear fission cannot be held responsible, because of the low abundance in the sun of elements that will undergo fission. In fact, the main part of the sun's mass is formed by light elements, hydrogen and helium accounting for 90%.

The present thinking is that the constant and large solar emission is in the main due to a series of exothermic nuclear reactions in which hydrogen nuclei are transmuted into helium nuclei in a cyclic sequence; one example is the so-called *proton-proton chain* neglecting neutrinos:

$$_1H^1 + {}_1H^1 \rightarrow {}_1H^2 + {}_{+1}e^0,$$

$$_1H^2 + {}_1H^1 \rightarrow {}_2He^3, \tag{38.26}$$

$$_2He^3 + {}_2He^3 \rightarrow {}_2He^4 + 2{}_1H^1.$$

In words: two protons *fuse* into a deuteron, with the emission of a positron; the deuteron encounters another proton and forms a light helium nucleus, $_2He^3$; finally, two light helium nuclei so generated join to form one α-particle and two protons. Note that two reactions of the first kind and two of the second are needed before one $_2He^4$ nucleus can be formed. The net result of this cycle of five fusion reactions is that four protons have been converted into one α-particle and two positrons (the latter are soon bound to encounter electrons and combine with them to form γ-photons). Also, a good deal of energy is made available by this cycle, as is clear from a comparison of the sum of the rest masses after and before conversion:

Mass of α-particle	4.0027 amu
Mass of 2 positrons	0.0011 amu
Sum	4.0038 amu
Mass of 4 protons	4.0304 amu
Difference	−0.0266 amu

This reduction of rest mass by nearly 0.027 amu must be accompanied by a corresponding release of about $0.027 \times 931 = 25$ Mev of energy, some as γ-photons but most of it in the form of kinetic energy of the product particles. The material in which these reactions are occurring will therefore be in a high state of agitation, which in turn corresponds to a high temperature; this would help to account for the enormous internal temperature of the sun, which is believed to be about twenty million degrees Celsius. The estimate is that only about 1% of the sun's hydrogen is consumed in a billion years; still, many millions of tons of its mass are "lost" each minute by radiation of energy into space.

When it comes to the exploitation of these or similar fusion reactions for *terrestrial* applications, there is one obstacle not emphasized in the foregoing account. To enable nuclei to fuse, they must be brought close together and so must be given initial kinetic energy sufficient to overcome the electric force of repulsion between them. Cyclotrons and other particle accelerators can accomplish this easily enough for light nuclei, but they generally deal with relatively few nuclei at a time. In the sun, the high ambient temperature assures the necessary speeds of approach of nuclei before fusion. On earth, the high speeds for the atoms in a large mass of material can also be obtained by heating the material initially by means of a violent explosion—perhaps an explosive fission reaction set off in the sample.

Such a *thermonuclear reaction* is one of the processes involved in the so-called "hydrogen bomb," or "H-bomb," first tested in 1952, in which hydrogen fusion reactions are kindled by sudden local heating. The fusion process utilized may be a single reaction rather than a sequence as in Eq. (38.24). Three possibilities are

$$_1H^2 + {}_1H^2 \rightarrow {}_2He^3 + {}_0n^1, \qquad Q = 3.3 \text{ Mev}, \qquad (38.27)$$

$$_1H^2 + {}_1H^2 \rightarrow {}_1H^3 + {}_1H^1, \qquad Q = 4.0 \text{ Mev}, \qquad (38.28)$$

$$_1H^2 + {}_1H^3 \rightarrow {}_2He^4 + {}_0n^1, \qquad Q = 17.6 \text{ Mev}. \qquad (38.29)$$

The hydrogen isotope $_1H^3$, *tritium*, is not found in nature in significant quantities, but can be manufactured, for example by letting deuterium ($_1H^2$) absorb low-speed neutrons, or by the reaction in Eq. (38.31).

It has been suggested that thermonuclear weapons may utilize, in addition to fusion, a reaction such as

$$_3Li^6 + {}_1H^2 \rightarrow {}_2He^4 + {}_2He^4, \qquad Q = 22.4 \text{ Mev}, \qquad (38.30)$$

or

$$_3Li^6 + {}_0n^1 \rightarrow {}_1H^3 + {}_2He^4, \qquad Q = 4.9 \text{ Mev}. \qquad (38.31)$$

The tritium nucleus generated in the latter reaction might then fuse with separately supplied deuterons; a fission bomb might provide both the initial high temperature and the neutrons for the reaction with $_3Li^6$.

One of the most significant steps in the eventual application of the fusion process to peaceful uses was taken late in 1957, when researchers in British and United States laboratories succeeded in sending very large electric currents through tubes containing deuterium gases. If the temperature thereby can be raised above 10^6 °C, neutrons will be observed to be generated during the discharge, indicating that fusion was being achieved (see Eqs. 38.27 and 38.29). The perfection of a controlled fusion reaction will make the virtually unlimited quantity of heavy hydrogen (as in water) potentially available to us as a high-energy fuel.

ADDITIONAL PROBLEMS

38.28. Write a general nuclear-reaction expression for the disintegration occurring when a nucleus $_ZX^A$ captures an α-particle and immediately forms a new nucleus $_?Y^?$ by the ejection of (a) a proton, (b) a neutron.

38.29. When a particle of mass m and charge q in a cyclotron (Fig. 38.4) is moving with a constant speed v, it is acted on by a centripetal force of magnitude $\mu_0 Hqv$ that impels it to move at every moment in a circular arc of radius r. (a) Prove that the number of times per second that the particle crosses the gap between the segments A and B is given by $\mu_0 Hq/\pi m$. (b) Is this number constant for any given particle?

38.30. Show that 1 amu is equivalent to 1.49×10^{-10} j, or 931 Mev.

38.31. If a γ-photon of energy 5.6×10^{-13} j is transformed into an electron-positron pair, and if these two particles share equally in the excess energy, what is the kinetic energy of each at the instant of production?

38.32. In an experiment on the nuclear reaction of Eq. (38.2), the kinetic energy of each bombarding α-particle was 4.8 Mev. Compute (a) the nuclear reaction energy Q, and (b) the speed of the emerging neutrons. (The average kinetic energy of the beryllium atoms is negligibly small in comparison with that of the other particles in this reaction.)

38.33. In Eq. (38.8), what was the speed of the emerging α-particles, and what can one say about the directions they took?

38.34. Compute the ratio of relativistic mass to rest mass of an electron that is moving with a speed of (a) $0.01c$, (b) $0.2c$, (c) $0.7c$, and (d) $0.9c$.

38.35. (a) In a certain television tube, the electrons are accelerated to the screen of the tube by a potential difference of 5000 volts. Compute the relativistic increase in mass of each electron arriving at the screen. (b) Find the relativistic increase in mass and the speed of electrons in the 6-Bev electron accelerator (1 Bev = 10^9 ev).

38.36. (a) Which of the planets moves with the highest speed around the sun? Is the increase in its mass owing to this motion appreciable? (b) If a planet's relativistic mass were distinctly larger than its rest mass, how would this appear to affect our use of Newton's law of gravitation, namely, Eq. (11.7)?

SUPPLEMENTARY READING

BEYER, R. T., ed., *Foundations of nuclear physics* (Dover, 1949). Contains reprints of original papers of Chadwick, Cockcroft and Walton, Fermi, Hahn and Strassmann, and others.

BLACKWOOD, O. H., T. H. OSGOOD, and A. E. RUARK, *An outline of atomic physics* (Wiley, 1955), Chaps. 11–13.

BORN, M., *Einstein's theory of relativity* (Methuen, London, 1924). The only elementary book on relativity theory that is authoritative and, at the same time, has adequate physical and mathematical discussion of the main points. Highly recommended.

EINSTEIN, A., and L. INFELD, *The evolution of physics* (Simon and Schuster, 1939).

GLASSTONE, S., *Source book on atomic energy* (Van Nostrand, 1950, 1958), Chaps. 9–11, 13.

HECHT, S., *Explaining the atom* (Viking, 1954), Chaps. 4–12.

HEISENBERG, W., *Nuclear physics* (Philosophical Library, 1953), Chaps. 4–8.

KOLIN, A., *Physics, its laws, ideas, and methods* (McGraw-Hill, 1950), Chap. 40 on relativity theory.

CHAPTER 39

FURTHER DEVELOPMENTS OF NUCLEAR PHYSICS

39.1 Nuclear binding energy. Nuclei are made up of protons and neutrons, and these two particles have about the same mass, close to 1 amu; indeed, this fact served to explain why the masses of all nuclei are nearly whole-number multiples of 1 amu. However, as the precision of mass-spectrograph measurements increased, the approximate character of this whole-number rule became more and more evident. In fact, the mass of any nucleus turns out to be somewhat *smaller* than the sum of the masses of its protons and neutrons taken separately. For example, the mass of a deuteron ($_1H^2$) is smaller by 0.0024 amu than the sum of the masses of a free proton and a free neutron. For every nucleus it is true that the whole weighs less than the sum of the parts. This difference in masses for any particular nucleus is called its *mass defect,* and signifies a mass loss which may have been incurred when the constituent particles were originally packed together to form the nucleus.*

The mass defect becomes understandable when considered in the light of the principle of conservation of mass-energy. Imagine that a proton and a neutron are brought together to form a deuteron. Since the mass defect in this case is 0.0024 amu, the process must involve the release of energy of amount 0.0024 amu $\times$ 1.49 $\times$ 10^{-10} j/amu = 3.6 $\times$ 10^{-13} j, or 2.2 Mev. Only if this energy can be and is lost (say, by the emission of a photon) will the two particles be bound together in a stable configuration. Thus, for any stable nucleus to be formed by the binding together of individual nuclear particles, the process must be accompanied by the release of energy. This energy is called the *binding energy* of the nucleus, for it is the energy that must be *given up* if the nuclear particles are to remain bound together. On the other hand, when the corresponding amount of energy is put back into a nucleus, the individual particles can again dissociate. An example already given was that of photodisintegration (Problem 38.16), where a deuteron, on absorbing a γ-photon of energy 2.2 Mev or larger, can break up into a free proton and a free neutron. Thus the binding energy (the term "unbinding energy" might be more descriptive) may also be defined as the energy that would be needed to separate any nucleus $_ZX^A$ into its Z protons and $(A - Z)$ neutrons.

---

*Aston, who formulated the whole-number rule, originally defined mass defect as atomic weight minus atomic number. The convention used here, however, makes closer contact with the physical significance of the term.

Clearly, for each nucleus,

binding energy (in joules)
$$= \text{mass defect (in kgm)} \times c^2 \text{ (in m}^2/\text{sec}^2). \quad (39.1)$$

PROBLEM 39.1. Use the information in Table 38.1 to calculate the frequency of γ-rays which you would employ if you were to look for the possibility of a complete photodisintegration of tritium nuclei. (*Note:* Recall that Table 38.1 lists the masses of *neutral* atoms.)

PROBLEM 39.2. With the help of Table 38.1, compute the mass defect and binding energy of (a) $_1\text{H}^2$, (b) $_2\text{He}^4$, (c) $_3\text{Li}^7$, (d) $_{92}\text{U}^{235}$. (*Note:* Recall that Table 38.1 lists the masses of *neutral* atoms.)

39.2 Nuclear forces. The discussion of mass defects and binding energies suggests a simple hypothesis of the origin of atoms. We may speculate that once there existed a great gaslike cloud of protons, neutrons, and electrons, all in a state of rapid random motion, perhaps as the result of some primeval explosion and subsequent partial decay of a quantity of free neutrons. The free protons and neutrons eventually combined to form nuclei, which in turn captured the appropriate numbers of free electrons to form neutral atoms. But why do the nuclear particles hold together as they do? With the nuclear particles crowded together in a space of diameter roughly 10^{-13} cm to 10^{-12} cm, why do they not fly apart as the result of the mutual forces of repulsion between the positively charged protons?

In trying to answer this question, we are led to propose the existence of forces of attraction, *nuclear forces*, which presumably are neither electric nor gravitational in character, and which are peculiar to nuclear particles. Although these nuclear forces are still imperfectly understood, several of their properties are now well established. For one thing, they are of very "short range," that is, they decrease rapidly to zero as the distance between nuclear particles exceeds about 10^{-12} cm. Again, the nuclear force between two neutrons is about the same as that between a neutron and a proton, or between two protons. However, between protons there is also the ordinary electric ("Coulomb-law") repulsion in addition to the nuclear force of attraction, giving a net force between a proton and a proton-containing nucleus which varies with distance between them roughly as indicated in Fig. 39.2.

A mechanical analogy will help to make clear the nature of nuclear forces and of binding energies. Consider a marble rolling at some initial speed v_0 on a flat surface toward a hole or well which is surrounded by a steep wall (see Fig. 39.1); let the friction be negligible. Clearly, if the marble is to have any hope of falling into the well, it must have at least enough initial kinetic energy to climb the wall and surmount the gravitational "barrier" at its highest point B. As the marble now descends into the well, it gathers speed, and arrives at the bottom with a final velocity v

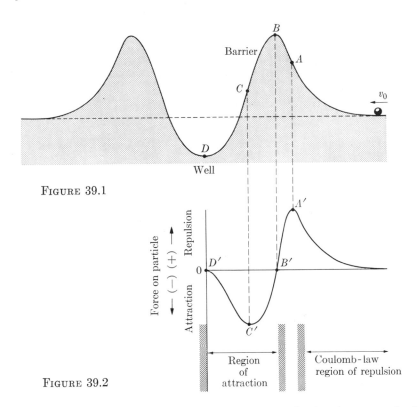

FIGURE 39.1

FIGURE 39.2

FIG. 39.1. The marble must be able to roll over the barrier to reach the bottom of the well. To stay in the well, the marble must be able to give up some of its energy. The analogy applies to the case of a positively charged particle approaching a nucleus.

FIG. 39.2. Graph of net force on a particle as it moves toward the center of the well. The distance $D'B'$ corresponds to the radius of the well. For small distances from the center, the force of attraction (negative) predominates over the force of repulsion (positive).

which is greater than v_0. Ordinarily, the marble will then simply go on and roll over the barrier on the other side, and escape from the wall. To capture the marble we must take away some of its kinetic energy while it is inside the hole. Similarly, the proton will not stay in the nucleus once it conquers the "barrier" due to the Coulomb-law force of repulsion unless it can give up energy (binding energy), perhaps in the form of γ-emission. And having lost energy, the system also has lost mass.

The net force acting on the marble as it moves toward the well behaves in the manner indicated by the graph of force vs. distance, Fig. 39.2. At the steepest part of the hill (A) the force opposing the forward motion is largest (A'); at the top of the barrier (B) the net force is momentarily zero (B'); at the steepest point inside the well (C) and at the very bottom (D), respectively, the magnitudes of the net forces are those shown on the graph at C' and D'. In terms of the analogy, the force on a proton approaching a positively charged nucleus changes in a very similar way: the Coulomb-law force of repulsion on the approaching particle grows to a maximum, and then is overbalanced by a nuclear force of attraction at shorter ranges.

PROBLEM 39.3. Since there is no "Coulomb-law" repulsion between a nucleus and a neutron approaching it, the graphs of Figs. 39.1 and 39.2 do not apply to such a case. How should the analogy be modified to fit neutron capture?

39.3 A reinterpretation of nuclear reactions. The introduction of a new term will make our subsequent discussions more concise. The particles of the nucleus, protons and neutrons, are usually both referred to simply as *nucleons*. Now the larger the number of nucleons in the nuclear "well," the greater is the binding energy of the nucleus. But we should not expect that the mass defect or binding energy increases in a linear fashion with increase in the number of nucleons. After all, the short-range nuclear attractive forces between protons are not necessarily quite the same as those between a proton and a neutron or between two neutrons, and in any case they depend on the pattern in which the nucleons assemble.

In Fig. 39.3, the binding energies determined for various nuclei are plotted as a function of the number of nucleons, which is the same as the mass number A. Instead of a straight line, which would result if each nucleon made the same contribution to the total binding energy of the nucleus, we have a curve with valleys and convexities. This fact stands out more clearly in Fig. 39.4, which shows the average binding energy *per nucleon* for the various nuclei, i.e., the total binding energy divided by the number of nucleons. Note particularly that nuclei having between about 50 and 90 nucleons have a greater binding energy *per nucleon* than those for the rest of the curve. Thus the binding energy for $_{29}Cu^{63}$ is 8.75 Mev per nucleon, whereas for $_{92}U^{235}$ it is only 7.61 Mev per nucleon, and for $_1H^2$ only 1.12 Mev per nucleon. It follows that nuclei of copper and other elements high on the curve are the more difficult to unravel or disturb; they are among the most stable nuclei because they are, in a sense, the most economically packed. Also note the steep hump for $_2He^4$—a very stable nucleus, as we could have predicted from the fact that the four nucleons composing it are ejected in one unit as an α-particle from many radioactive nuclei.

These curves hold the key to the question whether any particular nuclear reaction is endothermic or exothermic. As we saw earlier, the answer can be found by experiment or predicted from the measured difference between the rest masses of the products and of the original

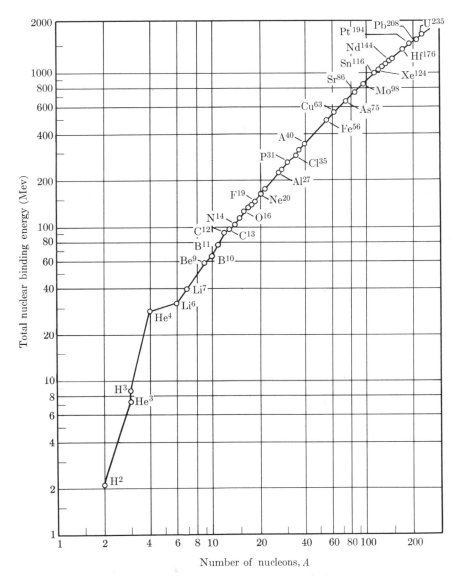

FIG. 39.3. Total binding energies of nuclei as a function of the number of nucleons, A. (The "compressed" scale is logarithmic for both ordinate and abscissa.)

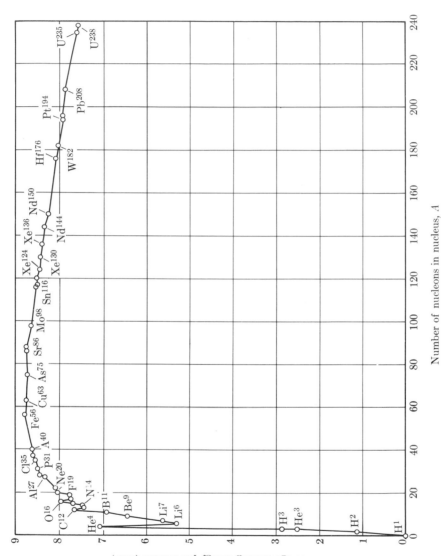

FIG. 39.4. Average binding energy per nucleon as a function of the number of nucleons, A.

constituents (Section 38.9). But now the problem can be reinterpreted and simplified by using Figs. 39.3 and 39.4. For example, consider the reaction of Eq. (38.8), namely $_3Li^7 + _1H^1 \rightarrow _2He^4 + _2He^4$. As has been computed in Problem 39.2 and as is shown in Fig. 39.3, the binding energy is about 39 Mev for the $_3Li^7$ nucleus (the incident proton itself has no binding energy), and is about 28 Mev for each resulting α-particle. Thus the two product particles together have 17 Mev more binding energy, owing to their more economical packing, than has the parent nucleus. This difference represents energy that must be disposed of, in this case in the form of kinetic energy of the two α-particles; thus the reaction is exothermic. *In general, when the total binding energy of the products exceeds that of the original constituents, the reaction is exothermic.* Or to put it in terms of Fig. 39.4, whenever the products lie higher on the curve than do the reacting nuclei, they have more binding energy per nucleon and so must release the difference.

Notice how readily the curves afford information about the processes of fission and fusion. In Fig. 39.4 the nuclei of either the right-hand or the left-hand parts of the curve indicate by their smaller binding energy per nucleon that they may possibly change to the more stable nuclei of the middle portion with release of energy. It follows that the most massive nuclei will release energy when they undergo *fission*, the least massive nuclei when they undergo *fusion*.

PROBLEM 39.4. What is the justification for saying that the number of nucleons in the nucleus is numerically equal to the mass number A of the atom?

PROBLEM 39.5. If the curve in Fig. 39.3 had been a straight line, what would this have meant physically? What would Fig. 39.4 look like in that case?

PROBLEM 39.6. (a) Using Fig. 39.3, find the energy obtainable by fission of $_{92}U^{235}$ into two fragments of equal mass. (b) Using Fig. 39.4, find the energy obtainable by fission of $_{92}U^{238}$ (as can be achieved with fast neutrons) into two fragments, one of which has about twice the mass of the other.

PROBLEM 39.7. Using Figs. 39.3 and 39.4, show that the following fusion processes are exothermic: (a) $_1H^2 + _1H^1 \rightarrow _2He^3$; (b) $_1H^2 + _1H^3 \rightarrow _2He^4 + _0n^1$; (c) $_1H^2 + _1H^2 \rightarrow _2He^3 + _0n^1$.

PROBLEM 39.8. Ions of nitrogen $_7N^{14}$, accelerated in a cyclotron, have been used to produce fusion with oxygen $_8O^{16}$ nuclei. Determine the product compound nucleus, and whether the fusion process has a net yield of energy.

39.4 The "liquid-drop" model of the nucleus. The observed properties of material bodies, especially their chemical and thermal properties, led to the model of matter as an aggregate of atoms (Dalton, Joule). The atom, in turn, was described by a model (initially that of Rutherford and Bohr) in which a nucleus is pictured at the center of a swarm of electrons. But nuclei themselves are responsible for a wide variety of phenomena, ranging from particle emission in radioactive decay to fission, and to explain these phenomena, a model of the nucleus is needed. Currently, use is being made of several different models, each helpful for explaining a specific group of phenomena. Two of these are of special interest to us, the *liquid-drop model* and the *shell model*. Although both are basically mathematical, yielding quantitative results, we shall see some of their scope and power even in the following qualitative descriptions. We turn first to the liquid-drop model of the nucleus.

It will be recalled that one of the outstanding problems of nuclear physics has been to understand the stability of a nucleus despite the presence in it of the positively charged protons. The solution given was the proposal that the Coulomb-law repulsion between the protons is overwhelmed at short distances by attractive nuclear forces between the nucleons (Fig. 39.2). This solution is in accord with a suggestion by G. Gamow (1930) and the detailed analysis by Niels Bohr and J. A. Wheeler (1939). The nucleus is regarded as analogous to a (charged) drop of liquid, for in a drop the molecules are also held in a spherical form by short-range forces, namely those of surface tension. Moreover, nuclei and the drops of a given liquid have something else in common: the volumes of both increase fairly linearly with their masses. In other words, the nucleons of all nuclei are crowded together about equally densely, giving all nuclei the same density of about 10^{14} gm/cm^3. This tight packing of nucleons is, of course, in great contrast to the scattered structure of the electron cloud around the nucleus.

On this model, the nucleons, like the molecules in a drop of liquid, are pictured as being in random motion. As in the evaporation of molecules from the surface of a liquid, a group of nucleons may pick up enough speed through chance collisions with other nucleons to break through the barrier of the cohesive nuclear forces and thus escape from the nucleus; this would correspond to spontaneous α-particle emission. Or a particle may enter the nucleus from the outside and impart enough additional kinetic energy to the nucleons to permit the escape of a proton, a neutron, or an α-particle; this would correspond to reactions such as those in Eqs. (38.1), (38.2), or (38.6).

The power of the liquid-drop model is best exhibited by its ability to explain the nuclear fission process, at least in its general outline. As we have seen, the capture of even a very slow particle by a nucleus can cause it to explode with a release of a good deal of energy; examples were the reaction $_3\text{Li}^7 + {}_1\text{H}^1 \rightarrow {}_2\text{He}^4 + {}_2\text{He}^4$, and the fission of uranium. Such violent effects indicate that the introduction of a particle into a nucleus can make available to the nucleons in it enough energy to upset the balance of forces which previously held them together.

A quantitative consideration confirms this guess. For example, the simplest of all reactions in which a slow particle is captured by the nucleus, the reaction

$$_1H^1 + {_0}n^1 \rightarrow {_1}H^2 \tag{39.2}$$

by which a proton is converted into a deuteron, must leave the $_1H^2$ nucleus in a highly excited state, for the sum of the rest masses of $_1H^1$ and $_0n^1$ is 2.01712 amu, and the rest mass of $_1H^2$ *in the ordinary state* is only 2.01474 amu. The excess of 0.00238 amu must mean that the newly formed $_1H^2$ nucleus in Eq. (39.2) has an excess of $0.00238 \times 931 = 2.22$ Mev of energy, which it must get rid of before it can be a stable $_1H^2$ nucleus. (In this particular case this is accomplished by the emission of a γ-photon from the excited nucleus, evidently just the reverse of the process of photodisintegration of the deuteron by absorption of a γ-photon.) Note again that the excess energy of about 2.2 Mev is due to the large mass defect of $_1H^2$, and not due to the bombarding neutron's initial kinetic energy; the latter has been assumed to be negligible.

PROBLEM 39.9. We may assume that when $_3Li^7$ is bombarded with $_1H^1$, a nucleus of $_4Be^8$ forms momentarily before it disintegrates into two $_2He^4$ particles in the reaction

$$_3Li^7 + {_1}H^1 \rightarrow [{_4}Be^8] \rightarrow {_2}He^4 + {_2}He^4.$$

Use the data in Table 38.1 to compute the excess energy which the temporary $_4Be^8$ nucleus has.

A similar calculation can be made for the energy released in the nucleus when $_{92}U^{235}$ captures a slow neutron to form *momentarily* $_{92}U^{236}$. The mass of ordinary $_{92}U^{236}$ would be 236.1191 amu, but the mass of $_{92}U^{235}$ and one neutron together is $235.1170 + 1.0090 = 236.1260$ amu. Thus the compound nucleus formed by the capture of a slow neutron in a $_{92}U^{235}$ nucleus has a surplus of mass of 0.0069 amu, representing $0.0069 \times 931 = 6.4$ Mev of excess energy. This may be called the *excitation energy* due to neutron capture.

What happens to the excited $_{92}U^{236}$ nucleus? On the Bohr-Wheeler liquid-drop model, the nucleus will behave rather like a drop of mercury when "excited" by being given mechanical energy, e.g., by being shaken: the nucleus is deformed momentarily into an elongated or dumbbell-like shape whose two parts are beyond the effective range of the nuclear attractive forces. At that point the electric force of repulsion between the two parts of the nucleus predominates over the short-range forces of inter-nucleon attraction; it causes the nucleus to split, that is, to undergo fission, and the fragments to separate with high velocity. Each of the two main fragments will on its own quickly assume a spherical form, because within them the attractive nuclear forces again predominate (Fig. 39.5).

The liquid-drop model also provides a simple answer to the question why only very few types of nuclei are observed to undergo fission. To

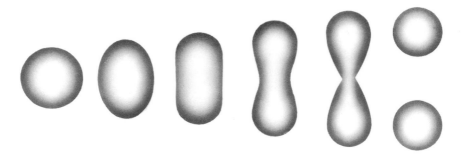

FIG. 39.5. Schematic representation of steps leading to the fission of a compound nucleus, according to the liquid-drop model.

deform the "drop" against the initial force of attraction sufficiently for the repelling forces between its parts to predominate requires a certain minimum amount of energy. This may be called *activation energy*, by analogy with chemical reactions such as explosions that are initiated only when enough energy is supplied to trigger them off. The activation energies for fission can be calculated on the basis of the liquid-drop model. For $_{92}U^{236}$, for example, the activation energy is found to be smaller than the excitation energy which becomes available in the nucleus owing to the capture of a neutron by $_{92}U^{235}$. Hence even a *slow* neutron (one with a kinetic energy of only a small fraction of an electron volt) should be able to produce fission, and experiment of course confirms this prediction. But for $_{92}U^{239}$ the model predicts that the activation energy is larger by 0.6 Mev than the excitation energy produced by slow-neutron capture of $_{92}U^{238}$ nuclei. Hence fission of $_{92}U^{238}$ should occur only if the neutron enters with a kinetic energy of at least 0.6 Mev, and within the sizeable uncertainty of the calculation this prediction coincides with the experimental observations. Thus when a $_{92}U^{238}$ nucleus captures a *slow* neutron rather than a fast one it does not undergo fission, but becomes $_{92}U^{239}$; this nucleus spontaneously and rapidly disintegrates by the emission of two successive β-particles and neutrinos to form the transuranic element plutonium, $_{94}Pu^{239}$, which is an α-emitter with a half-life of 24,000 yr that has been found in only minute quantities in nature.

Fast, charged particles and γ-photons can be used to produce fission of various nuclei, including some of intermediate atomic mass. All these various fission processes are explainable in terms of the liquid-drop model.

PROBLEM 39.10. The uranium isotope $_{92}U^{233}$ does not exist naturally, but results after the thorium nucleus $_{90}Th^{232}$ has captured a neutron. (a) Give the probable steps leading from $_{90}Th^{232}$ to $_{92}U^{233}$. (b) Knowing that the activation energy needed for fission of the compound nucleus $_{92}U^{234}$ is 4.6 Mev, and given the data in Table 38.1, discuss the possibility of fission of $_{92}U^{233}$ by bombardment with slow neutrons.

39.5 The shell model of the nucleus. A second, different model of the nucleus is required and used to explain quite another set of properties of the nucleus, for example the experimental finding that nuclei having 2, 8, 20, 50, or 82 protons, or 2, 8, 20, 50, 82, or 126 neutrons, are unusually numerous and stable. Binding energies per nucleon exceed those of nuclei with one nucleon fewer or more; they are also somewhat smaller in volume than normal, and often have other exceptional properties. In nuclear theory, these six numbers are called "magic numbers." Nuclei consisting of 14, 28, and 40 protons or neutrons also have these exceptional properties, but in lesser degree.

It will be recalled that chemical evidence revealed the remarkable stability of *atoms* of atomic numbers 2, 10, 18, 36, 54, and 86—the rare, or inert, gases helium to radon. Their valence is zero, the atomic volumes are unusually small, and more energy is needed to wrench an electron from any of these atoms in ionizing it than for its neighbors in the periodic table. These properties of the rare gases were explained in the Bohr-Rutherford model of the atom by the conception that the electrons around each nucleus tend to arrange themselves in concentric shells, with each shell able to accommodate only a certain maximum number of electrons, 2 for the innermost shell, 8 for the next, and so on (Section 35.3).

It is therefore not surprising that an analogous scheme was introduced in nuclear physics in order to explain *nuclear* stability in terms of internal structure. A shell structure was proposed by W. Elsasser (1934) and is supported by a variety of experimental evidence. We can speculate that in the magic-number nuclei the shells are "filled." Indeed, this is the basic assumption of the shell model of the nucleus, which has been worked out in considerable quantitative detail.

The successes of the nuclear shell model include explanations of α-, β-, and γ-emission, and of the nature of the electric and magnetic fields that surround nuclei. But it does not help us to understand nuclear fission, and there are several other fundamental differences between this model and the one previously discussed. For example, the shell model accentuates definite patterns of arrangements and definite sets of energy levels, whereas the liquid-drop model envisages the nucleons in random motion. Both models have their successes, but both cannot be completely valid.

Similar situations have arisen many times with physical theory, and all are symptomatic of the same difficulty. For example, we found that the electromagnetic wave theory and the photon theory give two models for light which in many ways seem contradictory (Section 32.4), yet both are firmly based on experimental facts in their respective domains of application. In such situations, the contradictions usually disappear when we are able to develop a more general point of view that encompasses each of the special pictures as a valid consequence of the particular limited circumstances in which it serves well. One of the profound discoveries of modern physical science is that nature often exhibits a *complementarity* among the different aspects of some one fundamental phenomenon, a coexistence of seemingly divergent evidences. In the same sense, a biologist may regard man as an organism described by the laws of natural science, whereas a philosopher may regard him as an embodiment of moral principles and problems. Neither view by itself is either wrong or completely right; insofar as truth can be found in such matters, it lies in recognizing man as a being with complementary aspects.

In the case of nuclear theory, the first steps to the formulation of a more general model of the nucleus, called the *collective model*, have now been taken, for example by Aage Bohr (the son of Niels Bohr). Perhaps the main difficulty to overcome now is the enormous amount of detailed knowledge that the greatly expanded efforts of physical science have recently made available to us. There is much to be explained, and the important clues are often hidden in the camouflaging growth of interesting-looking details.

PROBLEM 39.11. Is it true in every case that capture of a slow neutron makes energy available to the nucleus? Which nuclei will get the largest amount of energy, and which the smallest amount?

PROBLEM 39.12. (a) If, in the reaction $_{92}U^{238} + _0n^1 \rightarrow _{92}U^{239} + \gamma$-photon, the kinetic energy of the captured neutron is 25 ev, what is the energy of the γ-photon? (b) $_{92}U^{239}$ decays with β-emission to form the transuranic element neptunium (Np), thence with β-emission forms plutonium. Write the symbolic expressions for these two disintegrations.

PROBLEM 39.13. Explain what you understand the term "complementarity" to mean in physical science, and illustrate its possible applicability to one or more situations outside the sciences.

39.6 Applications of nuclear physics. Reactors. The conditions under which nuclear energy can be released in practical amounts by fission were discovered in the U.S.A. during World War II by joint research of large numbers of scientists and engineers from many countries, principally Americans, Britons, and European refugees from fascism. As we have noted in Section 38.14, there were two distinct results: the *nuclear reactor* (Fig. 39.6), in which a chain reaction without multiplication allows the rate of energy release to be controlled; and the so-called *atomic bomb*, a chain reaction with rapid multiplication. In the first case, only one of the neutrons at each fission process on the average causes fission in another nucleus; in the second case, more than one neutron from each fission does so.

In the nuclear reactor, as in the bomb, the operation depends on reducing to a minimum all factors that tend to prevent neutrons from reaching

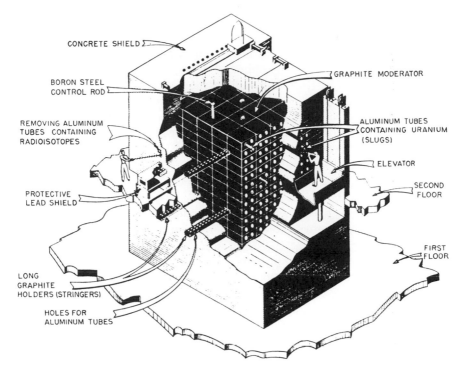

CONCRETE SHIELD

GRAPHITE MODERATOR

BORON STEEL
CONTROL ROD

REMOVING ALUMINUM
TUBES CONTAINING
RADIOISOTOPES

ALUMINUM TUBES
CONTAINING URANIUM
(SLUGS)

ELEVATOR

PROTECTIVE
LEAD SHIELD

SECOND
FLOOR

FIRST
FLOOR

LONG
GRAPHITE
HOLDERS (STRINGERS)

HOLES FOR
ALUMINUM TUBES

Fig. 39.6. Schematic diagram of a nuclear reactor for research and production of fissionable materials. The uranium "slugs" are embedded in the graphite pile behind the concrete shield. (Courtesy Atomic Energy Commission.)

the necessary number of fissionable nuclei. As a concrete example, consider separately each of the processes in a typical nuclear reactor in which the energy released by fission yields useful power (by heating a circulating liquid which operates a steam turbine generating electric power).

(a) *Neutron leakage.* We may wish to start constructing our reactor by obtaining a piece of pure, natural uranium metal. We know that the proportion of isotopes will be 99.3% U^{238} and 0.7% U^{235}, with a negligible trace (0.006%) of U^{234}. An externally supplied stream of neutrons will help to start off the fission reaction which we hope will maintain itself as a chain reaction. Fission of U^{238} and U^{235} nuclei yields, in addition to the primary fission fragments (Eq. 38.25), on the average about 2.5 neutrons each for every neutron used to induce fission. But this promising figure is deceptive. Of a given quantity of fission-produced neutrons in a typical reactor, 26.7% are lost by leakage out through the surface.

The probability that the neutron escapes is proportional to the surface area of the reactor, which is $4\pi R^2$ for a sphere. On the other hand, the probability that a neutron induces fission depends on the amount of fissionable material it can encounter in the reactor, and this in turn is a function of the volume of the reactor; for a sphere of radius R this probability is proportional to $\frac{4}{3}\pi R^3$. Thus, the larger R is, the larger is the probability of fission ($\propto R^3$) compared with the probability of escape ($\propto R^2$). Each type of reactor (including the fission bomb) has therefore a *critical size* below which maintenance of a chain reaction is not possible.

Some of the escaping neutrons can be turned back ("reflected") by surrounding the reactor with a mantle of material which serves to scatter neutrons in all directions, including backward into the reactor; graphite (pure carbon) has been used for this purpose. The remaining flux of escaping neutrons must, of course, be absorbed by protective shielding to avoid serious health hazards.

(b) *Fast neutron fission.* The neutrons released during fission of U^{235} or U^{238} nuclei emerge with average energies of about 1 or 2 Mev, corresponding to speeds of some 10,000 mi/sec. They are *fast* neutrons, about 99.3% of them emitted within perhaps 10^{-12} sec of the formation of the primary fission fragments ("prompt neutrons"), and the rest as "delayed neutrons," following on the average a few seconds later. These fast neutrons can indeed induce fission, both in U^{238} and in U^{235}, but in the typical reactor the competition of all processes for the available neutrons leaves only about 0.4% of the fast neutrons for the direct fission process in U^{238} and 0.4% more for U^{235}. At the rate of 2.5 neutrons emitted per fission, this provides for a replacement of only 2.0% of the original neutron flux. Clearly, "fast" fission is quite insufficient to provide the replacement of neutrons needed to assure a chain reaction. (However, if the content of U^{235} is increased by "enriching" the fuel in this isotope above the natural proportion of 0.7%, the relative amount of fast fission also increases.)

(c) *Nonfission capture of neutrons.* A fast neutron, just released in a fission process, is far less likely to induce fast fission in a uranium nucleus than it is to be scattered inelastically, at somewhat lower speed, or to be absorbed or "captured" by the nucleus. In a typical reactor using unenriched uranium, 30.8% of the neutrons of a given generation are likely to be so captured (10% while they are still "fast" and 20.8% at various lower speeds). Thereby $_{92}U^{235}$ nuclei are converted to $_{92}U^{236}$, and $_{92}U^{238}$ nuclei to $_{92}U^{239}$, the latter experiencing subsequent β-decay to form first $_{93}Np^{239}$ and then the fissionable nuclide $_{94}Pu^{239}$ [see Problem 39.12(b)]. U^{238} does not have a significant fission probability for neutrons below about 1 Mev, and is a particularly effective neutron absorber in the range of moderate neutron speeds corresponding to 6 ev to 100 ev energy. A resonance effect analogous to the ability of a tuning fork to absorb sound energy most effectively at the frequency to which it resonates can be thought to exist; hence the term "resonance capture" identifies this process.

The large share of neutrons so trapped without resulting in fission is the main reason why no chain reaction can be sustained in a piece of ordinary pure uranium metal, no matter how large it is. On the other hand, resonance capture is essential for producing plutonium; this will be discussed further below.

(d) *Slow neutron fission.* So far we have accounted for 58.3% of a given initial neutron flux, and have found that the replacement (by fast fission) amounts to only 2.0%. The whole operation of reactors therefore depends on an additional process: When slow neutrons encounter nuclei of U^{235}, fission is very likely to occur. E. Fermi and L. Szilard therefore proposed that the uranium "fuel" in the reactor be intermixed with a material, called a *moderator*, that serves to put obstacles in the path of the neutrons. During these collisions many of the fast fission neutrons can give up their energy safely, and so pass through the intermediate energy range in which they are prey to resonance capture. When they encounter a U^{238} nucleus at low speeds (at energies below 6 ev), they are generally merely scattered, but the slower they go, the more likely they are to cause fission in a U^{235} nucleus; 38.0% of the initial neutrons are destined to do this in a typical reactor, and thereby yield a replacement of neutrons amounting to 95.0% ($=38.0\% \times 2.5$).

From the point of view of mechanics, ordinary hydrogen (either liquefied or, more inexpensively, in ordinary water molecules) would be the most effective moderator among all the elements, for the mass of the hydrogen nucleus is most nearly that of the neutron itself, and therefore it can most effectively accept energy during collision. But hydrogen offers a considerable capture probability to neutrons by the reaction $_1H^1 + _0n^1 \rightarrow$ $_1H^2 + \gamma$-photon, and hence is useful as a moderator only if the fuel is sufficiently enriched to offset this source of neutron loss.

The larger the mass of the nucleus of the moderator, the more collisions a neutron has to make before it is "thermalized," i.e., has reached the low speed at which it retains only the energy of ordinary thermal motion of the reactor material, namely about 0.03 ev. After $_1H^1$, the nuclide $_1H^2$ is most effective as a moderator (as in "heavy water"); it does not withdraw a significant amount of neutrons by capture, but is expensive. Helium cannot be used effectively, since it is ordinarily a gas and hence not dense enough. Lithium and boron absorb neutrons very strongly. Pure carbon has been most often used as a moderator material; but it is poor structurally, absorbs neutrons a little even if prepared in very pure form, and requires a larger bulk since it takes four collisions with a nucleus of carbon before a neutron loses the same energy it would give to a nucleus of $_1H^2$ in one collision.

The reactor may be a matrix of graphite blocks in which rods of uranium metals are distributed as in Fig. 39.7 (hence the original name "pile" for

FIG. 39.7. The loading face of the Oak Ridge reactor X-10 (compare with Fig. 39.6). Uranium slugs in the tubes can be pushed out for chemical processing on the other side of the reactor. (Courtesy Oak Ridge National Laboratory.)

the whole structure). Other reactors consist of uranium rods inside a tank containing a liquid moderator. These are examples of "heterogeneous" reactors. In "homogeneous" reactors, a suitable compound containing uranium is dissolved or suspended in a liquid moderator.

PROBLEM 39.14. (a) Explain why neutrons are slowed down very effectively by a moderator of ordinary water, and why heavy water and graphite are less effective. (b) A "thermal neutron" is one having an average energy of about 0.025 ev at ordinary temperatures. Calculate roughly how many collisions a 1.0-Mev neutron would have to make (1) with protons and (2) with carbon nuclei, to be left with thermal energy. (c) What happens to the speed of a "thermalized" neutron if it continues to collide with nuclei of the moderator?

(e) *Other capture of neutrons.* Previous fission products, the structural material of the reactor, and the moderator are all traps for neutrons; they may account for 2.7% of the initial flux.

The capture of neutrons by impurities in the reactor material must of course be kept as low as possible, and for this reason the fission fragments have to be removed from time to time. (Most of the nearly 200 artificially produced nuclides are radioactive, and these "ashes" provide a useful supply of materials, for research as well as industrial and medical applications.) However, for control of the rate of fission and for the occasional complete shutdown of the reactor, special *control rods* containing such neutron-absorbing material as boron or cadmium may be pushed into the structure as required.

(f) *Fission of neutron capture products.* The nuclide Pu^{239}, produced in the reactor by nonfission capture of neutrons by U^{238}, is itself fissionable. This fuel, bred in the reactor, can itself contribute to the chain reaction; in a typical case, it accounts for the capture of 1.0% of the initial flux and so contributes about 3.0% of the next generation of neutrons, the average number of neutrons released in the fission of Pu^{239} being 3.0.

The data given above permit setting up a budget for the neutrons, showing on the one hand what share of the initial number each process takes, and on the other hand how many new neutrons are produced. The ratio of these two quantities is the effective "multiplication factor" or "reproduction constant" for the reactor. Clearly it has to be 1.00 if the chain reaction is to be maintained at an even rate, as was assumed in the example on which the figures above were based. Such a reactor is termed "critical." For ratios above and below 1.00 the corresponding terms are "supercritical" and "subcritical."

The products of an operating nuclear reactor are of three types: heat, neutrons and radiation, and fission fragments and fissionable material.

The quantity of *heat* produced can be very great and, if not removed by a cooling system, may destroy a reactor. This removed heat can be converted to obtain electrical or mechanical energy; thus it can produce steam for driving a turbine coupled with an electric generator, or can be used for the propulsion of ships, submarines, perhaps large aircraft, and eventually space vehicles.

The *neutrons and radiation* (mainly γ-photons) that are produced in the reactor may escape, presenting a grave health hazard unless thick and massive shielding, usually of concrete, is used to protect the operators. However, many reactors are provided with special channels through the shielding so that streams of well-defined neutrons are obtainable for monitoring and research purposes. Materials can be exposed to neutrons

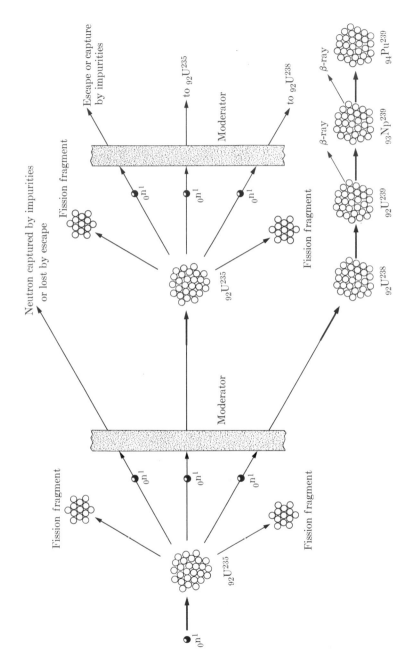

FIG. 39.8. Schematic diagram of main events in chain reaction in uranium, as in a nuclear reactor.

inside the reactor, to induce changes in structure or to manufacture radioactive nuclides. As a source of neutrons, the reactor far surpasses any other, and has made possible many important experiments and practical uses.

Most of the *products resulting from fission* are radioactive. Thus in an operating reactor a great many nuclear species coexist, some of them unobtainable otherwise. The production of $_{94}Pu^{239}$ by the capture by $_{92}U^{238}$ of slow neutrons has been mentioned. Like $_{92}U^{235}$, plutonium $_{94}Pu^{239}$ is fissionable with both slow and fast neutrons, and has two big advantages over the former: first, being derived from the 140-times more plentiful isotope $_{92}U^{238}$, plutonium is potentially available in much larger quantities than the scarce isotope $_{92}U^{235}$; second, it is chemically different from uranium and thus, if required in pure form, can be separated from the parent element by relatively straightforward chemical processes, whereas the separation of $_{92}U^{235}$ from uranium containing mostly $_{92}U^{238}$ is difficult and slow, requiring a physical process such as diffusion.

The first nuclear reactor was put into use in the United States on December 2, 1942, by a research team under the direction of Enrico Fermi. At the time it was feared that the relatively small world supply of $_{92}U^{235}$, on which the operation of the reactor depended, would preclude the long-range use of nuclear energy on a large scale. But in 1953 the United States Atomic Energy Commission announced a far-reaching development: the design of a special reactor in which more $_{94}Pu^{239}$ is produced than the amount of $_{92}U^{235}$ or $_{94}Pu^{239}$ needed to keep the reactor going.

This process, in which large amounts of energy still continue to be released, is called *breeding of nuclear fuel*. It results when for every fission of $_{92}U^{235}$ or $_{94}Pu^{239}$, more than one of the resulting neutrons, on the average, will be captured by $_{92}U^{238}$, thus leading to the formation of $_{94}Pu^{239}$. It is as though a motor car could not only transport its load, but also produce more fuel than it consumes during the trip. Thus the expected shortage of $_{92}U^{235}$ is now less of a problem, and the way is open for the exploitation of nuclear energy on a large scale, particularly for nonmilitary uses.

Breeder reactors have become even more promising through the discovery that the plentiful thorium isotope $_{90}Th^{232}$ can capture neutrons and undergo two successive β-decays to become $_{92}U^{233}$. This uranium isotope, not found in nature, turns out to be quite as fissionable as $_{92}U^{235}$ (see Problem 39.10). A quantity of $_{90}Th^{232}$ introduced into a reactor will make possible the production of fissionable $_{92}U^{233}$.

39.7 Military and nonmilitary applications. The *nuclear fission bomb*, commonly but less accurately called the "atomic bomb," relies on a fast chain reaction in pure fissionable material. The mass of material necessary is said to be of the order of magnitude of several pounds, but the associated equipment, for example the triggering mechanism, may add much to the total weight and size. As in the controlled reactor, no chain reaction occurs unless the fissionable material is assembled in a quantity equal to or larger than a certain critical size. Presumably, therefore, the bomb is exploded by suddenly bringing together two or more subcritical pieces to form one larger piece. An envelope of a nonfissionable material may act as a "tamper," that is, serve to scatter back escaping neutrons and also to hold together the exploding mass long enough to permit the reaction to spread throughout the bomb. The energy explosively released by the largest of these bombs has been compared to more than 500,000 tons of TNT; the flash of one of the test blasts was seen more than 1000 miles away. This bespeaks of a many-fold increase of effectiveness over the very first test bomb (in New Mexico, July 16, 1945) and the two bombs that were reported to have killed and wounded 190,000 human beings in Hiroshima and Nagasaki, Japan, near the end of World War II. Apart from this fearful weapon, other fission weapons have been under development, specifically nuclear artillery shells.

The *hydrogen bomb*, or "H-bomb," a weapon that relies on thermonuclear reactions, has been mentioned in Section 38.15. These nuclear fusion bombs have even more dreadful potentiality for destruction than have the fission bombs, for there may be no upper limit to their size. With ordinary fission bombs, little is added to their effect by making them much larger than the critical size, for the violence of the explosion tends to disperse the fissionable material located at the outer portions before it can participate in an efficient chain reaction. On the other hand, radioactive fall-out is a necessary consequence of fission rather than fusion weapons. One of the most abundant and long-lived products of the fission of U^{235} and Pu^{239} is strontium-90 ($_{38}Sr^{90}$), which, being chemically like calcium, finds its way to the bone when ingested as food contamination. There, strontium-90 decays to $_{39}Y^{90}$ by emission of 0.6-Mev β-particles (half-life = 28 years). If present in large quantities, the radiation can cause somatic damage in the body, particularly in growing children (e.g., leukemia, bone tumor). As with all other high-energy radiations, there exists here also the danger of harmful genetic effects due to the increase of mutation rate of cells in the presence of radiation; for this effect there is no threshold below which radiation is too weak to affect the rate of mutation.

Both for research in biology and for setting safety standards, the concept of *radiation dosage* is of greatest interest. The quantity of any radioactive material undergoing 3.70×10^{10} disintegrations per second is termed 1 *curie* (1 c); this is virtually the number of radioactive disintegrations per second in a 1.00-gm sample of pure radium. With respect to somatic effects the maximum permissible body content of Sr^{90} is believed to be at most 1 microcurie (1 μc).

PROBLEM 39.15. To locate brain tumors, use can be made of the selective absorption of the artificially prepared radioisotope $_{15}P^{32}$ by the tumor. If a dosage of five millicuries of P^{32} (half-life = 14.3 days) is administered intravenously to a patient, and if the tumor tissue absorbs 2% of the material selectively, how many disintegrations per second will occur in the whole diseased tissue three days after administration? (Thus, a counter can guide the surgeon.)

Another aspect of dosage is not, as above, the number of disintegrations which are responsible for radiation, but rather the energy absorbed by the body from the radiation which passes into it. The quantity of x- or γ-radiation which produces by ionization 1 statcoulomb of positive or negative electric charge in 1 cm^3 of dry air at 0°C and 1 atm is called 1 roentgen (1 r); it has been found to produce 2.08×10^9 pairs of ions in 1.00 cm^3 of air under the stated conditions. Since the density of air is 0.00129 gm/cm^3, this corresponds to 1.61×10^{12} ion pairs in 1 gm of air. At the experimentally determined rate of 33.5 ev energy lost per ion pair produced, 1.00 r corresponds to 86.0 ergs or 8.60×10^{-6} j energy absorbed from the passing radiation. For convenience, the new unit *rad* has been proposed, where 1 rad is the absorbed quantity of any ionizing radiation which liberates 100 ergs (10^{-5} j) of energy per gram of absorbing material; we note that for x- and γ-radiation 1 r is approximately 1 rad.

Not surprisingly, these units of physical dosage of absorbed radiation do not tell the whole story of biological effect, for different radiations have different biological effectiveness on, say, the metabolism of the cell. For example, one gram of human tissue absorbs about as much energy from x- or γ-radiation as 1 gm of air, but when the same amount of energy is released in 1 gm of tissue by fast neutron radiation, the biological effectiveness is 10 times that of the x- or γ-radiation; for thermal (slow) neutrons, the corresponding factor is about 5, and for α-particles it is 10 to 20. To assess the full effect on living persons, dosage is therefore often specified in the units of *rem* (roentgen equivalent, man), where for fast neutrons 1 rad = 10 rem, for thermal neutrons 1 rad = 5 rem, for α-particles 1 rad = 10 to 20 rem, for β-radiation (as for x- and γ-radiation) 1 rad = 1 rem.

PROBLEM 39.16. During one year, a person may receive the following dosages from radiation: 0.04 rad from cosmic rays (largely γ-radiation); 0.06 rad from natural radioactivity in the earth and surroundings (largely β- and γ-radiation, since α-radiation is absorbed by a few centimeters travel in air); 0.02 rad natural radioactivity of potassium (K^{40}) and carbon (C^{14}) in the human body (β- and γ-radiation); 0.04 rad (β- and γ-radiation) from the luminous dial of his wrist watch containing 1 μc of radium; and 0.003 rad from fall-out (mainly β-radiation) of past weapons tests. Find (a) the total energy absorbed by an average adult owing to these radiations, (b) the total annual dosage in rems.

Research has shown that the maximum permissible dose of radiation from all sources for the *general population* should be substantially less than used to be thought in the past. There being no clear threshold for genetic effects of radiation, and in view of the cumulative nature of the damage, the following standards are now generally considered reasonable: no more than 0.5 rem in any year, and no more than 0.1 rem in any one week. For specialists working with radiation and for persons undergoing medical therapy, specific higher permissible dosages have been allowed under controlled conditions.

As for further *nonmilitary uses of nuclear energy*, these will undoubtedly in the long run overshadow the military uses. We have mentioned the adaptability of nuclear reactors as energy sources for ship engines and possibly space vehicles. In stationary installations, reactors should be particularly useful in localities where other fuels are expensive and energy is needed on a large scale.

But the consequences of research on nuclear energy reach into practically every field of science; a few examples will speak for thousands of cases. Impressive advances in biology are being made with the aid of radioactive isotopes (radioisotopes) obtained either by subjecting nonradioactive elements to neutron bombardment in a reactor or by extracting them from fission products. With the Geiger counter we can accurately follow the course of minute quantities of such *isotopic tracers*, or "tagged atoms," and so study the role of various chemical substances in the metabolism of plants and animals. Agricultural experiments with fertilizers containing radioactive isotopes have shown at what point in the growth of a plant the fertilizer is most needed. A good attack is being made with tracers on the puzzle of micronutrients, the vanishingly small quantities of elements that are essential for the well-being of plants and animals. In chemistry, radioisotopes help in the determination of the details of chemical reactions and the structures of complex molecules.

Perhaps the most rewarding consequence of nuclear-energy developments has been the immensely beneficial role of radioisotopes in medical research, diagnosis, and therapy. For example, tracers can help to find the rate of flow of blood through the heart or to the limbs, thus aiding in the diagnosis of abnormal conditions. Because some parts of the body tend to take up particular elements preferentially, specially prepared radioactive isotopes of such elements can be administered to the victims of certain diseases, thus producing the desired radioactive emissions right at the site of the disease for the control of leukemia, polycythemia, and some thyroid cancers, or aiding the surgeon or diagnostician (see Problem 39.15 and Figure 39.9).

Table 39.1 summarizes the uses of a few radioisotopes, most of them produced with the aid of nuclear reactors. It is such uses that best symbolize the great promise of nuclear energy for the future. Indeed, they dramatize the meaning of science at its best: *research in science lays open to our understanding the secrets of nature, and the applications of this knowledge to problems of scientific interest and human needs can benefit all mankind.*

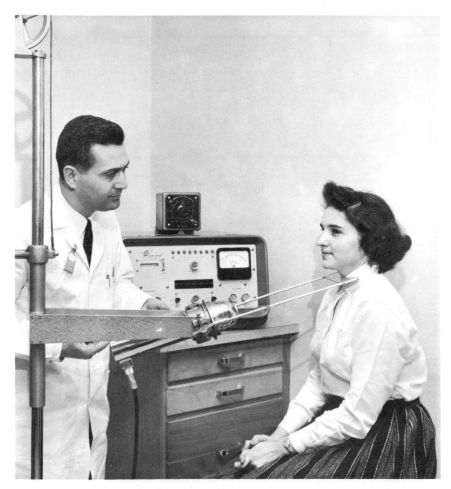

FIG. 39.9. Medical use of artificially prepared radioactive isotopes. A day previously, the patient received a tracer dose of radioactive iodine I^{131} which decays with β- and γ-emission with a half-life of 8.04 days. The amount of this nuclide remaining in the thyroid gland in the neck of the patient is being determined with a counter tube in front of the patient, kept at a fixed distance by the two-pronged spacer. The "percentage uptake" of radioactive iodine can be calculated, and determines whether the thyroid gland is functioning normally or abnormally. (Courtesy Dr. H. A. Selenkow; photograph by Harvard News Office.)

Table 39.1. Representative uses of artificially prepared radioisotopes. [Based on Blackwood, Osgood, and Ruark, *An outline of atomic physics* (Wiley, 1955), p. 402].

Isotope	Half-life	Important uses
$_1H^3$	11 yr	Used as a tag in organic substances.
$_6C^{14}$	4700 yr	Used as a tag in studying the synthesis of many organic substances. When $_6C^{14}$ is incorporated in food material, the metabolic products of the organism are marked with it.
$_{11}Na^{24}$	15 hr	Useful in a wide variety of biochemical investigations because of its solubility and chemical properties.
$_{15}P^{32}$	14 days	For the study of bone metabolism, the treatment of blood diseases, and the specific uptake in tumor tissue.
$_{16}S^{35}$	87 days	Has numerous chemical and industrial applications.
$_{27}Co^{60}$	5.3 yr	Because of its intense γ-emission, may be used as a low-cost substitute for radium in radiography and therapy.
$_{53}I^{131}$	8 days	For the study of thyroid metabolism and the treatment of thyroid diseases.

ADDITIONAL PROBLEMS

39.17. Recent figures indicate that the installations for producing electric power in the United States have a combined capacity of about 10^9 kw, that is, 10^{12} j/sec. (a) If one central plant were to provide this power by direct conversion of nuclear energy into electrical energy, what mass of nuclear "fuel" would be converted per day? (b) If only 0.08% of the material employed were converted in this process, what total mass of material would have to be handled per year?

39.18. How is the principle of conservation of momentum to be formulated in relativistic mechanics?

39.19. Use Figs. 39.3 and 39.4 to determine whether each of the following reactions is endothermic or exothermic (but indicate where these two curves do not give enough data to answer the question):

(a) $_5B^{11} + _1H^1 \rightarrow _2He^4 + _2He^4 + _2He^4$;

(b) $_8O^{18} + _1H^1 \rightarrow _9F^{18} + _0n^1$;

(c) $_7N^{14} + _0n^1 \rightarrow _6C^{14} + _1H^1$;

(d) $_5B^{10} + _0n^1 \rightarrow _3Li^7 + _2He^4$;

(e) $_{13}Al^{27} + \gamma\text{-photon} \rightarrow _{11}Na^{24} + _1H^1 + _1H^1 + _0n^1$;

(f) $_{16}S^{32} + _0n^1 \rightarrow _{15}P^{32} + _1H^1$;

(g) $_{92}U^{238} + _0n^1 \rightarrow _{92}U^{239} + \gamma\text{-photon}$;

(h) $_3Li^6 + _0n^1 \rightarrow _1H^3 + _2He^4$.

39.20. In 1934 J. Chadwick and M. Goldhaber used γ-photons from $_{81}Tl^{208}$ (ThC″), for which the energy $h\nu$ is 2.62 Mev, to disintegrate deuterons. They found the total kinetic energy of the released proton and neutron to be 0.45 Mev. (a) What is the value for the binding energy of the deuteron on the basis of this experiment? (b) Compare this value with that computed from the mass defect of deuterons.

39.21. (a) Given that the value of Q for the reaction in Eq. (38.25) is 3.2×10^{-11} j, show that 8.2×10^{13} j of energy would be released by the complete fission of 1 kgm of $_{92}U^{235}$. (b) If 1 kgm of TNT can release 4×10^6 j of energy, how much TNT would be needed to provide as much energy as is released by the complete fission of 1 kgm of $_{92}U^{235}$? (c) How much coal having a heat of combustion of 3×10^7 j/kgm would have to be burned to provide a like amount of energy?

39.22. In the breeder reactor described in Section 39.6, both energy and more fuel is obtained. Does one thereby "get something for nothing"? Is any law of physics violated?

SUPPLEMENTARY READING

ASME NUCLEAR ENERGY GLOSSARY COMMITTEE, *A glossary of terms in nuclear science and technology* (American Society of Mechanical Engineers and National Research Council, 1957).

BLÜH, O., and J. D. ELDER, *Principles and applications of physics* (Interscience Publishers, 1955), Chap. 31.

COOK, J. M., *Radioactivity and nuclear physics* (Van Nostrand, 3rd edition, 1957).

DUNNING, J. R., "Atomic structure and energy" and "The future of atomic energy," *American Scientist*, v. 37, no. 4 (1949) and v. 38, no. 1 (1950).

EDITORS OF SCIENTIFIC AMERICAN MAGAZINE, *Atomic power* (Simon and Schuster, 1955).

GAMOW, G., *Atomic energy in cosmic and human life* (Cambridge University Press, 1947); *The birth and death of the sun* (Viking, 1940); *The creation of the universe* (Viking, 1952).

HALLIDAY, D., *Introductory nuclear physics* (Wiley, 1950, 1955).

KAPLAN, I., *Nuclear physics* (Addison-Wesley, 1955).

LAPP, R. E., and H. L. ANDREWS, *Nuclear radiation physics* (Prentice Hall, 1948, 1954).

OLDENBERG, O., *Introduction to atomic physics* (McGraw-Hill, 1954), Chaps. 18 and 19.

POLLARD, E. C., and W. L. DAVIDSON, *Applied nuclear physics* (Wiley, 2nd edition, 1951).

SEMAT, H., *Introduction to atomic and nuclear physics* (Rinehart, 1954), Part 3.

SMYTH, H. D., *A general account of the development of methods of using atomic energy* . . . (Superintendent of Documents, U. S. Government Printing Office, Washington, D. C., 1945). The famous report on the development of the nuclear fission bomb in the U.S.A.

APPENDIXES

APPENDIX A

FUNDAMENTAL CONSTANTS

Largely based on values in the *American Institute of Physics Handbook* (1957). The probable error for each value has been omitted here; it should properly be considered part of the datum.

Name of Quantity	Symbol	Value
Velocity of light in vacuum	c	2.9979×10^8 m/sec
Charge of electron	q_e	-1.602×10^{-19} coul = -4.803×10^{-10} statcoul
Rest mass of electron	m_e	9.108×10^{-31} kgm
Ratio of charge to mass of electron	q_e/m_e	1.759×10^{11} coul/kgm = 5.273×10^7 statcoul/gm
Planck's constant	h	6.625×10^{-34} j·sec
Boltzmann's constant	k	1.380×10^{-23} j/°K
Avogadro's number (chemical scale)	N_0	6.023×10^{23} molecules/mole
Universal gas constant (chemical scale)	R	8.314 j/mole·°K
Mechanical equivalent of heat	J	4.185×10^3 j/kcal
Standard atmospheric pressure	1 atm	1.013×10^5 new/m²
Volume of ideal gas at 0°C and 1 atm (chemical scale)		22.415 liter/mole
Absolute zero of temperature	0°K	-273.16°C
Acceleration due to gravity (sea level, at equator)		9.78049 m/sec²
Universal gravitational constant	G	6.673×10^{-11} new·m²/kgm²
Mass of earth	m_E	5.975×10^{24} kgm
Mean radius of earth		6.371×10^6 m = 3959 mi
Equatorial radius of earth		6.378×10^6 m = 3963 mi
Mean distance from earth to sun	1 AU	1.49×10^{11} m = 9.29×10^7 mi
Eccentricity of earth's orbit		0.0167
Mean distance from earth to moon		3.84×10^8 m $\doteq$ 60 earth radii
Diameter of sun		1.39×10^9 m = 8.64×10^5 mi
Mass of sun	m_S	1.99×10^{30} kgm = 333,000 × mass of earth
Coulomb's law constant	C	8.98×10^9 new·m²/coul²
Faraday's constant (1 faraday)	F	96,500 coul/mole
Mass of neutral hydrogen atom	m_{H^1}	1.008142 amu
Mass of proton	m_p	1.007593 amu
Mass of neutron	m_n	1.008982 amu

FUNDAMENTAL CONSTANTS—*Continued*

Name of Quantity	Symbol	Value
Mass of electron	m_e	5.488×10^{-4} amu
Ratio of mass of proton to mass of electron	m_p/m_e	1836.12
Rydberg constant for nucleus of infinite mass	R_∞	109,737 cm^{-1}
Rydberg constant for hydrogen	R_H	109,678 cm^{-1}
Wien displacement law constant		0.2898 cm·°K

Numerical constants: $\pi = 3.142$; $e = 2.718$; $\sqrt{2} = 1.414$; $\sqrt{3} = 1.732$

APPENDIX B

CONVERSION FACTORS

LENGTH

1 meter: 1.000×10^{-3} km, 100.0 cm, 1000 mm, 6.214×10^{-4} mi, 1.094 yd, 3.281 ft, 39.37 in

1 kilometer: 1.000×10^3 m

1 centimeter: 1.000×10^{-2} m

1 angstrom unit: 1.000×10^{-10} m

1 micron: 1.000×10^{-6} m

1 inch: 2.540×10^{-2} m

1 foot: 0.3048 m

1 yard: 0.9144 m

1 mile: 1609 m

1 light-year: 9.464×10^{15} m

AREA

1 square meter: 1.000×10^4 cm^2, 10.76 ft^2, 1.550×10^3 in^2

1 square inch: 6.452×10^{-4} m^2

1 square foot: 0.0929 m^2

1 square yard: 0.8361 m^2

1 square mile: 2.590×10^6 m^2

VOLUME

1 cubic meter: 1.000×10^6 cm^3, 35.31 ft^3, 6.102×10^4 in^3, 264.2 gallons (U.S.)

1 cubic inch: 1.639×10^{-5} m^3

1 cubic foot: 0.02832 m^3

1 liter: 1.000×10^3 cm^3, 1.000×10^{-3} m^3, 0.2642 gallon (U.S.)

SPEED

1 meter per second: 0.3728 mi/min, 3.281 ft/sec, 196.8 ft/min, 3.600 km/hr

1 foot per second: 0.3048 m/sec

1 mile per minute: 88.00 ft/sec, 26.82 m/sec

1 mile per hour: 1.467 ft/sec, 0.4470 m/sec

ACCELERATION

1 meter per second, per second: 3.281 ft/sec^2, 2.237 mi/hr·sec

1 foot per second, per second: 0.3048 m/sec^2

1 mile per hour, per second: 0.4470 m/sec^2

FORCE

1 newton: 1.000×10^5 dynes, 0.2247 lbf, 7.233 pdl

1 pound-force: 4.448 new, 32.17 pdl

1 poundal: 0.1383 new, 0.03108 lbf

Mass

1 kilogram: 1.000×10^3 gm, 2.205 lb, 0.0685 slug, 6.0248×10^{26} amu
1 pound: 0.4536 kgm, 0.0311 slug
1 atomic mass unit (physical scale): 1.65980×10^{-27} kgm

Pressure

1 atmosphere: 1.013×10^5 new/m^2, 14.70 lbf/in^2, 472.7 pdl/in^2

Energy

1 joule (abs.): 1.000×10^7 ergs, 1.000 new·m, 2.389×10^{-4} kcal, 23.73 ft·pdl
1 electron volt: 1.602×10^{-19} j, 1.074×10^{-9} amu
1 atomic mass unit (physical scale): 1.492×10^{-10} j, 931.1 Mev

Electric Charge

1 coulomb (absolute): 2.998×10^9 statcoul (esu)
1 statcoulomb (esu): 3.336×10^{-10} coul

Greek Letter Symbols

A	α	Alpha	N	ν	Nu
B	β	Beta	Ξ	ξ	Xi
Γ	γ	Gamma	O	o	Omicron
Δ	δ	Delta	Π	π	Pi
E	ϵ	Epsilon	P	ρ	Rho
Z	ζ	Zeta	Σ	σ	Sigma
H	η	Eta	T	τ	Tau
Θ	θ	Theta	Y	υ	Upsilon
I	ι	Iota	Φ	ϕ	Phi
K	κ	Kappa	X	χ	Chi
Λ	λ	Lambda	Ψ	ψ	Psi
M	μ	Mu	Ω	ω	Omega

APPENDIX C

ALPHABETIC LIST OF THE ELEMENTS

Element	Symbol	Atomic number Z	Element	Symbol	Atomic number Z
Actinium	Ac	89	Holmium	Ho	67
Aluminum	Al	13	Hydrogen	H	1
Americium	Am	95	Indium	In	49
Antimony	Sb	51	Iodine	I	53
Argon	A	18	Iridium	Ir	77
Arsenic	As	33	Iron	Fe	26
Astatine	At	85	Krypton	Kr	36
Barium	Ba	56	Lanthanum	La	57
Berkelium	Bk	97	Lead	Pb	82
Beryllium	Be	4	Lithium	Li	3
Bismuth	Bi	83	Lutetium	Lu	71
Boron	B	5	Magnesium	Mg	12
Bromine	Br	35	Manganese	Mn	25
Cadmium	Cd	48	Mendelevium	Md	101
Calcium	Ca	20	Mercury	Hg	80
Californium	Cf	98	Molybdenum	Mo	42
Carbon	C	6	Neodymium	Nd	60
Cerium	Ce	58	Neon	Ne	10
Cesium	Cs	55	Neptunium	Np	93
Chlorine	Cl	17	Nickel	Ni	28
Chromium	Cr	24	Niobium	Nb	41
Cobalt	Co	27	Nitrogen	N	7
Copper	Cu	29	Nobelium	No	102
Curium	Cm	96	Osmium	Os	76
Dysprosium	Dy	66	Oxygen	O	8
Einsteinium	E	99	Palladium	Pd	46
Erbium	Er	68	Phosphorus	P	15
Europium	Eu	63	Platinum	Pt	78
Fermium	Fm	100	Plutonium	Pu	94
Fluorine	F	9	Polonium	Po	84
Francium	Fr	87	Potassium	K	19
Gadolinium	Gd	64	Praseodymium	Pr	59
Gallium	Ga	31	Promethium	Pm	61
Germanium	Ge	32	Protactinium	Pa	91
Gold	Au	79	Radium	Ra	88
Hafnium	Hf	72	Radon	Rn	86
Helium	He	2	Rhenium	Re	75

ALPHABETIC LIST OF THE ELEMENTS—*Continued*

Element	Symbol	Atomic number Z	Element	Symbol	Atomic number Z
Rhodium	Rh	45	Terbium	Tb	65
Rubidium	Rb	37	Thallium	Tl	81
Ruthenium	Ru	44	Thorium	Th	90
Samarium	Sm	62	Thulium	Tm	69
Scandium	Sc	21	Tin	Sn	50
Selenium	Se	34	Titanium	Ti	22
Silicon	Si	14	Tungsten	W	74
Silver	Ag	47	Uranium	U	92
Sodium	Na	11	Vanadium	V	23
Strontium	Sr	38	Xenon	Xe	54
Sulfur	S	16	Ytterbium	Yb	70
Tantalum	Ta	73	Yttrium	Y	39
Technetium	Tc	43	Zinc	Zn	30
Tellurium	Te	52	Zirconium	Zr	40

PERIODIC TABLE OF THE ELEMENTS.

Atomic weights are based on the most recent values adopted by the International Union of Chemistry. (For artificially produced elements, the approximate atomic weight of the most stable isotope is given in brackets.) The full names of the elements are given in Appendix C.

Group→		I	II	III	IV	V	VI	VII	VIII			O
Period	Series											
1	1	1 H 1.0080										2 He 4.003
2	2	3 Li 6.940	4 Be 9.013	5 B 10.82	6 C 12.011	7 N 14.008	8 O 16.0000	9 F 19.00				10 Ne 20.183
3	3	11 Na 22.991	12 Mg 24.32	13 Al 26.98	14 Si 28.09	15 P 30.975	16 S 32.066	17 Cl 35.457				18 A 39.944
4	4	19 K 39.100	20 Ca 40.08	21 Sc 44.96	22 Ti 47.90	23 V 50.95	24 Cr 52.01	25 Mn 54.94	26 Fe 55.85	27 Co 58.94	28 Ni 58.71	
	5	29 Cu 63.54	30 Zn 65.38	31 Ga 69.72	32 Ge 72.60	33 As 74.91	34 Se 78.96	35 Br 79.916				36 Kr 83.80
5	6	37 Rb 85.48	38 Sr 87.63	39 Y 88.92	40 Zr 91.22	41 Nb 92.91	42 Mo 95.95	43 Tc [99]	44 Ru 101.1	45 Rh 102.91	46 Pd 106.4	
	7	47 Ag 107.880	48 Cd 112.41	49 In 114.82	50 Sn 118.70	51 Sb 121.76	52 Te 127.61	53 I 126.91				54 Xe 131.30
6	8	55 Cs 132.91	56 Ba 137.36	57–71 Lanthanide series*	72 Hf 178.50	73 Ta 180.95	74 W 183.86	75 Re 186.22	76 Os 190.2	77 Ir 192.2	78 Pt 195.09	
	9	79 Au 197.0	80 Hg 200.61	81 Tl 204.39	82 Pb 207.21	83 Bi 209.00	84 Po 210	85 At [210]				86 Rn 222
7	10	87 Fr [223]	88 Ra 226.05	89– Actinide series**								

*Lanthanide series:

57 La 138.92	58 Ce 140.13	59 Pr 140.92	60 Nd 144.27	61 Pm [147]	62 Sm 150.35	63 Eu 152.0	64 Gd 157.26	65 Tb 158.93	66 Dy 162.51	67 Ho 164.94	68 Er 167.27	69 Tm 168.94	70 Yb 173.04	71 Lu 174.99

**Actinide series:

89 Ac 227	90 Th 232.05	91 Pa 231	92 U 238.07	93 Np [237]	94 Pu [242]	95 Am [243]	96 Cm [245]	97 Bk [249]	98 Cf [249]	99 E [253]	100 Fm [255]	101 Md [256]	102 No	103

SUMMARY OF SOME TRIGONOMETRIC RELATIONS

(1) **Right triangles:** (a) The sum of the angles in any plane triangle being 180°, and angle γ in Fig. A.1 being 90°, it follows that $\alpha + \beta = 90°$.
(b) By the Pythagorean theorem, $c^2 = a^2 + b^2$.

(2) **Definitions:** We can *define* six functions of any one angle in a right triangle, namely sine (sin), cosine (cos), tangent (tan), cotangent (cot), secant (sec), and cosecant (cosec). Specifically,

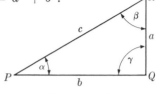

FIGURE A.1

$$\sin \alpha = \frac{\text{opposite side}}{\text{hypotenuse}} = \frac{a}{c}, \qquad \cos \alpha = \frac{\text{adjacent side}}{\text{hypotenuse}} = \frac{b}{c},$$

$$\tan \alpha = \frac{a}{b}, \qquad \cot \alpha = \frac{b}{a}, \qquad \sec \alpha = \frac{c}{b}, \qquad \cosec \alpha = \frac{c}{a}.$$

(For the first three functions, these numerical values are given in Appendix F.) It follows directly from these definitions that

(a) $\tan \alpha = \dfrac{\sin \alpha}{\cos \alpha}, \qquad \cot \alpha = \dfrac{\cos \alpha}{\sin \alpha} = \dfrac{1}{\tan \alpha}, \qquad \sec \alpha = \dfrac{1}{\cos \alpha},$

$$\cosec \alpha = \frac{1}{\sin \alpha};$$

therefore only the sine and cosine functions of an angle need be discussed in detail.

(b) $\sin^2 \alpha = (\sin \alpha)^2 = \dfrac{a^2}{c^2}, \qquad \cos^2 \alpha = (\cos \alpha)^2 = \dfrac{b^2}{c^2};$

thus,

$$\sin^2 \alpha + \cos^2 \alpha = \frac{a^2 + b^2}{c^2} = 1$$

by the Pythagorean theorem.

(c) Because $\sin \beta = b/c$, $\cos \beta = a/c$, and so on,

$$\sin \alpha = \cos \beta, \qquad\qquad \cos \alpha = \sin \beta,$$

$$\sin \alpha = \cos (90 - \alpha), \qquad \cos \alpha = \sin (90 - \alpha).$$

EXAMPLE 1. In a right triangle ($\gamma = 90°$), $\alpha = 35°$, length $b = 4.0$ cm; what is length a?

$\tan \alpha = a/b$, therefore $a = b \tan \alpha = 4.0 \times 0.700 = 2.8$ cm.

EXAMPLE 2. In a right triangle, $a = 8.3$ cm, $c = 21$ cm; what are α and β?

$$\sin \alpha = \frac{a}{c} = \frac{8.3}{21} = 0.395.$$

As seen in Appendix F, this value lies between $\sin 23° = 0.391$ and $\sin 24° = 0.407$. But

$$\frac{0.395 - 0.391}{0.407 - 0.391} = \frac{0.004}{0.016} = \frac{1}{4}.$$

Thus angle α is (roughly) $\frac{1}{4}$ of $1°$ larger than $23°$, or $23° \, 15'$. And $\beta = 90° - \alpha = 66° \, 45'$.

(3) We can define the same trigonometric functions for any angle, even for an angle not in a triangle but enclosed between an inclined line and the horizontal (Fig. A.2). If r is the length of the line and (x,y) the x- and y-coordinates of its end point P, the other end being at the origin of the coordinate system, then

$$\sin \theta = \frac{y}{r}, \qquad \cos \theta = \frac{x}{r}, \qquad \tan \theta = \frac{y}{x}.$$

By convention, θ is measured counterclockwise from the right (positive) segment of the abscissa.

(4) If θ is larger than $90°$, its trigonometric functions are defined as before; for example, $\sin \theta = y/r$:

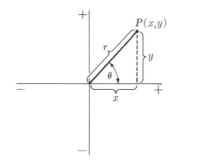

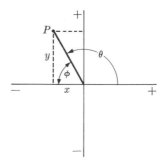

FIGURE A.2   FIGURE A.3

(a) $\theta = 90°$ to $180°$ (Fig. A.3). Note that x has a negative value, being on the left side of the x-y coordinate system, or in the second quadrant. Thus

$$\cos \theta = \frac{x}{r} = -\cos \phi = -\cos (180° - \theta),$$

$$\sin \theta = \frac{y}{r} = \sin \phi = \sin (180° - \theta).$$

(b) $\theta = 180°$ to $270°$ (Fig. A.4); $\phi = \theta - 180°$. Both x and y have negative values:

$$\sin \theta = -\sin \phi = -\sin (\theta - 180°),$$

$$\cos \theta = -\cos \phi = -\cos (\theta - 180°).$$

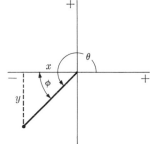

FIGURE A.4   FIGURE A.5

(c) $\theta = 270°$ to $360°$ (Fig. A.5); $\phi = 360° - \theta$. Now y has a negative value, x a positive one:

$$\sin \theta = -\sin \phi = -\sin (360° - \theta),$$

$$\cos \theta = \cos \phi = \cos (360° - \theta).$$

These relations show that trigonometric tables computed for the range $0°$ to $90°$ will serve for all angles.

EXAMPLE 3. To find $\sin \theta$ and $\tan \theta$ if $\theta = 295°$. Note that θ is between $270°$ and $360°$: $\sin \theta = -\sin (360° - \theta) = -\sin 65° = -0.906$; $\tan \theta = \sin \theta / \cos \theta = -0.906/0.423 = -2.15$.

(5) **General triangles:** Even when a triangle does not have a right angle, as in Fig. A.6, there still exist several simple relations between the sides and the angles.

(a) *Law of cosines:* The square of any one side is equal to the sum of the squares of the other two sides minus twice the product of those two and the cosine of their included angle. For example,

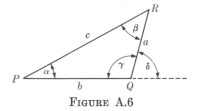

$$c^2 = a^2 + b^2 - 2ab \cos \gamma.$$

Thus one may find one side in terms of two others and one angle, or one angle in terms of three sides. Because the complementary angle $\delta = 180 - \gamma$, and $\cos \delta = \cos (180 - \gamma) = -\cos \gamma$, we may write

$$c^2 = a^2 + b^2 + 2ab \cos \delta.$$

(b) *Law of sines:* In any triangle, the ratio of any side and the sine of the opposite angle is constant, or

$$\frac{a}{\sin \alpha} = \frac{b}{\sin \beta} = \frac{c}{\sin \gamma}.$$

Thus, two sides and one angle determine the remaining angles and side, and so forth.

(6) **Other useful trigonometric relations:**

$\sin (\alpha + \beta) = \sin \alpha \cos \beta + \cos \alpha \sin \beta,$

$\cos (\alpha + \beta) = \cos \alpha \cos \beta - \sin \alpha \sin \beta,$

$2 \sin \alpha \cos \alpha = \sin 2\alpha.$

$\cos 2\alpha = \cos^2 \alpha - \sin^2 \alpha = 2 \cos^2 \alpha - 1 = 1 - 2 \sin^2 \alpha.$

APPENDIX F
NATURAL TRIGONOMETRIC FUNCTIONS

Angle		Sine	Cosine	Tan-gent	Angle		Sine	Cosine	Tan-gent
Degree	Radian				Degree	Radian			
0°	.000	0.000	1.000	0.000					
1°	.018	.018	1.000	.018	46°	0.803	0.719	0.695	1.036
2°	.035	.035	0.999	.035	47°	.820	.731	.682	1.072
3°	.052	.052	.999	.052	48°	.838	.743	.669	1.111
4°	.070	.070	.998	.070	49°	.855	.755	.656	1.150
5°	.087	.087	.996	.088	50°	.873	.766	.643	1.192
6°	.105	.105	.995	.105	51°	.890	.777	.629	1.235
7°	.122	.122	.993	.123	52°	.908	.788	.616	1.280
8°	.140	.139	.990	.141	53°	.925	.799	.602	1.327
9°	.157	.156	.988	.158	54°	.942	.809	.588	1.376
10°	.175	.174	.985	.176	55°	.960	.819	.574	1.428
11°	.192	.191	.982	.194	56°	.977	.829	.559	1.483
12°	.209	.208	.978	.213	57°	.995	.839	.545	1.540
13°	.227	.225	.974	.231	58°	1.012	.848	.530	1.600
14°	.244	.242	.970	.249	59°	1.030	.857	.515	1.664
15°	.262	.259	.966	.268	60°	1.047	.866	.500	1.732
16°	.279	.276	.961	.287	61°	1.065	.875	.485	1.804
17°	.297	.292	.956	.306	62°	1.082	.883	.470	1.881
18°	.314	.309	.951	.325	63°	1.100	.891	.454	1.963
19°	.332	.326	.946	.344	64°	1.117	.899	.438	2.050
20°	.349	.342	.940	.364	65°	1.134	.906	.423	2.145
21°	.367	.358	.934	.384	66°	1.152	.914	.407	2.246
22°	.384	.375	.927	.404	67°	1.169	.921	.391	2.356
23°	.401	.391	.921	.425	68°	1.187	.927	.375	2.475
24°	.419	.407	.914	.445	69°	1.204	.934	.358	2.605
25°	.436	.423	.906	.466	70°	1.222	.940	.342	2.747
26°	.454	.438	.899	.488	71°	1.239	.946	.326	2.904
27°	.471	.454	.891	.510	72°	1.257	.951	.309	3.078
28°	.489	.470	.883	.532	73°	1.274	.956	.292	3.271
29°	.506	.485	.875	.554	74°	1.292	.961	.276	3.487
30°	.524	.500	.866	.577	75°	1.309	.966	.259	3.732
31°	.541	.515	.857	.601	76°	1.326	.970	.242	4.011
32°	.559	.530	.848	.625	77°	1.344	.974	.225	4.331
33°	.576	.545	.839	.649	78°	1.361	.978	.208	4.705
34°	.593	.559	.829	.675	79°	1.379	.982	.191	5.145
35°	.611	.574	.819	.700	80°	1.396	.985	.174	5.671
36°	.628	.588	.809	.727	81°	1.414	.988	.156	6.314
37°	.646	.602	.799	.754	82°	1.431	.990	.139	7.115
38°	.663	.616	.788	.781	83°	1.449	.993	.122	8.144
39°	.681	.629	.777	.810	84°	1.466	.995	.105	9.514
40°	.698	.643	.766	.839	85°	1.484	.996	.087	11.43
41°	.716	.656	.755	.869	86°	1.501	.998	.070	14.30
42°	.733	.669	.743	.900	87°	1.518	.999	.052	19.08
43°	.751	.682	.731	.933	88°	1.536	.999	.035	28.64
44°	.768	.695	.719	.966	89°	1.553	1.000	.018	57.29
45°	.785	.707	.707	1.000	90°	1.571	1.000	.000	∞

APPENDIX G

VECTOR ADDITION AND SUBTRACTION

The addition of two vector quantities **P** and **Q** may be written **P** + **Q** = **R**. In interpreting such equations, we must realize that, in general, **R** is not obtained simply by adding the magnitudes of **P** and **Q**, but that one must find **R**, in direction as well as magnitude, by means of a graphical or a trigonometric solution (see Fig. A.7).

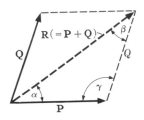

$$\mathbf{R} = \mathbf{P} + \mathbf{Q}.$$

Magnitude of **R**, from law of cosines:

$$R = \sqrt{P^2 + Q^2 - 2PQ \cos \gamma}.$$

Direction of **R**, from law of sines, that is, from

$$\sin \alpha / Q = \sin \gamma / R = \sin \beta / P.$$

FIG. A.7. Vector addition, graphically and trigonometrically.

In the same manner, the equation **B** − **A** = **C** refers to a vector subtraction such as is graphically and trigonometrically presented in Fig. A.8. Note that **C** is drawn so that when **C** is added to **A** the result is **B**. That this is correct becomes clear when one writes out the last sentence, replacing **C** by its definition, namely "the difference between **B** and **A**."

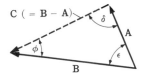

$$\mathbf{C} = \mathbf{B} - \mathbf{A}.$$

Magnitude of **C**, from law of cosines:

$$C = \sqrt{A^2 + B^2 - 2AB \cos \epsilon}.$$

Direction of **C**, from law of sines, that is, from

$$\sin \phi / A = \sin \epsilon / C = \sin \delta / B.$$

FIG. A.8. Vector subtraction, graphically and trigonometrically.

EXAMPLE OF VECTOR ADDITION. Two men are pulling on ropes attached to a heavy object; the first pulls with force $F_1 = 90$ new ($\doteq$ 20 lbf) at 40° east of north, the second with force $F_2 = 45$ new ($\doteq$ 10 lbf) in a direction 30° west of north. Find the resultant of these two forces, i.e., the vector sum, the single equivalent force **R** that might just as well be applied to this object instead of $\mathbf{F}_1$ and $\mathbf{F}_2$.

SOLUTION: First, we make a sketch in terms of the chosen arrow symbolism of the relative magnitudes, directions, and placement of vectors $\mathbf{F}_1$ and $\mathbf{F}_2$ [Fig. A.9(a)]. Then complete the parallelogram; the diagonal corresponds to $\mathbf{R}$, the vectorial sum of $\mathbf{F}_1$ and $\mathbf{F}_2$. The right half of the parallelogram is a triangle composed of $\mathbf{R}$, $\mathbf{F}_1$, and a side corresponding to $\mathbf{F}_2$; the angle opposite $\mathbf{R}$, indicated as γ, is directly given by $\gamma = 180° - (\theta_1 + \theta_2)$, in this case 180° —

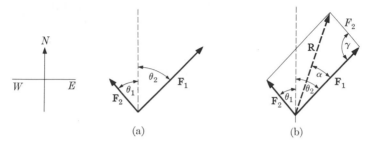

(a)   (b)

FIG. A.9. Vector addition.

70°, or 110°.* Now we find the magnitude of $\mathbf{R}$ by

$$R = \sqrt{F_1^2 + F_2^2 - 2F_1F_2 \cos \gamma}$$

$$= \sqrt{8.1 \times 10^2 + 2.03 \times 10^2 - 2 \times 90 \times 45 \times (-0.34)} \text{ new}$$

$$= 114 \text{ new } (\doteq 26 \text{ lbf}).$$

The direction of $\mathbf{R}$ may be found in several equivalent ways, but here it would seem most practicable to determine α, then $(\theta_2 - \alpha)$, the angle of $\mathbf{R}$ with respect to the north direction:

$$\sin \alpha = F_2 \frac{\sin \gamma}{R} = 45 \text{ new} \times \frac{0.94}{114 \text{ new}} = 0.37; \qquad \alpha \doteq 22°,$$

and

$$(\theta_2 - \alpha) = 18°.$$

The answer to the original question, then, is that the resultant force is 114 new, in a direction 18° east of north. And incidentally, the same procedure is applicable for calculating the sum of *any* two vector quantities of the same kind, for instance, two displacements or two accelerations, regardless of what the angle between them may be. Even the special cases where a right angle exists between the two vectors are, in substance, the same problem, simplified by the convenient facts that there the factor corresponding to $2F_1F_2 \cos \gamma$ under the square root is zero (since $\cos 90° = 0$), and that $\sin \alpha = F_2 \sin \gamma/R = F_2/R$ (since $\sin 90° = 1$).

---

*Recall that for angles between 90° and 180° the following relations apply: $\sin \gamma = \sin (180° - \gamma)$; $\cos \gamma = -\cos (180° - \gamma)$; see Appendix E. Therefore $\sin 110° = \sin 70° = 0.94$; $\cos 110° = -\cos 70° = -0.34$.

A moment's thought proves that one may abbreviate the process of vector addition. Both in Fig. A.7 and Fig. A.9(b) only the right half of the parallelogram is really needed; the left half is a congruent triangle, and therefore superfluous for our construction. Therefore, to add two vector quantities, we can draw their arrowlike representation and join them head to tail [Fig. A.10(a), (b)], the resultant **R** then being represented by the arrow running from the tail of the first-drawn to the head of the last-drawn arrow. When there are more than two vector quantities to be added, we may do this either by adding two of them, then adding a third one to their resultant, then a fourth to *that* resultant, and so forth; or more conveniently, though less accurately, graphically by adding the corresponding arrows head to tail, as in Fig. A.10(c).

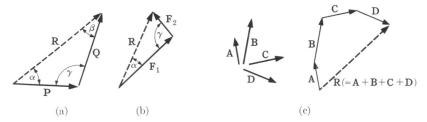

(a)   (b)   (c)

FIG. A.10. Vector addition.

EXAMPLE OF VECTOR SUBTRACTION. A bullet is shot in a direction 40° above the horizontal plane and with an initial velocity $v_1 = 3.5 \times 10^4$ cm/sec. After 46 sec the bullet returns to the same plane with a velocity v_2 having the same magnitude as v_1, namely, 3.5×10^4 cm/sec, but directed 40° below the horizontal. What was the change of velocity Δv during that time interval (magnitude and direction)?

SOLUTION: First make a sketch of the physical situation [Fig. A.11(a)], and then a sketch of the scheme for the subtraction of vector quantities [Fig. A.11 (b)]. This is done by joining the two arrows representing $\mathbf{v}_1$ and $\mathbf{v}_2$ tail-to-tail, and drawing an arrow representing the difference $\Delta \mathbf{v}$ between $\mathbf{v}_2$ and $\mathbf{v}_1$ from the tip of $\mathbf{v}_1$ to the tip of $\mathbf{v}_2$, as in Fig. A.8. Here the angle opposite the side representing $\Delta \mathbf{v}$ is ($\theta_1 + \theta_2$), or 80°; therefore the magnitude of $\Delta \mathbf{v}$ is

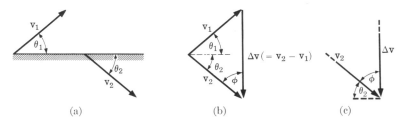

(a)   (b)   (c)

FIG. A.11. Vector subtraction.

$$\Delta v = \sqrt{v_1^2 + v_2^2 - 2v_1v_2 \cos(\theta_1 + \theta_2)}$$

$$= \sqrt{12.25 \times 10^8 + 12.25 \times 10^8 - 2 \times 3.5 \times 10^4 \times 3.5 \times 10^4 \times 0.174}$$

$$= 4.5 \times 10^4 \text{ cm/sec.}$$

The direction of $\Delta \mathbf{v}$ "obviously" is vertically downward, but it is important that this be confirmed rigorously. In Fig. A.11(c), angle $(\theta_2 + \phi)$ gives the inclination of Δv with the vertical; θ_2 is known, ϕ can be easily computed by the law of sines from $\sin \phi = (v_1/\Delta v) \sin(\theta_1 + \theta_2)$, and the sum, $\theta_2 + \phi$, is thereby confirmed to be 90°; i.e., $\Delta \mathbf{v}$ is perpendicular to the horizontal plane.

APPENDIX H

COMMON LOGARITHMS

N	0	1	2	3	4	5	6	7	8	9
0	....	0000	3010	4771	6021	6990	7782	8451	9031	9542
1	0000	0414	0792	1139	1461	1761	2041	2304	2553	2788
2	3010	3222	3424	3617	3802	3979	4150	4314	4472	4624
3	4771	4914	5051	5185	5315	5441	5563	5682	5798	5911
4	6021	6128	6232	6335	6435	6532	6628	6721	6812	6902
5	6990	7076	7160	7243	7324	7404	7482	7559	7634	7709
6	7782	7853	7924	7993	8062	8129	8195	8261	8325	8388
7	8451	8513	8573	8633	8692	8751	8808	8865	8921	8976
8	9031	9085	9138	9191	9243	9294	9345	9395	9445	9494
9	9542	9590	9638	9685	9731	9777	9823	9868	9912	9956
10	0000	0043	0086	0128	0170	0212	0253	0294	0334	0374
11	0414	0453	0492	0531	0569	0607	0645	0682	0719	0755
12	0792	0828	0864	0899	0934	0969	1004	1038	1072	1106
13	1139	1173	1206	1239	1271	1303	1335	1367	1399	1430
14	1461	1492	1523	1553	1584	1614	1644	1673	1703	1732
15	1761	1790	1818	1847	1875	1903	1931	1959	1987	2014
16	2041	2068	2095	2122	2148	2175	2201	2227	2253	2279
17	2304	2330	2355	2380	2405	2430	2455	2480	2504	2529
18	2553	2577	2601	2625	2648	2672	2695	2718	2742	2765
19	2788	2810	2833	2856	2878	2900	2923	2945	2967	2989
20	3010	3032	3054	3075	3096	3118	3139	3160	3181	3201
21	3222	3243	3263	3284	3304	3324	3345	3365	3385	3404
22	3424	3444	3464	3483	3502	3522	3541	3560	3579	3598
23	3617	3636	3655	3674	3692	3711	3729	3747	3766	3784
24	3802	3820	3838	3856	3874	3892	3909	3927	3945	3962
25	3979	3997	4014	4031	4048	4065	4082	4099	4116	4133
26	4150	4166	4183	4200	4216	4232	4249	4265	4281	4298
27	4314	4330	4346	4362	4378	4393	4409	4425	4440	4456
28	4472	4487	4502	4518	4533	4548	4564	4579	4594	4609
29	4624	4639	4654	4669	4683	4698	4713	4728	4742	4757
30	4771	4786	4800	4814	4829	4843	4857	4871	4886	4900
31	4914	4928	4942	4955	4969	4983	4997	5011	5024	5038
32	5051	5065	5079	5092	5105	5119	5132	5145	5159	5172
33	5185	5198	5211	5224	5237	5250	5263	5276	5289	5302
34	5315	5328	5340	5353	5366	5378	5391	5403	5416	5428
35	5441	5453	5465	5478	5490	5502	5514	5527	5539	5551
36	5563	5575	5587	5599	5611	5623	5635	5647	5658	5670
37	5682	5694	5705	5717	5729	5740	5752	5763	5775	5786
38	5798	5809	5821	5832	5843	5855	5866	5877	5888	5899
39	5911	5922	5933	5944	5955	5966	5977	5988	5999	6010
40	6021	6031	6042	6053	6064	6075	6085	6096	6107	6117
41	6128	6138	6149	6160	6170	6180	6191	6201	6212	6222
42	6232	6243	6253	6263	6274	6284	6294	6304	6314	6325
43	6335	6345	6355	6365	6375	6385	6395	6405	6415	6425
44	6435	6444	6454	6464	6474	6484	6493	6503	6513	6522
45	6532	6542	6551	6561	6571	6580	6590	6599	6609	6618
46	6628	6637	6646	6656	6665	6675	6684	6693	6702	6712
47	6721	6730	6739	6749	6758	6767	6776	6785	6794	6803
48	6812	6821	6830	6839	6848	6857	6866	6875	6884	6893
49	6902	6911	6920	6928	6937	6946	6955	6964	6972	6981
50	6990	6998	7007	7016	7024	7033	7042	7050	7059	7067
N	0	1	2	3	4	5	6	7	8	9

APPENDIX H

COMMON LOGARITHMS

N	0	1	2	3	4	5	6	7	8	9
50	6990	6998	7007	7016	7024	7033	7042	7050	7059	7067
51	7076	7084	7093	7101	7110	7118	7126	7135	7143	7152
52	7160	7168	7177	7185	7193	7202	7210	7218	7226	7235
53	7243	7251	7259	7267	7275	7284	7292	7300	7308	7316
54	7324	7332	7340	7348	7356	7364	7372	7380	7388	7396
55	7404	7412	7419	7427	7435	7443	7451	7459	7466	7474
56	7482	7490	7497	7505	7513	7520	7528	7536	7543	7551
57	7559	7566	7574	7582	7589	7597	7604	7612	7619	7627
58	7634	7642	7649	7657	7664	7672	7679	7686	7694	7701
59	7709	7716	7723	7731	7738	7745	7752	7760	7767	7774
60	7782	7789	7796	7803	7810	7818	7825	7832	7839	7846
61	7853	7860	7868	7875	7882	7889	7896	7903	7910	7917
62	7924	7931	7938	7945	7952	7959	7966	7973	7980	7987
63	7993	8000	8007	8014	8021	8028	8035	8041	8048	8055
64	8062	8069	8075	8082	8089	8096	8102	8109	8116	8122
65	8129	8136	8142	8149	8156	8162	8169	8176	8182	8189
66	8195	8202	8209	8215	8222	8228	8235	8241	8248	8254
67	8261	8267	8274	8280	8287	8293	8299	8306	8312	8319
68	8325	8331	8338	8344	8351	8357	8363	8370	8376	8382
69	8388	8395	8401	8407	8414	8420	8426	8432	8439	8445
70	8451	8457	8463	8470	8476	8482	8488	8494	8500	8506
71	8513	8519	8525	8531	8537	8543	8549	8555	8561	8567
72	8573	8579	8585	8591	8597	8603	8609	8615	8621	8627
73	8633	8639	8645	8651	8657	8663	8669	8675	8681	8686
74	8692	8698	8704	8710	8716	8722	8727	8733	8739	8745
75	8751	8756	8762	8768	8774	8779	8785	8791	8797	8802
76	8808	8814	8820	8825	8831	8837	8842	8848	8854	8859
77	8865	8871	8876	8882	8887	8893	8899	8904	8910	8915
78	8921	8927	8932	8938	8943	8949	8954	8960	8965	8971
79	8976	8982	8987	8993	8998	9004	9009	9015	9020	9025
80	9031	9036	9042	9047	9053	9058	9063	9069	9074	9079
81	9085	9090	9096	9101	9106	9112	9117	9122	9128	9133
82	9138	9143	9149	9154	9159	9165	9170	9175	9180	9186
83	9191	9196	9201	9206	9212	9217	9222	9227	9232	9238
84	9243	9248	9253	9258	9263	9269	9274	9279	9284	9289
85	9294	9299	9304	9309	9315	9320	9325	9330	9335	9340
86	9345	9350	9355	9360	9365	9370	9375	9380	9385	9390
87	9395	9400	9405	9410	9415	9420	9425	9430	9435	9440
88	9445	9450	9455	9460	9465	9469	9474	9479	9484	9489
89	9494	9499	9504	9509	9513	9518	9523	9528	9533	9538
90	9542	9547	9552	9557	9562	9566	9571	9576	9581	9586
91	9590	9595	9600	9605	9609	9614	9619	9624	9628	9633
92	9638	9643	9647	9652	9657	9661	9666	9671	9675	9680
93	9685	8689	9694	9699	9703	9708	9713	9717	9722	9727
94	9731	9736	9741	9745	9750	9754	9759	9763	9768	9773
95	9777	9782	9786	9791	9795	9800	9805	9809	9814	9818
96	9823	9827	9832	9836	9841	9845	9850	9854	9859	9863
97	9868	9872	9877	9881	9886	9890	9894	9899	9903	9908
98	9912	9917	9921	9926	9930	9934	9939	9943	9948	9952
99	9956	9961	9965	9969	9974	9978	9983	9987	9991	9996
100	0000	0004	0009	0013	0017	0022	0026	0030	0035	0039
N	0	1	2	3	4	5	6	7	8	9

ANSWERS TO SELECTED ODD-NUMBERED PROBLEMS

1.1. 10 ft/sec. **1.3.** (a) 30 mi/hr, (b) 24 mi/hr, (c) 26.7 mi/hr. **1.5.** (c) 30 mi; 65 mi; 105 mi. **1.7.** $\frac{1}{5}$ ft/sec^2; 75 sec. **1.9.** 4.32 sec; 139 ft/sec. **1.11.** 2 mi/hr/sec or 2.9 ft/sec^2; 330 ft. **1.13.** $\frac{2}{5}$ mi/hr/min; 1.6 mi. **1.19.** 1.43 sec; 2.02 sec; 2.47 sec; 2.86 sec. **1.21.** 27 ft/sec.

3.1. 30 ft. **3.3.** 350 m, 530 from horizontal. **3.5.** 24 m/sec 36° below horizontal. **3.9.** 39 ft, 1.7 ft/sec up. **3.11.** (a) 202 m/sec, 2.51 × 10^3 m; 104 m/sec, 4.04 × 10^3 m; 6 m/sec, 4.59 × 10^3 m; −92 m/sec, 4.16 × 10^3 m; −190 m/sec, 2.75 × 10^3 m; −288 m/sec, 0.360 × 10^3 m; (b) 61.2 sec. **3.15.** (a) 84 ft; 155 ft; 0; (b) 68 ft/sec up; 3.6 ft/sec up; 0; (c) 2.48 sec and 3.73 sec. **3.17.** (a) 559 sec, (b) 318 mi, (c) 614 sec, (d) uniform acceleration during firing; no air resistance; very poor. **3.19.** 3.57 × 10^3 ft/sec.

4.3. 2 kgm. **4.7.** 90 new; by the car seat; forward. **4.9.** (a) 1 kgm, (b) 9.809 new; 9.801 new, (c) 0; 0.08%. **4.13.** (a) 0.915 m; 1.61 × 10^3 m, (b) 9.30 × 10^{-2} m^2; 6.46 × 10^{-4} m^2, (c) 1.64 × 10^{-5} m^3; 2.84 × 10^{-2} m^3, (d) 711 new, (e) 9.8 m/sec^2. **4.17.** 0.20. **4.19.** 3.27 m/sec^2. **4.23.** zero.

5.1. (a) 0.209, (b) 0.401, (c) 0.855. **5.3.** 96 min; 0.625 rev/hr; 7.56 × 10^3 m/sec. **5.5.** (a) 2.45 × 10^3 rad; 1.40 × 10^5 deg, (b) 25 in/sec; 98 in/sec, (c) 8.2 rad/sec. **5.9.** 8.25 m/sec^2. **5.11.** 1.36 × 10^3 m. **5.15.** 26 rad/sec or 4 rev/sec. **5.19.** (a) 0.18 m/sec^2; 54 new. **5.23.** (a) 64 new, (b) 74 new. **5.25.** 4.1 × 10^2 m/sec^2.

6.3. 1:1; 3:1.

11.7. (a) 10^{-11} new·m^2/kgm^2. **11.9.** 16%.

12.3. 0.3 m. **12.9.** 5.5 × 10^3 kgm/m^3, 2.7 × 10^3 kgm/m^3, 1.3 × 10^3 kgm/m^3. **12.11.** (a) by one-half, (b) to zero, (c) to 9.5 × 10^{-4} of the original weight.

17.1. 1.7 sec. **17.3.** (a) 82.6 kgm·m/sec, (b) 143 kgm·m/sec. **17.7.** 0.96 m/sec to right. **17.17.** 1.5. **17.21.** (a) 1.7 × 10^7 new, (b) 1.7 × 10^7 new.

18.1. 300 ft. **18.3.** 5.4 × 10^6 j. **18.5.** (a) 2.3 × 10^3 j, (b) 1.6 × 10^3 j, (c) −2.3 × 10^3 j, (d) 0. **18.7.** 2.8 × 10^5 j. **18.9.** 7.5 × 10^8 j. **18.13.** (a) 2.2 × 10^4 j, (b) 2.2 × 10^4 j. **18.23.** 4 ft from his end. **18.25.** (a) 2.0 m, (b) 200 j, 250 j, (c) 0.80. **18.27.** 6.7 m/sec. **18.29.** (a) 2.4 j, (b) 0.62 new

19.1. 65°C. **19.3.** 3 × 10^{-2} kgm. **19.5.** 0.18 kcal/kgm·°C. **19.11.** 1.6 kcal. **19.15.** (a) 1080 kcal, (b) 179 kcal. **19.17.** (a) 9.7 × 10^2 kcal, (b) 8.2 kcal.

20.3. (a) 2 × 10^{-2} °C.

21.3. (b) 2.69 × 10^{-3} m^3, (c) 4.15 j/°K. **21.5.** 3.4 atm.

22.1. (a) 5.25, 15.75, 1.75, (b) 1 kgm nitrogen, 0.2 kgm hydrogen. **22.3.** (a) 3.6, 3.6, 2.7, (b) 1.8, 1.8, 1.8. **22.5.** 1:16, 1:24, 1:32, . . . , 1:4, 1:2, 1:1, ...

23.9. 19.000, 39.944, 30.98. **23.13.** 1.43. **23.15.** (a) 0.0587 mole, (b) 3.54×10^{22} molecules, (c) 1.42×10^{23} atoms, (d) 0.359 liter, (e) 1.82 moles. **23.19.** 1, 2, 3, 4, 5.

25.11. (c) 1.07.

26.5. 9×10^9 new; no. **26.7.** 5×10^{42} **26.15.** (a) 3.4 m/sec, (b) 14 m/sec. **26.19.** (a) 62 dyne, (b) 37 statcoul.

27.1. (a) 4.0×10^{-6} new toward nearer sphere, (b) 4.1×10^{-6} new toward other spheres. **27.13.** (a) 9×10^2 new/coul, (b) 3.7×10^5 new/coul, 54° above horizontal. **27.27.** 3×10^{-4} coul. **27.29.** 18×10^{-13} j, 9×10^6 ev.

28.3. (a) 32 gm, (b) 108 gm, (c) 41 gm. **28.5.** 0.34 gm. **28.11.** west, east, zero.

29.1. (b) 1.02 m.

30.1. (a) 0°, 28°, (b) 50°. **30.5.** (a) 18.85°, (b) 19.17°. **30.9.** $5 \times 10^{-5}\%$. **30.15.** (a) 6.41×10^3 A, 4.68×10^{14} cycles/sec.

31.1. 6232°K. **31.3.** (a) 1.2×10^4 A, (b) 1.1×10^5 A. **31.5.** (a) 1.7×10^{13} °K, (c) zero.

32.3. (b) 4.0×10^{-19} j. **32.7.** (a) 0, (b) 3.7 v. **32.11.** (a) 1.5×10^8 m/sec, (b) 0.21 A. **32.13.** (a) 6.6×10^{-34} j·sec.

33.3. (b) 3645.6 A. **33.5.** (a) 972.5 A, (b) 911.8 A.

34.3. 1:5000. **34.5.** 4.23×10^{-26} j.

35.1. 1026 A, 1216 A, 6565 A. **35.11.** 3.02 A.

36.1. eastward. **36.5.** 6.01×10^{23} atoms/mole. **36.11.** $\frac{1}{64}$. **36.13.** $\frac{1}{8}$.

37.3. (a) 238.11 amu, (b) 238.03 awu. **37.13.** 4.00335 amu, 6.65×10^{-24} gm. **37.15.** 1.52×10^4 m/sec. **37.17.** 37.96 awu, yes.

38.5. (a) $_1H^1 + _4Be^9 \rightarrow _4Be^8 + _1H^2$, $_1H^1 + _3Li^6 \rightarrow _2He^3 + _2He^4$,
  (b) $_1H^2 + _6C^{12} \rightarrow _6C^{13} + _1H^1$, $_1H^2 + _{11}Na^{23} \rightarrow _{11}Na^{24} + _1H^1$.
38.9. (a) $_1D^2 + _5B^{11} \rightarrow _1p^1 + _5B^{12}$, (b) 0.28 mev, (c) 0.00122 amu. **38.13.** infinite. **38.17.** (c) 2.70×10^8 m/sec. **38.21.** (a) $_5B^{10} + _0n^1 \rightarrow _2\alpha^4 + _3Li^7$. **38.23.** 2×10^{-34} kgm, 7×10^{-26} kgm·m/sec, 2×10^{-17} j. **38.31.** 1.2×10^{-19} j. **38.33.** 2.1×10^7 m/sec. **38.35.** (a) 5.370×10^{-6} amu, (b) 6.45 amu.

39.1. 2.1×10^{21} cycles/sec. **39.15.** 3×10^6 dis/sec. **39.17.** (a) 1 kgm, 5×10^5 kgm or 500 tons.

INDEX

absolute temperature system, 370
absolute zero, 370, 445
absorption, of radiation, 634
  spectra, 604
acceleration, 9
  average, 93
  centripetal, 93, 97
  constant, 9
    equations of motion for, 11 ff.
  due to gravity, 14, 70, 71
  for uniform circular motion, 94
accelerators, particle, 696
action, 581
  and reaction, 82
  through a distance, 495
activation energy for fission, 735
Adams, J. C., 197, 200
Almagest, 112, 118
alpha particles, 289, 291, 661
alpha-particle scattering, 614 ff.
alpha rays, 661
amber effect, 464
Anderson, C. D., 698, 700
Angström, A. J., 568, 608
angular distance, 92
angular speed, 91, 92
aphelion, 146
apogee, 145
Aquinas, Thomas, 118, 124, 171
Archimedes of Syracuse, 315
areas, law of equal, 147
Aristarchus of Samos, 110, 120, 126
Aristotelian, *see* Scholastics
Aristotelian cosmology, 106, 107, 109
Aristotle, 19, 20, 21, 32, 109, 365, 543
asteroids, 200
Aston, F. W., 683, 725
Aston's whole-number rule, 685
Astronomia nova, 287
astronomical unit, 111
atmosphere, escape of the, 446
  homogeneity of the, 445
atom, 365
  liquid-drop model of, 731
  nuclear model of, 613 ff.
  planetary model of, 620

shell structure of, 637
size of, 408, 678
tagged, 745 ff.
x-ray spectra of, 644, 646
atomic bomb, 736, 742
atomic mass, 407
  electromagnetic determination of,
    682
  unit, 685
atomic models, 613 ff., 651, 731
atomic number, 426, 618, 647
atomic theory, 363 ff.
  Dalton's, 377 ff.
atomic volume, 421
atomic weight, 384, 388, 401
  physical determination of, 680
  relative, 384
atoms, compound, 380, 381
attraction, electrical, 463
  gravitational, 174
  magnetic, 517
Atwood's machine, 77, 268
Avogadro, Amedeo, 393, 415, 429
Avogadro's law, 394, 406
Avogadro's model for gases, 393
Avogadro's number, 405, 406, 433,
    444, 515, 516

Bacon, Francis, 126, 131, 139, 366
Bainbridge, K. T., 682
balance, equal-arm, 72
  spring, 65
  torsion, 188
ballistic pendulum, 322
Balmer series, 611
Balmer's formula, 607 ff.
Barberini, Maffeo, 161
barometer, 367
barrier, nuclear, 726, 727
Becquerel, Henri, 657, 674
Benedetti, Giovanni, 253
Bernoulli, Daniel, 374 ff., 432, 476
Berzelius, Jöns Jacob, 381, 413
beta particles, 661
beta rays, 661
binding energy, nuclear, 725, 728, 729

772